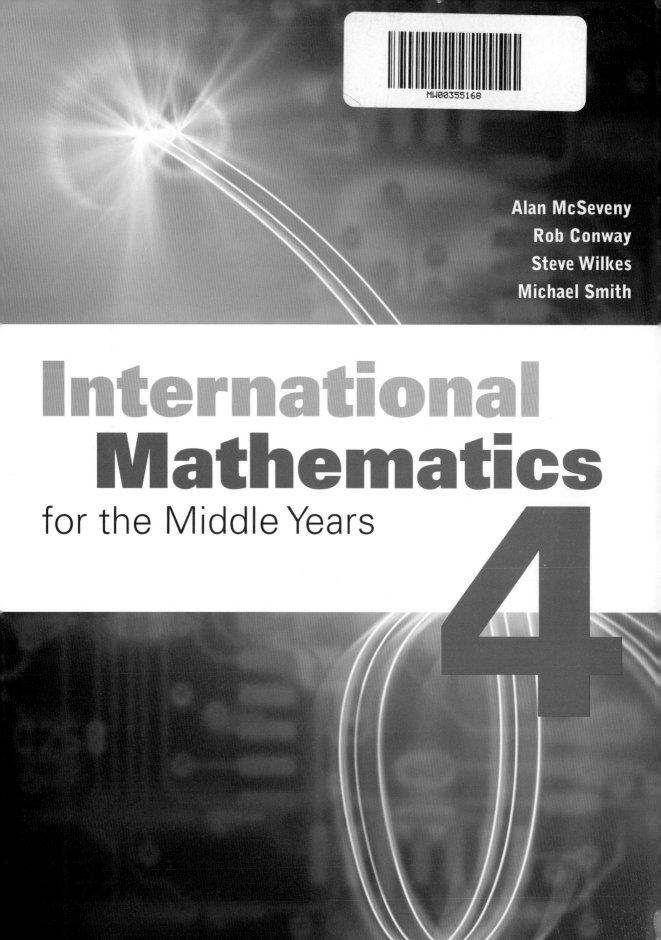

Alan McSeveny

Rob Conway

Steve Wilkes

Michael Smith

International Mathematics

for the Middle Years

4

Pearson Australia
(a division of Pearson Australia Group Pty Ltd)
707 Collins Street, Melbourne, Victoria 3008
PO Box 23360, Melbourne, Victoria 8012
www.pearson.com.au

Editor: Fiona Brodribb
Designer: Pier Vido and Anita Adams
Copyright and Picture Editor: Jacqui Ligget
Illustrators: Michael Barter, Bruce Rankin and Boris Silvestri
Typeset by Sunset Digital Pty Ltd, Brisbane
Printed in China (SWTC/13)

National Library of Australia
Cataloguing-in-Publication data

International mathematics for the middle years 4

1st ed.
Includes index.
For secondary school students.
ISBN 978-0-7339-8519-5 (pbk: CD-ROM)

1. Mathematics – Textbooks. I. McSeveny, A. (Alan).

510

Pearson Australia Group Pty Ltd   ABN 40 004 245 943

Acknowledgements

Pearson Australia would like to thank Luke Borda for his assistance in reviewing and writing some of the material in *International Mathematics for the Middle Years Book 4*. Luke is the Mathematics Coordinator for the Middle and Senior Schools at Mercedes College in Adelaide, Australia, where he has been teaching MYP mathematics for the last 5 years. Luke has been involved in submitting year 5 MYP moderation and has focussed on the assessment criteria and their application and interpretation.

We would like to thank the following for permission to reproduce photographs, texts and illustrations.

iStockphoto: pp. 338, 364, 428, 496, 499.
Larry Bagnell: p. 329.
Pearson Australia: Karly Abery: p. 118; Kim Nolan: p. 284.
Photolibrary Pty Ltd: pp. 201, 465, 501.
Shutterstock: pp. 20r, 39, 117, 133, 150, 245, 258, 270, 327, 378, 386, 437, 448, 459, 466.
Sven Klinge: pp. 198, 201, 211, 319, 336, 368, 375.

Cover: Getty Images

Every effort has been made to trace and acknowledge copyright. However, should any infringement have occurred, the publishers tender their apologies and invite copyright owners to contact them.

Contents

Chapter 6

Chapter 7

Chapter 8

Chapter 9

Chapter 10

Chapter 11

Interactive Student CD

You can access this material by clicking on the links provided on the Interactive Student CD. Go to the Home Page for information about these links.

Worksheet Answers

Challenge Worksheets

Worksheet Answers

Technology Applications

The material below is found in the Companion Website which is included on the Interactive Student CD as both an archived version and a fully featured live version.

Activities and Investigations

Drag and Drops

Animations

Chapter Review Questions

These can be used as a diagnostic tool or for revision. They include multiple choice, pattern-matching and fill-in-the-gaps style questions.

Destinations

Links to useful websites that relate directly to the chapter content.

Features of *International Mathematics for the Middle Years*

International Mathematics for the Middle Years is organised with the international student in mind. Examples and exercises are not restricted to a particular syllabus and so provide students with a global perspective.

Each edition has a review section for students who may have gaps in the Mathematics they have studied previously. Sections on the language of Mathematics and terminology will help students for whom English is a second language.

Areas of Interaction are given for each chapter and Assessment Grids for Investigations provide teachers with aids to assessing Analysis and Reasoning, Communication, and Reflection and Evaluation as part of the International Baccalaureate Middle Years Program (IBMYP). The Assessment Grids will also assist students in addressing these criteria and will enhance students' understanding of the subject content.

How is *International Mathematics for the Middle Years* organised?

As well as the student coursebook, additional support for both students and teachers is provided:
- Interactive Student CD — **free** with each coursebook
- Companion Website
- Teacher's Resource — printout and CD.

Coursebook

Chapter-opening pages summarise the key content and present the learning outcomes addressed in each chapter.

Areas of Interaction references are included in the chapter-opening pages to make reporting easier. For example, Homo faber.

Prep Quizzes review skills needed to complete a topic. These anticipate problems and save time in the long run. These quizzes offer an excellent way to start a lesson.

Well-graded exercises — Within each exercise, **levels of difficulty** are indicated by the colour of the question number.

1 green ... foundation　　**4** blue ... core　　**9** red ... extension

---

2 a　An equilateral triangle has a side of length 4.68 m. What is its perimeter?

7　Solve the following equations.

a　$\dfrac{x}{2} + \dfrac{x}{3} = 5$　　　　b　$\dfrac{p}{6} + \dfrac{p}{2} = 8$

8 a　A radio on sale for $50 is to be reduced in price by 30%. Later, the discounted price is increased by 30%. What is the final price? By what percentage (to the nearest per cent) must the first discounted price be increased to give the original price?

Worked examples are used extensively and are easy for students to identify.

worked examples

1　Express the following in scientific notation.
　　a　243　　　　　　b　60 000　　　　　　c　93 800 000

Important rules and concepts are clearly highlighted at regular intervals throughout the text.

Cartoons are used to give students friendly advice or tips.

The table of values looks like this!

Foundation Worksheets provide alternative exercises for students who need to consolidate earlier work or who need additional work at an easier level. Students can access these on the CD by clicking on the Foundation Worksheet icons. These can also be copied from the Teacher's Resource CD or from the Teacher's Resource Centre on the Companion Website.

Foundation Worksheet 4:01A
Grouping symbols
1 a $(3 + 2) \times 10$
2 a $(8 - 2) \times 3$
3 a $10 - (4 + 3)$

Challenge activities and worksheets provide more difficult investigations and exercises. They can be used to extend more able students.

challenge

Fun Spots provide amusement and interest, while often reinforcing course work. They encourage creativity and divergent thinking, and show that Mathematics is enjoyable.

fun spot

Investigations and **Practical Activities** encourage students to seek knowledge and develop research skills. They are an essential part of any Mathematics course. Where applicable, investigations are accompanied by a set of assessment criteria to assist teachers in assessing criteria B, C and D as prescribed by the MYP.

investigation

Diagnostic Tests at the end of each chapter test students' achievement of outcomes. More importantly, they indicate the weaknesses that need to be addressed by going back to the section in the text or on the CD listed beside the test question.

diagnostic test

Assignments are provided at the end of each chapter. Where there are two assignments, the first revises the content of the chapter, while the second concentrates on developing the student's ability to work mathematically.

assignment

The See cross-references direct students to other sections of the coursebook relevant to a particular section.

see

The Algebra Card (see p xx) is used to practise basic algebra skills. Corresponding terms in columns can be added, subtracted, multiplied or divided by each other or by other numbers. This is a great way to start a lesson.

The Language of Mathematics

Within the coursebook, Mathematics literacy is addressed in three specific ways:

ID Cards (see pp xiv–xix) review the language of Mathematics by asking students to identify common terms, shapes and symbols. They should be used as often as possible, either at the beginning of a lesson or as part of a test or examination.

Mathematical Terms met during the chapter are defined at the end of each chapter. These terms are also tested in a **Drag and Drop** interactive that follows this section.

Reading Mathematics help students to develop maths literacy skills and provide opportunities for students to communicate mathematical ideas. They present Mathematics in the context of everyday experiences.

An **Answers** section provides answers to all the exercises in the coursebook, including the ID Cards.

Interactive Student CD

This is provided at the back of the coursebook and is an important part of the total learning package.

Bookmarks and links allow easy navigation within and between the different electronic components of the CD that contains:

- A copy of the student coursebook.
- Appendixes A–D for enrichment and review work, linked from the coursebook.
- Printable copies of the Foundation Worksheets and Challenge Worksheets, linked from the coursebook.
- An archived, offline version of the Companion Website, including:
  - Chapter Review Questions and Quick Quizzes
  - All the Technology Applications: activities and investigations and drag-and-drops
  - Destinations (links to useful websites)

All these items are clearly linked from the coursebook via the Companion Website.

- A link to the live Companion Website.

Companion Website

The Companion Website contains a wealth of support material for students and teachers:

- **Chapter Review Questions** which can be used as a diagnostic tool or for revision. These are self-correcting and include multiple-choice, pattern-matching and fill-in the-gaps-style questions. Results can be emailed directly to the teacher or parents.
- **Quick Quizzes** for most chapters.
- **Destinations** — links to useful websites which relate directly to the chapter content.
- **Technology Applications** — activities that apply concepts covered in most chapters and are designed for students to work independently:

Activities and investigations using technology, such as Excel spreadsheets and The Geometer's Sketchpad.

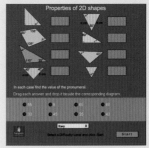

 Drag and Drop interactives to improve mastery of basic skills.

Sample Drag and Drop

Animations to develop key skills by manipulating visually stimulating and interactive demonstrations of key mathematical concepts.

Sample Animation

- **Teacher's Resource Centre** — provides a wealth of teacher support material and is password protected:
  — Coursebook corrections
  — Topic Review Tests and answers
  — Foundation and Challenge Worksheets and answers

Teacher's resource

 This material is provided as both a printout and as an electronic copy on CD:

- Teaching Program, including treatment of learning outcomes, in both PDF and editable Microsoft Word formats
- Practice Tests and Answers
- Foundation and Challenge Worksheets and answers
- Answers to some of the Technology Application Activities and Investigations

Most of this material is also available in the Teacher's Resource Centre of the Companion Website.

Using this Book for Teaching MYP for the IB

- Holistic Learning
- Intercultural Awareness
- Communication

These elements of the MYP Mathematics course are integrated throughout the text. Links are made possible between subjects, and different methods of communicating solutions to problems through investigations allow students to explore their own ideas.

The Areas of Interaction

- Approaches to Learning
- Community and Service
- Health and Social Education
- Environment
- Homo Faber

Areas of Interaction covered are outlined at the start of each chapter, allowing teachers to develop links between subjects and formulate their own Interdisciplinary Units with additional assistance in the Teacher's Resource.

Addressing the Objectives

Assessment grids are provided for Investigations throughout the text to not only help teachers assess criteria B, C and D of the MYP, but also to assist students in addressing the criteria. The assessment grids should be modified to suit the student where necessary.

A **Knowledge and Understanding**
This criterion is addressed in the Diagnostic Tests and Revision Assignments that accompany each chapter. Teachers can also use the worksheets from the CD to add to material for this criterion.

B **Investigating Patterns**
It is possible to address this criterion using the Working Mathematically sections accompanying each chapter, and also using the Investigations throughout the text.

C **Communication**
This can be assessed using the Investigations throughout the book.

D **Reflection in Mathematics**
This can be assessed using the Investigations throughout the book.

Fulfilling the Framework for Mathematics

The content of the text covers the five broad areas required to fulfil the Framework:

- Number
- Algebra
- Geometry
- Statistics
- Discrete Mathematics

Although the material in the text is not exhaustive, it covers the required areas in sufficient depth. Teachers can use the text as a resource to build on as they develop their own scheme of work within their school.

Metric Equivalents

Length
1 m = 1000 mm
= 100 cm
= 10 dm
1 cm = 10 mm
1 km = 1000 m

Area
$1 \text{ m}^2 = 10\,000 \text{ cm}^2$
$1 \text{ ha} = 10\,000 \text{ m}^2$
$1 \text{ km}^2 = 100 \text{ ha}$

Mass
1 kg = 1000 g
1 t = 1000 kg
1 g = 1000 mg

Volume
$1 \text{ m}^3 = 1\,000\,000 \text{ cm}^3$
$= 1000 \text{ dm}^3$
1 L = 1000 mL
1 kL = 1000 L
$1 \text{ m}^3 = 1 \text{ kL}$
$1 \text{ cm}^3 = 1 \text{ mL}$
$1000 \text{ cm}^3 = 1 \text{ L}$

Time
1 min = 60 s
1 h = 60 min
1 day = 24 h
1 year = 365 days
1 leap year = 366 days

Months of the year
30 days each has September,
April, June and November.
All the rest have 31, except February alone,
Which has 28 days clear and 29 each leap year.

Seasons
Southern Hemisphere
Summer: December, January, February
Autumn/Fall: March, April, May
Winter: June, July, August
Spring: September, October, November
Northern Hemisphere
Summer: June, July, August
Autumn/Fall: September, October, November
Winter: December, January, February
Spring: March, April, May

The Language of Mathematics

You should regularly test your knowledge by identifying the items on each card.

ID Card 1 (Metric Units)			
1 m	2 dm	3 cm	4 mm
5 km	6 m^2	7 cm^2	8 km^2
9 ha	10 m^3	11 cm^3	12 s
13 min	14 h	15 m/s	16 km/h
17 g	18 mg	19 kg	20 t
21 L	22 mL	23 kL	24 °C

See page 610 for answers.

ID Card 2 (Symbols)			
1 =	2 ÷ or ≈	3 ≠	4 <
5 ⩽	6 ≮	7 >	8 ⩾
9 4^2	10 4^3	11 $\sqrt{2}$	12 $\sqrt[3]{2}$
13 ⌐	14 ∥	15 ≡	16 ⫴
17 %	18 ∴	19 eg	20 ie
21 π	22 Σ	23 $\bar{x}$	24 P(E)

See page 610 for answers.

See 'Maths Terms' at the end of each chapter.

ID Card 3 (Language)			
1 6 minus 2	**2** the sum of 6 and 2	**3** divide 6 by 2	**4** subtract 2 from 6
5 the quotient of 6 and 2	**6** $$2\overline{)6}^{\,3}$$ the divisor is	**7** $$2\overline{)6}^{\,3}$$ the dividend is	**8** 6 lots of 2
9 decrease 6 by 2	**10** the product of 6 and 2	**11** 6 more than 2	**12** 2 less than 6
13 6 squared	**14** the square root of 36	**15** 6 take away 2	**16** multiply 6 by 2
17 average of 6 and 2	**18** add 6 and 2	**19** 6 to the power of 2	**20** 6 less 2
21 the difference between 6 and 2	**22** increase 6 by 2	**23** share 6 between 2	**24** the total of 6 and 2

See page 610 for answers.

We say 'six squared' but we write 6^2.

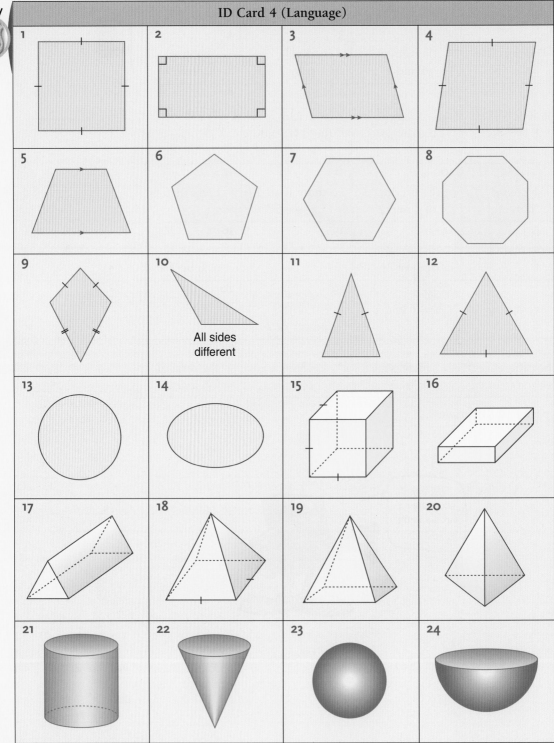

See page 610 for answers.

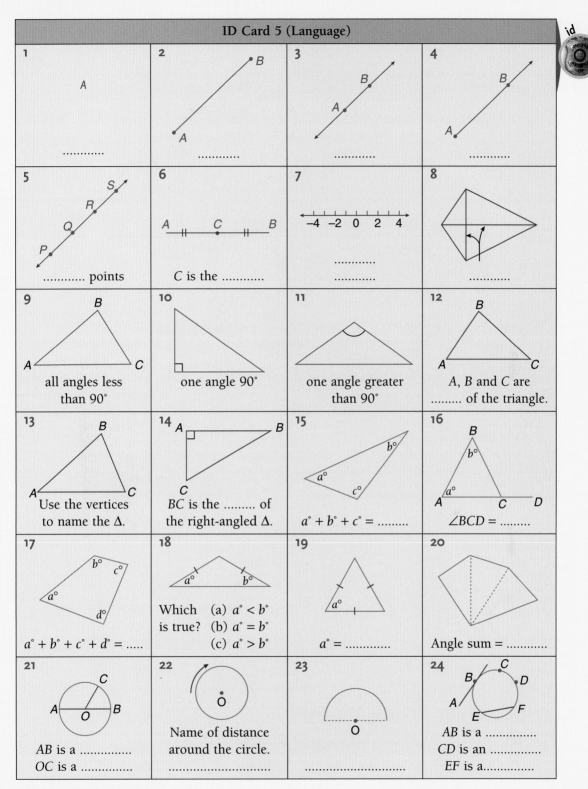

ID Card 5 (Language)

1 A ....

2 B · A ....

3 B A ....

4 B A ....

5 S R Q P .... points

6 A ‖ C ‖ B C is the ....

7 −4 −2 0 2 4 ....

8 ....

9 B A C all angles less than 90°

10 one angle 90°

11 one angle greater than 90°

12 B A C A, B and C are .... of the triangle.

13 B A C Use the vertices to name the Δ.

14 A B C BC is the .... of the right-angled Δ.

15 $b°$ $a°$ $c°$ $a° + b° + c° = ...$

16 B $b°$ $a°$ A C D ∠BCD = ...

17 $b°$ $c°$ $a°$ $d°$ $a° + b° + c° + d° = ...$

18 $a°$ $b°$ Which is true? (a) $a° < b°$ (b) $a° = b°$ (c) $a° > b°$

19 $a°$ $a° = ...$

20 Angle sum = ...

21 C A O B AB is a .... OC is a ....

22 O Name of distance around the circle. ....

23 O ....

24 C B D A F E AB is a .... CD is an .... EF is a...............

See page 610 for answers.

ID Card 6 (Language)

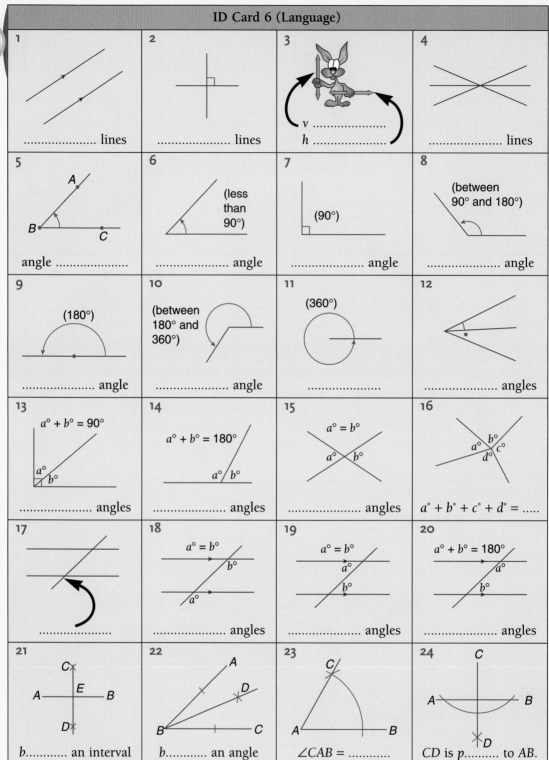

1 .... lines

2 .... lines

3 v .... h ....

4 .... lines

5 angle ....

6 (less than 90°) .... angle

7 (90°) .... angle

8 (between 90° and 180°) .... angle

9 (180°) .... angle

10 (between 180° and 360°) .... angle

11 (360°) ....

12 .... angles

13 $a° + b° = 90°$ .... angles

14 $a° + b° = 180°$ .... angles

15 $a° = b°$ .... angles

16 $a° + b° + c° + d° = $ .....

17 ....

18 $a° = b°$ .... angles

19 $a° = b°$ .... angles

20 $a° + b° = 180°$ .... angles

21 b............ an interval

22 b............ an angle

23 $\angle CAB = $............

24 CD is p.......... to AB.

See page 610 for answers.

ID Card 7 (Language)

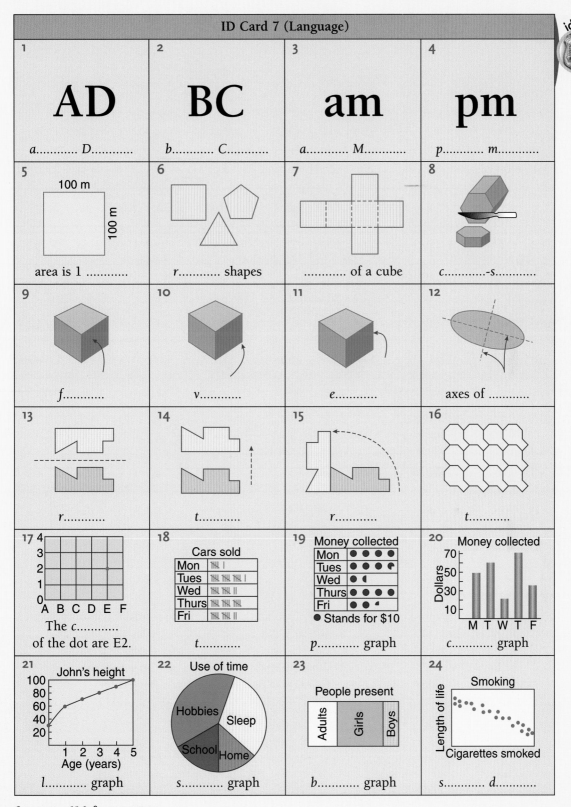

1 AD
a............ D............

2 BC
b............ C............

3 am
a............ M............

4 pm
p............ m............

5 100 m / 100 m
area is 1 ....

6 r............ shapes

7 .... of a cube

8 c............-s............

9 f............

10 v............

11 e............

12 axes of ....

13 r............

14 t............

15 r............

16 t............

17
The c............ of the dot are E2.

18 Cars sold

Mon	𝍷
Tues	
Wed	
Thurs	
Fri	

t............

19 Money collected

Mon	
Tues	
Wed	
Thurs	
Fri	

● Stands for $10

p............ graph

20 Money collected
c............ graph

21 John's height
Age (years)
l............ graph

22 Use of time
Hobbies, Sleep, School, Home
s............ graph

23 People present
Adults, Girls, Boys
b............ graph

24 Smoking
Length of life
Cigarettes smoked
s............ d............

See page 610 for answers.

xix

Algebra Card

	A	B	C	D	E	F	G	H	I	J	K	L	M	N	O
1	3	2.1	$\frac{1}{4}$	m	$\frac{2m}{3}$	$-3m$	$5m^2$	$-5x$	$\frac{x}{6}$	$-3x$	$-\frac{x}{2}$	$x+2$	$x-3$	$2x+1$	$3x-8$
2	-1	-0.4	$\frac{1}{8}$	$-4m$	$\frac{m}{4}$	$2m$	$-2m^3$	$3x$	$-\frac{x}{3}$	$5x^2$	$\frac{x}{4}$	$x+7$	$x-6$	$4x+2$	$x-1$
3	5	0.8	$\frac{1}{3}$	$10m$	$-\frac{m}{4}$	$-5m$	$8m^5$	$10x$	$-\frac{2x}{7}$	$-8x$	$\frac{2x}{5}$	$x+5$	$x+5$	$6x+2$	$x-5$
4	-2	1.5	$\frac{1}{20}$	$-8m$	$-\frac{3m}{2}$	$7m$	$6m^2$	$-15x$	$\frac{x}{10}$	$-4x^4$	$-\frac{x}{5}$	$x+1$	$x-9$	$3x+3$	$2x+4$
5	-8	-2.5	$\frac{3}{5}$	$2m$	$-\frac{m}{5}$	$10m$	m^2	$7x$	$\frac{2x}{3}$	$2x^3$	$\frac{x}{3}$	$x+8$	$x+2$	$3x+8$	$3x+1$
6	10	-0.7	$\frac{2}{7}$	$-5m$	$-\frac{3m}{7}$	$-6m$	$-9m^3$	$9x$	$-\frac{2x}{5}$	x^2	$\frac{3x}{5}$	$x+4$	$x-7$	$3x+1$	$x+7$
7	-6	-1.2	$\frac{3}{8}$	$8m$	$-\frac{m}{6}$	$9m$	$2m^6$	$-6x$	$\frac{5x}{6}$	$5x^2$	$\frac{2x}{3}$	$x+6$	$x-1$	$x+8$	$2x-5$
8	12	0.5	$\frac{9}{20}$	$20m$	$\frac{2m}{5}$	$-4m$	$-3m^3$	$-12x$	$\frac{3x}{4}$	$4x^3$	$-\frac{x}{7}$	$x+10$	$x-8$	$5x+2$	$x-10$
9	7	0.1	$\frac{3}{4}$	$5m$	$\frac{3m}{5}$	$-10m$	m^7	$5x$	$-\frac{3x}{7}$	$-3x^5$	$\frac{3x}{7}$	$x+2$	$x+5$	$2x+4$	$2x-4$
10	-5	-0.6	$\frac{7}{10}$	$-9m$	$-\frac{4m}{5}$	$-7m$	$-8m^4$	$-3x$	$-\frac{x}{6}$	$-7x^5$	$\frac{2x}{9}$	$x+1$	$x-7$	$5x+4$	$x+7$
11	-11	-1.8	$\frac{1}{10}$	$-7m$	$\frac{m}{5}$	$-8m$	$-4m$	$-4x$	$\frac{x}{5}$	$-x^3$	$\frac{x}{3}$	$x+9$	$x+6$	$2x+7$	$x-6$
12	4	-1.4	$\frac{2}{5}$	$3m$	$\frac{m}{3}$	$12m$	$7m^2$	$-7x$	$-\frac{3x}{4}$	x^{10}	$\frac{x}{6}$	$x+3$	$x-10$	$2x+3$	$2x+3$

How to use this card

If the instruction is 'column D + column F', then you add corresponding terms in columns D and F.

eg

1   $m + (-3m)$ 2 $(-4m) + 2m$ 3 $10m + (-5m)$

4   $(-8m) + 7m$ 5 $2m + 10m$ 6 $(-5m) + (-6m)$

7   $8m + 9m$ 8 $20m + (-4m)$ 9 $5m + (-10m)$

10   $(-9m) + (-7m)$ 11 $(-7m) + (-8m)$ 12 $3m + 12m$

Basic Skills and Number — Review of Book 3

Chapter Contents

Learning Outcomes

Students will be able to:
- Compare, order and calculate with integers.
- Operate with fractions, decimals, percentages, ratios and rates.
- Identify special angles and make use of the relationships between them.
- Classify, construct and determine the properties of triangles and quadrilaterals.

Areas of Interaction

Approaches to Learning (Knowledge Acquisition, Problem Solving, Logical Thinking, Reflection)

Note: A complete review of Book 3 content is found in Appendix A located on the Interactive Student CD.

This chapter is a summary of the work covered in *International Mathematics 3*. For an explanation of the work, refer to the cross-reference on the right-hand side of the page which will direct you to the Appendix on the Interactive Student CD.

1:01 | Basic Number Skills

Rational numbers: Integers, fractions, decimals and percentages (both positive and negative) are rational numbers. They can all be written as a terminating or recurring decimal. The following exercises will remind you of the skills you should have mastered.

A Order of operations

Exercise 1:01A

CD Appendix

Answer these questions without using a calculator.

1
  a $4 - (5 - 3)$
  b $6 - (9 - 4)$
  c $-4 + (3 + 1)$
  d $6 + 4 \times 2$
  e $9 - 3 \times 4$
  f $16 + 4 \div 4$
  g $10 \times 4 - 4 \times 7$
  h $30 \div 3 + 40 \div 2$
  i $5 \times 8 + 6 \times 5$
  j 5×2^2
  k 3×10^2
  l $3^2 + 4^2$
  m $6 + 3 \times 4 + 1$
  n $8 + 4 \div 2 + 1$
  o $6 - (-6 - 6)$

A:01A

2
  a $6 \times (5 - 4) + 3$
  b $27 \div (3 + 6) - 3$
  c $16 - [10 - (6 - 2)]$
  d $\dfrac{30 + 10}{30 - 10}$
  e $\dfrac{15 + 45}{45 + 5}$
  f $\dfrac{14}{14 - 7}$
  g $(6 + 3)^2$
  h $(10 + 4)^2$
  i $(19 - 9)^2$

A:01A

B Fractions

Exercise 1:01B

CD Appendix

1 Change to mixed numerals.
  a $\dfrac{7}{4}$
  b $\dfrac{49}{6}$
  c $\dfrac{15}{4}$
  d $\dfrac{11}{8}$

A:01B₁

2 Change to improper fractions.
  a $5\frac{1}{2}$
  b $3\frac{1}{7}$
  c $8\frac{3}{4}$
  d $66\frac{2}{3}$

A:01B₂

3 Simplify the fractions.
  a $\dfrac{48}{80}$
  b $\dfrac{70}{150}$
  c $\dfrac{200}{300}$
  d $\dfrac{250}{450}$

A:01B₃

4 Complete the following equivalent fractions.
  a $\dfrac{3}{4} = \dfrac{\square}{24}$
  b $\dfrac{2}{5} = \dfrac{\square}{50}$
  c $\dfrac{2}{7} = \dfrac{\square}{28}$
  d $\dfrac{1}{3} = \dfrac{\square}{120}$

A:01B₄

5
  a $\dfrac{7}{15} + \dfrac{1}{15}$
  b $\dfrac{13}{20} - \dfrac{2}{5}$
  c $\dfrac{5}{8} + \dfrac{3}{10}$
  d $\dfrac{6}{7} - \dfrac{3}{5}$

A:01B₅

6
  a $6\frac{1}{2} + 2\frac{3}{5}$
  b $4\frac{3}{4} - 2\frac{3}{10}$
  c $4\frac{3}{4} + 6\frac{1}{10}$
  d $5\frac{3}{8} - 1\frac{9}{10}$

A:01B₆

7
  a $\dfrac{3}{5} \times \dfrac{4}{7}$
  b $\dfrac{18}{25} \times \dfrac{15}{16}$
  c $\dfrac{4}{9} \times \dfrac{3}{10}$
  d $\dfrac{7}{10}$ of $\dfrac{2}{3}$

A:01B₇

8
  a $6 \times \dfrac{3}{4}$
  b $2\frac{1}{2} \times 1\frac{4}{5}$
  c $1\frac{1}{3} \times 15$
  d $10\frac{1}{2} \times 1\frac{3}{7}$

A:01B₈

9
  a $\dfrac{9}{10} \div \dfrac{2}{3}$
  b $\dfrac{3}{8} \div \dfrac{3}{5}$
  c $\dfrac{4}{5} \div 6$
  d $2\frac{3}{4} \div 1\frac{1}{2}$

A:01B₉

C Decimals

Exercise 1:01C

CD Appendix

A:01C₁

1 Put in order, smallest to largest.
   a {0·606, 0·6, 0·66, 0·066}   b {1·53, 0·153, 1·053}
   c {0·7, 0·017, 7, 0·77}   d {3·5, 3·45, 3·05, 3·4}

A:01C₂

2 Do not use your calculator to do these.
   a $7·301 + 2$ b $3·05 + 0·4$
   c $0·004 + 3·1$ d $6 + 0·3 + 0·02$
   e $8·67 - 6·7$ f $9·12 - 1·015$
   g $8 - 3·112$ h $162·3 - 3$

3 a $0·012 \times 3$ b $0·03 \times 0·2$ c $0·45 \times 1·3$ d $(0·05)^2$ A:01C₃
4 a $3·14 \times 10$ b $0·5 \times 1000$ c $0·0003 \times 100$ d $3·8 \times 10^4$ A:01C₄
5 a $0·15 \div 5$ b $1·06 \div 4$ c $15·35 \div 5$ d $0·01 \div 4$ A:01C₅
6 a $1·3 \div 3$ b $9·1 \div 11$ c $14 \div 9$ d $6 \div 7$ A:01C₆
7 a $48·04 \div 10$ b $1·6 \div 100$ c $0·9 \div 1000$ d $6·5 \div 10^4$ A:01C₇
8 a $8·4 \div 0·4$ b $0·836 \div 0·08$ c $7·5 \div 0·005$ d $1·4 \div 0·5$ A:01C₈

9 Express as a simplified fraction or mixed numeral. A:01C₉
   a $3·017$ b $0·04$ c $0·86$ d $16·005$

10 Express as a decimal. A:01C₁₀
   a $\dfrac{4}{5}$ b $\dfrac{7}{200}$ c $\dfrac{5}{8}$ d $\dfrac{8}{11}$

11 Express these recurring decimals as fractions. A:01C₁₁
   a $0·5555...$ b $0·257\ 257\ 2...$ c $0·7\dot{2}$ d $0·6\dot{4}\dot{2}$

12 Express these recurring decimals as fractions. A:01C₁₁
   a $0·8333...$ b $0·915\ 151\ 5...$ c $0·43\dot{5}$ d $0·8\dot{9}4\dot{2}$

D Percentages

Exercise 1:01D

CD Appendix

A:01D₁

1 Express as a fraction.
   a 54%   b 203%   c $12\frac{1}{4}\%$ d 9·1%

A:01D₂

2 Express as a percentage.
   a $\dfrac{11}{20}$ b $\dfrac{4}{9}$ c $1\frac{1}{4}$ d $\dfrac{2}{3}$

A:01D₃

3 Express as a decimal.
   a 16%   b 8·6%   c 3%   d $18\frac{1}{4}\%$

A:01D₄

4 Express as a percentage.
   a 0·47   b 0·06   c 0·375   d 1·3

5 a 36% of 400 m   b 9% of 84 g   c $8\frac{1}{2}\%$ of $32 A:01D₅
   d At the local Anglican church, the offertories for 2005 amounted to $127 000.
   If 68% of this money was used to pay the salary of the two full-time ministers,
   how much was paid to the ministers?

6   a   9% of Dahn's money was spent on fares. If $5.40 was spent on fares, how much money did Dahn have?

     b   70% of Alana's weight is 17·5 kg. How much does Alana weigh?

     c   Lyn bought a book for a reduced price of 70 cents. This was 14% of the book's recommended retail price. What was the recommended retail price?

     d   54 minutes of mathematics lesson time was lost in one week because of other activities. If this represents 30% of the allocated weekly time for mathematics, what is this allocated time?

A:01D$_6$

7   a   Express 85 cents as a percentage of $2.

     b   4 kg of sugar, 9 kg of flour and 7 kg of mixed fruit were mixed. What is the percentage (by weight) of flour in the mixture?

     c   Of 32 birds in Rachel's aviary, 6 are canaries. What percentage of her birds are canaries?

     d   When Australian cricketer Steve Waugh retired from test cricket in 2003, he had scored 32 centuries from 260 innings. In what percentage of his innings did he score centuries?

A:01D$_7$

E   Ratio

Exercise 1:01E

CD Appendix

1   a   Simplify each ratio.

       i $15 : $25   ii   9 kg : 90 kg   iii   75 m : 35 m   iv   120 m^2 : 40 m^2

     b   Find the ratio in simplest terms of 5·6 m to 40 cm.

     c   Giang spends $8 of $20 she was given by her grandparents and saves the rest. What is the ratio of money spent to money saved?

     d   Three-quarters of the class walk to school while $\frac{1}{5}$ ride bicycles. Find the ratio of those who walk to those who ride bicycles.

     e   At the end of their test cricket careers, Australian Steve Waugh had scored 50 fifties and 32 hundreds from 260 innings, while his brother Mark Waugh had scored 47 fifties and 20 hundreds from 209 innings.

       i   Find the ratio of the number of hundreds scored by Steve to the number scored by Mark.

       ii   Find the ratio of the number of times Steve scored 50 or more to the number of innings.

     f   Express each ratio in the form $X : 1$.

       i   3 : 5   ii   2 : 7   iii   10 : 3   iv   25 : 4

     g   Express each ratio in f in the form $1 : Y$.

A:01E$_1$

2   a   If $x : 15 = 10 : 3$, find the value of x.

     b   If the ratio of the populations of Africa and Europe is 5 : 4, find the population of Africa if Europe's population is 728 million.

     c   The ratio of the average population density per km^2 of Asia to that of Australia is 60 : 1. If the average in Asia is 152 people per km^2, what is the average in Australia?

     d   The ratio of the population of Sydney to the population of Melbourne is 7 : 6. If 4.2 million people live in Sydney, how many people live in Melbourne?

A:01E$_2$

3 **a** If 84 jellybeans are divided between Naomi and Luke in the ratio $4:3$, how many jellybeans does each receive?

  b The sizes of the angles of a triangle are in the ratio $2:3:4$. Find the size of each angle.

  c A total of 22 million people live in the cities of Tokyo and Moscow. If the ratio of the populations of Tokyo and Moscow is $6:5$, what is the population of each city?

  d At Christ Church, Cobargo, in 1914, there were 60 baptisms. The ratio of males to females who were baptised was $3:2$. How many of each were baptised?

A:01E₃

F Rates

Exercise 1:01F

CD Appendix

1 Complete these equivalent rates.

  a 5 km/min = . . . km/h   **b** 8 km/L = . . . m/mL
  c 600 kg/h = . . . t/day   **d** 2·075 cm³/g = . . . cm³/kg

A:01F

2 **a** At Cobargo in 1915, the Rector, H. E. Hyde, travelled 3396 miles by horse and trap. Find his average speed (to the nearest mile per hour) if it took a total of 564 hours to cover the distance.

  b Over a period of 30 working days, Adam earned \$1386. Find his average daily rate of pay.

  c Sharon marked 90 books in 7 hours. What rate is this in minutes per book?

  d On a hot day, our family used an average of 36 L of water per hour. Change this rate to cm³ per second (cm³/s).

A:01F

G Significant figures

Exercise 1:01G

CD Appendix

1 State the number of significant figures in each of the following.

a 21	**b** 4·6	**c** 2·52	**d** 0·616
e 16·32	**f** 106	**g** 3004	**h** 2·03
i 1·06	**j** 50·04	**k** 0·5	**l** 0·003
m 0·000 32	**n** 0·06	**o** 0·006	**p** 3·0
q 25·0	**r** 2·60	**s** 13·000	**t** 6·40
u 41 235	**v** 600 (to nearest	**w** 482 000 (to nearest	**x** 700 (to nearest
y 1600	hundred)	thousand)	ten)
z 16 000			

A:01G

2 State the number of significant figures in each of the following.

a 3·0	**b** 3·00	**c** 0·3	**d** 0·03
e 0.030	**f** 0.0030	**g** 0.0300	**h** 3.0300

A:01G

H Approximations

Exercise 1:01H

1 Approximate each of the following correct to one decimal place.

   a 4·63   b 0·81   c 3·17   d 0·062
   e 15·176   f 8·099   g 0·99   h 121·62
   i 0·119   j 47·417   k 0·35   l 2·75

A:01H

2 Approximate each of the following correct to two decimal places.

   a 0·537   b 2·613   c 7·134   d 1·169
   e 12·0163   f 8·399   g 412·678   h 0·0756
   i 0·4367   j 100·333   k 0·015   l 0·005

A:01H

3 Approximate each number correct to: i 1 sig. fig. ii 2 sig. figs.

   a 7·31   b 84·9   c 0·63   d 2·58
   e 4·16   f 0·0073   g 0·0828   h 3·05
   i 0·009 34   j 0·0098   k 7·52   l 0·0359

A:01H

4 Approximate each of the following numbers correct to the number of significant figures indicated.

   a 2·3 (1 sig. fig.)   b 14·63 (3 sig. figs.)   c 2·15 (2 sig. figs.)
   d 0·93 (1 sig. fig.)   e 4·07 (2 sig. figs.)   f 7·368 94 (3 sig. figs.)
   g 0·724 138 (3 sig. figs.)   h 5·716 (1 sig. fig.)   i 31·685 (4 sig. figs.)
   j 0·007 16 (1 sig. fig.)   k 0·78 (1 sig. fig.)   l 0·007 16 (2 sig. figs.)

A:01H

5 Approximate each of the following numbers correct to the number of decimal places indicated.

   a 5·61 (1 dec. pl.)   b 0·16 (1 dec. pl.)   c 0·437 (2 dec. pl.)
   d 15·37 (1 dec. pl.)   e 8·333 (2 dec. pl.)   f 413·789 (1 dec. pl.)
   g 71·98 (1 dec. pl.)   h 3·0672 (3 dec. pl.)   i 9·99 (1 dec. pl.)
   j 4·7998 (3 dec. pl.)   k 0·075 (2 dec. pl.)   l 0·0035 (3 dec. pl.)

A:01H

I Estimation

Exercise 1:01I

1 Give estimates for each of the following.

   a $12·7 \times 5·8$

   b $0·55 \times 210$

   c $17·8 \times 5·1 \times 0·336$

   d $15·6 \div 2·165$

   e $(4·62 + 21·7) \times 4·21$

   f $7·8 \times 5·2 + 21·7 \times 0·89$

   g $(0·93 + 1·72)(8·5 - 1·7)$

   h $\dfrac{43·7 + 18·2}{7·8 + 2·9}$

   i $\dfrac{101·6 - 51·7}{21·3 - 14·8}$

   j $\dfrac{0·68 \times 51}{0·25 \times 78}$

   k $\dfrac{11·6 - 3·92}{12·7 + 6·58}$

   l $3·52^2 \times \sqrt{17·9}$

   m $\sqrt{41·7 \times 5·6}$

   n $\sqrt{4·26} \times \sqrt{105·6}$

   o $3·1^3 \times 1·8^4$

   p $\dfrac{4·1 \times \sqrt{48·12}}{26·23}$

   q $\dfrac{15·7^2}{11·3 \times 3·1}$

   r $\dfrac{16·7}{2·15} + \dfrac{41·6}{4·7}$

   s $\dfrac{0·65}{0·01} - \dfrac{0·75 \times 3·6}{0·478}$

A:01I

1:02 | Algebraic Expressions

Exercise 1:02

CD Appendix

1. Simplify these expressions.

A:02A

   a $a + 5a$
   b $5y + 3y + 2y$
   c $5m - 3m$
   d $3x^2 - 2x^2$
   e $7k + 3k - 2k$
   f $20y - 10y - 5y$
   g $3a + 2b + 5a$
   h $7n + 10m - 3m$
   i $6m - 5 + 5m + 7$
   j $6x - y^2 + x + 2y^2$
   k $3ab - 5a + 2ab$
   l $7x^2 + 2xy - x^2 + 3xy$
   m $5a + 7 - 2a + 4b$
   n $9k + 5m - 3 - 2m$
   o $8x + 2y - 3z - 7x$

2. Simplify these products.

A:02B

   a $5y \times 7$
   b $\frac{1}{2} \times 10q$
   c $2x \times 3y$
   d $5a \times 4b$
   e $9m \times n$
   f $3m \times 2m$
   g $5ab \times 2a$
   h $5mn \times 2mn$
   i $(-5x) \times 4$
   j $(-4y) \times (-3)$
   k $(-10pq) \times (-\frac{1}{2}pq)$
   l $2m \times 3n \times 7$
   m $6a \times 2b \times 5a$
   n $(-5p) \times 2q \times (-3r)$

1:03 | Probability

Exercise 1:03

CD Appendix

1. Using the figures shown in the table, find the probability of selecting at random a matchbox containing:

A:03A

Number of matches	48	49	50	51	52
Number of boxes	3	6	10	7	4

   a 50 matches
   b 48 matches
   c more than 50
   d at least 50

2. A single dice is rolled. What is the probability of getting:

A:03B

   a a five?
   b less than 3?
   c an even number?
   d less than 7?

3. A bag contains 3 red, 4 white and 5 blue marbles. If one is selected from the bag at random, find the probability that it is:

A:03B

   a white
   b red or white
   c *not* red
   d pink

4. A pack of cards has four suits, hearts and diamonds (both red), and spades and clubs (both black). In each suit there are 13 cards: Ace, 2, 3, 4, 5, 6, 7, 8, 9, 10, Jack, Queen and King. The Jack, Queen and King are called *court* cards.

A:03C

   A card is drawn from a standard pack. What is the probability that the card is:

   a red?
   b not red?
   c a six?
   d not a six?
   e a court card?
   f a red Ace?
   g a spade?
   h a red thirteen?
   i either a red five or a ten?
   j either a heart or a black Ace?
   k either a blue five or a seven?
   l either a heart or a black card?

In each of these cases, the events may not be mutually exclusive.

m either a court card or a diamond?

n either a number larger than two or a club?

o either a heart or a five?

p either a Queen or a black court card?

q either a number between two and eight or an even-numbered heart?

> ■ Since there are 4 suits with 13 cards in each suit, the number of cards in a standard pack is 52. (In some games a Joker is also used.)

1:04 | Geometry

Exercise 1:04

CD Appendix

A:04A

1 a

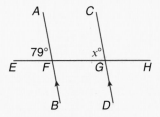

Find x.
Give reasons.

b

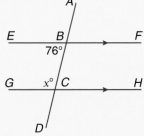

Find the size of x.
Give reasons.

c

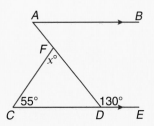

Find the size of x.
Give reasons.

d

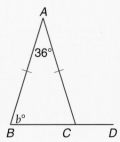

Find the value of b.
Give reasons.

e

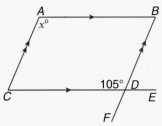

ABDC is a parallelogram. Find the size of x. Give reasons.

f

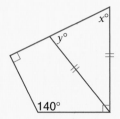

Find the value of x and y.
Give reasons.

2 a What is the sum of the interior angles of:
  i a hexagon?   **ii** a decagon?

    b What is the size of each interior angle in these regular polygons?
  i   **ii**

    c What is the sum of the exterior angles of an octagon?

    d Find the size of each exterior angle of these regular polygons.
  i   **ii**

A:04B

1:05 | Indices

Exercise 1:05

CD Appendix

1 Write in index form.

A:05A

    a $a \times a \times a$ **b** $2 \times 2 \times 2 \times 2$
    c $n \times n \times n \times n \times n$ **d** $10 \times 10 \times 10$

2 Simplify, giving your answers in index form.

A:05B

    a $2^4 \times 2^5$ **b** $a^3 \times a^2$ **c** $m \times m^4$ **d** $10^6 \times 10^2$
    e $a^{10} \div a^2$ **f** $y^4 \div y^3$ **g** $b^3 \div b$ **h** $10^5 \div 10^2$
    i $(m^3)^4$ **j** $(a^2)^3$ **k** $(x^4)^2$ **l** $(10^5)^2$
    m $a^0 \times 3$ **n** $b^0 + c^0$ **o** $6y^0$ **p** $e^6 \div e^6$
    q $6a^2 \times 5$ **r** $6m^3 \div 3$ **s** $6a \times 5a$ **t** $(4x^4)^2$

3 Simplify.

A:05B

    a $6a^4 \times 5ab^3$ **b** $7a^2b^2 \times 8a^3b$ **c** $4a^2b^3 \times 6a^2b^4$
    d $10a^7 \times a^3b^3$ **e** $(7x^3)^2$ **f** $(2m^2)^4$
    g $(x^2y^3)^3$ **h** $(5xy^2)^4$ **i** $30a^5 \div 5a^3$
    j $100x^4 \div 20x$ **k** $36a^3b^4 \div 12a^2b^4$ **l** $8y^7z^2 \div y^7z^2$

4 Rewrite without a negative index.

A:05C

    a 4^{-1} **b** 10^{-1} **c** x^{-1} **d** $2a^{-1}$
    e 5^{-2} **f** 2^{-3} **g** m^{-3} **h** $5x^{-2}$

5 Rewrite each of the following with a negative index.

A:05C

    a $\dfrac{1}{3}$ **b** $\dfrac{1}{8}$ **c** $\dfrac{1}{a}$ **d** $\dfrac{3}{x}$

    e $\dfrac{1}{2^4}$ **f** $\dfrac{1}{10^6}$ **g** $\dfrac{1}{y^4}$ **h** $\dfrac{5}{n^3}$

6 Find the value of the following.

A:05D

    a $9^{\frac{1}{2}}$ **b** $36^{\frac{1}{2}}$ **c** $8^{\frac{1}{3}}$ **d** $27^{\frac{1}{3}}$

7 Rewrite, using fractional indices.

    a $\sqrt{a}$ **b** $\sqrt[3]{y}$ **c** $5\sqrt{m}$ **d** $\sqrt{16x}$

A:05D

8 Write these numbers in scientific (or standard) notation.

    a 148 000 000   **b** 68 000   **c** 0·000 15   **d** 0·000 001 65

A:05E

9 Write these as basic numerals.

    a $6\cdot2 \times 10^4$ **b** $1\cdot15 \times 10^6$ **c** $7\cdot4 \times 10^{-3}$ **d** $6\cdot91 \times 10^{-5}$

A:05E

1:06 | Measurement

Exercise 1:06

CD Appendix

1 Find the perimeter of the following figures.

A:06A

  a   **b**   **c**

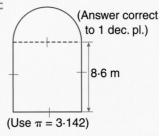

(Answer correct to 1 dec. pl.)

(Use π = 3·142)

2 Find the area of each plane shape. (Answer to 2 dec. pl.)

A:06B

  a   **b**   **c**

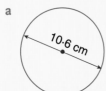

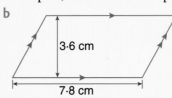

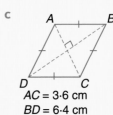

$AC = 3\cdot6$ cm
$BD = 6\cdot4$ cm

3 Find the area of the following shaded figures (correct to 3 sig. figs.).

A:06C

  a   **b**   **c**

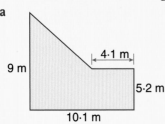

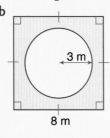

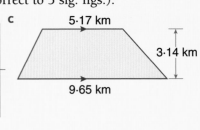

4 Find the surface area of the following solids.

A:06D

  a   **b**   **c**

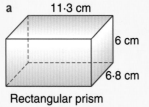

Rectangular prism

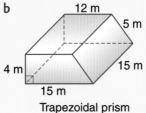

Trapezoidal prism

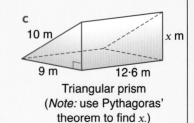

Triangular prism
(*Note:* use Pythagoras' theorem to find *x*.)

1:07 | Equations and Inequations

CD Appendix

1 Solve the following.

a $a + 7 = 25$ b $m - 6 = -1$ c $5x = 75$

d $10 - y = 12$ e $3p = 7$ f $\dfrac{n}{4} = 3$

g $2x + 3 = 7$ h $3q - 5 = 1$ i $8m + 5 = 21$

j $5y + 2 = 3$ k $2x - 7 = 10$ l $9k - 1 = 5$

m $5 + 3x = 11$ n $10 - 7y = 3$ o $15 - 2q = 8$

A:07A

2 Solve the following.

a $5m + 2 = 4m + 7$ b $3x - 7 = 2x - 3$ c $5x + 2 = 6x - 5$

d $4p + 2 = 2p + 10$ e $5n - 6 = 3n + 2$ f $7m - 3 = 2m + 7$

g $2a + 3 = 3a - 5$ h $3m - 2 = 5m - 10$ i $q + 7 = 8q + 14$

j $10 - 2x = x + 4$ k $2y + 5 = 2 - y$ l $3 + 8p = 29 - 5p$

m $2k - 3 = 4k + 8$ n $3z + 7 = z + 10$ o $6y - 3 = 2y + 8$

p $5n + 4 = 8n + 2$ q $10 - q = 9 + 3q$ r $13 - 2m = 9 - 5m$

A:07B

3 Solve these equations involving grouping symbols.

a $5(a + 1) = 15$ b $4(x - 3) = 16$ c $4(5 - x) = 8$

d $3(2x + 5) = 33$ e $9(1 + 2m) = 0$ f $2(2k - 7) = 15$

g $3(5 - 2a) = 27$ h $4(3 - 2x) = 36$ i $3(2m - 5) = 11$

j $3(a + 2) + 2(a + 5) = 36$ k $2(p + 3) + p + 1 = 31$

l $2(x + 5) = x + 16$ m $2(y - 3) = 3(y + 1)$

n $4(2b + 7) = 2(3b - 4)$ o $4(2y + 3) + 3(y - 1) = 2y$

p $3(m - 4) - (m + 2) = 0$ q $2m - 3(1 - m) = 22$

r $5(y - 3) - 3(1 - 2y) = 4$ s $4(2x - 1) - 2(x + 3) = 5$

A:07C

4 Solve these equations.

a $\dfrac{5x}{2} = 10$ b $\dfrac{2a}{3} = 6$ c $\dfrac{3m}{5} = 4$

d $\dfrac{n + 1}{5} = 2$ e $\dfrac{x - 4}{2} = 1$ f $\dfrac{2p + 5}{3} = 1$

A:07D

5 Write the set of x that has been graphed below.

a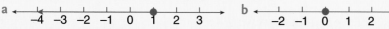
b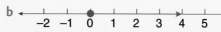

c
d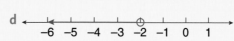

A:07E

6 Solve these inequations and show the solution to each on a number line.

a $x + 7 > 11$ b $a - 5 < 3$ c $10 - y \geq 8$

d $3m \leq 21$ e $15 < 4x$ f $\dfrac{m}{4} \leq 1$

g $2x + 1 > 5$ h $5m - 3 \geq 6$ i $7 - 3n \geq 4$

j $5x + 6 > x + 18$ k $3x - 5 < x + 6$ l $m + 3 \geq 2m - 7$

m $3 - a \leq 5 - 2a$

A:07E

1:08 | Coordinate Geometry

Exercise 1:08

CD Appendix

1 a What are the coordinates of the origin?
   b What is the name of the vertical axis?
   c What is the name of the horizontal axis?
   d In which quadrant does $(-3, -2)$ lie?

A:09A

2 On the same number plane, graph these straight lines.
   a $y = 3x - 2$ b $x + y = 4$ c $y = -2x + 3$

A:09B

3 a Which of the following points lie on the line $y = 3x - 11$?
      $\{(0, 0), (3, -2), (1, 4), (5, 4), (10, 41)\}$
   b Which of the following lines pass through the point $(0, 2)$?
      $\{y = 2x, y = 2x - 2, y = x + 2, y = 5x + 2, x + y = 2\}$

A:09C

4 a Write down the equation of the line which is:
       i parallel to the x-axis and 2 units above it
      ii parallel to the x-axis and 3 units below it
     iii the x-axis
      iv parallel to the y-axis and 2 units to the right of it
       v parallel to the y-axis and 1 unit to the left of it
      vi the y-axis
   b On the same number plane, graph the following lines.
       i $y = 3$ ii $y = -1$ iii $x = 4$ iv $x = -2$

A:09D

5 a Find the gradient of AB in each case.
   i 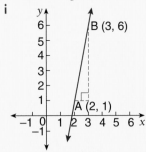   ii 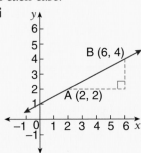   iii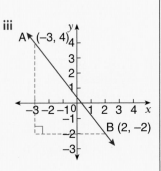

A:09G

6 Find the gradient and y-intercept of the following lines.
   a $y = 4x + 7$ b $y = x - 3$ c $y = -2x + 5$

A:09H

7 Find the equation of a line that has:
   a a gradient of 4 and a y-intercept of 5
   b a gradient of $-\frac{1}{2}$ and a y-intercept of 3
   c a gradient of 2 and passes through the point $(0, -4)$
   d a y-intercept of -3 and a gradient of -7

A:09H

12 INTERNATIONAL MATHEMATICS 4

1:09 | Statistics

Exercise 1:09

CD Appendix

1 In a game, a dice was rolled 50 times, yielding the results below. Organise these results into a frequency distribution table and answer the questions.

A:10A

5	4	1	3	2	6	2	1	4	5
5	1	3	2	6	3	2	4	4	1
6	2	5	1	6	6	6	5	3	2
6	3	4	2	4	1	4	2	4	4
2	3	1	5	4	2	2	3	2	1

    a Which number on the dice was rolled most often?

    b Which number had the lowest frequency?

    c How often did a 3 appear?

    d For how many throws was the result an odd number?

    e On how many occasions was the result greater than 3?

2 Use the information in question **1** to draw, on separate diagrams:

    a a frequency histogram

    b a frequency polygon

A:10B

3 **a** For the scores 5, 1, 8, 4, 3, 5, 5, 2, 4, find:

       i the range   **ii** the mode   **iii** the mean   **iv** the median

    b Use your table from question **1** to find, for the scores in question **1**:

       i the range   **ii** the mode   **iii** the mean   **iv** the median

    c Copy your table from question **1** and add a cumulative frequency column.

       i What is the cumulative frequency of the score 4?

       ii How many students scored 3 or less?

       iii Does the last figure in your cumulative frequency column equal the total of the frequency column?

A:10C

4 Use your table in question **3** to draw on the same diagram:

    a a cumulative frequency histogram

    b a cumulative frequency polygon

A:10D

5 The number of cans of drink sold by a shop each day was as follows:

30	28	42	21	⑤④	47	36
37	22	⑱	25	26	43	50
23	29	30	19	28	20	40
33	35	31	27	42	26	44
53	50	29	20	32	41	36
51	46	37	42	27	28	31
29	32	41	36	32	41	35
41	29	39	46	36	36	33
29	37	38	25	27	19	28
47	51	28	47	36	35	40

It's fizz–tastic!

DRINK...

The highest and lowest scores are circled.

a Tabulate these results using classes of 16–22, 23–29, 30–36, 37–43, 44–50, 51–57. Make up a table using these column headings: Class, Class centre, Tally, Frequency, Cumulative frequency.

b What was the mean number of cans sold?

c Construct a cumulative frequency histogram and cumulative frequency polygon (or ogive) and find the median class.

d What is the modal class?

e Over how many days was the survey held?

1:10 | Formulae and Problem-Solving

Exercise 1:10

1 Write down expressions for:

a the sum of $3a$ and $4b$

b the product of $3a$ and $4b$

c the difference between k and m, if k is greater than m

d the average of x, y and z

e twice the sum of m and 5

f the square of the difference between a and b

g the square root of the sum of $5m$ and $4n$

h the sum of three consecutive integers, if the first one is m

2 If $a = 3$, $b = 5$ and $c = -6$, find the value of:

a $a + c$

b $2a + 3b$

c $a + b + c$

d $\frac{1}{2}c^2$

e $ac - b^2$

f $a^2 + c^2$

g $\frac{3b - c}{2a}$

h $\sqrt{ab + c}$

i $\sqrt{\dfrac{3c}{a - b}}$

3 If $x = 2.1$, $y = 3.5$ and $z = 2.8$, evaluate P if:

a $P = 2x + 3y$

b $P = \dfrac{x + y}{z}$

c $P = \dfrac{x + z}{x - z}$

4 **a** If $s = ut + \frac{1}{2}at^2$, find s if $u = 9$, $t = 4$ and $a = 7$.

b Given $F = p + qr$, find F if $p = 2.3$, $q = 3.9$ and $r = 0.9$.

c For the formula $T = a + (n - 1)d$, find T if $a = 9.2$, $n = 6$ and $d = 1.3$.

1:11 | Graphs of Physical Phenomena

Exercise 1:11

CD Appendix

1

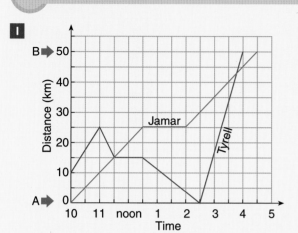

The travel graph shows the journeys of Jamar and Tyrell between town A and town B. (They travel on the same road.)

A:12A

a How far from A is Tyrell when he commences his journey?

b How far is Jamar from B at 2:30 pm?

c When do Jamar and Tyrell first meet?

d Who reaches town B first?

e At what time does Tyrell stop to rest?

f How far does Jamar travel?

g How far apart are Jamar and Tyrell when Tyrell is at town A?

h How far does Tyrell travel?

2 a What did the baby weigh at birth?

b What was the baby's weight at 4 weeks of age?

c By how much did the baby's weight increase in the first two weeks of age?

d By how much did the baby's weight increase from 2 weeks of age to 4 weeks of age?

e Considering your answer to parts **c** and **d**, in which period, (0–2) or (2–4) was the baby's rate of growth the greatest?

A:12B

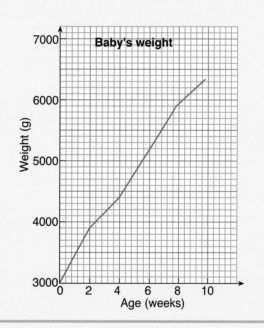

Chapter 1 | Working Mathematically

1 Complete a table of values for each matchstick pattern below, and hence find the rule for each, linking the number of coloured triangles (t) to the number of matches (m).

a

t	1	3	5
m			

b

t	2	4	6
m			

c

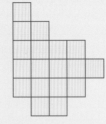

t	1	3	6
m			

2 Divide this shape into three pieces that have the same shape.

3 Ryan answered all 50 questions in a maths competition in which he received 4 marks for each correct answer but lost one mark for each incorrect answer.
   a What is Ryan's score if he answered 47 questions correctly?
   b How many answers did he get right if his score was 135?

4 It takes 3 min 15 s to join two pieces of pipe. How long would it take to join 6 pieces of pipe into one length?

5 A number of cards can be shared between 4 people with no remainder. When shared between 5 or 6 people, there are two cards left over. If there are fewer than 53 cards, how many are there?

6 From August 2003 to August 2004, the unemployment rate fell from 6·0% to 5·6%.

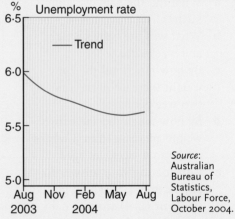

% Unemployment rate

Source: Australian Bureau of Statistics, Labour Force, October 2004.

   a If the number of unemployed in August 2000 was 576 400, how many were unemployed in August 2003? Answer correct to four significant figures.
   b If 576 400 represents 5·6% of the total workforce, what is the size of the total workforce? Answer correct to four significant figures.
   c If the rate of 5·6% is only correct to one decimal place, the rate could really be from 5·55% to 5·65%. How many people does this approximation range of 0·1% represent?

2
Proportion

Chapter Contents

Learning Outcomes

Students will be able to:
- Solve problems relating to direct proportion.
- Solve problems relating to inverse proportion.

Areas of Interaction

Approaches to Learning (Knowledge Acquisition, Reflection), Human Ingenuity,
Environments, Community & Service

2:01 | Review — Proportional Change

In Book 3 you learnt that if all parts of an object or shape are increased or decreased by the same ratio or fraction then the original shape or object and the new shape or object are said to be in proportion.

worked examples

1 A photograph and its enlargement are in proportion. One of the photographs measures 10 cm long and 8 cm wide. If the other is 15 cm long, how wide is it?

A ratio is the same as a fraction.

2 Three girls can paint 18 m of fence in one day. How many metres of fence can 5 girls paint if they all paint at the same rate?

Solutions

1 The two lengths and the two widths go together. Let the unknown width be w.

$$\therefore \frac{w}{8} = \frac{15}{10}$$

> ■ The ratio of the widths = the ratio of the lengths

$$w = \frac{15}{10} \times 8$$

$$w = 12 \text{ cm}$$

2 The number of girls and the amount of fencing go together. Let the unknown amount of fencing be f.

$$\therefore \frac{f}{18} = \frac{5}{3}$$

> ■ The ratio of the number of girls = the ratio of the fencing

$$f = \frac{5}{3} \times 18$$

$$f = 30 \text{ m}$$

These are examples of **direct proportion** because as one item increases (eg: the number of girls) the other item (the amount of fencing) increases as well. Sometimes these examples are also called **direct variation**.

Exercise 2:01

1 150 kg of fertiliser costs $975. How much would 180 kg of the same fertiliser cost?

2 It costs Ben €3.36 in fuel costs to drive his car 550 km.
   a How much would it cost him to drive 800 km?
   b How far can he drive for $100? (Answer to the nearest whole kilometre.)

3 Cycling at a steady pace, Bob can cycle 260 km in 4 days.
   a How long would it take him to cycle 585 km?
   b How far would he be able to cycle in 6 days?

4 When making a cake for 4 people, Lotty needs 6 eggs.
  a How many eggs would she need if she were making a cake for 10 people?
  b How big a cake could she make with 9 eggs?

5 It has been estimated that 38 000-kilojoule survival pack would be enough to sustain 4 people for a period of 5 days. Keeping this proportion:
  a How many kilojoules would be required for 7 people for 3 days?
  b How many days would a 133 000 kilojoule pack last 4 people?
  c How many people could survive on a 114 000 kilojoule pack for 3 days?

6 As a general rule a minimum of 60 m² is required for every 5 people working in an office. Keeping this proportion:
  a How much space would be required for 4 people?
  b What would be the maximum number of people that could work in a space of 200 m²?

7 A telephone call lasting 4 minutes 20 seconds cost $6.50. If the cost is proportional to the length of the call:
  a How much would be the cost of a 5 minute, 10 second call?
  b How long could your call be if you had $9.00 to spend?

8 A leaky tap leaks 2.25 L of water in 3 hours. At this rate:
  a How much will leak in 5 hours?
  b How long will it take for 5 litres to leak?

9 Fourteen cans of cat food can feed 10 cats for 3 days. At this rate:
  a How many days would 21 cans feed 10 cats?
  b How many cans would be needed to feed 10 cats for 9 days?
  c How many cans would be needed to feed 15 cats for 3 days?

10 For a certain species of tree, 5 mature trees can produce the same amount of oxygen inhaled by 250 people over a 4-year period.
  a Over a 4-year period, how many people inhale the oxygen produced by 7 mature trees?
  b How many trees would be required to produce the oxygen needed for 100 people over a 4-year period?
  c How many trees would be required to produce the oxygen inhaled by 250 people over a 10-year period?

2:02 | A New Approach

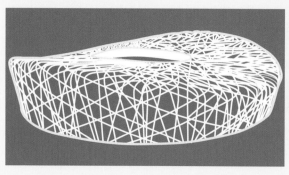

The symbol $\propto$ means 'is proportional to' so if we look again at example 1 from the previous section:

Any length on the enlargement (L) is proportional to the corresponding length on the original photograph (l).

We can write this as $\qquad L \propto l$

Since, to be in proportion, all the lengths are multiplied by the same factor we can write

$$L \propto l$$

$$\therefore L = kl \quad \text{where } k = \text{the \textbf{proportional constant} or \textbf{constant of variation}}$$

So for example 1 $\qquad L \propto l$

$\therefore\ L = kl \qquad$ Now substitute values that are known:

$\therefore 15 = k \times 10 \quad$ the lengths of the two photographs.

$\therefore\ k = \dfrac{15}{10}$

So now we know that for any length on the original photograph (l), the corresponding length on the enlargement (L) is given by

$$L = \frac{15}{10}l$$

So if the width of the original is 8 cm, the corresponding width of the enlargement is given by

$$L = \frac{15}{10} \times 8 = 12 \text{ cm}$$

You can see the same ratio appearing in the working out for both methods.

Now, let's try example 2 from the previous section:

We are looking for the amount of fencing (f) which is proportional to the number of girls (g).

$$f \propto g$$
$$\therefore\ f = kg$$
$$\therefore 18 = k \times 3$$
$$\therefore\ k = \frac{18}{3} = 6$$
$$\therefore\ f = 6g$$
$$\text{Now} \qquad f = 6 \times 5$$
$$\therefore\ f = 30 \text{ m}$$

This may seem like a long way round to get to the answer but it will help in the next section.

Exercise 2:02

Set up a proportion statement using the proportional constant to solve the following questions.

1 The height (h) of a plant is directly proportional to the number of days (d) it has been growing.
  a Write a proportional statement to help you find the height of the plant.
  b If the plant is 80 cm high after 3 days
    i what is the proportional constant?
    ii how high will it be after 5 days?

2 The mass (m) of a liquid varies directly as its volume (v).
  a Write a proportional statement to help you find the volume of the liquid.
  b Four litres of the liquid has a mass of 11 kg.
    i What is the constant of variation?
    ii If the mass of the liquid is 5 kg, what volume is present?

3 The amount of sealing paint (p) required for a job is proportional to the area (a) to be painted.
  a Write a proportional statement to help you find the area to be painted.
  b If 5 litres of paint covers an area of 37 m²
    i what is the proportional constant?
    ii what area could be covered with 9 litres of paint?

4 The number of toys (n) produced by a machine is directly proportional to the length of time (t) it operates.
  a Write a proportional statement to help you find the number of toys made.
  b If the machine can make 19 toys in 5 hours
    i what is the proportional constant?
    ii how many *whole* toys could be made in 12 hours?

5 The length of a ditch (l) is directly proportional to both the number of men (n) and the amount of time (t) they spend digging it.
  a Write two proportional statements to help you find the length of the ditch.
  b If it takes 6 men 4 days to dig a ditch 10 m long, find the length of a ditch that could be dug by 9 men in 6 days.
  c Write the ratio of men:days:length for each case. What do you notice?

Investigation 2:02 | A proportional flip

Please use the Assessment Grid on the following page to help you understand what is required for this Investigation.

Consider the following situations:

1 It takes 5 men 15 hours to build brick wall. How long would it take:

  a 1 man?   **b** 3 men?

2 Four women can row a boat 25 km in 3 hours. How long will it take:

  a 1 woman to row the same distance?

  b 3 women to row the same distance?

3 18 tins of 'Yum' dog food can will last 3 dogs an average of 5 days.

  How long will the same amount of dog food last:

  a 1 dog?   **b** 5 dogs?

4 12 boy scouts can paint a fence in a day.

  How long would it take:

  a 1 scout?   **b** 15 scouts?

Complete the table with answers from the questions.

1	Time for 5 men	Time for 1 man	Time for 3 men
	15 hours		
2	Time for 4 women	Time for 1 woman	Time for 3 women
	3 hours		
3	Time for 3 dogs	Time for 1 dog	Time for 5 dogs
	5 days		
4	Time for 12 scouts	Time for 1 scout	Time for 15 scouts
	1 day		

5 What do you notice about the answers for the time in each case as the number of men, women, dogs and scouts

  i decreases?   **ii** increases?

6 Do you think that these types of problems still refer to proportion? Explain your answer in as much detail as you can.

7 Try to write two more examples of this type of situation.

Assessment Grid for Investigation 2:02 | **A proportional flip**

The following is a sample assessment grid for this investigation. You should carefully read the criteria *before* beginning the investigation so that you know what is required.

			Assessment Criteria (B, C, D) for this investigation		Achieved ✓
Criterion B Investigating Patterns	a		None of the following descriptors has been achieved.	0	
	b		Some help was needed to apply mathematical techniques and problem solving to recognise the patterns.	1	
				2	
	c		Mathematical problem solving techniques have been applied and patterns recognised. A general rule has been suggested.	3	
				4	
	d		The correct techniques have been applied and patterns recognised are described as a general rule. Conclusions have been drawn consistent with the results.	5	
				6	
	e		All of the above have been achieved and conclusions are justified with a proof or further examples.	7	
				8	
Criterion C Communication in Mathematics	a		None of the following descriptors has been achieved.	0	
	b		There is a basic use of mathematical language and representation. Lines of reasoning are hard to follow.	1	
				2	
	c		There is a sufficient use of mathematical language and representation. Lines of reasoning are clear but not always logical or complete.	3	
				4	
	d		A good use of mathematical language and representation. Lines of reasoning are complete and concise.	5	
				6	
Criterion D Reflection in Mathematics	a		None of the following descriptors has been achieved.	0	
	b		An attempt has been made to explain whether the results make sense. An attempt has been made to draw a connection to real-life problems.	1	
				2	
	c		There is a correct but brief explanation of whether the results make sense. A description of a real life application is given in question 7.	3	
				4	
	d		There is a critical explanation of whether the results make sense. Examples given in question 7 provide detailed applications of inverse proportion.	5	
				6	

2:03 | Inverse Proportion (Inverse Variation)

In Investigation 2:02 you found that as the number of one thing in the problem decreased, the other increased.

For example, if it takes 5 men 15 hours to do a job, it will take 1 man $15 \times 5 = 75$ hours to do the same job. So, as the number of men decreases, the time taken to do the job increases.

Likewise, if it takes 1 man 75 hours to do the job, it will take 3 men $\dfrac{75}{3} = 25$ hours to do the same job. So, as the number of men increases, the time taken to do the job decreases.

These are examples of **inverse proportion** (sometimes referred to as **inverse variation**).

worked example

If I travel at 50 km/h it will take me 3 hours to complete my journey. How long will it take to complete the journey if I travel at 60 km/h?

The faster I travel, the less time it takes, so this is an example of inverse proportion.

There are 2 methods of solving problems of this type:

Method 1:   Unitary method
This requires us to find out how long it takes when travelling at 1 km/h and then at 60 km/h.

At 50 km/h it takes 3 hours
At 1 km/h it will take $3 \times 50 = 150$ hours
At 60 km/h it will take $\dfrac{150}{60} = 2\frac{1}{2}$ hours

The time taken is inversely proportional to the speed travelled. In other words: hasta la vista baby!

Method 2:   Using a proportional statement
Since this is an example of inverse proportion, time (t) is inversely proportional to speed (s).

$\therefore t \propto \dfrac{1}{s}$

$\therefore t = \dfrac{k}{s}$ this is $k \times \dfrac{1}{s}$

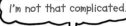

Remember: write the proportional statement then work out k.

I'm not that complicated.

Using the information we have been given: $3 = \dfrac{k}{50}$

$\therefore k = 3 \times 50 = 150$

$\therefore k = \dfrac{150}{s}$

So to solve the problem: $t = \dfrac{150}{60}$

$\therefore t = 2\frac{1}{2}$ hours

Exercise 2:03

1 A water tank is leaking so that after 4 hours the water in the tank is only 20 cm deep. How deep will the water be after 10 hours?

2 Eight people can survive on the provisions in a life raft for 6 days. For how long could 3 people survive on the same provisions?

3 If 4 boys can mow 10 lawns in three days, how many days would it take 6 boys?

4 Five teenage boys can eat 3 jumbo pizzas in 30 minutes. How long would the pizzas last if there were 4 teenage boys sharing them?

5 A Boeing 747 jumbo jet with a cruising speed of Mach 0.85 flies from Singapore to London in 14 hours. How long would it take an Airbus A320 with a cruising speed of Mach 0.82 to fly the same route? Answer to the nearest minute.

6 A team of 10 fruit pickers can clear 4 hectares of fruit in a week.
  a How many days would it take 14 fruit pickers?
  b If the 4 hectares had to be cleared in 2 days, how many fruit pickers would be needed?

7 Typing at 30 words per minute, Michael will be able to finish his essay in 2 hours. His friend Michelle says that she would be able to finish it in 1 and a half hours. At what speed must she be able to type to do this?

8 If it takes 5 cats 2 days to catch 6 mice, how many days will it take 3 cats to catch 9 mice? *Hint*: It might be useful to set up a table with the headings shown.

Cats	Days	Mice

9 If 3 boys take 2 days to mow 3 lawns, how many boys can mow 6 lawns in 3 days?

10 If 2 workers can paint 12 metres of fence in 3 hours, how many metres of fence can 4 workers paint in 2 hours?

Mathematical Terms 2

Ratio
- A comparison of two quantities

Proportion
- When all aspects of an object or shape are increased or decreased by the same amount

Proportional constant
- The numerical factor by which both objects are increased or decreased in the given ratio

Direct proportion
- When both variables increase at a given ratio, ie if one number is multiplied by a constant then the other is multiplied by the same value

Inverse proportion
- When one variable increase at a given ratio as the other decreases, ie if one number is multiplied by a constant then the other is divided by the same value

Mathematical terms 2

Diagnostic Test 2: | Proportion

- Each section of the test has similar items that test a certain type of example.
- Failure in more than one item will identify an area of weakness.
- Each weakness should be treated by going back to the section listed.

		Section
1	Which of the following are examples of direct proportion and which are examples of inverse proportion? a The ingredients of a cake and the number of people that are going to eat it. b The number of people eating a cake and the time taken to eat it. c The speed at which you travel and the time taken to finish the journey. d The speed at which you travel and the distance you are from your starting point. e The number of horses in a stable and the amount of fodder for required to feed them.	2:01 to 2:03
2	If I am travelling at 50 km/h, I am 40 km from my starting point. How far would I be if I had been travelling at 80 km/h?	2:01
3	The SRC has estimated that 30 pieces of pizza will be needed to feed the 12 people attending a meeting. How many pieces would be needed to feed 18 people?	2:01
4	The 30 pieces of pizza in the previous question will last the 12 people 20 minutes. How long would the same number of pieces last 18 people?	2:03
5	The amount of water in a leaking tank is inversely proportional to the time it has been leaking. If, after 4 hours there are 50 litres left in the tank, how many litres will be left after 5 hours?	2:03

6 It is estimated that when travelling from Singapore to Frankfurt, a distance of approximately 10 000 km, a person is responsible for releasing 1300 kg of CO_2 into the atmosphere. If emissions are proportional to the distance flown

   a what is the proportional constant and what does it represent?

   b how many kilograms of CO_2 is a person responsible for if they fly from Bangkok to Sydney, a distance of 7500 km? Answer to the nearest kilogram.

7 At a particular, time Emma's distance from home is directly proportional to the speed at which she travels. If her proportional constant is 8

   a how far is she from home if she travels at 55 km/h?

   b at what speed must she be traveling if she is 240 km from home?

   c what does the proportional constant represent in the context of the problem?

8 When swimming the 1500 m freestyle, the time Marko has remaining to swim is inversely proportional to the speed at which he is swimming. If his proportional constant is 600:

   a What time has he left when swimming at 100 metres/minute?

   b How fast must he be swimming if he has $12\frac{1}{2}$ minutes left?

   c What does the proportional constant represent?

Chapter 2 | Revision Assignment

1 When cooking rice, the ratio of water to rice is 4:3. How much water will I need to cook 500 grams of rice?

2 Jasmine receives a pay increase in the ratio 9:7. If her weekly income was $550, what will be her new weekly wage?

3 A 4 litre can of paint will cover 18 m² of wall. Write down a formula connecting the number of litres, n, and the area covered, A. How many litres would be needed to paint a room with wall area 40·5 m²?

4 The speed of a falling object is directly proportional to the time from release. If the speed after 5 seconds is 49 m per second:
   a what will the speed of the object be at 8 seconds?
   b how long till the object reaches 100 m/sec?

5 In order to buy goods from overseas you must work out how many Australian dollars (AUD$) are equal to the amount in the overseas currency.

Eg, if AUD$1.00 is worth USD$0.7370, then USD$15.00 ÷ 0·7370 = AUD$20.35. Use the information above and below to answer parts **a** and **b**:
AUD$1.00 is worth 6·03 Chinese yuan, or 78·14 Japanese yen.
   a Convert these amounts to AUD$.
      USD$50.00
      30.00 yuan
      2000 yen
   b When arriving overseas, Australian tourists convert Australian dollars into the local currency. Convert AUD$100.00 into USD$, Chinese yuan and Japanese yen.

6 If it takes me 2 hours to drive to my beach house at 80 km/h, how long would it take me if I drove at 100 km/h?

7 If 35 workers could do a job in 5 days
   a how long would it take 20 workers?
   b how many workers are required to complete the job in 3 days?

3

Consumer Arithmetic

Chapter Contents

Learning Outcomes

Students will be able to:

• Solve problems involving earning and spending money.
• Solve problems involving compound interest, depreciation and successive discounts.

Areas of Interaction

Approaches to Learning (Knowledge Acquisition, Reflection), Human Ingenuity, Environments, Community & Service

3:01 | Working for Others

Some people work for themselves and charge a fee for their services or sell for a profit, but most people work for others to obtain an income. In the chart below, the main ways of earning an income from an employer are introduced.

Employment				
Salary	*Piece work*	*Casual*	*Commission*	*Wages*
Meaning				
A fixed amount is paid for the year's work even though it may be paid weekly or fortnightly.	The worker is paid a fixed amount for each piece of work completed.	A fixed rate is paid per hour. The person is not permanent but is employed when needed.	This payment is usually a percentage of the value of goods sold.	Usually paid weekly to a permanent employee and based on an hourly rate, for an agreed number of hours per week.
Advantages				
Permanent employment. Holiday and sick pay. Superannuation. A bonus may be given as an incentive or time off for working outside normal working hours.	The harder you work, the more you earn. You can choose how much work you do and in some cases the work may be done in your own home.	A higher rate of pay is given as a compensation for other benefits lost. Part time work may suit some or casual work may be a second job. Superannuation.	The more you sell the more you are paid. Some firms pay a low wage plus a commission to act as an incentive.	Permanent employment. Holiday and sick pay. Superannuation. If additional hours are worked, additional money is earned, sometimes at a higher hourly rate of pay.
Disadvantages				
During busy periods, additional hours might be worked, without additional pay. Very little flexibility in working times eg 9 am–5 pm	No holiday or sick pay. No fringe benefits. No permanency of employment in most piece work.	No holiday or sick pay. No permanency of employment. Few fringe benefits. Less job satisfaction.	There may be no holiday or sick pay. If you sell nothing you are paid nothing. Your security depends on the popularity of your product.	There is little incentive to work harder, since your pay is fixed to time not effort. Little flexibility in working times eg 9 am–5 pm
Salary	*Piece work*	*Casual*	*Commission*	*Wages*
teachers	dressmakers	swimming instructors	sales people	mechanics

Superannuation, sometimes called a *pension fund* or *pension plan*, is an investment fund usually contributed to by both employer and employee on the employee's behalf. It provides benefits for employees upon retirement, or for the widow or widower if the member dies.

worked examples

1   Use the information on the right to answer these questions.

a   How much would an employee earn in a week if no sales were made?

b   If Jane sold $18 000 worth of building products in one week, how much would she earn?

c   If Peter sold $24 000 worth of materials in one week and $5000 worth in the next, find his average weekly income for the two weeks.

> **POSITIONS VACANT**
> 5 people required to promote our nationally known building product in the suburbs.
> Pay: $100 pw and 2% commission.
> Please phone YRU-POOR during business hours.

2   Luke has a casual job from 4:00 pm till 5:30 pm Monday to Friday. He also works from 9 am till 12:30 pm on Saturdays. Find his weekly income if his casual rate is $8.80 per hour Monday to Friday, and $11.50 an hour on Saturdays.

Solutions

1   a   Week's earnings = $100 + 2% of $0
$$= \$100 + \$0$$
∴ Employee making no sales is paid $100.

b   Jane's earnings = $100 + 2% of $18 000
$$= \$100 + 0 \cdot 02 \times \$18\,000$$
$$= \$460 \text{ in the week}$$

c   *Week 1*
Peter's earnings = $100 + 2% of $24 000
$$= 100 + 0 \cdot 02 \times 24\,000$$
∴ Earnings week 1 = $580

Week 2
Peter's earnings = $100 + 2% of $5000
$$= \$100 + 0 \cdot 02 \times \$5000$$
∴ Earnings week 2 = $200

∴ Peter's average weekly wage = ($580 + $200) ÷ 2
$$= \$390$$

2   Luke's weekly income = (hours, Mon–Fri) × $8.80 + (hours, Sat) × $11.50
$$= (1\tfrac{1}{2} \times 5) \times \$8.80 + 3\tfrac{1}{2} \times \$11.50$$
$$= 1 \cdot 5 \times 5 \times \$8.80 + 3 \cdot 5 \times \$11.50$$
$$= \$106.25$$

Exercise 3:01

1 Write answers in your own words. Refer to page 30 if necessary.
  a What are the advantages of working for a wage?
  b What is piece work?
  c What is a salary?
  d What form of payment gives the worker a percentage of the value of goods sold?
  e What advantages are there in casual work?
  f What are the disadvantages of being on a salary?
  g What are wages?
  h Which forms of payment depend on success or the amount of work completed?
  i What are the disadvantages of casual work?
  j Which two forms of payment are often combined in determining a worker's pay?

Wages and salaries

Use your calculator!

2 a A man is paid $18.50 an hour for a 35-hour week. What is his normal weekly wage?
  b A boy is paid a wage based on $9.15 an hour. How much is he paid for an 8-hour day of work?
  c For a 38-hour working week a woman is paid $731.50. Find her hourly rate of pay?
  d Adam is paid €16.05 an hour for a 35-hour week. Luke receives €15.75 for a 38-hour week. Who has the higher weekly wage and by how much?
  e Irene is paid $594.70 for a 38-hour week, while Shireen is paid $565.25 for a 35-hour week. Who has the higher rate of pay and by how much?
  f A painter works a 38-hour week for an hourly rate of £19.65. An extra height allowance of 95 pence per hour is paid. Find his total weekly wage.
  g A woman is paid a salary of $46 089 per year. How much would she receive each week if it is calculated on 52·178 weeks in a year? (Answer to nearest dollar.)
  h Find the weekly income (assuming there are 52·178 weeks in the year) for a salary of:
  i €43 000   ii $26 400
  iii ¥895 000   iv $58 200
  (Give answers to the nearest cent.)
  i Find the yearly salary of a person whose monthly income is:
  i €4600   ii $3150.50   iii $5305   iv CNY 194 750
  j Two jobs are advertised: one with a salary of $55 000, the other a salary with a fortnightly payment of $2165.60. Which is the greater weekly salary and by how much? Use 'one year equals 52·178 weeks.' (Give your answer correct to the nearest cent.)

> **Salary**
> It is assumed that each day of the year, the salaried person earns
> $\dfrac{1}{365\frac{1}{4}}$ of the salary.
>
> There are $365\frac{1}{4}$ days, on average, in a year.
> ∴ On average, 52·178 (approximately) weeks are in each year.

k Two jobs are advertised. One is based on 37 hours per week at $20.15 an hour, the other is a yearly salary of $39 400. If one year is taken to be 52·178 weeks, which weekly income is higher and by how much? (Answer to the nearest cent.)

Commission, piece work and casual work

3 a

i Does this job guarantee an income?

ii If you have never heard of the products of this company, is it likely that you will sell much of their product?

iii Is any compensation mentioned for petrol used or provision of a vehicle?

iv Find the commission paid on sales of:
   1 €300   2 €743
   3 €1658   4 €92

> **CLEAN-U-UP PTY LTD**
> Selling cleaning machinery, equipment and chemicals.
> *Sales people required* to sell on total commission of 23% of sales.
> Great potential!
> Excellent reward!
> Ring: Ugo Broke. YRU-000.

b Janice is offered a sales position with a retainer (guaranteed wage) of $140 plus a commission of 7% on sales.

i How much could she make in one week if her weekly sales total were:
   1 $800?   2 $3500?   3 $4865?   4 $5213?

ii She is told that the average weekly sales per person is $6300. What is the average weekly income?

iii If Janice is a shy person who has no previous sales experience, is it likely that she will succeed in this job?

c John works as a sales assistant receiving $300 per week plus 10% commission on sales in excess of $5000. Find his weekly income if, in one week, the amount of his sales was:
   i $3400   ii $5700   iii $8424   iv $6129.50

4 a Heather works in a supermarket on a casual basis. She is paid £16.60 an hour from Monday to Friday and £20.85 an hour on Saturdays. Find her week's income if she works from 3:30 pm till 5:30 pm, Monday to Friday, and from 8:30 am till 1:00 pm on Saturday.

b Edward works as a waiter from 6:00 pm till 1:30 am four days in one week. His hourly rate of pay is £18.35 and he gets an average of £6.50 as tips per working night. Find his income for the week. (A 'tip' is a payment in appreciation of good service.)

c An electrician charged £35.80 per hour for labour. Find the charge for labour if he works from 11:20 am till 1:50 pm.

5 a A factory worker was paid $2.16 for each garment completed. How much would be earned if 240 garments were completed?

b A doctor charges each patient $37.50 for a consultation. If she works for 5 hours during one day and sees an average of six patients per hour, find the amount of money received that day. Her costs per day are $343. What was her profit for the day?

c Smokey and Smiley were two shearers who were paid $2.15 for each sheep shorn. By how much was Smokey's pay greater than Smiley's, if Smokey was able to shear 673 sheep while Smiley was able to shear only 489?

d A tiler charges $30.40 per square metre to lay tiles. Find how much he would charge to lay an area of:

    i 9·4 m²   **ii** 6·25 m²   **iii** 18·2 m²   **iv** $15\frac{3}{4}$ m²

e Flo works at home altering dresses for a dress shop. She is paid €14.95 for a major alteration and €6.80 for a small alteration. In the week before Christmas she completed 13 major alterations and 27 small alterations. Find her income for the week. If she spent 39 hours working on the alterations what was her hourly rate of pay? (Answer to the nearest cent.)

3:02 | Extra Payments

There are several additional payments that may add to a person's income. Terms needed are listed below.

1 **Overtime:** This is time worked in excess of a standard day or week. Often rates of $1\frac{1}{2}$ or 2 times the normal rate of pay are paid for overtime.

2 **Bonus:** This is money, or an equivalent, given in addition to an employee's usual income.

3 **Holiday bonus:** A payment calculated as a fixed percentage of the normal pay over a fixed number of weeks. It may be paid at the beginning of annual holidays to meet the increased expenses often occurring then.

4 **Time card:** This card is used to record the number of hours worked in a week. A time clock is used to stamp the times onto the card. Therefore a worker 'clocks on' in the morning and 'clocks off' in the evening.

No. 53 **Name:** Tom McSeveny		**TIME CARD**							**Whit. Pty Ltd**	
Week ending	**Fri 21 Jan**		**Fri 28 Jan**		**Fri 4 Feb**		**Fri 11 Feb**		**Fri 18 Feb**	
Day	**IN**	**OUT**	**IN**	**OUT**	**IN**	**OUT**	**IN**	**OUT**	**IN**	**OUT**
Sat	–	–	–	–	8:00	10:02	8:00	12:00	8:02	11:30
Sun	–	–	–	–	–	–	–	–	–	–
Mon	7:57	4:00	8:00	4:04	7:59	4:00	8:00	4:02	7:57	3:59
Tues	7:58	4:02	7:55	3:59	7:56	4:02	8:00	4:05	8:00	4:05
Wed	8:00	4:01	8:00	4:02	8:03	4:01	7:56	3:02	7:58	4:07
Thu	8:02	4:05	7:58	7:00	7:58	4:03	8:01	4:02	7:55	6:00
Fri	8:00	4:00	8:00	4:00	8:00	4:01	8:02	6:31	7:59	6:30

Hourly rate: $16.20
Lunch: 12 noon till 1:00 pm (unpaid)
Normal hours: Mon-Fri, 8:00 a.m. – 4:00 p.m.
Overtime: 'Time-and-a-half' is paid and 'double-time' for overtime in excess of 3 hours (on any one day)

Note: **1** In the week ending 21 Jan, no overtime was worked.
Total of hours worked = (8 hours × 5) − 5 hours for lunch
= 35 hours

2 In the week ending 11 Feb, only 34 normal hours were worked, as Tom left work 1 hour early on Wednesday. However, $2\frac{1}{2}$ hours overtime was worked on Friday and 4 hours on the Saturday. Three of the hours worked on Saturday are time-and-a-half and one (that in excess of 3 h) was at double-time.

> ■ A few minutes variation from the hour or half-hour will not be considered in determining hours worked.

worked examples

1 During one week Peter worked 35 hours at the normal rate of $11.60 per hour. He also worked 6 hours overtime: 4 at 'time-and-a-half' and 2 at 'double-time'. How much did he earn?

2 Use the time card on the previous page to calculate Tom McSeveny's wage for the week ending Friday, 18 February.

3 Calculate Diane's holiday bonus if she is given $17\frac{1}{2}$% of four weeks salary and she earns $980 per fortnight.

I don't get paid for lunch . . .

Solutions

time-and-a-half   double-time

1 Peter's earnings = (35 h at $11.60) + (4 h at $11.60 × $1\frac{1}{2}$) + (2 h at $11.60 × 2)

$$= (35 × 11·6) + (4 × 11·6 × 1·5) + (2 × 11·6 × 2) \text{ dollars}$$

$$= \$522 \quad \text{(using a calculator)}$$

2 For the week ending Friday, 18 February, Tom worked:

'Normal hours': 35 hours (8–4, Mon–Fri with 1 hour lunch)

Overtime—'Time-and-a-half': $7\frac{1}{2}$ hours (8–11 on Sat, 4–6 on Thur, 4–6:30 on Fri)

'Double-time': $\frac{1}{2}$ hour (11–11:30 on Sat as double-time is paid only after 3 hours)

∴ Tom's earnings = (35 h at $16.20) + ($7\frac{1}{2}$ h at $16.20 × $1\frac{1}{2}$) + ($\frac{1}{2}$ h at $16.20 × 2)

$$= (35 × 16·2) + (7·5 × 16·2 × 1·5) + (0·5 × 16·2 × 2) \text{ dollars}$$

$$= \$765.45 \text{ (using a calculator)}$$

3 Diane's holiday loading = $17\frac{1}{2}$% of four weeks salary

$$= 17\frac{1}{2}\% \text{ of } (\$980 × 2)$$

$$= 0·175 × (980 × 2) \text{ dollars}$$

$$= \$343$$

> ■ $17\frac{1}{2}\% = \dfrac{17·5}{100}$
> $= 17·5 ÷ 100$
> $= 0·175$

Exercise 3:02

1 **a** Bill earns $9.60 per hour. Calculate his wages for the week if he worked 35 hours at the normal rate and 5 hours overtime at 'time-and-a-half'.

b At Bigfoot Enterprises a wage rate of $12.70 per hour is paid on the first 37 hours and 'time-and-a-half' after that. What is the wage for a 42-hour week?

c Each day Pauline receives $18.10 per hour for the first 7 hours, 'time-and-a-half' for the next 2 hours, and 'double-time' thereafter. Find her wage for:
  i a 6-hour day
  ii a 9-hour day
  iii an $8\frac{1}{2}$-hour day
  iv an 11-hour day

d An electrician earns a wage of €22.40 per hour for a 35-hour week and 'time-and-a-half' after that. How much would he earn in a week in which he works:
  i 30 hours
  ii 37 hours
  iii $41\frac{1}{2}$ hours
  iv $45\frac{1}{2}$ hours

e A pipe factory asks a labourer to work 8 hours on Saturday at 'time-and-a-half' for the first 3 hours and 'double-time' after that. If his normal rate of pay is $20.40, how much is he paid for the day's work?

f Brian earns $17.60 an hour, while his boss earns $23.20 an hour. How much more than Brian is the boss paid for a 7-hour day? If Brian gets 'time-and-a-half for overtime, how many additional hours would he need to work in a day to get the same wage as his boss?

> ■ The tricky parts of the time card on page 34 are in colour.

g By referring to the time card on page 34, complete the summary below.

No. 53 Name: Tom McSeveny		Time Card Summary			Whit. Pty Ltd. Rate: $16.20 ph
Week ending	Number of hours at:				Wage
	normal rates	time-and-a-half	double-time		
21 Jan					
28 Jan					
4 Feb					
11 Feb					
18 Feb					

2 a If $17\frac{1}{2}$% holiday bonus is given on 4 weeks normal pay, find the holiday bonus for:
  i John, who earns $4000 in 4 weeks
  ii Mary, who earns $822 in a fortnight
  iii Wilkes, who earns $495 a week
  iv Conway, who earns $19.80 an hour (for a 35-hour week)
  (Assume that in each case no extra payments are included.)

b When June was given her holiday pay she received 4 weeks pay and a $17\frac{1}{2}$% holiday bonus. If her normal wage is €427 per week, how much holiday pay did she receive?

c Franko works a 35-hour week at a rate of $17.60 per hour. Calculate his holiday bonus if $17\frac{1}{2}$% is given on 4 weeks wage.

d Mr Bigsuccess earns a salary of $96 000 per year. At the end of the year he is given a bonus equal to 80% of one month's pay. How much did he earn in the year?

e Alana managed a small business for a salary of $56 400. At the end of a successful year in which the business made a profit of $211 000, she was given a bonus of 1·2% of the profits. What was her bonus and what was her income for the year?

f Luke works for a mining company at a wage rate of $22.80 per hour. If he works underground he is paid a penalty rate of $3.65 per hour in addition to his normal pay. Find his weekly wage if during the normal 38 hours he works underground for 16 hours.

g Mary works in a food processing plant at a wage rate of $15.95 per hour. From time to time she is required to work beside ovens where the temperature is uncomfortable. When this is necessary she is paid an additional 95 cents an hour. Calculate her wage for a normal working week of 36 hours where 5 hours were beside the ovens.

h Lyn received a $17\frac{1}{2}$% holiday bonus on four weeks normal wages. (She works a 36-hour week.) Find her normal weekly wage if the total of four weeks wages and the holiday bonus was:
  i $2350   **ii** $2162

i Sundeep received a holiday bonus payment of £364 that represented $17\frac{1}{2}$% on four weeks wages. What is his weekly wage? What percentage of his total income for the year (containing 52 weeks) does the holiday bonus represent? (Answer correct to 2 decimal places.)

3 Ayse's salary is €47 300, but she expects it to rise 2% each year to keep pace with inflation.
  a After the beginning of the second year, what would Ayse expect her salary to be?
  b What would the salary be at the beginning of the third year?
  c What would the salary be at the beginning of:
    i the sixth year?   **ii** the eleventh year?

Investigation 3:02 | Jobs in the papers

3:02

1 Look in the careers section of a newspaper to see what salaries are offered for various employment opportunities.
2 Examine the positions vacant columns for casual jobs. How many mention the pay offered? What level of pay is offered in different fields of employment?
3 What other benefits are mentioned in employment advertisements, other than the wage or salary?

3:03 | Wage Deductions

A person's weekly wage or salary is referred to as the weekly *gross* pay. After deductions have been made the amount actually received is called the weekly *net* pay.

Possible deductions

1. **Income tax** — The Commonwealth government takes a part of all incomes earned to finance federal, state and local government activities. Employers deduct this tax on the government's behalf at the end of each pay period. It is called PAYE (pay-as-you-earn). The rate of tax varies according to the amount of money earned and the number of dependants.

2. **Superannuation or pension fund** — This is a form of insurance or investment. Usually both the employee and the employer contribute to this fund on behalf of the employee. It provides for an income or lump-sum payment on retirement, and in the event of the member's death, it provides a pension for the family.

3. **Miscellaneous** — Other deductions could be for medical insurance, life insurance, home payments, credit union savings and union membership fees.

Here is a pay advice slip representing two weeks' pay.

Peter Newby	Serial No.	Dept.	Location	Gross Salary or Wage Rate	Super Units		Fortnight Ended	Net Pay	Pay Advice No.
					Entld.	Held			
	6552750	AA	8436	46884.70	113	113	4/11/02	1192.20	12381

* Reasons for Adjustments

A – increment	B – award agreement	C – national wage	D – promotion
E – L.W.O.P	F – allowance	G – termination	H – resumed duty
I – reduction in salary		Z – combination of reasons	

Deductions this fortnight				Pay this fortnight			
Taxation	S'annuation	M'laneous	Total	Normal Pay	Adjustments	Overtime	Gross Earnings
400.50	40.60	163.80	604.90	1797.10	–	–	1797.10

Peter Newby has a gross yearly salary or wage ① of $46 884.70, earns $1797.10 ② per fortnight and in the fortnight ending 4/11/02 had no adjustments or overtime ③. This means that his gross earnings were $1797.10 ④. His net pay ⑤ was only $1192.20 because his total deductions ⑥ were $604.90.

Peter paid $400.50 tax ⑦ on an income of $1797.10. This is about 22%. His contribution to superannuation ⑧ was $40.60.

worked examples

Find the net pay for the week if John earns $423.60, is taxed $67.80, pays $32.10 for superannuation and has miscellaneous deductions totalling $76.30. What percentage of his gross pay did he pay in tax?

Solution

Total deductions = Tax + Superannuation + Miscellaneous
$$= \$67.80 + \$32.10 + \$76.30$$
$$= \$176.20$$
∴ John's net pay $= \$423.60 - \$176.20$
$$= \$247.40$$
John's tax payment $= \$67.80$

Tax as a percentage of gross pay
$$= \frac{\text{tax}}{\text{gross pay}} \times 100\%$$

$$= \frac{\$67.80}{\$423.60} \times 100\%$$

$$\doteqdot 16\%$$

I've just collected my net pay.

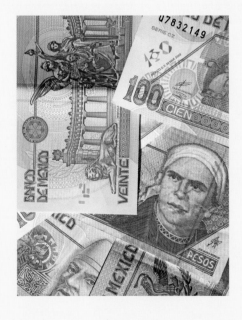

1 Find the net pay if:

a gross pay is $315.60 and total deductions are €115

b gross pay is $518.20, tax is $99.70, superannuation is $20.70 and miscellaneous is $94.80

c gross pay is $214.55, tax is $22.20, superannuation is $4.80 and union fees are $2.60

d gross pay (for a fortnight) is £1030.40, superannuation is £48.50, miscellaneous is £174.70 and tax is £303.55

e gross salary is $612.10, superannuation is $31.90, medical insurance is $21.60, life insurance is $4.10, house payment is $76.50, credit union savings are $11.00, union fees are $2.45 and tax is $131.60

Wow! You must have some fishing spot! Where'd you net this stuff?

At the river bank!

GROAN!

2 a Vicki Turner receives a yearly salary of $32 096, pays 16% of her weekly gross (calculated on 52·18 weeks in the year) in income tax, pays 5% of her weekly gross to her superannuation fund and has $86 in miscellaneous deductions each week. Find her:

   i weekly gross salary

   ii weekly tax deductions

   iii weekly superannuation payment

   iv weekly net pay

> ■ 'Net pay' is what you take home.

b Use question **2a** to complete this pay advice slip.

Turner, Vicki	Serial No.	Gross Salary or Wage Rate	Super Units		Week Ended	Net Pay	Pay Advice No.
			Entld.	Held			
	6841672		98	98	18/11/02		11364

* Reasons for Adjustments

A – increment	B – award agreement	C – national wage	D – promotion
E – L.W.O.P	F – allowance	G – termination	H – resumed duty
I – reduction in salary		Z – combination of reasons	

Deductions this week				Pay this week			
Taxation	S'annuation	M'laneous	Total	Normal Pay	Adjustments	Overtime	Gross Earnings
					–	–	

3 Find the net pay and the tax as a percentage of the gross pay for each person.

	Name	Gross Pay	Tax	Net Pay	Tax as % of Gross Pay
a	R. Collison	$ 385.70	$ 56.40		
b	G. Foster	$1450.00	$500.75		
c	B. Jones	$ 947.50	$265.15		
d	R. Sinclair	$ 591.60	$124.65		

4 **a** Upon retirement, Joe Simmons received annual superannuation payments of 68% of his final year's salary. If his salary at that time was €62 600, how much is his annual superannuation (before tax)?

b Ellen's annual superannuation is 63% of her finishing wage of €52 186. How much would her net monthly income be if she pays 22% of her gross income in taxation payments? (Answer correct to the nearest cent.)

c John earns €32 492 a year. If he were to die, his widow would receive 65% of this figure in superannuation payments each year. What would be her weekly income (before tax) taking 1 year to be 52·18 weeks?

d Jim has just retired. He has the option of receiving a monthly payment of €3667 or €330 000 as a 'lump sum' (a final single payment).

  i Find the yearly superannuation payment.

  ii What yearly income would result if the lump sum could be invested at 12% p.a.?

  iii Which option seems most attractive and why?

  iv What would his yearly income be if he elected to receive 30% of the monthly payment, and 70% of the lump sum of which he invested 40% at 12% p.a.?

> ■ *Challenge*
> 1 Expected returns in superannuation, based on average life span, could be calculated.
> 2 Effects of inflation (with or without indexation) on these expected returns could be considered.

e Janice retired in 1995 on a fixed income of €2400 per month. How many toothbrushes costing €1.80 could she buy with a month's income? One year later inflation had caused the cost of toothbrushes to rise by 8%. How many toothbrushes could she buy with a month's income after the rise? (*As years pass, inflation greatly affects the purchasing power of people on fixed incomes.*)

5 Maryanne's gross pay for a week is $874.20. Her employer must pay an additional 9% of this amount into a superannuation fund for Maryanne. Maryanne chooses to also pay 5% of her weekly pay into this fund.

a How much is being paid into the superannuation fund each week?

b What is the total cost to the employer each week of employing Maryanne?

c Maryanne receives a 4% pay rise. By how much will the superannuation contributions increase?

3:04 | Taxation

- Many countries have an *Income Tax Return* form which is filled out each year, to determine the exact amount of tax that has to be paid, for the preceding 12 months. Since most people have been paying tax as they have earned their income, this exercise may mean that a *tax refund* is given.

- Some expenses, such as those necessary in the earning of our income, are classified as *tax deductions* and the tax we have paid on this money will be returned to us. On the other hand, if we have additional income (such as interest on savings) that has not yet been taxed, additional taxes will have to be paid.

  The tax deductions are subtracted from the total income to provide the *taxable income*.

- The table below gives an example of an *index taxation system* in which the amount of tax you pay varies according to your *taxable income*.

TABLE 1—Resident for full year	
Taxable income	*Tax on this income*
$1–$6000	Nil
$6001–$20 000	17 cents for each $1 over $6000
$20 001–$50 000	$2380 + 30 cents for each $1 over $20 000
$50 001–$60 000	$11 380 + 42 cents for each $1 over $50 000
$60 001 and over	$15 580 + 47 cents for each $1 over $60 000

worked examples

Alan received a salary of $47 542 and a total from other income (investments) of $496. His total tax deductions were $1150. During the year he had already paid tax instalments amounting to $10 710.75. Find:

1 his total income
2 his taxable income
3 the tax payable on his taxable income
4 his refund due or balance payable
5 how much extra Alan would receive each week if he is given a wage rise of $10 per week

Solution

1 Alan's total income
   = $47 542 + $496
   = $48 038

2 Alan's taxable income
   = total income − tax deductions
   = $48 038 − $1150
   = $46 888

3   Taxable income = $46 888 (or $20 000 + $26 888)
          Tax on $20 000 = $2380.00 (from the table on page 304) . . . (A)
   Tax on $26 888 at 30 cents = $8066.40 (30c/$ for amount over $20 000) . . . (B)

          ∴ Tax on $46 888 = (A) + (B)
                           = $2380 + $8066.40
                           = $10 446.40

4   Tax on $46\,888$ $= \$10\,446.40$

       Tax instalments paid $= \$10\,710.75$

           $\therefore$ Refund due $= \$10\,710.75 - \$10\,446.40$

                     $= \$264.35$

5   For salaries over $\$20\,000$ and less than $\$50\,001$, for each additional $\$1$ earned you pay 30 cents tax.

     $\therefore$ Tax on an extra $\$10$ per week $= 10 \times \$0.30$

                           $= \$3.00$

       $\therefore$ Amount left after tax $= \$10 - \$3.00$

                              $= \$7.00$ per week

Exercise 3:04

1   Use the table on page 42 to determine the tax payable on a taxable income of:

    a $3963   **b** $12\,587   **c** $31\,460

    d $67\,346   **e** $284\,914

2   Mrs Short has a salary of $33\,600, receives income from other sources of $342, has tax deductions of $655, and has paid PAYE tax instalments throughout the year of $6570. Find:

    a   her total income

    b   her taxable income

    c   tax payable on her taxable income

    d   her refund or balance payable

3   When Joy left school she had a weekly wage of $488. During the financial year, there were 52 weeks' pay received. (*Note*: In a normal year of 52 weeks and one day, there could be 53 paydays.) She had no extra income and calculated her tax deductions to be $217. Find the tax payable on her taxable income.

4   Karl earned $52\,850 as a tiler in 2002/03. His employer deducted tax payments of $13\,110. However, Karl earned a further $4156 on weekends and during his holidays. His tax deductions came to $2096 as his expenses in earning the additional income were considerable. Find:

    a   Karl's total income

    b   Karl's taxable income

    c   the tax on his taxable income

    d   additional tax payable (balance).

5   Eight workers in a factory were each given a pay rise of $2000 per annum. How much of the $2000 would each have received after tax?

   Their yearly taxable incomes are listed below.

   (Use the tax table on page 42.)

    a   M. Callow: $3900   **b**   A. Smith: $9322

    c   P. Farmer: $16\,112   **d**   M. Awad: $28\,155

    e   R. Sissi: $41\,300   **f**   P. Mifsud: $55\,788

    g   R. Ringe: $63\,950   **h**   S. Sze: $82\,000

Fun Spot 3:04 | What is brought to the table, cut, but never eaten?

Work out the answer to each question and put the letter for that part in the box that is above the correct answer.

Express as a percentage:

A 0·76   **A** 0·125   **A** $\frac{3}{5}$

O 12% of $81 250   **C** $13.50 × 38 + $20.25 × 6

C Sid is paid $22.80 an hour for a 40-hour week. What is his normal weekly wage?

D For a 38-hour week Naomi is paid $744.80. Find her hourly rate of pay.

F My salary is $31 306.80 per year. How much would I receive each week if it is calculated on 52·178 weeks in a year?

S Alana has a casual job from 4:00 pm till 5:30 pm Monday to Friday. What is her weekly income if her casual rate is $9.20 per hour?

P A tiler charges $28.50 per square metre to lay tiles. How much would he charge to lay an area of 8 square metres?

K Find the net pay for one week if Anne earns $520.50, is taxed $104.10, pays $8 for superannuation and has miscellaneous deductions totalling $77.40.

R In the previous question, what percentage of Anne's gross pay was paid in tax?

60% $228   76% $634.50 $331 $9750 $600 $912   12·5%   20% $19.60 $69

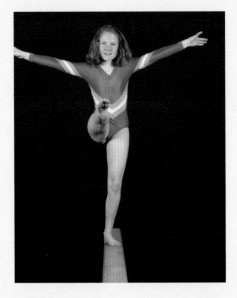

- It is important to balance your budget!

3:05 | Budgeting

A budget is a plan for the use of expected income.

A budget helps to keep the balance!

Budgeting is money management.

Suggested steps for compiling a budget

1 **Determine expected income.**
2 **Analyse present spending habits.**
3 **Minimise non-essential expenses.**
4 **Tabulate income versus expenses.**
5 **Determine savings.**

When trying to minimise non-essential expenses it is helpful to group expenses under the heading 'fixed' and 'variable'. Fixed expenses would include rent, electricity, water, local government rates, insurance and hire purchase repayments. Variable expenses would include food, clothing, fares, entertainment, gifts, petrol and car repairs, dentist and the like.

worked examples

Mr Jones analysed the family income to see if €800 could be found for a holiday. He decided to make up a monthly budget.

Monthly income (net)	
Job ($4\frac{1}{3}$ weeks)	€2480
Investments	€ 83
Casual work	€ 310
Children's board	€ 433
Other	€ 43
Total: €3349	

Fixed expenses	
House payment	€ 740
Car payment	€ 280
Electricity	€ 80
Water	€ 46
Local government rates	€ 62
Insurance	€ 70
Medical	€ 104
Other	€ 20
€1402	

Variable expenses	
Food	€ 740
Clothing	€ 250
Fares	€ 60
Entertainment	€ 190
Petrol & Repairs	€ 185
Telephone	€ 88
Other	€ 360
€1873	

Assume that Mr Jones has already paid the tax.

continued ➜ ➜ ➜

1   What is the monthly balance (surplus)? Could they save enough for the holiday in 12 months?
2   How much is left of the yearly balance if holiday money is removed?
3   Is it wise to save so little, or should the variable expenses be reduced?
    Where could the reductions most easily be made?

Solutions

1   Balance (surplus) = income − expenses
                    = €3349 − €3275
    ∴ Monthly balance = €74
        ∴ Yearly balance = €74 × 12 or €888
    ∴ Sufficient money can be saved.

2   Money left = yearly balance − €800
              = €888 − €800
              = €88

3   It is not wise to save so little unless savings are already substantial. Emergencies are likely to occur that will destroy your budget unless you have savings on hand. If the holiday is important, then sacrifices can be made in the areas of entertainment, food, clothing, telephone and especially 'other'.

Exercise 3:05

1   Rhonda earns $200 per month from odd jobs, $42 as an allowance from her parents and $24 average from other sources. In each month she must spend $50 on food, $36 repaying a loan and $16 on school needs. She would like to save $20 per month and divide what remains equally between clothes, entertainment and gifts.
    a   Make up a budget as in the example above.
    b   What percentage of her total income does she save?

2   James earns €428 a week gross. His weekly tax payment is €86. Here is a list of his monthly expenses. Rent €608; electricity/telephone/water €86; medical expenses €164; food €182; fares €72; clothing €44; entertainment/sport €84 and other €50.
    a   Make up a budget as in the example, using $4\frac{1}{3}$ weeks for 1 month.
    b   How much can James save each month? What is this as a percentage of his net income?
    c   James would like to buy a car. He estimates that payments, including registration, would amount to €180 per month; repairs and servicing the car, €60 per month; and petrol €36 per month. He no longer would have to pay fares. Is it possible? Can you suggest a solution?

3   Using similar headings to those in question 2, make up a budget for a school-leaver with an income of $500 per week who is:
    a   living at home
    b   renting a room for $80 a week

4   Make up your own monthly budget based on your real income and expenses. Consider all sources of income, essential expenditure, non-essential expenditure and savings.

3:06 | Best Buy, Shopping Lists and Change

Let's consider the signs above.

1. **a** $\frac{1}{2}$ price   **b** Save $6   **d** 10–50% off
   k 20% off   **l** Were $12, now $10.20
   q Save up to $20   **s** Save over 30%   **v** Save 40%

   These statements assume that the original price was reasonable. I could have a pencil for sale for $9, reduce its price by 90% or $8.10 (whichever sounds best) and attempt to sell it for 90 cents. If the pencil is worth only 30 cents this is not a bargain.

> ■ When shopping ask:
> 1 Do I really need this item?
> 2 Is this the best price available?
> 3 Is it worth the price?
> 4 Is it good quality? (Will it last?)

2. **c** Sale   **e** Special   **n** Value   **o** Bargain   **t** Low prices
   u Super Special

   Some stores have 'sale' signs displayed all year round. When advertising, stores are more interested in selling their product than in examining the meaning of words.

3. **f** Buy 3, get one free   **g** Prizes to be won   **h** Free trip   **i** Free tin of stain

   You never really get anything for nothing. The 'free' gift or slim chance at a prize are alternatives to giving you a lower price. In most competitions, the value of the postage stamps used to send in the entries would be greater than the total value of the prizes.

4. **j** From $9.50   **q** Save up to $20

   It is amazing how often the lower priced items are those you don't want.

5. **f** Buy 3, get one free   **m** 3 for $30.00   **p** Limit of 3

   Do you really need three hammers, or whatever they are? Even when they seem to be restricting you to three, you may not need them.

6. **r** Buy direct

   Many firms give companies and tradespeople a good discount but they charge the ordinary customer as much as they can.

worked examples

1 Determine the best buy on a 'front door'. Assume that the quality of each door is the same.
   Y-Mart: 32% off marked price of $435.
   N-Boss Discounts: $120 off marked price of $426.
   Cottonworths: Buy 3 doors for $1005 and get one free.
   Walgrams: Buy a door for $360 and get a tin of stain free.

2 *Smooth* coffee costs $14.80 for 500 g, *Ringin* coffee costs $9.60 for 300 g. Which brand is the best value? (Assume similar quality.)

Solutions

1
Y-MART

Cost = $435 − 0·32 × $435
     = $295.80

N-BOSS DISCOUNTS

Cost = $426 − $120
     = $306

COTTONWORTHS

Cost = 4 doors for $1005
     = $251.25 per door

WALGRAMS

Cost = $360 less value of stain
Is a tin of stain worth $64.20?

The cheapest cost per door is from Cottonworths but we want to buy *one* front door not four, so the best buy is from Y-Mart.

2 500 g of *Smooth* coffee costs $14.80
   ∴ 100 g of *Smooth* coffee costs
   $14.80 ÷ 5 = $2.96

   300 g of *Ringin* coffee costs $9.60
   ∴ 100 g of *Ringin* coffee costs
   $9.60 ÷ 3 = $3.20

Clearly *Smooth* coffee is less expensive.

Exercise 3:06

Foundation Worksheet 3:06
Best buy, shopping lists, change
1 Find:
   a 15% of $25   b 20% of $140
2 What percentage is:
   a $5 of $25?   b $7.50 of $60?
2 Which is cheaper:
   a 500 g for $12 or 750 g for $17?

1 a If the marked price of an item is €137 find the price that must be paid if the discount in sign **a** from page 47 were applied. Do the same for signs **b** **f** **k** and **v**. For sign **q** give the range of prices that might have to be paid.

   b An item has a marked price of €85 in two shops. One offers a 14% discount (reduction in price) and the other a discount of €10.65. Which is the better buy and by how much?

   c Paint is advertised: 'Was €12. Now €10.20.'
      i What has been the reduction?
      ii Express the reduction as a percentage of the original price.

d John travelled to a factory for a 'direct buy' purchase of 60 litres of paint for €690. He noticed that the same paint was being sold at a local store for a 'sale' price of €46.60 for 4 litres. Which was the less expensive and by how much? If John spent an hour of travelling and €4.60 worth of petrol, which do you think was the better buy? Why?

e Jane bought a new tyre for €160, Robyn bought one for €130 and Diane bought a retread for €76. If Jane's tyre lasted 32 000 km, Robyn's 27 500 km, and Diane's 16 000 km, which was the best buy? (Assume that safety and performance for the tyres are the same.)

2 **a** Frozen peas come in three brands, *Yip* peas at 84c for 200 g, *Hap* peas at $1.56 for 440 g and *Nap* peas at $1.84 for 600 g. Which is the best buy?

b If *Coco Pops* are sold at $4.90 per 750 g box, *Rice Bubbles* at $3.20 per 500 g box and *Corn Flakes* at $1.30 per 250 g box, which is the cheapest per unit of weight?

c James and Maree go shopping for ice-cream. James like Strawberry and Maree likes Vanilla. They decide to buy the container that represents the best value. The Strawberry is $6.90 for 4 L or $3.90 for 2 L, the Vanilla is $5.20 for 3 L or $10 for 6 L. Which did they buy? What is their change from $20?

d Alice wants to buy the least expensive tea. Which will she buy if *Paa* tea costs $2.50 for 250 g, *Katt* tea costs $6.20 for 600 g, *Jet* tea costs $11 for 1 kg and *Yet* tea costs $7.65 for 800 g?

e Which is the least expensive sauce: Soy at $1.45 for 200 mL, Barbecue at $2.30 for 250 mL, Chilli at $2.25 for 300 mL or Tomato sauce at $1.80 for 750 mL? Which is the most expensive?

3

A quick way to find change
eg Change from \$20 if \$3.75 is spent.
\$3.75 up to \$4   is 25 cents
\$4 up to \$20   is \$16   +
∴ Change   is \$16.25

Do you have any change?

No, but if you read the box behind you, you'll find some . . .

a Use the method in the box to find the change from \$20 if the bill is:
    i \$2.95   **ii** \$7.80   **iii** \$12.15   **iv** \$17.10   **v** \$8.05   **vi** \$4.30

b Find the total cost of each list below and find the change from \$100.

i

Item	Price	No.	Cost
Peanut butter	\$1.40	2	
Vegetable soup	\$0.80	5	
Vitamin C	\$1.70	1	
Mousetrap	\$0.30	7	
Icing mix	\$0.80	2	
100 mL oil	\$2.40	1	
Tin of cream	\$0.85	3	
Flavouring	\$2.20	2	

Total =
Change from \$100 =

ii

Item	Price	No.	Cost
Pickles	\$0.85	3	
Cake mix	\$2.30	1	
Baby food	\$0.55	15	
Strawberry jam	\$3.95	1	
Gravy mix	\$2.55	2	
Vitamins	\$5.30	1	
Honey	\$1.30	2	
Salt	\$0.75	1	

Total =
Change from \$100 =

c Make up your own table to find the cost of the following list and change from \$100.
    • 3 packets of tea at \$2.45
    • 2 tins of mixed vegetables at \$2.10
    • a bottle of tomato sauce at \$1.80
    • 2 packets of instant pudding at 95 cents
    • 2 jars of stock cubes at \$2.15
    • 3 tins of tuna at \$3.95
    • 5 tins of mushrooms at 70 cents
    • 8 tins of sardines at 70 cents
    • 7 tins of cat food at \$1.75
    • 1 tub of ice-cream at \$7.45
    • 4 tins of beans at 80 cents

• I do my shopping on the internet!

3:07 | Sales Tax

Find 10% of:	**1** $20	**2** $3.50	**3** $7.10	**4** $14.36
Calculate:	**5** $66 \div 11$	**6** $9.24 \div 11$	**7** 5.6×1.1	**8** 127×1.1
	9 $66 \times \dfrac{10}{11}$	**10** $9.24 \times \dfrac{10}{11}$		

A sales tax is a broad-based tax on most goods and services you buy. Usually the sales tax is included in the price you pay. However, in some countries no sales tax is applied to some items such as basic food goods. In these cases a bill or shopping receipt may itemise each product showing whether the sales tax was charged and how much tax was included in the bill.

A sales tax is sometimes called a goods and services tax (GST) or value added tax (VAT).

In the following exercises the sales tax will be referred to as a GST which will be taxed at a rate of 10%. It is simple to calculate the GST included in a price in these cases by dividing by 11, since the base price has been increased by 10% or $\frac{1}{10}$.

worked examples

1 Find the GST that needs to be applied to a price of $325.
2 What is the retail price of a DVD player worth $325 after the GST has been applied?
3 How much GST is contained in a price of $357.50?
4 What was the price of an item retailing at $357.50 before the GST was applied?

Solutions

1 The GST is 10% of the price.
   $\therefore$ GST $= \$325 \times 10\%$
   $= \$32.50$

> To calculate the GST to add on to a price, simply find 10% of the price.

2 The GST is added on to get the retail price.
   $\therefore$ Retail price $= \$325 + \$32.50$
   $= \$357.50$

   Note: The retail price can also be calculated by multiplying the original price by 110% (or 1·1) since 10% is added on
   ie   Retail price $= \$325 \times 1.1$
   $= \$357.50$

3 To find the GST contained in a price, we divide it by 11.
   (If the original price is increased by $\frac{1}{10}$, then the retail price, including the GST, is $\frac{11}{10}$ of the original price.)
   $\therefore$ GST $= \$357.50 \div 11$
   $= \$32.50$

> To find the GST included in a price, divide the price by 11.

continued ➜➜➜

4 To find the original price, simply subtract the GST from the retail price.

∴ Original price = $357.50 − $32.50

= $325

Note: The original price can also be found by multiplying the retail price by $\frac{10}{11}$.

ie Original price = $357.50 × $\frac{10}{11}$

= $325

Exercise 3:07

Foundation Worksheet 3:07

Goods and services tax

1 Find 10% of:
  a $17   b $23.50   c $1125

2 Find $\frac{1}{11}$ of:
  a $13.20   b $26.40   c $62.48

1 Determine the GST that needs to be added to original prices of:

  a $70   b $120

  c $46.20   d $59.70

  e $863   f $12 740

  g $97.63   h $142.37

  i $124.55   j $742.15

2 Determine the retail price after the GST of 10% is added to the following.

  a €60   b €150   c €220   d €740

  e €75   f €112   g €343   h €947

  i €8.60   j €27.40   k €56.45   l €19.63

3 How much GST is contained in the following retail prices?

  a $22   b $110   c $165   d $286

  e $61.60   f $57.20   g $13.20   h $860.20

  i $46.75   j $349.80   k $1004.30   l $1237.50

• Find the total GST paid on the camping gear shown if its retail price is $1130.

4 What was the original price before the GST of 10% was added to each of these retail prices?

a	$77	**b**	$132	**c**	$198	**d**	$275
e	$15.40	**f**	$28.60	**g**	$106.70	**h**	$126.50
i	$13.86	**j**	$41.25	**k**	$237.05	**l**	$1238.38

5 When retailers sell a mixture of goods where the GST is only applied to some, they normally indicate which items on the bill include the GST. This bill indicates the items which include the GST with an asterisk (*). Determine the amount of GST that would be included in the total on this bill.

SHOPQUICK	
Sauce	$ 1.20
Biscuits*	$ 1.35
Bread	$ 3.60
Toothbrush*	$ 3.10
Soap*	$ 1.93
Total	$11.18
GST incl =	?

6 The retailer indicates the GST items with a percentage sign (%). Determine the GST included in these bills.

a

% Magazine	$ 2.85
% Deodorant	$ 4.00
Milk	$ 5.60
Muffins	$ 2.60
% Biscuits	$ 2.17
Total	$17.22
GST incl =	?

b

Bread	$ 2.70
Flour	$ 0.90
% Ice creams	$ 4.48
% Soap pads	$ 0.98
% Tissues	$ 5.10
Total	$14.16
GST incl =	?

c

Bananas	$ 3.50
% Soap	$ 3.92
% Detergent	$ 3.31
Tea bags	$ 4.46
Eggs	$ 2.89
% Bath salts	$ 6.05
Rice	$ 1.54
% Biscuits	$ 2.56
Total	$28.23
GST incl =	?

7
a The prices of three items were €10.56, €10.30 and €21.00. The total of the GST included in the bill was €0.96. Which was the only price that included a 10% GST?
b Four prices on a bill were €5.60, €7.70, €9.30 and €10.56. The total of the bill, excluding GST, was €31.50. Which of the four prices did not include GST?
c Five articles cost €20.90, €37.40, €52.80, €61.60 and €45.10. GST of 10% was then added to some of these prices. The total bill was then €230.56. Which prices had GST added to them?

Investigation 3:07 | Shopper dockets

1 Collect 'shopper dockets' from as many different supermarkets you can. Examine them to see how they indicate the GST charges.

2 Draw up a list of all the items you can that *do not* include GST.

3 When was the GST introduced in Australia?

investigation

3:07

3:08 | Ways of Paying and Discounts

When buying the things we need, we can pay cash (or cheque or use electronic transfer of funds), buy on terms or use credit cards. The wise buyer will seek discounts wherever possible, comparing prices at different stores.

Using money			
Seeking discount	*Buying with credit card*	*Buying on terms*	*Paying cash or transferring funds*
Meaning			
A process of bargaining to seek a reduced price.	A readily acceptable method of making credit purchases. 'Buy now pay later'.	A way of having the item and spreading the payment over a period of time. (Hire-purchase)	An immediate payment with cheque, electronic transfer of funds card or money.
Advantages			
You pay less because you can challenge one shop to beat the price of another. Taking time allows you to compare the quality of items.	Convenient. Safer than carrying large sums of money. Useful in meeting unexpected costs. If payment is made promptly the charge is small. Many stores accept credit cards.	You can buy essential items and make use of them as you pay. Buying a house on terms saves rent. The item bought may be used to generate income. Little immediate cost.	Paying cash may help you get a discount. Money is accepted anywhere. You own the item. You keep out of debt. It doesn't encourage impulse buying. With cheque or electronic transfer of funds card you don't have to carry a lot of money.
Disadvantages			
It takes time and energy to compare prices. To get the best price you may have less choice in things like colour, after sales service and maybe condition of the item. 'Specials' are discounts.	There is a tendency to overspend, buy on impulse and not out of need. The interest charged on the debt is high. Hidden costs (stamp duty and charge on stores) generally lift prices.	Relies on a regular income and, if you cannot continue payments, the item can be repossessed, sold and, if its value has depreciated (dropped), you still may owe money. High interest rates. You are in debt.	Carrying large sums of money can be dangerous (risk of loss) and many shops won't accept cheques or electronic transfer of funds cards. You may miss out on a good buy if you don't carry much money with you.

Using money			
Seeking discount	*Buying with credit card*	*Buying on terms*	*Paying cash or transferring funds*

worked examples

1   Brenda bought a car on terms of $100 deposit and 60 monthly repayments of $179.80. The price of the car was $5000.
   a   How much did she pay for the car?
   b   How much interest did she pay on the money borrowed?
   c   How much money had she borrowed?

2   a   Greg was given $12\frac{1}{2}$% discount on a rug with a marked price of $248. How much did he pay?
   b   A television marked at $2240 was eventually sold for $2128. What was the discount and what was the percentage discount given on the marked price?
   c   After a discount of 14% was given, I paid $5848 for my yellow Holden. What was the original marked price?

3   Brenda bought a TV priced at $1200 after it was discounted by 10%. Brenda received a further 5% discount because she was a member of staff. How much did she pay for the TV?

Solutions

1   a   Total payments for car = deposit + payments
$$= \$100 + 60 \times \$179.80$$
$$= \$10\,888$$

   b   Interest = extra money paid
$$= \$10\,888 - \$5000$$
$$= \$5888$$

   c   Amount borrowed = price of car − deposit
$$= \$5000 - \$100$$
$$= \$4900$$

2   a   Discount on rug = 12·5% of $248
$$= 0·125 \times \$248$$
$$= \$31$$
   Amount paid = $248 − $31
$$= \$217$$

continued →→→

b   Discount on TV = $2240 − $2128

$$= \$112$$

Percentage discount = ($112 ÷ $2240) × 100%

$$= 5\%$$

c   Price paid = (100 − 14)% of marked price

$$= 86\% \text{ of marked price}$$

1% of marked price = $5848 ÷ 86

$$= \$68$$

100% of marked price = $6800

3   Price after original 10% discount = (100 − 10)% of $1200

$$= 90\% \text{ of } \$1200$$
$$= \$1080$$

Price after a further 5% discount = (100 − 5)% of $1080

$$= 95\% \text{ of } \$1080$$
$$= \$1026$$

(*Note:* This is not the same as a 15% discount off the original price
ie 85% of $1200 = $1020)

Exercise 3:08

1   Use the table on page 54 to answer these questions in your own words.
  a   What are the disadvantages of buying on terms?
  b   What are the advantages of paying cash?
  c   What are the advantages of seeking out discounts?
  d   What are the disadvantages of buying with credit cards?

2   **a**   Find the amount John will pay for a fishing line worth $87 if he pays $7 deposit and $5.70 per month for 24 months. How much extra does he pay in interest charges?
  b   How much will Ingrid pay for her wedding dress worth $1290 if she pays $90 deposit and $74 per month for two years? How much interest did she pay on the money borrowed?
  c   When Robyn said that she could buy an item marked at $640 for $610 at another store, the salesman offered her the item for $601.60 if she bought it immediately. She bought it on terms, paying a deposit of $20 and monthly repayments of $23.30 for four years. How much did she pay all together? How much extra did she pay in interest charges?
  d   Joshua wants to buy a tent with a marked price of $730. He wants to pay it off on terms. For each of the following, work out how much he pays altogether and the interest charged.
    i   Deposit of $100 and monthly payments of $64.50 for one year.
    ii   Deposit of $100 and monthly payments of $38.30 for two years.
    iii   Deposit of $100 and monthly payments of $29.60 for three years.
    iv   Deposit of $100 and monthly payments of $25.20 for four years.
    v   Deposit of $100 and monthly payments of $22.60 for five years.
    vi   Deposit of $100 and monthly payments of $17.35 for ten years.

e A man bought a car for $8250 paying a deposit of $250, $130 in extra charges, and paying $280 per month over five years. How much would he have to pay altogether? After paying four payments he finds it too expensive. The car is repossessed and sold for $6400. The finance company then sent him a bill for $1066.70 being the difference between what he owed and what they received for the car. He paid the bill and had no car. How much money had he paid altogether?

When borrowing money:
1 read the terms
2 work out the costs
3 be prepared to say NO

3 a Rachel was given a discount of 45% on a T-shirt with a marked price of €32. How much did she pay?

b Katherine was given a 7% discount on all purchases because she was a store employee. If the total of her purchases came to €85, how much did she pay?

c After bargaining, I purchased a chess set for €240 that was originally advertised for €320. What discount was I given and what is this as a percentage of the advertised price?

d My airline ticket was to cost me €550 but, because I booked more than six weeks ahead, I was given a discount price of €385. What percentage discount was I given?

e After a discount of 10% was given, Luke paid €585 for an additional hard disk drive for his computer. What was the original price of this hard disk drive?

f My mother paid €21.70 to attend the exhibit. She had been given a discount of 65% because she was a pensioner. What was the original price?

g Because Helen was prepared to pay cash for a yellow car with a marked price of €9200, she was given a discount of €1012. What percentage was the discount of the marked price?

h Greg was given a discount of 10% on the marked price of a kitchen table. If the discount was €22, how much did he pay?

4 Calculate the final price if successive discounts of 20% and 10% were applied to a price of $100.

5 A bookstore discounted all its books by 15%. A further discount of 10% was given to the local school. How much did they pay for books which originally sold for a total of $1750?

6 Apply the following successive discounts to the given prices.

a 10%, 10%, $500

b 15%, 25%, $720

c 5%, 20%, $260

d $12\frac{1}{2}$%, 15%, $965

e $7\frac{1}{2}$%, $17\frac{1}{2}$%, $2230

Does it matter in which order the discounts are applied?

7 a A radio on sale for £50 is to be reduced in price by 30%. Later, the discounted price is then increased by 30%. What is the final price? By what percentage (to the nearest per cent) must the first discounted price be increased to give the original price?

b   Edna bought a caravan, priced at £10 050, on terms of £300 deposit and 60 monthly repayments of £369.30. Find the total amount paid. Find also the interest paid expressed as a percentage of the money borrowed. (Answer correct to 1 decimal place.)

Only £9750 was borrowed.

c   Stephen bought a computer that had a marked price of £960. He received a discount of 15%. He paid a deposit of £81.60 and monthly repayments of £67.30 for one year. Find the interest paid expressed as a percentage of the money borrowed.

d   John had to pay interest on his credit card. He pays 1·7% per month on the greatest amount owing during each month. The greatest amount owing in April was £166, in May £294 and, in June, £408. Find the total interest charged for the three months.

8   A hardware store was offering multiple discounts of 12% and 15% on a chain saw with a list price of $480. The first discount is given on the list price, the second on the first net price.

a   What is the final purchase price?

b   What is the final purchase price, if the 15% discount is applied first?

c   Are the answers to **a** and **b** the same?

d   Is the multiple discount equivalent to a single discount of 27%?

e   What single discount is equivalent to multiple discounts of 12% and 15%?

f   What single discount is equivalent to multiple discounts of 10% and 20%?

9   The following formula converts multiple discounts to a single discount. Single discount rate $= [1 - (1 - d_1)(1 - d_2)(1 - d_3) \dots] \times 100\%$ where $d_1, d_2, d_3, \dots$ are the successive discounts expressed as decimals. Use the formula to find a single discount equal to the multiple discounts of:

a   11% and 8%

b   16%, 12% and 7%

c   10%, 9% and 5%

d $12\frac{1}{2}\%$, $4\frac{1}{4}\%$ and 2·1%

fun spot

3:08

Fun Spot 3:08 | The puzzle of the missing dollar

Three men had lunch in a busy restaurant. When it came time to pay their bill, each of the men gave to the waiter a ten-dollar note. Thus the waiter received $30 altogether.

But when the waiter added up the bill, he found it only came to $25. Knowing that $5 would not divide among the three men evenly, the waiter decided to give each of the men $1 change and put the remaining $2 in his pocket.

Now it appears that each of the men have paid $9 for their meal, and the waiter has $2; a total of $29.

Where is the missing dollar?

3:09 | Working for a Profit

People who work for themselves may charge a fee for their services or sell for a profit. However, they are not the only people concerned with profit and loss. We all, from time to time, will need to consider whether our investment of time, money and effort is justified by the results. This may be in our work for charity, organisations or in our hobbies.

- **When buying and selling:**

  ## Selling price = Cost price + Profit
  or
  ## Profit = Selling price − Cost price

  Note: **If the *profit is negative* we have made a *loss*.**

- **When calculating money made:**

  ## Profit = Money received − Expenses

worked examples

1 Rhonda bought a parachute for $80 and sold it for $340. Find the profit as a percentage of the cost.

2 We held a dance at school to make money to support the work of a charity organisation. We charged each of the 400 people who came an entrance fee of $8. The band cost $780, decorations cost $88.50, prizes $36, food $180, cleaning $147 and advertising $385. How much money did we make and what percentage is this of the sum received?

Okay, anything! I'll pay! Just give me the parachute!

Solutions

1 Rhonda's profit = Selling price − Cost price
   = $340 − $80
   = $260

Percentage profit = $\dfrac{\text{Profit}}{\text{Cost price}} \times 100\%$

= $\dfrac{\$260}{\$80} \times 100\%$

= 325%

continued ➜➜➜

2

$$\text{Income} = \text{Money received} - \text{Expenses}$$
$$\text{Money received} = 400 \times \$8$$
$$= \$3200$$
$$\text{Expenses} = \$780 + \$88.50 + \$36 + \$180 + \$147 + \$385$$
$$= \$1616.50$$
$$\text{Income} = \$3200 - \$1616.50$$
$$= \$1583.50$$
$$\text{Percentage of sum received} = \frac{\text{Income}}{\text{Money received}} \times 100\%$$
$$= \frac{\$1583.50}{\$3200} \times 100\%$$
$$\doteqdot 49.5\%$$

Exercise 3:09

1 Complete the tables below.

	Selling price	Cost price	Profit (or loss)
a	$2146	$1645	
b	$468		−$179
c	$58.75	$95.50	
d	$27 940	$13 650	
e		$85 420	$36 190

	Money received	Expenses	Profit (or loss)
f	€3816.50	€1308.50	
g	€491.80	€846.60	
h		€916	€8423
i	€27 648		€2494
j		€7684	€15 686

2 For parts **a** to **e** of question 1, find the profit or loss as a percentage of the cost price. (Answer correct to 1 decimal place.)

3 For parts **f** to **j** of question 1, find the profit or loss as a percentage of the money received. (Answer correct to 1 decimal place.)

4 For parts **i** to **j** of question 1, find the profit as a percentage of the expenses (correct to 1 decimal place).

5 Luke bought a microphone for $28 and sold it for $50. Find:
   a his profit from the sale
   b the profit as a percentage of the cost price
   c the profit as a percentage of the selling price

6 When selling products in a store, a percentage mark-up is added to the cost price to obtain the marked (or selling) price. If sporting gear has a mark-up of 60%, toys 40% and clothing 45% what will be the marked price of:
   a a baseball bat with a cost price of £24?
   b a doll with a cost price of £15?
   c a T-shirt with a cost price of £8.60?

7 A discount of 10% is given on the price of a car marked at $32 860. Find the discount price of the car.

8 Heather works for a toy store where the percentage mark-up is 40% of the cost price. She is offered 10% discount on any item and can have this on the cost price before mark-up occurs, or on the marked price. Use each method to find the discount price Heather would have to pay on a game that has a cost price of $32. What do you notice?

worked example

A shop owner marks everything up by 30% and the selling price of an article is $78.
What is the cost price and the profit on this article?

Solution

First, find the ratio of Cost : Profit : Selling price.

$$\therefore \text{C} : \text{P} : \text{SP} = 100 : 30 : 130$$

$$\frac{\text{Cost}}{\text{Selling price}} = \frac{100}{130}$$

$$\frac{\text{Cost}}{\$78} = \frac{100}{130}$$

$$\therefore \text{Cost} = \frac{100}{130} \times \$78$$

$$= \$60$$

$$\frac{\text{Profit}}{\text{Selling price}} = \frac{30}{130}$$

$$\frac{\text{Profit}}{\$78} = \frac{30}{130}$$

$$\therefore \text{Profit} = \frac{30}{130} \times \$78$$

$$= \$18$$

9 A store marks up everything by 40%. If the selling price of a tennis racquet is $308, what is the cost price and the profit on the racquet?

10 A travelling salesman marks up each item by 110%. Find the cost price and the profit on an item with a selling price of:
a $630   b $8.40   c $127.05

11 During a clearance sale, clothing was sold for 20% below cost. A dress was sold for $144. Calculate the cost price and the loss.

12 Unwanted stock was sold for 70% of the cost. If the amount received from sales was ¥1 092 000, what was the cost price of the stock sold and what was the loss?

13 The ratio Cost price : Profit : Selling price is 100 : 30 : 130. If the profit is $24 what is the selling price?

14 The ratio Cost price : Profit : Selling price is 8 : 3 : 11. If the cost price is $74.20 what will be the selling price?

15 Michael bought DVD players for $320 each. He wants to make a profit of 30% after passing on a 10% GST to the government. How much should he charge for each DVD player?

16 Lounge suites initially bought for $1100 each are to be sold at a loss of 40%. However, GST must still be charged and passed on to the government. What must be the sale price of each suite?

17 A machine was sold for a 25% profit of €270 on the cost price.
a   What was the selling price if an additional GST of 10% has to be added?
b   What was the cost price?
c   What percentage was the selling price, including the GST, of the cost price?

Investigation 3:09 | Let's plan a disco

3:09

Please use the Assessment Grid on the following page to help you understand what is required for this Investigation.

Plan a disco to raise money for charity.

Step 1
Estimate the cost of music, decorations, prizes, tickets, food, cleaning, advertising, etc.

Step 2
Estimate the number of people you expect to come.

Step 3
Set a ticket price to provide a profit of $300.

Use these estimates to draw on the same set of axes:
- a graph of *costs* ($) versus *number of tickets sold* (*n*)
- a graph of *income* ($) versus *number of tickets sold* (*n*)

Use the graphs to determine how many tickets need to be sold to:
- break even   • make $200   • make $300

Mathematical Terms 3

budget
- A plan for the use of expected income.

commission
- Income usually calculated as a percentage of the value of the goods sold.

discount
- To reduce the price of goods sold (*v*).
- The amount or percentage a price is reduced (*n*).

GST
- Goods and services tax.
- 10% of a base price is added onto the cost of most goods and services and included in the advertised retail price.

gross pay
- The amount of pay before any deductions such as income tax are subtracted.

income tax
- Tax paid to the government which is based on the level of income received.

net pay
- The amount of pay an employee receives after deductions such as income tax have been subtracted.

overtime
- Time worked by an employee in excess of a standard day or week.

- Usually rates of pay $1\frac{1}{2}$ or 2 times the normal rate of pay are paid for overtime.

profit
- The gain when a good is sold for a higher price than its cost price.
- If the selling price is lower a negative profit, or loss, is made.

salary
- A fixed amount paid for a year's employment. It may be paid weekly or fortnightly.

superannuation
- An investment fund usually contributed to by both employer and employee on the employee's behalf.
- It provides benefits for employees upon retirement, or for relatives if the member dies.

taxable income
- Amount after allowable deductions are subtracted from the gross pay.
- Income tax is calculated on this amount.

wages
- Pay given to an employee often based on an agreed hourly rate.
- Usually paid weekly or fortnightly.

Mathematical terms 3

Assessment Grid for Investigation 3:09 | **Let's plan a disco**

The following is a sample assessment grid for this investigation. You should carefully read the criteria *before* beginning the investigation so that you know what is required.

		Assessment Criteria (B, C, D) for this investigation		Achieved ✓
Criterion B Investigating Patterns	a	None of the following descriptors has been achieved.	0	
	b	Some help was needed to apply mathematical techniques and to graph the linear relationships given.	1	
			2	
	c	Mathematical problem-solving techniques have been selected and applied to accurately graph the lines required.	3	
			4	
	d	The student has graphed the required lines and attempted to use their graphs to determine the ticket sales required.	5	
			6	
	e	The student has effectively graphed the required lines and been able to use and interpret their graphs to determine the correct ticket sales required, with some reference to the equation of a line.	7	
			8	
Criterion C Communication in Mathematics	a	None of the following descriptors has been achieved.	0	
	b	There is a basic use of mathematical language and representation. Lines of reasoning are insufficient.	1	
			2	
	c	There is satisfactory use of mathematical language and representation. Graphs and explanations are clear but not always logical or complete.	3	
			4	
	d	A good use of mathematical language and representation. Graphs are accurate, to scale and fully labelled. Explanations are complete and concise.	5	
			6	
Criterion D Reflection in Mathematics	a	None of the following descriptors has been achieved.	0	
	b	An attempt has been made to explain whether the results make sense. An attempt has been made to make connection to the real-life aspects raised.	1	
			2	
	c	There is a correct but brief explanation of whether results make sense and how they were found. A description of the important aspects of the graphs is given along with their relation to finding ticket sales.	3	
			4	
	d	There is a critical explanation of the graphs obtained and their related equations. The ticket sales are explained with consideration of the accuracy of the results obtained and possible further applications discussed.	5	
			6	

Diagnostic Test 3 | Consumer Arithmetic

- These questions reflect the important skills introduced in this chapter.
- Errors made will indicate areas of weakness.
- Each weakness should be treated by going back to the section listed.

	Section
1 a John sells cars for a living. He is paid a retainer (a base wage) of $150 a week as well as 2% commission on sales made. Find his income for the week, if in one week he sells cars to the value of: i $8000 ii $21 500 **b** Luke has a casual job from 4:00 pm till 5:30 pm Monday to Friday. He also works from 9 am till 12:30 pm on Saturdays. Find his weekly income if his casual rate is $9.80 per hour Monday to Friday, and $14.70 an hour on Saturdays.	3:01
2 a During one week Petra worked 35 hours at the normal rate of €12.60 per hour. She also worked 6 hours overtime: 4 at 'time-and-a-half' and 2 at 'double-time'. How much did she earn? **b** Calculate Diane's holiday loading if she is given $17\frac{1}{2}$% of four weeks salary and she earns €860 per fortnight.	3:02
3 a Find the net pay for the week if John earns £586.80, is taxed £107.95, pays £43.50 for superannuation and has miscellaneous deductions totalling £79.40. **b** What percentage of John's gross pay did he pay in tax?	3:03
4 Alana received a salary of $38 465 and a total from other income (investments) of $965. Her total tax deductions were $2804. During the year she had already paid tax instalments amounting to $13 800.50. Find: **a** her total income **b** her taxable income **c** the tax payable on her taxable income using the table on page 42 **d** her refund due or balance payable **e** how much extra Alana would receive each week if she is given a wage rise of $100 per week.	3:04
5 a A lawn fertiliser comes in three sizes: 20 kg (for $11.60), 50 kg (for $24.80) and 110 kg (for $56.60). Which size is the best buy? **b** *Rich Red* strawberry flavouring can be purchased at 240 mL for $1.70, 660 mL for $3.75, or 1 L for $6.25. Which buy represents the best value?	3:06
6 a Determine the GST that needs to be added to a base price of $73.70. **b** Determine the retail price after 10% GST is added to a base price of $53.90. **c** How much GST is contained in a retail price of $32.45? **d** What was the base price before 10% GST was added to give a retail price of $21.45?	3:07

7 a Jim bought a car with a marked price of €3000. He paid a deposit of €100 and 36 monthly payments of €136.20. How much did he pay? How much more than the marked price did he pay?

b Pauline bought a lawnmower marked at $692. She paid a deposit of $40 and 24 monthly payments of $39.20. How much did she pay? By how far did that exceed the marked price?

8 a Naomi was given $12\frac{1}{2}\%$ discount on a rug with a marked price of $460. How much did she pay?

b A television marked at $4200 was eventually sold for $3612. What was the discount and what was the percentage discount given on the marked price?

c After a discount of 13% was given, I paid $27 840 for my yellow Holden. What was the original marked price?

9 a Jane bought a desk with a marked price of $650. She was given a discount of 10% for paying cash, and then received a further 10% off the discounted price because it was scratched. How much did she pay?

b What is the final price if successive discounts of 15% and 20% are applied to a retail price of $1250?

10 a Rachel bought a painting for $250 and sold it for $575. Find the profit as a percentage of the cost.

b We held a games night to raise money for *The House with no Steps*. We charged each of the 287 people who came an entrance fee of $17.50. Hire of the hall cost $110, decorations cost $63, prizes $185.60, food $687, cleaning $96 and advertising $240.
How much money did we make and what percentage is this of the money received?

Chapter 3 | Revision Assignment

1 **a** A woman works for wages of $16.80 per hour. How much will she earn in a week in which she works
   i 40 hours at normal time?
   ii 40 hours of normal time and 5 hours of overtime if overtime is paid at $1\frac{1}{2}$ times the normal rate of pay?

   b A salesman works for a wage of $500 per week plus 3% commission. How much will he earn in a week if he sells $4500 worth of goods?

   c A factory worker is paid a wage of $540 a week. The factory has a special bonus system which enables a worker to be paid an extra 25c per article for every article in excess of the weekly quota of 5000. How much will the worker earn in a week in which 7200 articles are made?

   d How much holiday pay will a girl receive if she is to be paid 4 weeks' holiday pay plus a holiday loading of $17\frac{1}{2}$% of 4 weeks' pay? Her weekly wage is $452.

2 **a** Fibreglass resin comes in the following sizes: 1 kg for $9.80; 5 kg for $26.80, and 21 kg for $59.60.
   i What is the best value for money?
   ii What is the most economical way of buying 17 kg?

   b A TV set with a cash price of $680 is bought for a deposit of $68 and 48 monthly payments of $15.68. Find the difference between the cash price and the price paid.

   c Calculate the amount of GST included in items which retailed for $736, $245 and $579.

3 Mary-Ann is paid an annual salary of $53 350. Her allowable tax deductions total $1340. During the year her employer paid income tax instalments on her behalf of $12 732.
   a What is Mary-Ann's taxable income?
   b How much income tax should she pay for the year?
   c What is the amount of her refund from the tax office?

4 Jeremy added 10% GST onto the price of a book valued at $29.90 to get its retail price. He then discounted the retail price by 10% to get a sales price.
   a What is the retail price?
   b What is the sales price?
   c Is the sales price the same as the original value of the book?
   d By what percentage should Jeremy have discounted the retail price to get back to the original value of the book?

5 **a** Vicki sold azaleas in her nursery for $15.90. She bought them for $11.35. What percentage profit does she make?
   b Michael sold a bike he bought for $350 to a friend two years later for $230. What percentage loss is this?

Technology Applications

Wages

Activities

Technology Applications

1 Finding the weekly wage
2 Going shopping
3 GST

Drag and Drops

Chapter Review

Questions

Chapter 3 | Working Mathematically

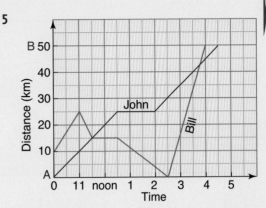

1 Use ID Card 2 on page xiv to identify:
   a 10   b 12   c 17   d 18   e 19
   f 20   g 21   h 22   i 23   j 24

2 Use ID Card 4 on page xvi to identify:
   a 1   b 2   c 3   d 4   e 5
   f 6   g 7   h 8   i 9   j 13

3 Through how many degrees does the hour hand of a clock turn in half an hour?

4 Tom was given a cheque for an amount between $31 and $32. The bank teller made a mistake and exchanged dollars and cents on the cheque. Tom took the money without examining it and gave 5 cents to his son. He now found that he had twice the value of the original cheque. If he had no money before entering the bank, what was the amount of the cheque.

$31.62 . . .
. . . $62.31?

5 This travel graph shows the journeys of John and Bill between town A and town B. (They travel on the same road.)
   a How far from A is Bill when he commences his journey?
   b How far is John from B at 2:30 pm?
   c When do John and Bill first meet?
   d Who reaches town B first?
   e At what time does Bill stop to rest?
   f How far does John travel?
   g How far apart are John and Bill when Bill is at town A?
   h How far does Bill travel?

6 A loan of $1000 is to be repaid at an interest rate of 20% pa. The faster the loan is repaid, the less interest is charged. The graph shows how the amount to be repaid varies according to the time taken to repay the loan.
   a How much has to be repaid if $3\frac{1}{2}$ years is taken to repay the loan?
   b If a person wished to repay the loan in 2 years what amount would have to be repaid?
   c How much must be paid monthly if this loan is to be repaid in 4 years?

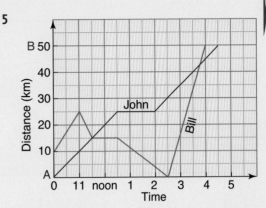

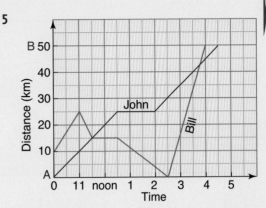

4

Algebraic Expressions

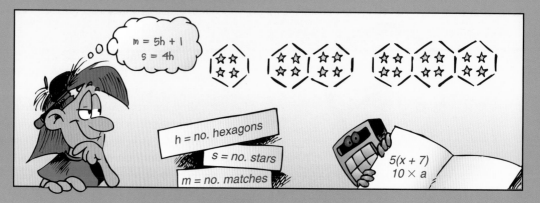

Chapter Contents

Learning Outcomes

Students will be able to:

- Use the algebraic symbols to represent word problems.
- Simplify, expand and factorise simple algebraic expressions.
- Work with expressions involving algebraic fractions.
- Expand binomial products.

Areas of Interaction

Approaches to Learning (Knowledge Acquisition, Problem Solving, Communication, Logical Thinking, Reflection), Human Ingenuity

4:01 | Generalised Arithmetic

prep quiz

4:01

Find:

1 the sum of 7 and 5
2 the difference between 9 and 2
3 the number 8 less than 25
4 the quotient of 48 and 6
5 the product of 7 and 3
6 12 more than 8
7 the average of 41 and 47
8 the total of 13 and 21
9 the number of times 23 can be taken from 138
10 the number 8 less than the product of 4 and 5

In mathematics, the method of solving a problem is sometimes hard to express in words. In cases like this, pronumerals are often used. The result could be a simple formula.

- Some numbers in a pattern are known. How can we find the others?
  For example: 9, 8, 7, 6, . . .   or   3, 5, 7, 9, . . .
  Patterns like these can be written in a table of values, where n represents the position of the number in the pattern, and T the actual number (or term).

n	1	2	3	4	5
T	9	8	7	6	

n	1	2	3	4	5
T	3	5	7	9	

Here we can see that:
$T = 10 - n$
So an algebraic expression that represents this pattern would be:
$10 - n$

Here we can see that:
$T = 2n + 1$
So an algebraic expression that represents this pattern would be:
$2n + 1$

- Two angles of a triangle are known. How can we find the third?

  A Consider a numerical example.
  $\theta = 180° - (72 + 54)°$
  $\quad = 54°$

  B Show the general result.
  $\theta = 180° - (a + b)°$
  or $180° - a° - b°$

  $180° - (a + b)°$ is called the *general case*.

The angle sum of a triangle is 180°.

---

worked examples

1   The sum of 8 and 12 $= 8 + 12$
    so the sum of x and y $= x + y$

2   The cost of 6 books at 30c each $= 6 \times 30c$
    so the cost of x books at 30c each $= x \times 30$
    $\qquad\qquad\qquad\qquad\qquad\qquad\quad = 30x$ cents

continued ➜➜➜

3 The average of 9 and 13 $= \dfrac{9+13}{2}$

so the average of a and b $= \dfrac{a+b}{2}$

4 The change from \$10 after buying 3 books
at \$2 each $= 10 - (2 \times 3)$ dollars
so the change from \$10 after buying x books
at \$2 each $= 10 - 2 \times x$
$\qquad\qquad = 10 - 2x$ dollars

> ■ The aim of 'generalised arithmetic' is to write an algebraic expression that shows the steps to be taken, no matter which numbers are involved.

Exercise 4:01

Foundation Worksheet 4:01

Generalised arithmetic
1 Write expressions for:
  a the sum of 3a and 2b
  b the average of m and n
2 a Find the cost of x books at 75c each.
  b Find the age of Bill, who is 25 years old, in another y years.

1 Match each table of values with the correct algebraic expression from the given list to complete the statement $T = \ldots$

a
n	1	2	3	4
T	3	4	5	6

b
n	1	2	3	4
T	−2	−1	0	1

c
n	1	2	3	4
T	3	6	9	16

d
n	1	2	3	4
T	5	8	11	18

e
n	1	2	3	4
T	1	4	9	16

f
n	1	2	3	4
T	1	3	5	7

> **A** $3n$
> **B** n^2
> **C** $n + 2$
> **D** $3n + 2$
> **E** $2n - 1$
> **F** $n - 3$

2 Write down an algebraic expression that represents each pattern of numbers, using n to represent the position of each number in the pattern.

a 2, 4, 6, 8, …
b 4, 5, 6, 7, …
c 7, 6, 5, 4, …
d 5, 7, 9, 11, …
e $\frac{1}{2}$, 1, $1\frac{1}{2}$, 2, …
f −3, −1, 1, 3, …

> ■ Use a table of values if you need to.

For questions 3 to 8 write expressions for each.

3 a the sum of 5 and 7
b the sum of 5 and y
c the sum of x and y

4 a the product of 3 and 7
b the product of a and 7
c the product of a and b

5 a the difference between 8 and 3
b the difference between 8 and p
c the difference between q and p

6 a the average of 8 and 12
b the average of 8 and x
c the average of w and x

7 a the cost of 5 books at 75c each
b the cost of a books at 75c each
c the cost of a books at b cents each

8 a dividing 30 cm into 5 equal lengths
b dividing 30 cm into t equal lengths
c dividing A cm into t equal lengths

9 **a** If Steve is 15 years old, how old will he be in 6 years?
 b How old will Steve be in y years?

10 **a** If a car travels at 60 km/h for 3 hours, how far does it travel?
 b If the same car travels for h hours, how far does it travel?

11 **a** If three lengths of rope, each 2 m long, are cut from a piece of rope 10 m long, what length is left?
 b If two lengths of rope, each x m long, are cut from a piece of rope X m long, what length is left?

12 **a** A student buys x books and y pens. If each book costs 85c and each pen costs 63c, what is the total cost?
 b If the books cost C cents each and the pens D cents each, what is the total cost?

13 Mr Smith is Y years old; his son is 22 years younger. How old is his son? How old will the son be in x years' time?

14 **a** If I travel x km in 2 hours, and then y km in the next 3 hours, how far have I travelled altogether?
 b What is my average speed for the whole journey?

15 Bob and Tom have $1 between them. If Bob has x cents, how much has Tom?

16 **a** What is the next even number after 6?
 b What is the next even number after y, if y is an even number?
 c What is the largest odd number less than y, if y is even?

17 The expression $2n$ will give an even number for all values of 'n', where n is an integer. Write down an expression that will always give an odd number.

18 **a** Two angles of a triangle are 25° and 79°. What is the size of the third angle?
 b Two angles of a triangle are $a°$ and $b°$. What is the size of the third angle?

19 **a** How far will a person walk at m km/h in h hours?
 b What is the average speed of a car that travels k km in h hours?
 c How long will it take to travel k km at m km/h?

20 **a** A TV set is bought for $P. If it is sold for $R, what is the profit?
 b If a gain of $G is to be made, what should the selling price of the TV be?

21 Write an expression for the perimeter of each figure below.
All measurements are in centimetres.

a
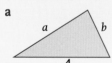

b
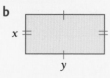

c

d
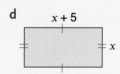

22 Write an expression for the area of each figure.

a

b 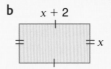 $x + 2$ ... x

c y ... x

d 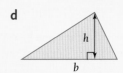 h ... b

23 In each of the following, use grouping symbols to make the meaning clear.

a the product of 4 and $a + 2$
b subtract $x + y$ from 8
c twice the sum of p and q
d the square of $2a$
e the difference between $3a$ and $b + c$
f the square of $x + 2$
g the product of x and $y - 5$
h the square root of $2m + 3n$

24 a What is the cost of 3 books at p cents and 4 pens at q cents each?
b What is the change from $5 (in cents)?

25 Translate the following algebraic expressions into words.

a xy
b $5 - a$
c $2p + q$
d $3m - 2n$
e $5(x + y)$
f $(a + b)^2$
g $\dfrac{x + y}{2}$
h $\dfrac{m - n}{a}$
i $\sqrt{u + v}$
j $\sqrt[3]{ab}$

26 Translate the following into words to explain the difference between each pair of expressions.

a abc and $a + b + c$
b $a - b$ and $b - a$
c $3(a + b)$ and $3a + b$
d $x^2 + y^2$ and $(x + y)^2$
e $\sqrt{a} + \sqrt{b}$ and $\sqrt{a + b}$
f $\dfrac{a}{b} + \dfrac{2}{3}$ and $\dfrac{a + 2}{b + 3}$

---

 challenge

4:01

Challenge 4:01 | Let's play with blocks

Eight blocks have been stacked together here to form a cube. If the outside of the cube were painted, how many sides of each block would be painted?

How many blocks make up the second cube? If this cube were painted, how many blocks would have 3 sides, 2 sides, 1 side or even no sides painted?

What would be the result of painting a cube that had four blocks along each edge?

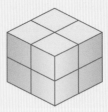

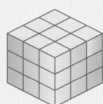

4:02 | Substitution

Write the following algebraic expressions in their simplest form.

1 $a \times b$ **2** $x \times y \times y$ **3** $2 \times x + 3 \times y$

Simplify the following:

4 $2 + 4 \times 3$ **5** $3 \times 4 + 2 \times 5$ **6** 4×5^2

7 $3(6 - 10)$ **8** $\frac{1}{2} \times 6 - 5$ **9** $\frac{8-2}{3}$

10 $\frac{5}{3} - \frac{3}{5}$

Algebra involves the use of 'pronumerals' as well as numbers. A pronumeral is usually a letter, such as x, that takes the place of a number in an expression like $3x + 7$.

If a number is substituted for each pronumeral, a value for the expression can then be obtained.

worked examples

Find the value of the following expressions, given that $a = 10$, $b = 4$, $x = 5$ and $y = -3$.

1 $3a + 2b$
$= 3 \times 10 + 2 \times 4$
$= 30 + 8$
$= 38$

2 $x^2 + y^2$
$= 5^2 + (-3)^2$
$= 25 + 9$
$= 34$

3 $\frac{1}{2}ab^2$
$= \frac{1}{2} \times 10 \times 4^2$
$= \frac{1}{2} \times 160$
$= 80$

4 $\frac{1}{x} + \frac{1}{y}$
$= \frac{1}{5} + \frac{1}{(-3)}$
$= \frac{1}{5} - \frac{1}{3}$
$= -\frac{2}{15}$

Exercise 4:02

Foundation Worksheet 4:02
Substitution
1 Find the value of:
  a $2x + 3y$ if $x = 3$, $y = -5$
2 If $a = 4$, $b = 5$, $c = -2$, find the value of:
  a $a^2 + bc$

1 Evaluate the following expressions if $x = 3$, $y = 4$ and $z = 8$.

a $x + y$ **b** $3x + 2y$ **c** $2x - y$

d x^2y **e** $(x + y)^2$ **f** $x^2 + y^2$

g $z(x + y)$ **h** $xz - 10$ **i** $xy - xz$

j $\frac{x + y}{2}$ **k** $\frac{x}{2} + \frac{y}{4}$ **l** $z^2 - z$

m $xy^2 + x^2y$ **n** $xz - yz$ **o** $4(x - 2y)$

p $x(y^2 - z^2)$ **q** $x - 3y$ **r** $y^2 - z^2$

s $z - xy$ **t** $\frac{x}{y} + \frac{y}{x}$ **u** $\frac{x + y}{xy}$

v $\frac{x + y}{x - y}$ **w** $\frac{1}{2}xyz^2$ **x** $\sqrt{3xy}$

Expressions have no equals symbols.

Technology Applications

4:02 Substitution
4:02 Magic squares

Activities

2 Find the value of the following expressions if $a = 3$, $b = -4$ and $c = \frac{1}{2}$.

- **a** $a + b$
- **b** $a - b$
- **c** ab
- **d** ab^2
- **e** $(ab)^2$
- **f** bc
- **g** abc
- **h** $10 - ab$
- **i** $\frac{1}{a} + \frac{1}{b}$
- **j** $c(2a + b)$
- **k** $\frac{1}{a} + c$
- **l** $(a + b)(a - b)$
- **m** $b^2 - b^3$
- **n** $\frac{1}{c} - \frac{1}{b}$
- **o** $\frac{a}{b} - \frac{b}{c}$
- **p** $\frac{a}{b} + \frac{b}{c} + \frac{c}{d}$
- **q** $ab + bc + ac$

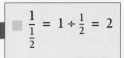

$\blacksquare \quad \dfrac{\frac{1}{1}}{\frac{1}{2}} = 1 \div \frac{1}{2} = 2$

3 a Find the value of $mx + c$ if:
- **i** $m = 3$, $x = 10$, $c = 1$
- **ii** $m = 5$, $x = 4$, $c = -3$
- **iii** $m = -2$, $x = 7$, $c = -4$

b Find the value of $\frac{h}{2}(a + b)$ if:
- **i** $h = 4$, $a = 7$, $b = 5$
- **ii** $h = 7$, $a = 4$, $b = 6$
- **iii** $h = 3\cdot4$, $a = 9\cdot2$, $b = 3\cdot7$

c Find the value of πr^2 if:
- **i** $\pi = 3\cdot1$, $r = 8$
- **ii** $\pi = 3\cdot14$, $r = 2\cdot5$
- **iii** $\pi = 3\cdot142$, $r = 100$

4:02

Investigation 4:02 | The history of algebra

Find out as much as you can about the early history of algebra.
You might consider:
- Ahmes Papyrus (Egyptian c. 1700 BC)
- Diophantus (Greek c. AD 250)
- Mohammed ibn Musa al-Khowarizmi (Arab c. AD 825)
- Bhaskara (Hindu c. AD 1150)

4:03 | Simplifying Algebraic Expressions

4:03

Write these expressions in their simplest forms.

1. $7x + 2x$
2. $9x - 8x$
3. $3x \times 2y$
4. $5x \times x$
5. $12x \div 4$
6. $10ab \div 5a$
7. $3a + 2b + 5a + 3b$
8. $6x + 2y - x - y$
9. $3 \times (-2a) \times 4a$
10. $3a \div (-9b)$

---

worked examples

Remember that only terms that are alike may be added or subtracted.

1. $5a + 2b - 3a + b = 5a - 3a + 2b + b$
   $\qquad = 2a + 3b$

2. $5p^2 + 2p - 3p^2 = 5p^2 - 3p^2 + 2p$
   $\qquad = 2p^2 + 2p$
   (*Note:* p^2 and p are *not* like terms.)

3. $6ab - 4ba = 6ab - 4ab$
   $\qquad = 2ab$

'Like' terms contain identical pronumeral parts. eg $5x + 2x$.

Did you realise that the + or − sign belongs to the term after it?

4 $-7x \times -3xy^2 = 21x^2y^2$

5 $3pq \times 4qr = 12pqqr$
$\qquad = 12pq^2r$

6 $12ac \div 8ab = \dfrac{^3\cancel{12}ac}{_2\cancel{8}ab}$
$\qquad = \dfrac{3c}{2b}$

7 $-6x \div 18xy = \dfrac{^{-1}\cancel{6}x}{_3\cancel{18}xy}$
$\qquad = -\dfrac{1}{3y}$

8 $10a - 3 \times 2a = 10a - 6a$
$\qquad = 4a$

9 $(5a + 7a) \times (3b - 2b) = 12a \times b$
$\qquad = 12ab$

10 $3m \times 2n \div mn = 6mn \div mn$
$\qquad = \dfrac{6\cancel{mn}}{\cancel{mn}}$
$\qquad = 6$

11 $\dfrac{7p + 8p - 3p}{2p \times 3q} = \dfrac{^2\cancel{12}\cancel{p}}{_1\cancel{6}\cancel{p}q}$
$\qquad = \dfrac{2}{q}$

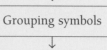
Remember the order in which operations should be done.

↓

Grouping symbols

↓

$\times \quad \div$

↓

$+ \quad -$

Multiply numbers first and then pronumerals.

In $12pq^2r$ only the 'q' is squared.

Exercise 4:03

1 Collect the like terms to simplify these expressions.

a $3x + 2x$	**b** $8a + 5a$	**c** $10p + 21p$	**d** $x + 7x$
e $7a - 4a$	**f** $9b - 3b$	**g** $11q - q$	**h** $12e + 9e$
i $3p + 5p - 6p$	**j** $4x + 2x + x$	**k** $10x - 9x + 3x$	**l** $x + 2x - 3x$
m $2a + p - a + 3p$	**n** $a + m - a + m$	**o** $8 + 2x - 5x - 7$	**p** $8y - 1 - 8y - 1$
q $x^2 + 2x + 2x^2 - x$	**r** $p^2 + 4p + 3p^2 + p$	**s** $3q^2 + 8q - 4q - q^2$	**t** $y^2 + y + y^2 - y$
u $7 - p^2 + p - 5$	**v** $2a + a^2 + 7 + a$	**w** $8x - 7 - 7x - 3x^2$	**x** $5ab - 7 + 3ba - 9$

2 Simplify these products.

a $8y \times 3$	**b** $4 \times 4a$	**c** $3x \times 2y$	**d** $8p \times 4q$	**e** $6a \times b$
f $5x \times x$	**g** $5a \times 3a$	**h** $ab \times ac$	**i** $3pq \times 2p$	**j** $5mn \times mp$
k $4mn \times \frac{1}{2}n$	**l** $9b \times a^2$	**m** $6a^2 \times (-7a)$	**n** $-5x \times -2x$	**o** $x \times 2y \times 3x$
p $14ab \times (-\frac{1}{2}ab)$	**q** $(-ab) \times (-bc)$	**r** $2k \times 3k \times 4k$	**s** $-2 \times 7x \times -5y$	**t** $\frac{1}{4}m \times 4n \times (-p)$

3 Simplify:

a $12x \div 4$ b $12x \div 4x$ c $9x^2 \div 3$ d $8x \div 8x$

e $15m \div 10n$ f $32a \div 12b$ g $5 \div 20a$ h $48ab \div 6b$

i $a \div 3a$ j $45ab \div 20ba$ k $-20p \div 4p$ l $-xy \div xz$

m $14a \div (-a)$ n $(-15x) \div (-5xy)$ o $-28mnp \div 7mp$ p $8a^2b \div 16ab^2$

4 Simplify:

a $mn \times np$ b $7 + m + 6 + 3m$ c $14 - 2a + 5$ d $5x^2 \times 0$

e $3xy \times 2yx$ f $8x^2 + 2x + 7x^2 + 3x$ g $3 \times 4y \times 5z$ h $-4x \times 7x$

i $15ab - 9ba + ab$ j $6m - 7m$ k $8b + 3b - 11b$ l $18ab \div 9bc$

m $x \div 3x$ n $2pq \times 9pq$ o $3a + b + 2a - c$ p $-3y \times (-5z)$

q $\frac{1}{2}y + \frac{1}{2}y$ r $m + n - m + n$ s $3a \times 2b \times c$ t $15at \div 10tx$

5 Write the simplest expression for:

a $(2a + 3a) \times 4$ b $(10x - 3x) \div 7$ c $(9b - 3b) \times 2$ d $(3m + 9m) \div 4$

e $12x \div (2x + x)$ f $5a \times (10a + 2a)$ g $3m \times (10m - 9m)$ h $15y \div (9y - 2y)$

i $5a \times 7 \div a$ j $8x \times 4y \div 2xy$ k $10a \div 5 \times 3a$ l $9xy \div 3x \times 2y$

m $2x + 3x \times 4$ n $5x \times 3x + 10x^2$ o $20y - 5 \times 2y$ p $18m - 12m \div 6$

q $3 \times 2n + 5n \times 4$ r $7x + 3 \times 2x - 10x$ s $8x \div 4 - x$ t $11m + 18m \div 2$

u $\dfrac{6 \times 3x}{2x \times 5}$ v $\dfrac{3p + 2p - 1p}{2 \times 2p}$ w $\dfrac{11y - y}{6y + 4y}$ x $\dfrac{5a \times 4b \times 2c}{10c \times b \times 8c}$

4:04 | Algebraic Fractions

4:04A   Addition and subtraction

Answer the following:

1 $\dfrac{3}{5} + \dfrac{1}{5}$ **2** $\dfrac{7}{10} - \dfrac{3}{10}$ **3** $\dfrac{1}{4} + \dfrac{1}{3}$

4 $\dfrac{1}{2} + \dfrac{3}{8}$ **5** $\dfrac{2}{5} - \dfrac{1}{4}$ **6** $\dfrac{7}{12} - \dfrac{1}{3}$

Simplify the expressions:

7 $7x + 4x$ **8** $3ab + ab$ **9** $6x - 5x$ **10** $9a - a$

 Rewrite each fraction as two equivalent fractions with a common denominator, then add or subtract the numerators.

---

worked examples

1 $\dfrac{3x}{5} + \dfrac{2x}{5} = \dfrac{3x + 2x}{5}$

$= \dfrac{{}^{1}\cancel{5}x}{\cancel{5}_{1}}$

$= x$

2 $\dfrac{5}{a} - \dfrac{3}{a} = \dfrac{5 - 3}{a}$

$= \dfrac{2}{a}$

> In these two examples, each fraction already had a common denominator.

3 $\dfrac{x}{3} + \dfrac{x}{2} = \dfrac{x \times 2}{3 \times 2} + \dfrac{x \times 3}{2 \times 3}$

$\qquad = \dfrac{2x}{6} + \dfrac{3x}{6}$

$\qquad = \dfrac{5x}{6}$

4 $\dfrac{4a}{5} - \dfrac{a}{3} = \dfrac{4a \times 3}{5 \times 3} - \dfrac{a \times 5}{3 \times 5}$

$\qquad = \dfrac{12a}{15} - \dfrac{5a}{15}$

$\qquad = \dfrac{7a}{15}$

5 $\dfrac{5m}{8} + \dfrac{m}{2} = \dfrac{5m}{8} + \dfrac{m \times 4}{2 \times 4}$

$\qquad = \dfrac{5m}{8} + \dfrac{4m}{8}$

$\qquad = \dfrac{9m}{8}$

6 $\dfrac{3x}{4} - \dfrac{2y}{3} = \dfrac{9x}{12} - \dfrac{8y}{12}$

$\qquad = \dfrac{9x - 8y}{12}$

7 $\dfrac{9}{x} + \dfrac{2}{3x} = \dfrac{27}{3x} + \dfrac{2}{3x}$

$\qquad = \dfrac{29}{3x}$

8 $\dfrac{5a}{2x} - \dfrac{2a}{3x} = \dfrac{15a}{6x} - \dfrac{4a}{6x}$

$\qquad = \dfrac{11a}{6x}$

Exercise 4:04A

1 Simplify the following.

a $\dfrac{3a}{2} + \dfrac{a}{2}$ **b** $\dfrac{3x}{5} - \dfrac{2x}{5}$ **c** $\dfrac{a}{3} + \dfrac{4a}{3}$ **d** $\dfrac{9m}{10} - \dfrac{3m}{10}$

e $\dfrac{x}{4} + \dfrac{y}{4}$ **f** $\dfrac{5a}{3} - \dfrac{2b}{3}$ **g** $\dfrac{2}{a} + \dfrac{3}{a}$ **h** $\dfrac{7}{x} + \dfrac{1}{x}$

i $\dfrac{3}{y} - \dfrac{2}{y}$ **j** $\dfrac{9}{m} - \dfrac{1}{m}$ **k** $\dfrac{5a}{x} + \dfrac{2a}{x}$ **l** $\dfrac{2x}{y} - \dfrac{3x}{y}$

m $\dfrac{5}{3n} + \dfrac{7}{3n}$ **n** $\dfrac{3}{2x} - \dfrac{1}{2x}$ **o** $\dfrac{8a}{5b} + \dfrac{2a}{5b}$ **p** $\dfrac{7m}{4x} - \dfrac{3m}{4x}$

2 Reduce each of these expressions to its simplest form.

a $\dfrac{x}{3} + \dfrac{x}{5}$ **b** $\dfrac{a}{2} + \dfrac{a}{5}$ **c** $\dfrac{y}{3} - \dfrac{y}{4}$ **d** $\dfrac{m}{2} - \dfrac{m}{4}$

e $\dfrac{2a}{3} + \dfrac{a}{2}$ **f** $\dfrac{5x}{3} + \dfrac{2x}{4}$ **g** $\dfrac{3n}{8} - \dfrac{n}{4}$ **h** $\dfrac{4p}{5} - \dfrac{3p}{10}$

i $\dfrac{x}{4} + \dfrac{y}{3}$ **j** $\dfrac{2a}{3} - \dfrac{3b}{2}$ **k** $\dfrac{3m}{5} + \dfrac{n}{2}$ **l** $\dfrac{k}{6} - \dfrac{2l}{4}$

m $\dfrac{2}{x} + \dfrac{4}{3x}$ **n** $\dfrac{1}{3a} + \dfrac{2}{4a}$ **o** $\dfrac{7}{2m} - \dfrac{2}{5m}$ **p** $\dfrac{5}{8x} - \dfrac{1}{2x}$

q $\dfrac{2a}{3x} + \dfrac{3a}{2x}$ **r** $\dfrac{x}{3m} - \dfrac{2x}{m}$ **s** $\dfrac{5m}{2n} + \dfrac{3m}{4n}$ **t** $\dfrac{2x}{3a} + \dfrac{y}{4a}$

4:04B   Multiplication and division

prep quiz

4:04B

Answer the following.

1 $\dfrac{1}{2} \times \dfrac{3}{4}$ **2** $\dfrac{2}{5} \times \dfrac{3}{4}$ **3** $\dfrac{4}{9} \times \dfrac{3}{8}$

4 $\dfrac{1}{2} \div \dfrac{3}{4}$ **5** $\dfrac{3}{5} \div \dfrac{3}{10}$ **6** $\dfrac{2}{3} \div \dfrac{5}{4}$

Simplify these expressions.

7 $5 \times 6x$ **8** $3a \times 2a$

9 $15a \div 5$ **10** $12ab \div 6b$

When **multiplying**
- Cancel any common factors, then
- multiply the numerators together and multiply the denominators together.

When **dividing**
- Turn the second fraction upside down, then
- multiply as above (invert and multiply).

worked examples

1 $\dfrac{2}{a} \times \dfrac{5}{b} = \dfrac{2 \times 5}{a \times b}$

$= \dfrac{10}{ab}$

2 $\dfrac{5}{x} \times \dfrac{x}{10} = \dfrac{5^1}{x_1} \times \dfrac{x^1}{10_2}$

$= \dfrac{1 \times 1}{1 \times 2}$

$= \dfrac{1}{2}$

3 $\dfrac{3b}{2} \times \dfrac{4}{5b} = \dfrac{3b}{2_1} \times \dfrac{4^2}{5b}$

$= \dfrac{3 \times 2}{1 \times 5}$

$= \dfrac{6}{5}$ or $1\dfrac{1}{5}$

4 $\dfrac{ab}{2} \div \dfrac{b}{5} = \dfrac{ab^1}{2} \times \dfrac{5}{b_1}$

$= \dfrac{a \times 5}{2 \times 1}$

$= \dfrac{5a}{2}$

5 $\dfrac{8a}{3b} \div \dfrac{2a}{9b} = \dfrac{^4 8a}{_1 3b} \times \dfrac{^3 9b}{_1 2a}$

$= \dfrac{4 \times 3}{1 \times 1}$

$= 12$

'Invert' means 'turn upside down'.

Don't forget to invert the second fraction when dividing.

Exercise 4:04B

Foundation Worksheet 4:04B

Simplifying algebraic fractions

1 Simplify: **a** $\dfrac{1}{3} \times \dfrac{4}{5}$

2 Simplify: **a** $\dfrac{a}{2} \times \dfrac{b}{5}$

3 Simplify: **a** $\dfrac{a}{2} \div \dfrac{a}{8}$

1 Simplify these products.

a $\dfrac{x}{2} \times \dfrac{y}{3}$ **b** $\dfrac{a}{4} \times \dfrac{b}{3}$ **c** $\dfrac{m}{2} \times \dfrac{m}{5}$ **d** $\dfrac{a}{4} \times \dfrac{a}{10}$

e $\dfrac{3}{a} \times \dfrac{4}{m}$ **f** $\dfrac{2}{x} \times \dfrac{1}{y}$ **g** $\dfrac{1}{p} \times \dfrac{4}{p}$ **h** $\dfrac{1}{n} \times \dfrac{1}{3n}$

i $\dfrac{p}{q} \times \dfrac{x}{y}$ j $\dfrac{2}{a} \times \dfrac{a}{4}$ k $\dfrac{m}{5} \times \dfrac{10}{n}$ l $\dfrac{3x}{5} \times \dfrac{2}{9x}$

m $\dfrac{ab}{3} \times \dfrac{2}{b}$ n $\dfrac{x}{y} \times \dfrac{y}{x}$ o $\dfrac{6m}{5a} \times \dfrac{15a}{2m}$ p $\dfrac{8x}{5p} \times \dfrac{2a}{3x}$

2 Simplify these divisions.

a $\dfrac{m}{2} \div \dfrac{m}{4}$ b $\dfrac{n}{3} \div \dfrac{n}{5}$ c $\dfrac{5a}{3} \div \dfrac{2a}{9}$ d $\dfrac{x}{5} \div \dfrac{3x}{10}$

e $\dfrac{5}{a} \div \dfrac{2}{a}$ f $\dfrac{3}{2m} \div \dfrac{1}{3m}$ g $\dfrac{a}{b} \div \dfrac{2a}{b}$ h $\dfrac{3x}{5y} \div \dfrac{x}{10y}$

i $\dfrac{a}{b} \div \dfrac{x}{y}$ j $\dfrac{2p}{3q} \div \dfrac{8p}{9q}$ k $\dfrac{10k}{3n} \div \dfrac{2k}{9n}$ l $\dfrac{a}{2} \div \dfrac{a}{3}$

m $\dfrac{xy}{2} \div \dfrac{y}{4}$ n $\dfrac{b}{2} \div \dfrac{ab}{6}$ o $\dfrac{xy}{c} \div \dfrac{y}{cx}$ p $\dfrac{9a}{b} \div \dfrac{4a}{3b}$

3 Simplify these expressions.

a $\dfrac{a}{3} \times \dfrac{12}{5a}$ b $\dfrac{2}{p} \times \dfrac{p}{3}$ c $\dfrac{15}{x} \div 5$ d $3b \div \dfrac{6}{b}$

e $\dfrac{xy}{z} \times \dfrac{2z}{x}$ f $\dfrac{ab}{c} \div \dfrac{a}{c}$ g $\dfrac{9m}{2} \times \dfrac{4m}{3}$ h $\dfrac{2x}{y} \div \dfrac{x}{2y}$

i $\dfrac{4}{pq} \times \dfrac{p}{q}$ j $\dfrac{3}{a} \times \dfrac{2}{b}$ k $\dfrac{4ab}{x} \times \dfrac{xy}{2ac}$ l $\dfrac{9bc}{2a} \div \dfrac{6b}{4a}$

m $\dfrac{2}{x} \times \dfrac{x}{3} \times \dfrac{9}{4}$ n $\dfrac{b}{c} \times \dfrac{c}{a} \times \dfrac{a}{b}$ o $\dfrac{8bc}{3a} \times \dfrac{9a}{b} \times \dfrac{1}{4c}$ p $\dfrac{8}{a} \times \dfrac{2a}{15} \div \dfrac{8}{3}$

Fun Spot 4:04 | Try this maths-word puzzle

Hidden in the maze of letters there are many words used in mathematics. Make a list of the words you find and, at the same time, put a line through the letters you use. Words may be written in any direction: up, down, backwards, even diagonally. Also, a letter may be used more than once, but you cannot change direction in order to form a word, ie the letters must be in a straight line.

When you have found all the words there should be four letters that have not been used. These four letters can be arranged to form another 'mystery' maths word.

4:04

4:05 | Simplifying Expressions with Grouping Symbols

Simplify: **1** $7x + 3x$ **2** $4a^2 - a^2$ **3** $4x + 3 + 2x + 5$ **4** $2x + 7 - x - 5$

        5 $3y^2 + 5y + 2y^2 - y$ **6** $7 - 3a + 6 + 5a$

Expand: **7** $3(x - 7)$ **8** $9(2 - 5y)$ **9** $2a(a + 3)$ **10** $-5(x + 7)$

The two most commonly used grouping symbols are:

     parentheses ( )

     brackets [ ]

$$a(b \pm c) = ab \pm ac$$

To expand an expression, such as $a(b + c)$, each term inside the grouping symbols is multiplied by the term outside the grouping symbols.

We are talking about symbols not cymbals.

worked examples

1 $p(p + 3) = p \times p + p \times 3$

           $= p^2 + 3p$

2 $3a(5 - 2a) = 3a \times 5 - 3a \times 2a$

               $= 15a - 6a^2$

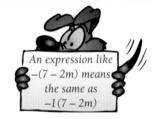

An expression like $-(7 - 2m)$ means the same as $-1(7 - 2m)$

3 $-5(3x + 4) = (-5) \times 3x + (-5) \times 4$

              $= -15x - 20$

5 $x(x - 1) - x^2 + 5 = x^2 - x - x^2 + 5$

                     $= -x + 5$

4 $-(7 - 2m) = (-1) \times 7 - (-1) \times 2m$

              $= -7 + 2m$

6 $2a(a + b) - a(3a - 4b) = 2a^2 + 2ab - 3a^2 + 4ab$

                             $= 6ab - a^2$

Exercise 4:05

> **Foundation Worksheet 4:05**
>
> Grouping symbols
> **1** Simplify: **a** $3 \times 4y$
> **2** Complete the following:
>   **a** $3(2m + 5) = 3 \times 2m + 3 \times \ldots$
> **3** Remove the grouping symbols.
>   **a** $3(2a + 5)$

1   The area of rectangle A = $3 \times n = 3n$

      The area of rectangle B = $3 \times 4 = 12$

      The area of the combined rectangle = $3(n + 4)$

                    $\therefore 3(n + 4) = 3n + 12$

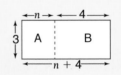

Following the example given above, write down the area of each of the following rectangles in two ways.

a   5, a, 7

b   7, x, 3

c m, n, 7

d

e

f

2 Expand:

a $3(x + 4)$ b $4(a + 5)$ c $3(y - 2)$ d $5(x - 3)$

e $3(2a + 3)$ f $4(m + n)$ g $6(3x + 2y)$ h $7(2a - 4b)$

i $x(x + 5)$ j $y(y - 2)$ k $2g(g - 1)$ l $3w(w + 2v)$

m $x(x + t)$ n $2h(3h - 1)$ o $2q(2 - q)$ p $8x(2 - 8x)$

q $y(s + t)$ r $ab(a + b)$ s $6xy(x - 5)$ t $5r(2r + 2s)$

3 Expand by removing the parentheses.

a $-3(x + 4)$ b $-4(a + 5)$ c $-4(a - 2)$ d $-3(p - 3)$

e $-7(2m + 5)$ f $-7(2m - 5)$ g $-7(5 - 2m)$ h $-8(1 - x)$

i $-(a - 3)$ j $-(4m - 3)$ k $-(3 + 6y)$ l $-(2a - 4c)$

m $-a(2a + 1)$ n $-3x(3x + 1)$ o $-3m(3m - 1)$ p $-9h(3h - j)$

4 Simplify:

a $4(x + 1) + x + 3$ b $3(x + 5) + 7x - 8$

c $5(y - 2) + 3y + 7$ d $4(a - 1) + 6a - 5$

e $3(p + 2) - 2p + 4$ f $10(m + 3) - 11m - 15$

g $5a + 6 + 2(a + 7)$ h $2x + 7 + 5(x - 1)$

i $7n - 4 + 3(n - 1)$ j $4h - 1 + 7(h + 2)$

k $6x + 2(x + 1) + 5$ l $4y + 6(y + 2) - 10$

m $3a + 10 - 2(a + 1)$ n $10m + 4 - 5(m + 4)$

o $6 - 2(y - 4) + 4y$ p $20 - 4(x - 2) + 5x$

q $5x + 7 + 2(2x + 7)$ r $4(3a + 1) - 10a + 2$

s $10m + 6 - 3(2m - 1)$ t $8x - 3(1 - 2x) + 10$

5 Simplify each expression by expanding the grouping symbols and then collecting like terms.

a $4(x + 1) + 2(x + 3)$ b $6(m + 3) + 3(m + 2)$

c $a(a + 4) + 3(a + 2)$ d $8(m - 3) + 5(m + 2)$

e $4(3x + 2) + 5(x - 4)$ f $6(x + 7) + 2(2x - 1)$

g $5(x + 7) - 3(x + 4)$ h $6(m + 1) - 3(m + 2)$

i $9(a + 5) - 7(a - 3)$ j $5(n - 5) - 3(n + 7)$

k $x(x + 3) + 3(x + 1)$ l $a(a + 3) + 7(a - 3)$

m $m(m + 3) - 4(m + 3)$ n $t(t - 5) - 4(t - 5)$

o $a(a + 2b) + a(2a + b)$ p $x(x + y) + y(x + y)$

Challenge worksheet 4:05 Fractions and grouping symbols

Fun Spot 4:05 | What is taken off last before you get into bed?

Work out the answer to each part and put the
letter for that part in the box that is above the
correct answer.

Write down the expression that is:

H 2 more than x **L** twice x

K half of x **N** 2 less than x

R the square of x

Find the value of $u + 10t$ if:

R $u = 12$, $t = 4$ **R** $u = -10$, $t = 2$

Simplify:

T $x \div x$ **T** $11x - x$

T $x + x + x$ **F** $x \times x \times 2$ **F** $x^2 - x - x$ **F** $7x + 3y - x + 3y$

F $3x \times 2y$ **A** $-2x \times -3x$ **A** $12x \div 2$ **Y** $12m \div 4m$

O $14 - 3x + 6$ **E** $\dfrac{x}{2} + \dfrac{x}{2}$ **O** $\dfrac{2x}{5} - \dfrac{x}{10}$ **O** $\dfrac{5}{x} \times \dfrac{x}{10}$

O $x - \dfrac{x}{10}$ **U** $x \div \dfrac{1}{8}$ **E** $\dfrac{x}{3} \div \dfrac{x}{6}$ **E** $\dfrac{x}{2} \div 2$

Write an expression for the perimeter of:

E   **E**

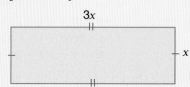

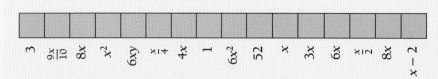

3	$\dfrac{9x}{10}$	$8x$	x^2	$6xy$	$\dfrac{x}{4}$	$4x$	1	$6x^2$	52	x	$3x$	$6x$	$\dfrac{x}{2}$	$8x$	$x - 2$

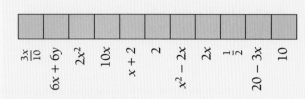

$\dfrac{3x}{10}$	$6x + 6y$	$2x^2$	$10x$	$x + 2$	2	$x^2 - 2x$	$2x$	$\dfrac{1}{2}$	$20 - 3x$	10

4:06 | Binomial Products

Simplify: **1** $5x + 7x$ **2** $2a - a$ **3** $x^2 + 3x - 5x + 3$

Expand: **4** $2(x + 5)$ **5** $x(x - 2)$ **6** $-3(a + 1)$

    7 $-y(5 - y)$

Expand and simplify: **8** $x(x + 1) + 3(x + 1)$ **9** $5(a + 5) - a(a + 5)$

    10 $2x(3x - 2) - 5(3x + 2)$

A binomial expression is one that contains two terms, such as $2x - 7$ or $a + b$. Thus a binomial product is the product of two such expressions. For example, $(2x + 7)(a + 5)$ is a binomial product.

Long multiplication is like a binomial product.

$26 \times 19 = (20 + 6) \times (10 + 9)$

$= 20(10 + 9) + 6(10 + 9)$
$= [20 \times 10] + [20 \times 9] + [6 \times 10] + [6 \times 9]$
$= 200 + 180 + 60 + 54$
$= 494$

Each part of one number must multiply each part of the other.

$(20 + 6) \quad (10 + 9)$

As you can see, the products form a *face*.

$$\begin{array}{r} 19 \\ \times\, 26 \\ \hline 54 \\ 60 \\ 180 \\ 200 \\ \hline 494 \end{array}$$

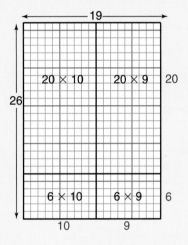

26 × 19 by areas

Multiplying binomial expressions
The expansion of binomial products may also be demonstrated by considering the area of a rectangle. This rectangle has dimensions $(2a + 6)$ and $(a + 9)$.

- The area of the whole rectangle must be equal to the sum of the four smaller areas.

- Area $= (2a + 6)(a + 9)$

$= 2a(a + 9) + 6(a + 9)$
$= 2a^2 + 18a + 6a + 54$
$= 2a^2 + 24a + 54$

- We can see that the product of two binomials yields four terms. Often two of these may be added together to simplify the answer.

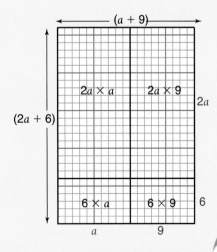

$(2a + 6)(a + 9)$ by areas

1 $(a + 2)(b + 4) = a(b + 4) + 2(b + 4)$
$\qquad\qquad = ab + 4a + 2b + 8$

2 $(a - 2)(a + 7) = a(a + 7) - 2(a + 7)$
$\qquad\qquad = a^2 + 7a - 2a - 14$
$\qquad\qquad = a^2 + 5a - 14$

3 $(x + 2y)(2x + y) = x(2x + y) + 2y(2x + y)$
$\qquad\qquad = 2x^2 + xy + 4xy + 2y^2$
$\qquad\qquad = 2x^2 + 5xy + 2y^2$

4 $(1 - x)(x - 3) = 1(x - 3) - x(x - 3)$
$\qquad\qquad = x - 3 - x^2 + 3x$
$\qquad\qquad = 4x - x^2 - 3$

You should notice that each term in the first binomial is multiplied by each term in the second; ie

That set-out looks familiar.

$= 2x^2 + 10x - 3x - 15$
$= 2x^2 + 7x - 15$

$$(a + b)(c + d) = a(c + d) + b(c + d)$$
$$= ac + ad + bc + bd$$

Exercise 4:06

1 Expand the following binomial products.

a $(a + 2)(b + 3)$ b $(x + 1)(y + 4)$ c $(m + 7)(n + 5)$ d $(a + 3)(x + 2)$
e $(p + 5)(q + 4)$ f $(2x + 1)(y + 3)$ g $(a + 6)(3p + 2)$ h $(4x + 1)(2y + 3)$
i $(3a + 1)(2b - 7)$ j $(7x + 5)(2p + 1)$ k $(5p + 3)(x - 4)$ l $(2x + y)(a + 2b)$

2 Expand the following and collect the like terms.

a $(a + 2)(a + 3)$ b $(x + 1)(x + 5)$ c $(n + 3)(n + 4)$ d $(p + 2)(p + 5)$
e $(m + 1)(m - 3)$ f $(y + 7)(y - 2)$ g $(x + 1)(x - 6)$ h $(t + 2)(t - 4)$
i $(x - 2)(x - 4)$ j $(n - 7)(n - 1)$ k $(a - 6)(a - 3)$ l $(x - 10)(x - 9)$
m $(y - 11)(y + 7)$ n $(a - 2)(a + 1)$ o $(x - 8)(x - 8)$ p $(m - 9)(m - 2)$
q $(a - 3)(a + 3)$ r $(x - 7)(x + 3)$ s $(y + 12)(y + 5)$ t $(a - 8)(a + 8)$
u $(q + 5)(q + 5)$ v $(x - 1)(x - 9)$ w $(t + 3)(t + 10)$ x $(k - 8)(k + 11)$

3 Find these products and simplify.

a $(a + 3)(2a + 1)$ b $(2x + 1)(x + 2)$ c $(3m + 2)(m + 5)$
d $(y + 3)(4y + 1)$ e $(2x + 1)(2x + 3)$ f $(3n + 2)(2n + 1)$
g $(2x + 3)(4x + 3)$ h $(5t + 2)(2t + 3)$ i $(2x - 2)(5x - 1)$
j $(8p + 1)(3p - 2)$ k $(5m - 2)(2m - 5)$ l $(3q + 1)(7q - 2)$
m $(3x + 2)(6x - 2)$ n $(2n + 3)(2n - 3)$ o $(8y - 1)(8y + 1)$
p $(3k - 2)(5k - 3)$ q $(7p - 1)(7p - 1)$ r $(3x - 1)(5x - 3)$
s $(5x + 4)(5x + 4)$ t $(9y - 4)(3y + 2)$ u $(5p + 2)(p - 7)$
v $(10q - 1)(q - 10)$ w $(4a + 3)(3a + 4)$ x $(7p + 5)(7p - 5)$

4 Expand and simplify:

a $(3 + x)(4 + x)$ b $(5 - a)(2 - a)$ c $(7 + m)(1 - m)$
d $(3 - n)(3 + n)$ e $(4 + y)(y + 5)$ f $(x - 7)(5 - x)$
g $(9 + k)(k + 10)$ h $(2a + 1)(3 + a)$ i $(3n + 1)(7 - 2n)$
j $(x + y)(x + 2y)$ k $(2n + m)(n + 2m)$ l $(a - b)(2a + 3b)$
m $(2p - q)(2p + q)$ n $(3x + y)(2x - 5y)$ o $(3a + 2b)(2a + 3b)$
p $(9w - 5x)(9w - 5x)$

4:07 | Special Products

Simplify:

1 4^2		**2** 7^2	**3** $(-2)^2$
4 $(-10)^2$		**5** $(3x)^2$	

Complete:

6 $(x + 2)(x + 7) = x^2 + 9x + \dots$

7 $(a + 3)(a + 3) = a^2 + 6a + \dots$

8 $(2m - 1)(2m - 1) = \dots m^2 - 4m + 1$

9 $(n + 5)(n + 5) = n^2 + \dots n + 25$

10 $(x - 3)(x - 3) = x^2 - \dots x + 9$

4:07A

4:07A   Perfect squares

When a binomial is multiplied by itself, we call this product
a perfect square. If a perfect square is expanded, we get:

$$(x + y)^2 = (x + y)(x + y)$$
$$= x(x + y) + y(x + y)$$
$$= x^2 + xy + yx + y^2$$
$$= x^2 + 2xy + y^2$$

Similarly $(x - y)^2 = x^2 - 2xy + y^2$

In words, we could say: 'The square of a binomial is equal to the square of the first term, plus twice
the product of the two terms, plus the square of the second term.'

worked examples

1 $(a + 3)^2 = a^2 + 2(3a) + 3^2$
  $= a^2 + 6a + 9$

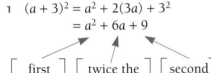

first term squared	twice the product of the 2 terms	second term squared

2 $(m - 5)^2 = m^2 - 2[5m] + 5^2$
  $= m^2 - 10m + 25$

first term squared	twice the product of the 2 terms	second term squared

3 $(3y - 7)^2 = [3y]^2 - 2[21y] + [-7]^2$
  $= 9y^2 - 42y + 49$

> ■ $(x + y)^2 = x^2 + 2xy + y^2$
> $(x - y)^2 = x^2 - 2xy + y^2$

---

investigation

4:07

Investigation 4:07 | The square of a binomial

Please use the Assessment Grid on the following page to help you understand what is required
for this Investigation.

The Prep Quiz above suggests that there might be a pattern formed when a binomial is squared.
Copy and complete this table.

x	y	x^2	y^2	xy	$(x + y)^2$	$x^2 + 2xy + y^2$	$(x - y)^2$	$x^2 - 2xy + y^2$
5	3							
6	1							
10	4							

What were your findings?

Assessment Grid for Investigation 4:07 | **The square of a binomial**

The following is a sample assessment grid for this investigation. You should carefully read the criteria *before* beginning the investigation so that you know what is required.

			Assessment Criteria (B, C) for this investigation		Achieved ✓
Criterion B Investigating Patterns		a	None of the following descriptors has been achieved.	0	
		b	Some help was needed to be able to expand the brackets and complete the table.	1	
				2	
		c	Mathematical techniques have been selected and applied to complete the table and suggest relationships or general rules.	3	
				4	
		d	The student has completed the table and accurately described the rules for the square of a binomial.	5	
				6	
		e	The above has been completed with justification using the patterns within the columns of the table and further examples.	7	
				8	
Criterion C Communication in Mathematics		a	None of the following descriptors has been achieved.	0	
		b	There is a basic use of mathematical language and representation. Lines of reasoning are insufficient.	1	
				2	
		c	There is satisfactory use of mathematical language and representation. Explanations are clear but not always complete.	3	
				4	
		d	An efficient use of mathematical language and representation has been shown. Explanations of all rules are complete and concise.	5	
				6	

1 Find the missing term in each example to make the statements true.

a $(x + 2)^2 = x^2 + 4x + ...$
b $(a + 6)^2 = a^2 + 12a + ...$
c $(y - 3)^2 = y^2 - 6y + ...$
d $(m - 10)^2 = m^2 - 20m + ...$
e $(x + 1)^2 = x^2 + ... + 1$
f $(y + 7)^2 = y^2 + ... + 49$
g $(n - 2)^2 = n^2 - .... + 4$
h $(p - 5)^2 = p^2 - .... + 25$
i $(q + 8)^2 = ... + 16q + 64$
j $(x - 4)^2 = ... -8x + 16$
k $(x + ...)^2 = x^2 + 6x + 9$
l $(a + ...)^2 = a^2 + 18a + 81$
m $(y - ....)^2 = y^2 - 14x + 49$
n $(m - ....)^2 = m^2 - 22m + 121$
o $(2x + 3)^2 = ... + 12x + 9$
p $(5n + 1)^2 = ... + 10n + 1$
q $(3m + 7)^2 = 9m^2 + ... + 49$
r $(4x + 5)^2 = 16x^2 + ... + 25$
s $(2a - 1)^2 = 4a^2 - .... + 1$
t $(9y - 7)^2 = 81y^2 - .... + 49$

Use the formula, it's quicker.

2 Expand these perfect squares and simplify.

a $(x + 3)^2$
b $(x + 5)^2$
c $(x + 1)^2$
d $(x - 6)^2$
e $(m - 1)^2$
f $(n - 5)^2$
g $(x + 2)^2$
h $(n - 8)^2$
i $(m + 11)^2$
j $(a + 12)^2$
k $(x + 10)^2$
l $(p - 9)^2$
m $(x + y)^2$
n $(a + m)^2$
o $(x + t)^2$
p $(a - b)^2$
q $(k - m)^2$
r $(p - q)^2$

3 Expand and simplify:

a $(2x + 3)^2$
b $(2x + 1)^2$
c $(3x + 5)^2$
d $(4a + 1)^2$
e $(3a + 7)^2$
f $(7t + 2)^2$
g $(2x - 1)^2$
h $(3a - 2)^2$
i $(5m - 4)^2$
j $(4t - 7)^2$
k $(6q - 1)^2$
l $(9n + 4)^2$
m $(2x + y)^2$
n $(a + 3b)^2$
o $(3t - 2x)^2$

4:07B   Difference of two squares

This is an investigation of a special relationship.

Evaluate:

1 $7^2 - 3^2$
2 $(7 + 3)(7 - 3)$
3 $4^2 - 2^2$
4 $(4 + 2)(4 - 2)$
5 $5^2 - 1^2$
6 $(5 - 1)(5 + 1)$
7 $6^2 - 3^2$
8 $(6 - 3)(6 + 3)$
9 $10^2 - 9^2$
10 $(10 + 9)(10 - 9)$

If the sum of two terms is multiplied by their difference, another special type of product is formed. If $(x + y)$ is multiplied by $(x - y)$ we get:

$$(x + y)(x - y) = x(x - y) + y(x - y)$$
$$= x^2 - xy + yx - y^2$$
$$= x^2 - y^2$$

In words, we could say: 'The sum of two terms multiplied by their difference is equal to the square of the first term minus the square of the second term.'

1   $(x + 3)(x - 3) = x^2 - 3^2$

$$\begin{bmatrix} \text{first term} \\ \text{squared} \end{bmatrix} \begin{bmatrix} \text{second term} \\ \text{squared} \end{bmatrix}$$

$= x^2 - 9$

2   $(2a - 3b)(2a + 3b) = (2a)^2 - (3b)^2$

$$\begin{bmatrix} \text{first term} \\ \text{squared} \end{bmatrix} \begin{bmatrix} \text{second term} \\ \text{squared} \end{bmatrix}$$

$= 4a^2 - 9b^2$

3   $(p - 7)(p + 7) = p^2 - 7^2$
    $= p^2 - 49$

4   $(5x + y)(5x - y) = (5x)^2 - y^2$
    $= 25x^2 - y^2$

$$\blacksquare \; (x + y)(x - y) = x^2 - y^2$$

Exercise 4:07B

1 Expand these products and simplify.

   a $(x + 4)(x - 4)$ **b** $(a + 1)(a - 1)$ **c** $(m + 2)(m - 2)$ **d** $(n + 7)(n - 7)$

   e $(p - 5)(p + 5)$ **f** $(q - 6)(q + 6)$ **g** $(x - 3)(x + 3)$ **h** $(y - 9)(y + 9)$

   i $(10 + x)(10 - x)$ **j** $(5 + a)(5 - a)$ **k** $(8 - x)(8 + x)$ **l** $(11 - m)(11 + m)$

   m $(x + t)(x - t)$ **n** $(a - b)(a + b)$ **o** $(m + m)(m - n)$ **p** $(p - q)(p + q)$

2 Express as the difference of two squares.

   a $(2a + 1)(2a - 1)$ **b** $(3x + 2)(3x - 2)$ **c** $(5m + 3)(5m - 3)$

   d $(9q + 2)(9q - 2)$ **e** $(4t - 3)(4t + 3)$ **f** $(7x - 1)(7x + 1)$

   g $(8n - 5)(8n + 5)$ **h** $(10x - 3)(10x + 3)$ **i** $(2x + y)(2x - y)$

   j $(4a + 3b)(4a - 3b)$ **k** $(5p + 2q)(5p - 2q)$ **l** $(3m - n)(3m + n)$

   m $(2m - 5n)(2m + 5n)$ **n** $(2p - 3q)(2p + 3q)$ **o** $(x - 5y)(x + 5y)$

   p $(12x - 5y)(12x + 5y)$

4:08 | Miscellaneous Examples

- It is important that you are able to expand and simplify algebraic expressions readily and accurately, if you are to use algebra in later problem-solving exercises.
- Work through the miscellaneous questions of Exercise 4:08 after examining the following two examples.

Watch out for tricky minus signs.

1   $(x + 3)^2 - (x - 1)(x + 2) = [x^2 + 6x + 9] - [x^2 + x - 2]$
    $= x^2 + 6x + 9 - x^2 - x + 2$
    $= 5x + 11$

2   $(3x + 5)(x - 1) + (x + 2)^2 - (2x + 1)(2x - 1) = [3x^2 + 2x - 5] + [x^2 + 4x + 4] - [4x^2 - 1]$
    $= 3x^2 + 2x - 5 + x^2 + 4x + 4 - 4x^2 + 1$
    $= 6x$

Exercise 4:08

Expand and simplify, where possible, each of the following expressions.

1
a $5x + 3(x - 7)$ **b** $(x + 2)(x - 1)$ **c** $(2x + 1)(x - 1)$
d $5(x + 2) - x(x + 1)$ **e** $(3x - 1)^2$ **f** $(x + 5)(x - 5)$
g $(2x - 7)(3x - 1)$ **h** $(5x - 1)(5x + 1)$ **i** $4x + 7 + x(x + 2)$
j $9x - (x + 5) + 5$ **k** $(x + 10)(x - 3)$ **l** $(9 - y)(9 + y)$
m $3x(x - 5) - 2x^2$ **n** $3(x + 2)(x + 1)$ **o** $(x + y)^2$
p $(x + 2y)(2x + y)$ **q** $5x - 2(x + y) + 2y$ **r** $(a + 2b)(a - 2b)$
s $a(x + 2) - x(a + 2)$ **t** $(3a + 7)(5a - 3)$ **u** $(2m - 5n)^2$
v $(1 - 5y)(1 + 5y)$ **w** $3x - 7(x - 3)$ **x** $(9x - 8y)(9x + 8y)$

2
a $(x + 1)^2 + 5(x + 2)$ **b** $(a - 3)^2 - 3(a + 1)$
c $(x + 2)(x + 3) - 7(x - 2)$ **d** $8(x + 2) + (x - 7)(x + 1)$
e $(x + 3)^2 + (x + 1)(x + 2)$ **f** $(a + 5)(a + 3) - (a + 4)^2$
g $(m + 6)^2 - (m - 1)(m + 1)$ **h** $(y + 7)(y - 7) - (y + 7)^2$
i $(x + 2)^2 + (x + 1)^2$ **j** $(a + 3)^2 - (a + 2)^2$
k $(x + 1)(x + 2) + (x + 2)(x + 3)$ **l** $(a + 1)(a - 2) + (a + 2)(a - 1)$
m $(x + 3)(x - 1) - (x + 2)(x - 5)$ **n** $(y + 7)(y - 2) - (y + 1)(y + 3)$
o $(2x + 1)^2 - 5(x + 3)$ **p** $2x(x + 5) + (x + 7)^2$
q $(5x + 1)(x - 3) + (2x + 1)^2$ **r** $(2x + 1)(3x + 1) - (2x - 1)(3x - 1)$
s $(p + 3)(p - 3) - (q + 3)(q - 3)$ **t** $(x + y)^2 - (x - y)(x + y)$
u $(a + b)(a + 2b) + (a + b)^2$ **v** $(m - n)^2 + (m + n)^2$
w $3(x + 1)^2 + 5(x + 1)$ **x** $2(x - 1)(x + 1) + 3(x + 1)^2$
y $(2x + 3y)^2 - (2x - 3y)(2x + 3y)$ **z** $(3a + 2b)(2a + 3b) - 6(a + b)^2$

3
a $(x + 1)^2 + (x + 2)^2 + (x + 3)^2$
b $(x + 1)(x + 2) + (x + 2)(x + 3) + (x + 3)(x + 4)$
c $(a - 1)(a + 1) + (a + 1)^2 + (a - 1)^2$
d $(x + 2)^2 + (x + 3)^2 - (x + 2)(x + 3)$
e $(3a + 2b)(2a + 3b) + (3a - 2b)(3a + 2b) + (2a + 3b)(2a - 3b)$
f $(4x + 1)(3x - 1) + (x + 2)^2 - (x - 3)(x + 3)$
g $5(m - 5)^2 - 8(m - 4)^2 + 3(m - 3)^2$
h $(3x + 2y)(3x - 2y) - (2x + y)(2x - y) - (x + 1)(x - 1)$
i $(x + 3y)^2 - (2x + 2y)^2 + (3x + y)^2$
j $2(x - y)(x + y) - (x + y)^2 - (x - y)^2$

Aha! A challenge!

Challenge 4:08 | Patterns in products

The examples below involve the sum of a series of products. Can you see the patterns involved and, hence, find the simplest expression for each sum?

1 $(x + 1)^2 + (x + 2)^2 \ldots + (x + 9)^2 + (x + 10)^2$
2 $(x + 1)(x + 2) + (x + 2)(x + 3) + \ldots + (x + 9)(x + 10)$
3 $(a - 5)^2 + (a - 4)^2 + \ldots + a^2 + \ldots + (a + 4)^2 + (a + 5)^2$
4 $(5m - n)(5m + n) + (4m - 2n)(4m + 2n) + (3m - 3n)(3m + 3n) +$
$(2m - 4n)(2m + 4n) + (m - 5n)(m + 5n)$

challenge

4:08

Investigation 4:08 | Using special products in arithmetic

A Perfect squares

Example 1

Using $(a \pm b)^2 = a^2 \pm 2ab + b^2$, evaluate $(103)^2$.

Solution 1

Writing 103 as $(100 + 3)$
Then $103^2 = (100 + 3)^2$
$= 100^2 + 2 \times 100 \times 3 + 3^2$
$= 10\,000 + 600 + 9$
$= 10\,609$

Similarly, the square of a number like 98 could be found by writing 98 as $(100 - 2)$.

Exercise A

Following the example above, evaluate:

a 101^2 b 205^2 c 1004^2 d 72^2

e 98^2 f 199^2 g 995^2 h 67^2

B Difference of two squares

Example 2

Using $(a - b)(a + b) = a^2 - b^2$, evaluate $100^2 - 97^2$.

Solution 2

$100^2 - 97^2 = (100 - 97)(100 + 97)$
$= 3 \times 197$
$= 591$

This method can be useful when finding a shorter side of a right-angled triangle.

eg

$x^2 = 50^2 - 48^2$
$= (50 - 48)(50 + 48)$
$= 2 \times 98$
$= 196$
$\therefore x = \sqrt{196}$
$= 14$

Exercise B

1 Evaluate:

a $100^2 - 98^2$ b $73^2 - 67^2$ c $145^2 - 140^2$ d $651^2 - 641^2$

2 Use the method above to find the value of x for each triangle. (Leave your answer in surd form.)

a

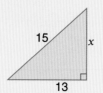

b

c

d

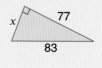

Mathematical Terms 4

algebra
- A branch of mathematics where numbers are represented by symbols, usually letters.

algebraic expression
- A group of terms that are joined by addition or subtraction signs.

binomial
- An algebraic expression consisting of two terms.
  eg $2x + 4$, $3x - 2y$

brackets
- The name given to these grouping symbols: [ ]

cancel
- To simplify a fraction by dividing the numerator and denominator by a common factor.
  eg $\dfrac{^3\cancel{21}xy \div 7x}{^2\cancel{14}x \div 7x} = \dfrac{3y}{2}$

denominator
- The bottom of a fraction.

difference of two squares
- The result of multiplying two binomials which are the sum and difference of the same terms.
  eg $(a + 3)(a - 3) = a^2 - 3^2$
  $\qquad\qquad\qquad = a^2 - 9$

expand
- To remove grouping symbols by multiplying the terms in each pair of grouping symbols by the term or terms outside.

like terms
- Terms that have identical pronumeral parts.
  eg $7x$ and $10x$
  $5a^2b$ and $-3a^2b$
- Only like terms may be added or subtracted together. This is called 'collecting like terms'.

numerator
- The 'top' of a fraction.

parentheses
- The name given to these grouping symbols: ( )

perfect square
- When a binomial is multiplied by itself.
  eg $(x + 5)^2$ or $(2a - 3b)^2$

pronumeral
- A symbol, usually a letter, that is used to represent a number.

substitution
- The replacing of a pronumeral with a numeral in an expression.
  eg to substitute 3 for a in the expression $4a - 2$ would give:
  $4(3) - 2 = 10$

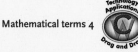

Mathematical terms 4

- A machine counts coins by weight. What is the value of a pile of \$M coins that weighs W grams if each coin weighs w grams?

Diagnostic Test 4: | Algebraic expressions

- These questions reflect the important skills introduced in this chapter.
- Errors made will indicate areas of weakness.
- Each weakness should be treated by going back to the section listed.

	Section

1 For each table of values, find the expression in x that completes the rule
$y = \ldots$

Section 4:01

a
x	0	1	2	3
y	0	4	8	12

b
x	5	6	7	8
y	12	14	16	18

c
x	1	2	3	4
y	1	4	9	16

2 Write an algebraic expression for the following:
   a the sum of x and y
   b the average of 5 and m
   c the cost of b books at p dollars each
   d $2 was shared between Sue and Jenny. If Sue received x cents, how many cents did Jenny receive?

4:01

3 If $m = 2$, $x = 6$, $c = 1$, $h = 10$, $a = 3$, $b = 6$, $\pi = 3.1$ and $r = 10$, evaluate:

   a $mx + c$ b $\dfrac{h}{2}(a + b)$ c πr^2

4:02

4 Simplify:
   a $7x + 6 - 3x - 2$ b $6q^2 + 7q - q^2$
   c $5xy - 3yx$ d $5m + 2n - 3m - 4 - 3n + 7$

4:03

5 Simplify:
   a $-5y \times a$ b $2xy \times x$
   c $12a \times (-3b)$ d $3x^2 \times 4xy$

4:03

6 Simplify:
   a $18m \div 6$ b $24ab \div 4a$
   c $\dfrac{16x^2}{8x}$ d $-5mn \div 10m^2$

4:03

7 Simplify:
   a $\dfrac{3x}{5} + \dfrac{2x}{5}$ b $\dfrac{x}{3} - \dfrac{x}{2}$

   c $\dfrac{4a}{5} - \dfrac{a}{3}$ d $\dfrac{5m}{8} + \dfrac{m}{2}$

4:04A

8 Simplify:
   a $\dfrac{3}{4} \times \dfrac{n}{3}$ b $\dfrac{2}{a} \times \dfrac{5}{b}$

   c $\dfrac{5}{x} \times \dfrac{x}{10}$ d $\dfrac{3b}{2} \times \dfrac{4}{5b}$

4:04B

9 Simplify:

a $\dfrac{3m}{2} \div \dfrac{1}{4}$

b $\dfrac{x}{3} \div \dfrac{x}{6}$

c $\dfrac{8a}{3b} \div \dfrac{2a}{9b}$

d $\dfrac{ab}{2} \div \dfrac{b}{5}$

4:04B

10 Expand:

a $4(x - 3)$

b $4(2x + 3)$

c $4x(2x - 3)$

d $3a(5 - a)$

4:05

11 Expand:

a $-4(x - 3)$

b $-4x(x + 3)$

c $-5m(3m - 3)$

d $-4a(3a + 7)$

4:05

12 Expand and simplify:

a $x(x - 1) - x^2$ b $7n - 4 + 3(n - 1)$ c $2a(a + b) - a(3a - 4b)$

4:05

13 Expand and simplify:

a $(x + 3)(x + 4)$ b $(a - 3)(2a - 1)$ c $(2 - y)(3 + y)$

d $(2x + y)(x - 3y)$

4:06

14 Expand and simplify:

a $(x + 2)^2$ b $(a - 7)^2$ c $(2y + 5)^2$ d $(m - n)^2$

4:07A

15 Expand and simplify:

a $(x + 3)(x - 3)$ b $(y - 7)(y + 7)$ c $(2a + 5)(2a - 5)$

d $(x + y)(x - y)$

4:07B

1 Three darts are thrown and all land in the '20' sector. What are the possible total scores for the three darts if all darts can land on either the 20, double 20 or triple 20?

2 Three darts are thrown and all land in the 'x' sector. Write an algebraic expression for the possible total scores.

3 Three darts are thrown and all land in the same sector. The total score is 102. In what sector did the darts land?

4A

1 Simplify the following.

a $6a + a$ b $6x \times 3x$
c $a - 5a$ d $x^2 + x^2$
e $18x \div 3x$ f $12y \div 8$
g $2x + 3y$ h $3ab \times 2b$
i $12a^2b \div 6a$ j $5ab + 7ab$
k $6a^2 - a$ l $4x - 3y - 5x$
m $12 + 6x + 7 - x$ n $6x + 2x \times 3$
o $x^2 - 3x + 2x + 3x^2$ p $12x - 6x \div 3$

2 Expand and simplify where possible.

a $(x - 1)(x + 2)$ b $5x + 3(x - 1)$
c $2(x + 3) - 2x - 3$ d $(2x + 1)(x - 7)$
e $(x + 5)(x - 5)$ f $(3x + 2)^2$
g $x(x - 3) + 2(x + 1)$ h $(2 - x)(3 - x)$
i $(x + y)(y - x)$ j $(2x - y)^2$
k $5[x + 3(x + 1)]$ l $[3x - (x - 2)]^2$

3 Simplify:

a $\dfrac{x}{2} + \dfrac{x}{3}$ b $\dfrac{2a}{5} - \dfrac{a}{10}$

c $\dfrac{3a}{2} \times \dfrac{5b}{6}$ d $\dfrac{10y}{3} \div 5y$

e $\dfrac{7x}{5} - \dfrac{x}{3}$ f $\dfrac{3m}{5} + \dfrac{m}{3} - \dfrac{m}{2}$

g $\dfrac{6n}{5} \times \dfrac{10}{7n} \div \dfrac{3}{2n}$ h $\dfrac{x+3}{2} + \dfrac{x+1}{3}$

4 Find the simplest expression for the perimeter of this figure. All angles are 90°.

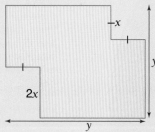

5 Find the algebraic rule for these tables of values.

a

x	0	1	2	3
y	12	9	6	3

b

t	−1	1	3	5
s	2	2	10	26

6 Find an expression for the shaded area of this rectangle. Expand and simplify your answer.

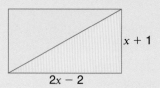

7 Find the simplest expression for the shaded area of each figure.

a

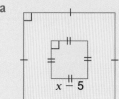

b

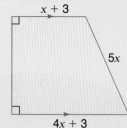

c

A ———————————— B
with $AC = (2x + 4)$

$ABCD$ is a square.
X and Y bisect AE
and CE respectively.

Chapter 4 | Working Mathematically

1 Use ID Card 4 on page xiv to give the mathematical term for:

   a 1   b 2   c 3   d 4   e 5
   f 6   g 7   h 8   i 9   j 11

2 a What geometric shape has inspired the design of this coffee cup?

   b What would you estimate the capacity of the cup to be?

3 Diane and Garry married and had three children. Each child married and had three children. Assuming that no one has died, how many people are now in this extended family altogether?

4 The numerals 1 to 10 are written on ten separate cards, one on each card.

   a How many pairs of cards have a sum of 10?

   b How many groups of three cards are there that have a sum of 18?

5 A particular country's exports are shown in the bar graph below (reduced in size). Find what percentage of the country's exports are taken up by:

   a beef   b minerals

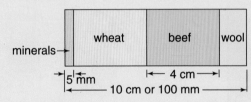

6

Education of children, ages 5 to 14

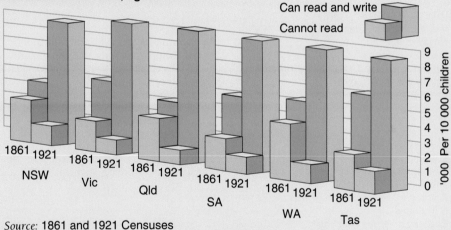

Source: 1861 and 1921 Censuses

   a In 1861, which state had the greatest number per 10 000 children that could read and write? What percentage was this?

   b In 1921, which state had the greatest percentage of children that could read and write? What percentage was this?

   c Which state had 4000 per 10 000 children that could read and write in 1861? About how many in that state could not read in 1861?

   d Consider Western Australia in 1861. Approximately what percentage could read and write? Approximately what percentage could not read? (To determine this, measure the height of this column and measure this height on the scale.)

Technology Applications

Drag and Drops

1 Addition and subtraction of algebraic fractions
2 Multiplication and division of algebraic fractions
3 Grouping symbols

4 Binomial products
5 Special products

Chapter Review Questions

5

Indices and Surds

What a great space saver!

Chapter Contents

Learning Outcomes

Students will be able to:

- Apply index laws to evaluate arithmetic expressions.
- Apply index laws to simplify algebraic expressions.
- Use standard (scientific) notation to write small and large numbers.
- Understand the difference between rational and irrational numbers.
- Perform operations with surds and indices.

Areas of Interaction

Approaches to Learning (Knowledge Acquisition, Logical Thinking, IT Skills, Reflection), Human Ingenuity

5:01 | Indices and the Index Laws

$5 \times 5 \times 5 \times 5 = 625$
$5^4 = 625$

- 5 is called the base.
- 4 is called the index.
- 625 is called the basic numeral.

5^4 is the 'index form' (base 5) of 625

$x^n = \underbrace{x \times x \times x \times \ldots \times x \times x}_{n \text{ factors}}$ (where n is a positive integer)

For: x^n x is the base
           n is the index.

5^4 is called a power of 5.

Multiplication using indices

$5^3 \times 5^2 = (5 \times 5 \times 5) \times (5 \times 5)$
$ = 5^5 \quad [= 5^{3+2}]$

$x^5 \times x^3 = (x \times x \times x \times x \times x) \times (x \times x \times x)$
$ = x^8 \quad [= x^{5+3}]$

Law 1   **When multiplying terms, *add* the indices: $x^m \times x^n = x^{m+n}$**

Division using indices

$5^6 \div 5^3 = \dfrac{5 \times 5 \times 5 \times \cancel{5} \times \cancel{5} \times \cancel{5}}{\cancel{5} \times \cancel{5} \times \cancel{5}}$
$ = 5^3 \quad [5^{6-3} = 5^3]$

$x^4 \div x^3 = \dfrac{x \times \cancel{x} \times \cancel{x} \times \cancel{x}}{\cancel{x} \times \cancel{x} \times \cancel{x}}$
$ = x^1 \quad [= x^{4-3}]$

Law 2   **When dividing terms, *subtract* the indices: $x^m \div x^n = x^{m-n}$**

Powers of indices

$(5^2)^3 = 5^2 \times 5^2 \times 5^2 \quad$ [Using Law 1]
$ = 5^{2+2+2} \quad [= 5^{2 \times 3}]$

$(x^5)^4 = x^5 \times x^5 \times x^5 \times x^5$
$ = x^{5+5+5+5} \quad$ [Using Law 1]
$ = x^{20} \quad [= x^{5 \times 4}]$

Law 3   **For powers of a power, *multiply* the indices: $(x^m)^n = x^{mn}$**

You should learn these laws.

If we simplify the division $x^n \div x^n$, using the second law above:
$$x^n \div x^n = x^{n-n}$$
$$= x^0$$
But any expression divided by itself must equal 1.
$$x^n \div x^n = 1$$
Therefore x^0 must be equal to 1.
$$x^0 = 1$$

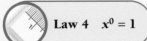
Law 4 $x^0 = 1$

1 Simplify:
   a 3^3 b 11^4 c $(-3)^2$

2 Simplify:
   a $5^2 \times 5^4$ b $a^2 \times a^4$ c $3x^4y \times 5x^2y^2$

3 Simplify:
   a $a^5 \div a$ b $18x^6 \div 6x^3$ c $24x^5y^3 \div 6xy$

4 Simplify:
   a $(x^5)^3$ b $(3x^3)^4$ c $(x^3)^4 \div (x^2)^3$

5 Simplify:
   a 7^0 b $18x^3 \div 6x^3$ c $(2y^3)^4 \div (4y^6)^2$

Solutions

1 a $3^3 = 3 \times 3 \times 3$
   $= 27$

   b $11^4 = 11 \times 11 \times 11 \times 11$
   Using the calculator
   to evaluate 11^4
   PRESS 11 $\boxed{x^y}$ 4 $\boxed{=}$
   $11^4 = 14\ 641$

   c $(-3)^2 = -3 \times -3$
   $= 9$

> ■ Another name for an INDEX is an EXPONENT.

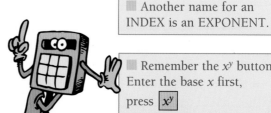

> ■ Remember the x^y button. Enter the base x first, press $\boxed{x^y}$ then enter the index y.

2 Using index law 1:
   a $5^2 \times 5^4 = 3^{2+4}$
   $= 5^6$

   b $a^2 \times a^4 = x^{2+4}$
   $= a^6$

   c $3x^4y \times 5x^2y^2 = 3 \times 5 \times x^{4+2} \times y^{1+2}$
   $= 15x^6y^3$

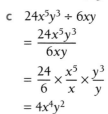

Note: $n = n^1$

3 Using index law 2:
   a $a^5 \div a = a^{5-1}$
   $= a^4$

   b $16x^6 \div 6x^3 = \dfrac{18x^6}{6x^3}$
   $= \dfrac{18}{6} \times \dfrac{x^6}{x^3}$
   $= 3x^3$

   c $24x^5y^3 \div 6xy$
   $= \dfrac{24x^5y^3}{6xy}$
   $= \dfrac{24}{6} \times \dfrac{x^5}{x} \times \dfrac{y^3}{y}$
   $= 4x^4y^2$

4 Using index law 3:
   a $(x^5)^3 = x^{5 \times 3}$
   $= x^{15}$

   b $(3x^3)^4 = 3^4 \times (x^3)^4$
   $= 81 \times x^{3 \times 4}$
   $= 81x^{12}$

   c $(x^3)^4 \div (x^2)^3 = x^{12} \div x^6$
   $= x^6$

5 Using index law 4:
   a $7^0 = 1$

   > ■ With practice, many of the steps in the above solutions can be left out.

   b $18x^3 \div 6x^3 = \dfrac{18x^3}{6x^3}$
   $= 3 \times x^{3-3}$
   $= 3x^0$
   $= 3 \times 1$
   $= 3$

   c $(2y^3)^4 \div (4y^6)^2 = \dfrac{2^4 \times (y^3)^4}{4^2 \times (y^6)^2}$
   $= \dfrac{16}{16} \times \dfrac{y^{12}}{y^{12}}$
   $= 1 \times y^0$
   $= 1$

Exercise 5:01

Foundation Worksheet 5:01

The index laws
1 Evaluate:
   a 2^3 **b** 3^4 **c** 5^3
2 Use your calculator to evaluate:
   a 6^3 **b** 4^5 **c** 8^4

1 Simplify each expression by writing in index form.
- **a** 3^4
- **b** 8^3
- **c** 12^2
- **d** 5^3
- **e** 6^4
- **f** $(-3)^4$
- **g** $3^2 \times 2^3$
- **h** $4^3 \times 2^3$
- **i** $9^4 \times 3^4$
- **j** $25^2 \times 5^4$

2 Determine the basic numeral for:
- **a** $5 \times 5 \times 5 \times 5$
- **b** $4 \times 4 \times 4$
- **c** $10 \times 10 \times 10 \times 10 \times 10 \times 10$
- **d** $x \times x \times x \times x \times x \times x \times x \times x \times x \times x \times x \times x$
- **e** $y \times y$
- **f** $x^3 \times x^2$
- **g** $a \times a^2 \times a^3$
- **h** $(m^2)^3$
- **i** $\dfrac{y^7}{y^2}$
- **j** $\dfrac{w^5 \times w^3}{w^4}$

This sure is powerful stuff!

3 Simplify the following, writing answers in index form.
- **a** $x^4 \times x^2$
- **b** $d^6 \times d$
- **c** $m^5 \times m^2$
- **d** $4a^6 \times 3a^3$
- **e** $-5y^2 \times 3y^3$
- **f** $x^9 \div x^3$
- **g** $m^6 \div m$
- **h** $a^6 \div a^3$
- **i** $16y^8 \div 4y^4$
- **j** $27d^{12} \div (-3d^4)$
- **k** $(x^3)^3$
- **l** $(m^6)^0$
- **m** $(3x^3)^2$
- **n** $(4a)^4$
- **o** $(6y^5)^3$

4 Simplify:
- **a** $4^2 \times 4^3$
- **b** 5×5^7
- **c** $7^2 \times 7^5$
- **d** 4×2^5
- **e** $10^4 \times 1000$
- **f** $5^7 \div 5$
- **g** $3^9 \div 3^3$
- **h** $10^4 \div 10^4$
- **i** $3^6 \div 9$
- **j** $3^5 \div 27$
- **k** $(5^2)^3$
- **l** $(7^7)^7$
- **m** $(2^3 \times 8)^2$
- **n** $(4 \times 16^3)^3$
- **o** $(27 \times 3^3)^4$

5 Simplify:
- **a** $8x^4 \times x^3$
- **b** $5a^2 \times a$
- **c** $4m^6 \times m^4$
- **d** $8x^4 \div x^3$
- **e** $5a^2 \div a$
- **f** $4m^6 \div m^4$
- **g** $10y^3 \times 5y$
- **h** $16m^2 \times 2m^2$
- **i** $8a^5 \times 4a^4$
- **j** $10y^3 \div 5y$
- **k** $16m^2 \div 2m^2$
- **l** $8a^5 \div 4a^4$
- **m** $12x^5 \times 6x^3$
- **n** $9a^7 \times 3a^2$
- **o** $18y^6 \times 6y$
- **p** $\dfrac{12x^5}{6x^3}$
- **q** $\dfrac{9a^7}{3a^2}$
- **r** $\dfrac{18y^6}{6y}$
- **s** $\dfrac{3a^5}{a^3}$
- **t** $\dfrac{10x^5}{5}$
- **u** $\dfrac{42a^7}{21a^6}$

6 Simplify:

a $6a^0$

b $6(a^3)^0$

c $(6a^3)^0$

d ab^0

e x^0y^3

f m^5n^0

g $(2m^2)^3$

h $(4n^3)^2$

i $(2p^3)^4$

j $x^2y^3 \times x^3$

k $a^2b^5 \times b^4$

l $xy^3 \times x^4$

m $x^2y^2 \times xy^2$

n $a^3b \times a^2b$

o $m^2n \times mn^3$

p $(x^2y^3)^2$

q $(abc)^2$

r $(pq^3)^3$

s $5x^2y \times 2xy$

t $4a^2b^2 \times 7ab^3$

u $11a^3 \times 4a^2b^2$

v $a \times a \times a \times 3a$

w $3a \times 2a \times -4a$

x $5c^4 \times 4c^2 \div 10c^5$

y $12x^2 - 5x^3 + 10x^2$

z $4x(3x + 2) - (x - 1)$

7 Simplify:

a $5x^2 \times 2x^3 \times 3x$

b $5 \times 2a \times 4a^2$

c $5y \times y^2 \times xy$

d $4x^4 \div 8x$

e $7y^3 \div 49y^2$

f $100x^3 \div 10x^4$

g $(x^2)^3 \times x^2$

h $(a^4)^2 \times a^5$

i $(y^7)^3 \times y^5$

j $(a^2)^3 \div a^4$

k $(m^3)^4 \div m^{10}$

l $n^8 \div (n^2)^3$

m $(y^5)^2 \times (y^3)^3$

n $(2a^4)^3 \times (a^3)^2$

o $(b^4)^3 \div (b^2)^5$

p $(x^4 \times x^7) \div x^9$

q $(4a^3 \times 5a^4) \div 10a^5$

r $7p^7q^5 \div (p^2q)^3$

s $\dfrac{5x^3 \times 4x^7}{10x^5}$

t $\dfrac{(3x^3)^2 \times 4x^5}{6x^4 \times x}$

u $\dfrac{x^2 \times (xy)^3}{(2x)^4}$

8 Expand and simplify:

a $x^2(x^2 - 1)$

b $a^3(5 - a^2)$

c $a^2(5a - a^3)$

d $x(x^2 + y)$

e $m(7 - m^2)$

f $y(y^2 - xy)$

g $3a^2(2a^3 + 3a)$

h $5x(3x^2 - x)$

i $2m^3(n^2 - m^2)$

j $x(5x^2 - 3x + 7)$

k $x^2(2x^2 + 7x - 14)$

l $y(y^2 - 7y - 1)$

m $x^2(x - 7) - x^3$

n $y(4y^3 + 2) - 2y$

o $x(x^2 - 7x + 1) - (x^3 - x^2)$

9 Simplify:

a $3^x \times 3^{x+1}$

b $5^{2y} \div 5^{y+1}$

c $(2^x)^2 \div (2^{1-x})^2$

d $e^{2x+1} \times e^x$

e $e^{2x+1} \div e^x$

f $(e^{x+2})^2 \div e^{x+1}$

5:02 | Negative Indices

Consider the problem $\dfrac{8}{32}$

By dividing by the highest common factor, 8: $\dfrac{8}{32} = \dfrac{1}{4}$

Also, $8 = 2^3$ and $32 = 2^5$

So $\dfrac{8}{32} = \dfrac{2^3}{2^5} = 2^3 \div 2^5$

$= 2^{3-5}$

$= 2^{-2}$

Therefore, $2^{-2} = \dfrac{1}{2^2} = \dfrac{1}{4}$

What happens if the index is negative?

Also $2^3 \div 2^5 = 8 \div 32$

$2^{-2} = \dfrac{1}{4}$

$= \dfrac{1}{2^2}$

 In general, the meaning of a negative index can be summarised by the rules:

x^{-m} is the reciprocal of x^m, since $x^m \times x^{-m} = 1$

$x^{-m} = \dfrac{1}{x^m}$, $(x \neq 0)$

worked examples

1 Simplify the following, writing answers with only positive indices.
  a 5^{-2} b 7^{-1} c $x^4 \times x^{-5}$ d $9a^3 \div 3a^5$ e $4y \div 12y^3$ f $(\tfrac{3}{5})^{-2}$

2 Evaluate, using the calculator.
  a 3^{-2} b $(\tfrac{3}{4})^{-3}$

Solutions

1 a $5^{-2} = \dfrac{1}{5^2}$

   $= \dfrac{1}{25}$

  b $7^{-1} = \dfrac{1}{7^1}$

   $= \dfrac{1}{7}$

  c $x^4 \times x^{-5} = x^{-1}$

   $= \dfrac{1}{x^1}$

   $= \dfrac{1}{x}$

  d $9a^3 \div 3a^5 = \dfrac{9}{3} a^{3-5}$

   $= 3 \times a^{-2}$

   $= 3 \times \dfrac{1}{a^2}$

   $= \dfrac{3}{a^2}$

  e $4y \div 12y^3 = \dfrac{4}{12} y^{1-3}$

   $= \dfrac{1}{3} \times y^{-2}$

   $= \dfrac{1}{3} \times \dfrac{1}{y^2}$

   $= \dfrac{1}{3y^2}$

  f $\left(\dfrac{3}{5}\right)^{-2} = \dfrac{1}{\left(\dfrac{3}{5}\right)^2}$

   $= \dfrac{1}{\left(\dfrac{9}{25}\right)}$

   $= \dfrac{25}{8}$

   $= 3\dfrac{1}{8}$

2 a $3^{-2} = \dfrac{1}{3^2}$ On the calculator 3 $\boxed{x^y}$ 2 $\boxed{=}$ 9

   $= \dfrac{1}{9}$

continued ➜➜➜

b $\left(\frac{3}{5}\right)^{-2} = \left(\frac{5}{3}\right)^2$ On the calculator 5 $\boxed{x^y}$ 2 $\boxed{=}$ 25

$= \frac{25}{9}$ On the calculator 3 $\boxed{x^y}$ 2 $\boxed{=}$ 9

$= 2\frac{7}{9}$

Exercise 5:02

Foundation Worksheet 5:02

Negative indices
1 Write down the value of:
 a 4^{-1} b 2^{-3} c 3^{-2}
2 Write with a negative index.
 a $\frac{1}{4}$ b $\frac{1}{2^3}$ c $\frac{1}{3^2}$

1 Write down the value of each of the following.
  a 3^{-1} b 5^{-1} c 2^{-1}
  d 6^{-2} e 4^{-2} f 10^{-3}
  g 2^{-4} h 10^{-4} i 5^{-2}

2 Write each with a negative index.
  a $\frac{1}{11}$ b $\frac{1}{3}$ c $\frac{1}{5}$ d $\frac{1}{7}$ e $\frac{1}{3^3}$ f $\frac{1}{5^4}$

  g $\frac{1}{2^8}$ h $\frac{1}{7^2}$ i $\frac{1}{10^2}$ j $\frac{1}{10^3}$ k $\frac{1}{10^6}$ l $\frac{1}{10^5}$

3 Write *true* or *false* for:
  a $1024 = 2^{10}$ b $8 = 2^4$ c $3^{-2} = \frac{1}{9}$ d $2(3)^2 = 36$
  e $2(3)^{-1} = \frac{1}{6}$ f $4^{-1} = \frac{1}{2}$ g $2^{-1} < 1$ h $-2^8 = (-2)^8$

4 Simplify, writing your answers without negative indices.
  a $x^3 \times x^{-2}$ b $a^{-2} \times a^5$ c $m^4 \times m^{-1}$ d $n^5 \times n^{-5}$
  e $3a^2 \times a^{-1}$ f $6x^{-2} \times 5x^4$ g $a^{-2} \times 5a^3$ h $15m^{-1} \times 2m^3$
  i $x^{-4} \times x$ j $2a^{-2} \times a^{-3}$ k $4y \times 2y^{-2}$ l $15m^{-4} \times 2m^{-1}$

5 Simplify, writing your answers without negative indices.
  a $m^4 \div m^{-1}$ b $x^2 \div x^{-2}$ c $y^{-6} \div y^{-8}$ d $x^3 \div x^{-1}$
  e $a^{-2} \div a^2$ f $y^{-1} \div y^3$ g $y^{-2} \div y$ h $x^{-3} \div x^{-1}$
  i $6x^2 \div 2x^{-1}$ j $10a^3 \div 5a^7$ k $24a^{-2} \div a^3$ l $18n^{-1} \div 9n^{-2}$

6 Simplify, writing your answers without negative indices.
  a $(a^{-3})^{-2}$ b $(x^2)^{-1}$ c $(y^{-3})^2$ d $(m^{-2})^{-2}$
  e $(2x^2)^{-1}$ f $(3x)^{-2}$ g $(5x^{-1})^2$ h $(7x^{-2})^2$
  i $(abc)^{-1}$ j $(a^2b^2c^2)^{-1}$ k $(2a^2b)^{-1}$ l $2(a^2b)^{-1}$

7 If $x = 2$, $y = 3$ and $z = \frac{1}{2}$, evaluate:
  a $x^{-1} + y^{-1}$ b $(xy)^{-1}$ c $(xz)^{-1}$ d $x^{-1}y^{-1}z$

8 Simplify:
  a $3^x \div 3^{-x}$ b $5^y \div 5^{2-y}$ c $e^{x+1} \div e^{1-x}$ d $(e^x)^2 \times e^{-(x-1)}$

- The formula for the volume of a sphere is:

  $V = \frac{4}{3}\pi r^3$

  where $\pi \doteqdot 3\cdot142$ and r is the radius of the sphere.

5:03 | Fractional Indices

Complete:

1 $5^2 = 25$
   $\sqrt{25} = \ldots$

2 $7^2 = 49$
   $\sqrt{49} = \ldots$

3 $2^3 = 8$
   $\sqrt[3]{8} = \ldots$

4 $5^3 = 125$
   $\sqrt[3]{125} = \ldots$

Consider the following:

5 $5^a \times 5^a = 5^{2a}$
If $5^n \times 5^n = 5^1$,
what is the value of n?

6 $8^a \times 8^a = 8^{2a}$
If $8^n \times 8^n = 8^1$,
what is the value of n?

7 $x^a \times x^a = x^{2a}$
If $x^n \times x^n = x^1$,
what is the value of n?

8 $y^a \times y^a = y^{2a}$
If $y^n \times y^n = y^1$,
what is the value of n?

9 $5^a \times 5^a \times 5^a = 5^{3a}$
If $5^n \times 5^n \times 5^n = 5^1$,
what is the value of n?

10 $x^a \times x^a \times x^a = x^{3a}$
If $x^n \times x^n \times x^n = x^1$,
what is the value of n?

What is the meaning of a fractional index?

The meaning is shown in the examples below.

1 $9^{\frac{1}{2}} \times 9^{\frac{1}{2}} = 9^{\left(\frac{1}{2} + \frac{1}{2}\right)}$
           $= 9^1$
           $= 9$

$3 \times 3 = 9$
$\sqrt{9} \times \sqrt{9} = 9$

$9^{\frac{1}{2}}$ multiplied by itself gives 9 and $\sqrt{9}$ multiplied by itself gives 9.

So $9^{\frac{1}{2}}$ is the square root of 9.

$\therefore \ 9^{\frac{1}{2}} = \sqrt{9}$

2 $5^{\frac{1}{2}} \times 5^{\frac{1}{2}} = 5^{\left(\frac{1}{2} + \frac{1}{2}\right)}$
           $= 5^1$
           $= 5$

Now $\sqrt{5} \times \sqrt{5} = 5$

So $5^{\frac{1}{2}} = \sqrt{5}$

That's neat!
$\left(5^{\frac{1}{2}}\right)^2 = 5$
That means that
$5^{\frac{1}{2}}$ is the square
root of 5.

$\left\{\begin{array}{l} \text{The number that multiplies itself to give 5} \\ \text{(ie } 5^{\frac{1}{2}}\text{) is the square root of 5.} \end{array}\right.$

3   Similarly:

$8^{\frac{1}{3}} \times 8^{\frac{1}{3}} \times 8^{\frac{1}{3}} = 8^{\left(\frac{1}{3} + \frac{1}{3} + \frac{1}{3}\right)}$
                  $= 8^1$
                  $= 8$

$2 \times 2 \times 2 = 8$
$\sqrt[3]{8} \times \sqrt[3]{8} \times \sqrt[3]{8} = 8$
Two is the cube root of 8.

So $8^{\frac{1}{3}} = \sqrt[3]{8}$, (the cube root of 8)

$\therefore \ 8^{\frac{1}{3}} = 2$

> ■ Since $\left(\sqrt[3]{x}\right)^3 = x$,
>
> $\sqrt[3]{x} = x^{\frac{1}{3}}$

$$x^{\frac{1}{2}} = \sqrt{x}, \qquad x^{\frac{1}{3}} = \sqrt[3]{x}, \qquad x^{\frac{1}{n}} = n\text{th root of } x$$

$x^{\frac{1}{3}}$ is the number that, when used three times in a product, gives x.

worked examples

1 Simplify the following:

a $25^{\frac{1}{2}}$　　b $27^{\frac{1}{3}}$　　c $3x^{\frac{1}{2}} \times 4x^{\frac{1}{2}}$　　d $(49m^6)^{\frac{1}{2}}$　　e $8^{\frac{2}{3}}$　　f $9^{-\frac{3}{2}}$

2 Evaluate using your calculator:

a $196^{\frac{1}{2}}$　　　　b $32^{\frac{1}{2}}$　　　　　　c $256^{-\frac{1}{4}}$　　　　　d $125^{-\frac{4}{3}}$

Solutions

1　a $25^{\frac{1}{2}} = \sqrt{25}$　　　　　　b $27^{\frac{1}{3}} = \sqrt[3]{27}$　　　　　c $3x^{\frac{1}{2}} \times 4x^{\frac{1}{2}} = 12x^{\frac{1}{2}+\frac{1}{2}}$
　　　　　$= 5$　　　　　　　　　　　　$= 3$　　　　　　　　　　　$= 12x$

　　d $(49m^6)^{\frac{1}{2}} = 49^{\frac{1}{2}} \times m^{6 \times \frac{1}{2}}$　　e $8^{\frac{2}{3}} = (8^{\frac{1}{3}})^2$　　　　f $9^{-\frac{3}{2}} = (9^{-\frac{1}{2}})^{-3}$
　　　　　　　$= \sqrt{49} \times m^3$　　　　　　　$= (\sqrt[3]{8})^2$　　　　　　　$= (\sqrt{9})^{-3}$
　　　　　　　$= 7m^3$　　　　　　　　　　$= 2^2$　　　　　　　　　$= \dfrac{1}{3^3}$
　　　　　　　　　　　　　　　　　　　　$= 4$　　　　　　　　　$= \dfrac{1}{27}$

Note from examples **e** and **f** the rule:

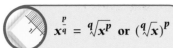

$$x^{\frac{p}{q}} = \sqrt[q]{x^p} \text{ or } (\sqrt[q]{x})^p$$

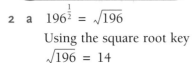

(f) is pretty tricky!

2　a $196^{\frac{1}{2}} = \sqrt{196}$

　　Using the square root key

　　$\sqrt{196} = 14$

For roots higher than a square root ($\frac{1}{2}$) [or cube root ($\frac{1}{3}$), if your calculator has a $\sqrt[3]{}$ key], the $x^{1/y}$ or $\sqrt[x]{}$ key can be used. You may need to use the inverse button.

　　b To evaluate $32^{\frac{1}{5}}$

　　　Press: 32 $\boxed{x^{1/y}}$ 5 $\boxed{=}$

　　　Answer: $32^{\frac{1}{5}} = 2$

　　c To evaluate $256^{-\frac{1}{4}}$　　　　　　d To evaluate $125^{-\frac{4}{3}}$

　　　Press: 256 $\boxed{x^{1/y}}$ 4 $\boxed{+/\!-}$ $\boxed{=}$　　　　Press 125 $\boxed{x^{1/y}}$ 3 $\boxed{x^y}$ 4 $\boxed{+/\!-}$ $\boxed{=}$

　　　Answer: $256^{-\frac{1}{4}} = 0 \cdot 25$　　　　　Answer: $125^{-\frac{4}{3}} = 0 \cdot 001\,6$

Exercise 5:03

Foundation Worksheet 5:03

Fractional indices

1 Simplify:

　a $\sqrt{36}$　　b $\sqrt{64}$　　c $\sqrt{121}$

2 Evaluate:

　a $36^{\frac{1}{2}}$　　b $64^{\frac{1}{2}}$　　c $121^{\frac{1}{2}}$

1 Write each of the following using a *square root sign*.

a $5^{\frac{1}{2}}$　　　　　　b $10^{\frac{1}{2}}$　　　　　　c $2^{\frac{1}{2}}$

d $3 \times 2^{\frac{1}{2}}$　　　　e $4 \times 3^{\frac{1}{2}}$　　　　f $7 \times 6^{\frac{1}{2}}$

2 Use a fractional index to write:

a $\sqrt{3}$　　　　　　b $3\sqrt{2}$　　　　　　c $\sqrt[3]{11}$　　　　　　d $7\sqrt{3}$

3 Find the value of the following:

a $4^{\frac{1}{2}}$ b $49^{\frac{1}{2}}$ c $8^{\frac{1}{3}}$ d $16^{\frac{1}{4}}$

e $16^{\frac{1}{2}}$ f $100^{\frac{1}{2}}$ g $144^{\frac{1}{2}}$ h $1^{\frac{1}{2}}$

i $121^{\frac{1}{2}}$ j $32^{\frac{1}{5}}$ k $81^{\frac{1}{2}}$ l $81^{\frac{1}{4}}$

4 Assuming that all pronumerals used are positive, simplify:

a $x^{\frac{1}{2}} \times x^{\frac{1}{2}}$ b $a^{\frac{1}{3}} \times a^{\frac{2}{3}}$ c $m^{\frac{1}{2}} \times m^{\frac{1}{2}}$

d $6x^{\frac{1}{2}} \times 2x^{\frac{1}{2}}$ e $3y^{\frac{1}{4}} \times 2y^{\frac{3}{4}}$ f $9n^{\frac{2}{3}} \times 2n^{\frac{1}{3}}$

g $(x^2)^{\frac{1}{2}}$ h $(y^6)^{\frac{1}{3}}$ i $(4a^6)^{\frac{1}{2}}$

j $(a^2b^4)^{\frac{1}{2}}$ k $(9x^4y^6)^{\frac{1}{2}}$ l $(8x^3y^3)^{\frac{1}{3}}$

■ $(x^a)^b = x^{ab}$

5 Evaluate:

a $9^{-\frac{1}{2}}$ b $25^{-\frac{1}{2}}$ c $8^{-\frac{1}{3}}$

d $9^{\frac{3}{2}}$ e $4^{\frac{3}{2}}$ f $4^{\frac{5}{2}}$

g $16^{\frac{3}{4}}$ h $125^{\frac{2}{3}}$ i $8^{-\frac{2}{3}}$

j $9^{\frac{5}{2}}$ k $32^{\frac{4}{5}}$ l $16^{-\frac{3}{4}}$

6 Evaluate using your calculator, leaving answers as decimal numerals:

a $225^{\frac{1}{2}}$ b $784^{\frac{1}{2}}$ c $1024^{\frac{1}{2}}$

d $729^{\frac{1}{3}}$ e $3375^{\frac{1}{3}}$ f $8000^{\frac{1}{3}}$

g $225^{\frac{3}{2}}$ h $729^{\frac{2}{3}}$ i $8000^{\frac{5}{3}}$

j $(0 \cdot 125)^{-\frac{2}{3}}$ k $(0 \cdot 25)^{-\frac{5}{2}}$ l $(0 \cdot 01)^{-\frac{3}{2}}$

■ $(ab)^{\frac{1}{3}} = a^{\frac{1}{3}} b^{\frac{1}{3}}$

7 If $a = 4$, $b = 8$ and $c = 9$, evaluate the following:

a $a^{\frac{1}{2}} + b^{\frac{1}{3}}$ b $(ab)^{\frac{1}{5}}$ c $2c^{\frac{3}{2}}$ d $\frac{1}{2}(ac)^{\frac{1}{2}}$

e $a^{-\frac{1}{2}} + b^{-\frac{1}{3}}$ f $(2b)^{-\frac{1}{4}}$ g $(2ab)^{-\frac{1}{6}}$ h $(2bc)^{\frac{1}{2}} - a^{\frac{3}{2}}$

8 Use the fact that $x^{\frac{p}{q}} = \sqrt[q]{x^p}$, to simplify:

a $(27a^3)^{\frac{2}{3}}$ b $(x^6y^{12})^{\frac{2}{3}}$ c $(8m^9)^{\frac{2}{3}}$

d $\left(\dfrac{a^3}{b^3}\right)^{\frac{2}{3}}$ e $\left(\dfrac{16}{x^4}\right)^{\frac{3}{4}}$ f $\left(\dfrac{y^6}{25}\right)^{\frac{3}{2}}$

■ As $x^{\frac{1}{2}} = \sqrt{x}$,
$x^{\frac{1}{2}}$ stands for the positive square root of x.
Note $\sqrt{x^2} = |x|$.

Technology Applications Activities

5:03 Who wants to be a millionaire?

Challenge worksheet 5:03 Algebraic expressions and indices

Fun Spot 5:03 | Why is a room full of married people always empty?

Work out the answer to each part and put the letter for that part in the box that is above the correct answer.

Write in index form:

E 10×10 **E** $8 \times 8 \times 8$ **E** $yyyyaa$

Find the value of:

E 3^2 **E** 2^3 **E** $5^2 - 5$

A 10^3 **A** $2^3 - 3^2$

Find the value of x in:

I $2^x = 16$ **I** $3^x = 9$

Write as a basic numeral:

I 1.7×10^2 **I** $6.04 \div 10$

Evaluate:

O x^0 **O** $7^0 + 9$ **U** $11y^0$

N 2^{-2} **N** 10^{-3} **N** $(\frac{2}{3})^{-1}$

N $36^{\frac{1}{2}}$ **B** $27^{\frac{1}{3}}$ **C** $7a \times a^{-1}$

H To fill a jar in 6 minutes, Jan doubled the number of peanuts in the jar every minute. After how many minutes was the jar half full?

Simplify:

S $3x - x$ **S** $3x \times x$ **T** $5 \times 5x$ **R** $10x \div 10$

T $x^2 \times x^3$ **T** $x^{10} \div x^2$ **S** $(x^2)^3$ **L** $60x^3 \div 5x^3$

S $\dfrac{4aab}{ab}$ **R** $x^{10} \times x^{-3}$ **P** $x^3 \div x^{-1}$ **G** $\dfrac{1}{10^2}$

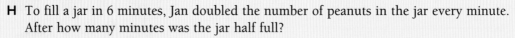

3	10^2	7	-1	11	$2x$	9	x^5	5	8^3	x	8	2	$3x^2$	$-\frac{1}{4}$	1	$25x$

1000	$4a$	0.604	$1\frac{1}{2}$	0.01	12	y^4a^2	x^4	20	x^7	x^6	10	6	4	$\frac{1}{1000}$	170	x^8

Investigation 5:03 | Reasoning with fractional indices

Please use the Assessment Grid on the following page to help you understand what is required for this Investigation.

- Write $\sqrt{x}$, $\sqrt{x^2}$, $\sqrt{x^3}$, $\sqrt{x^4}$, $\sqrt{x^5}$, ... as expressions with fractional indices and describe the pattern that emerges.

- Find the value of b if $(x^b)^3 = x$

- Explain why $\sqrt{8} = 2^{\frac{3}{2}} = 2\sqrt{2} = (\sqrt{2})^3$.

- Find some values that x, p and q could take if $x^{\frac{p}{q}} = 2$.

Assessment Grid for Investigation 5:03 | **Reasoning with fractional indices**

The following is a sample assessment grid for this investigation. You should carefully read the criteria *before* beginning the investigation so that you know what is required.

			Assessment Criteria (B, C) for this investigation		Achieved ✓
Criterion B Investigating Patterns	a		None of the following descriptors has been achieved.	0	
	b		Some help was needed to be able to write the fractional indices.	1	
				2	
	c		Mathematical techniques have been selected and applied to write each fractional index and suggest an emerging pattern.	3	
				4	
	d		The student has completed all fractional indices and accurately described the rules for the square of a binomial. Some attempt at the final two parts has been made.	5	
				6	
	e		The above has been completed with specific justification using the patterns and index lawns shown and the further questions have been completed accurately.	7	
				8	
Criterion C Communication in Mathematics	a		None of the following descriptors has been achieved.	0	
	b		There is a basic use of mathematical language and notation, with some errors or inconsistencies evident. Lines of reasoning are insufficient.	1	
				2	
	c		There is sufficient use of mathematical language and notation. Explanations are clear but not always complete.	3	
				4	
	d		Correct use of mathematical language and notation has been shown. Explanations of all rules are complete and concise.	5	
				6	

5:04 | Scientific (or Standard) Notation

5:04

Investigation 5.04 | Multiplying and dividing by powers of 10

Please use the Assessment Grid on the following page to help you understand what is required for this Investigation.

- Use the x^y button on your calculator to answer these questions.
- Look for a connection between questions and answers and then fill in the rules at the end of the investigation.

Exercise

1 a 1.8×10^1 b 1.8×10^2 c 1.8×10^3
   d 4.05×10^1 e 4.05×10^2 f 4.05×10^3
   g 6.2×10^4 h 6.2×10^5 i 6.2×10^6
   j 3.1416×10^2 k 3.1416×10^3 l 3.1416×10^4

> **To multiply by 10^n move the decimal point _____ places to the _____.**

2 a $1.8 \div 10^1$ b $1.8 \div 10^2$ c $1.8 \div 10^3$
   d $968.5 \div 10^2$ e $968.5 \div 10^3$ f $968.5 \div 10^4$

> **To divide by 10^n move the decimal point _____ places to the _____.**

The investigation above should have reminded you that:

1 when we *multiply* a decimal by 10, 100 or 1000, we move the decimal point 1, 2 or 3 places to the *right*
2 when we *divide* a decimal by 10, 100 or 1000, we move the decimal point 1, 2 or 3 places to the *left*.

> **When expressing numbers in scientific (or standard) notation each number is written as the product of a number between 1 and 10, and a power of 10.**

6.1×10^5

- This number is written in scientific notation (or standard form).
- The first part is between 1 and 10.
- The second part is a power of 10.

> 'Scientific notation' is sometimes called 'standard notation' or 'standard form'.

Scientific notation is useful when writing very large or very small numbers.

Numbers greater than 1

$5\,9\,7\,0. = 5.97 \times 10^3$

To write 5970 in standard form:

- put a decimal point after the first digit
- count the number of places you have to move the decimal point to the left from its original position. This will be the power needed.

To multiply 5·97 by 10^3, we move the decimal point 3 places to the right – which gives 5970.

The following is a sample assessment grid for this investigation. You should carefully read the criteria *before* beginning the investigation so that you know what is required.

		Assessment Criteria (B, C) for this investigation		Achieved ✓
Criterion B **Investigating Patterns**	a	None of the following descriptors has been achieved.	0	
	b	Some help was needed to complete the exercises.	1	
			2	
	c	The student independently completes the exercises.	3	
			4	
	d	The student has correctly done all exercises and attempted to complete the rules following.	5	
			6	
	e	All exercises and rules are completed correctly with thorough explanation and justification, possibly with further examples for support.	7	
			8	
Criterion C **Communication in Mathematics**	a	None of the following descriptors has been achieved.	0	
	b	There is a basic use of mathematical language and notation, with some errors or inconsistencies evident. Lines of reasoning are insufficient.	1	
			2	
	c	There is sufficient use of mathematical language and notation. Explanations are clear and the student generally moves between the different forms of representation well.	3	
			4	
	d	Correct use of mathematical language and notation has been shown with complete working. Explanations of all rules are complete and the student easily moves between the different forms of representation.	5	
			6	

1   Express the following in scientific notation.
   a   243   **b**   60 000   **c**   93 800 000

2   Write the following as a basic numeral.
   a 1.3×10^2 **b** 2.431×10^2 **c** 4.63×10^7

Solutions

1   **a** $243 = 2.43 \times 100$
                 $= 2.43 \times 10^2$

   b $60\,000 = 6 \times 10\,000$
                 $= 6 \times 10^4$

   c $93\,800\,000 = 9.38 \times 10\,000\,000$
                 $= 9.38 \times 10^7$

If end zeros are significant,
write them in your answer.
eg 60 000 (to nearest 100) $= 6.00 \times 10^4$

■ We have moved the decimal point
7 places from its original position.

2   **a** $1.3 \times 10^2 = 1.30 \times 100$
                 $= 130$

   b $2.431 \times 10^2 = 2.431 \times 100$
                 $= 243.1$

   c $4.63 \times 10^7 = 4.630\,000\,0 \times 10\,000\,000$
                 $= 46\,300\,000$

■ To multiply by 10^7, move the
decimal point 7 places right.

Numbers less than 1

$0.005\,97 = 5.97 \times 10^{-3}$

To write $0.005\,97$ in scientific notation:
- put a decimal point after the first non-zero digit
- count the number of places you have moved the
  decimal point to the right from its original position.
  This will show the negative number needed as
  the power of 10.

   5.97×10^{-3} is the same as $5.97 \div 10^3$.

5.97×10^{-3}
Multiplying by 10^{-3} is the
same as dividing by 10^3 so we
would move the decimal point
3 places left to get $0.005\,97$.

1   Express each number in scientific notation.
   a   0.043   **b**   0.000 059 7
   c   0.004

2   Write the basic numeral for:
   a 2.9×10^{-2} **b** 9.38×10^{-5}
   c 1.004×10^{-3}

■ Short-cut method:
                 0.043
- How many places must we move the
  decimal point for scientific notation?
  Answer = 2
- Is 0.043 bigger or smaller than 1?
  Answer = smaller
- So the power of 10 is '−2'.
  ∴ $0.043 = 4.3 \times 10^{-2}$

Solutions

1 a $0.043 = 4.3 \div 100$
        $= 4.3 \times 10^{-2}$

   b $0.000\,059\,7 = 5.97 \div 100\,000$
        $= 5.97 \times 10^{-5}$

   c $0.004 = 4 \div 1000$
        $= 4 \times 10^{-3}$

2 a $2.9 \times 10^{-2} = 002.9 \div 100$
        $= 0.029$

   b $9.38 \times 10^{-5} = 000009.38 \div 100\,000$
        $= 0.000\,093\,8$

   c $1.004 \times 10^{-3} = 0001.004 \div 1000$
        $= 0.001\,004$

Exercise 5:04

Foundation Worksheet 5:04

Scientific notation
1 Evaluate:
   a 6×10^1 b 6×10^2 c 6×10^3
2 Write in scientific notation.
   a 430   b 4300   c 43 000

1 a   Explain the difference between 2×10^4 and 2^4.
    b   Explain the difference between 5×10^{-2} and 5^{-2}.
    c   How many seconds are in 50 000 years?
    d   Have you lived 8.2×10^4 hours?
    e   Order the following, from smallest to largest.

   3.24×10^3 6 9.8×10^{-5} 5.6×10^{-2}
   1.2×10^4 2.04 5.499×10^2 0.0034

    f   Write the thickness of a sheet of paper in scientific notation if 500 sheets of paper have a thickness of 3.8 cm.
    g   Estimate the thickness of the cover of this book. Write your estimate in scientific notation.

2 Write the basic numeral for:
    a 2.1×10^1
    b $2.1 \div 10^1$
    c 2.1×10^{-1}
    d 7.04×10^2
    e $7.04 \div 10^2$
    f 7.04×10^{-2}
    g 1.375×10^3
    h $1.375 \div 10^3$
    i 1.375×10^{-3}

3 Express in scientific notation.
    (Assume that final zeros are not significant.)
    a   470
    b   2600
    c   53 000
    d   700
    e   50 000
    f   700 000
    g   65
    h   342
    i   90
    j   4970
    k   63 500
    l   2 941 000
    m   297.1
    n   69.3
    o   4976.5
    p   9 310 000
    q   67 000 000
    r   190 100
    s   600 000
    t   501 700
    u   100 000

If you're stuck with this exercise, think back to Investigation 6:02 . . .

4 Express in scientific notation.
    a   0.075
    b   0.0063
    c   0.59
    d   0.08
    e   0.0003
    f   0.009
    g   0.3
    h   0.0301
    i   0.000 529
    j   0.426
    k   0.001
    l   0.000 009 7
    m   0.000 06
    n   0.000 907
    o   0.000 000 004

Write the basic numeral for:

a 2.3×10^2	**b** 9.4×10^4	**c** 3.7×10^3	**d** 2.95×10^2
e 8.74×10^1	**f** 7.63×10^5	**g** 1.075×10^3	**h** 2.0×10^4
i 8×10^1	**j** 2.9×10^{-2}	**k** 1.9×10^{-3}	**l** 9.5×10^{-1}
m 3.76×10^{-3}	**n** 4.63×10^{-4}	**o** 1.07×10^{-2}	**p** 7×10^{-2}
q 8.0×10^{-1}	**r** 5×10^{-6}	**s** 9.73×10^5	**t** 6.3×10^{-3}
u 4.7×10^7	**v** 9.142×10^2	**w** 1.032×10^{-2}	**x** 1.0×10^8

5:05 | Scientific Notation and the Calculator

prep quiz

5:05

Write in scientific notation:

1 690 **2** 4000 **3** 963·2 **4** 0·073 **5** 0·0003

Rewrite as basic numerals:

6 2.9×10^3 **7** 8.0×10^5 **8** 4.6×10^{-2} **9** 5×10^{-7} **10** 8.14×10^{-1}

- On a calculator:

  5.517×10^{12} is shown as $\boxed{5.517 \quad 12}$

  3.841×10^{-6} is shown as $\boxed{3.841 \quad -06}$

  This is the calculator's way of showing scientific notation.

- To enter scientific notation, press:

  5.517 $\boxed{\text{Exp}}$ 12, to enter 5.517×10^{12}, and

  3.841 $\boxed{\text{Exp}}$ 6 $\boxed{^{+}/_{-}}$, to enter 3.841×10^{-6}.

> Some calculators are called 'Scientific Calculators' because they can give answers in scientific (or standard) notation.

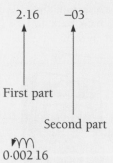

■ To convert calculator answers into decimal form:

$2.16 \quad -03$

First part

Second part

$0.002\,16$

1 Locate the decimal point in the first part of the number (the part between 1 and 10).
2 Look at the sign of the second part. This tells you in which direction to move the decimal point. If it is negative the point moves to the left. If it is positive the point moves to the right.
3 Look at the size of the second part. This tells you how many places the decimal point has to be moved.
4 Move the decimal point to its new position, filling in any gaps, where necessary, with zeros.

worked examples

Use a calculator to find the answers for:

1 $630\,000 \times (47\,000)^2$

2 $45 \div (8614)^3$

3 $(8.4 \times 10^6) + (3.8 \times 10^7)$

4 $\sqrt{1.44 \times 10^{-6}}$

> A calculator will give an answer in scientific notation if the number is too large or small to fit on the screen.

Solutions

1 $630\,000 \times (47\,000)^2$

$= \boxed{1.39167\ \ 15}$

$= 1.39167 \times 10^{15}$

$= 1\,391\,670\,000\,000\,000$

2 $45 \div (8614)^3$

$= \boxed{7.040409359\ \ -11}$

$= 7.040409359 \times 10^{-11}$

$\div 0.000\,000\,000\,070\,404\,093\,59$

The answers to **1** and **2** are too long to fit on the screen.

3 $(8.4 \times 10^6) + (3.8 \times 10^7)$

Press: 8.4 $\boxed{\text{Exp}}$ 6 $\boxed{+}$ 3.8 $\boxed{\text{Exp}}$ 7

$= 46\,400\,000$

4 $\sqrt{1.44 \times 10^{-6}}$

Press: $\boxed{\sqrt{}}$ 1.44 $\boxed{\text{Exp}}$ 6 $\boxed{^{+/}\!_-}$ $\boxed{=}$

$= 0.0012$

> ■ *Note:* Not all calculators work the same way.

Exercise 5:05

1 Enter each of these on your calculator using the $\boxed{\text{Exp}}$ key, and copy the calculator readout.
   a 6.3×10^{15} **b** 1.4×10^{-12} **c** 9.2×10^{11}

2 Rewrite these calculator readouts in scientific notation using powers of 10.
   a 3.02   05   **b** 4.631   09   **c** 1.37   15
   d 1.31   −04   **e** 6.9   −08   **f** 4.6327   −10
   g 7.6514   08   **h** 1.03124   −12   **i** 6.9333   −05

   Explain why a calculator readout of $\boxed{2.^{04}}$ has a different value to 2^4.

> ■ $\boxed{1.402 \times 10^7}$
>
> has 4 significant figures, as four figures are used in the decimal part.

3 Place the nine numbers in question **2** in order of size from smallest to largest.

4 Give the answers to these in scientific notation, correct to 5 significant figures.

> ■ Use index laws to check the size of your answer.

   a 3814^4 **b** $0.0004 \div 8400^2$
   c $(0.000\,7)^5$ **d** $93\,000\,000 \div 0.000\,13$
   e $(65 \times 847)^3$ **f** $(0.0045)^3 \times (0.0038)^2$
   g $\dfrac{9865 \times 8380}{0.000\,021}$ **h** $\dfrac{6800}{(0.0007)^5}$

5 Use a calculator to answer correct to 4 significant figures, then use the index laws to check your answer.
   a $13.85 \times (2.3 \times 10^4)$ **b** $(8.14 \times 10^{-2})^2$ **c** $(2.1 \times 10^8) \div (8.6 \times 10^8)$
   d $(3.8 \times 10^{-3})^2$ **e** $468 \times (1.8 \times 10^{-5})$ **f** $(9.1 \times 10^4) + (6.8 \times 10^5)$
   g $\sqrt{7.45 \times 10^9}$ **h** $\sqrt[3]{9.1 \times 10^{-8}}$ **i** $\sqrt[3]{6.714 \times 10^{-12}}$

6 **a** An American reported that the diameter of the sun is approximately 8.656×10^5 miles. Write this in kilometres, using scientific notation written correct to four significant figures. There are 1.609 km in a mile. If the sun's diameter is 109 times that of the earth, what is the earth's diameter, correct to three significant figures?
   b The distance to the sun varies from 1.47×10^8 km in January to 1.52×10^8 km in July. This is because the earth's orbit is an ellipse. What is the difference between these distances?

c If we use the average distance to the sun (1.50×10^8 km), how long would it take light travelling at 3.0×10^8 m/s to reach the earth? (Answer correct to the nearest minute.)

d The mass of the earth is approximately 6×10^{21} tonnes. The sun's mass is about 333 400 times greater than the mass of the earth. What is the mass of the sun correct to one significant figure?

e We belong to the galaxy known as the Milky Way. It contains about 1×10^{11} stars. If the sun is taken to have average mass [see part **d**], what is the total mass, correct to 1 significant figure, of the stars in the Milky Way?

investigation

5:05

Investigation 5:05 | Using scientific notation

1 The speed of light is 3.0×10^8 m/s. Use reference books and your calculator to complete this table for five stars of your choice (eg Vega, Dog Star, Pole Star, Sirius).

Name of star	Distance from the earth	Time taken for light to travel to the earth
The sun	1.5×10^8 km	
Alpha Centauri	4.2×10^{13} km	

> ■ 10^6 is 1 million.
> 10^9 is 1 billion.

Order the distances of the five stars from the earth, from smallest to largest.

2 Research *nanotechnology*, which involves the use of very small machine parts. Parts are often measured in micrometres. Make comparisons between the sizes of components.

- Distances in astronomy are measured in light years, which is the distance that light travels in a year. A light year is approximately 9.6×10^{12} km.

5:06 | The Real Number System

The real number system is made up of two groups of numbers: rational and irrational numbers.

Rational numbers

Any number that can be written as a fraction, $\frac{a}{b}$ where a and b are whole numbers and $b \neq 0$, is a rational number. These include integers, fractions, mixed numbers, terminating decimals and recurring decimals.

eg $\frac{7}{8}$, $6\frac{3}{5}$, 1.25, 0.07, $0.\dot{4}$, $\sqrt{81}$

These examples can all be written as fractions.

$$\frac{7}{8}, \frac{33}{5}, \frac{5}{4}, \frac{7}{100}, \frac{4}{9}, \frac{9}{1}$$

Note: An integer is a rational number whose denominator is 1.

Irrational numbers

It follows that irrational numbers cannot be written as a fraction, $\frac{a}{b}$ where a and b are whole numbers. We have met a few numbers like this in our study of the circle and Pythagoras' theorem.

eg π, $\sqrt{2}$, $\sqrt[3]{4}$, $\sqrt{3}+2$

The calculator can only give approximations for these numbers. The decimals continue without terminating or repeating.

$3.141\,592\,65\ldots$, $1.414\,213\,56\ldots$, $1.587\,401\,05\ldots$, $3.732\,050\,80\ldots$

Irrational numbers on the number line

Although irrational numbers cannot be given an exact decimal value, their positions can still be plotted on the number line. As can be seen from exercises on Pythagoras' theorem, a number such as $\sqrt{2}$ can correspond to the length of a side of a triangle, and so this length can be shown on a number line.

Examine the diagram on the right.

If the length of the hypotenuse of this triangle is transferred, using compasses, to the number line as shown, we have the position of $\sqrt{2}$ on the number line. (This agrees with the decimal approximation from the calculator of $1.414\,213\,56$.)

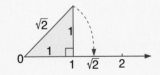

The previous construction can be extended to give the position of other square roots on the number line.

Another irrational number you have met before is π. You should know that it has an approximate value of 3.142, so it would lie on the number line in the position shown.

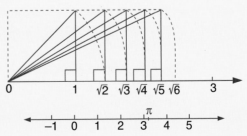

1 For each number write *rational* or *irrational*. (A calculator might help you to decide.)

a $\frac{7}{10}$ b $\sqrt{2}$ c 0.3 d $1\frac{1}{2}$

e 1.6 f π g $\sqrt{5}$ h $\frac{3}{4}$

i $\sqrt{16}$ j 0.99 k $\frac{22}{7}$ l 9

m $\sqrt{625}$ n 0.666 o 70 p $\sqrt{13}$

q $1\frac{1}{3}$ r $1+\sqrt{3}$ s $\sqrt{1}$ t $\sqrt{4}+\sqrt{9}$

u 0.0005 v $1-\sqrt{9}$ w $-\sqrt{3}$ x $\sqrt{7}+\sqrt{2}$

y $\sqrt[3]{27}$ z $\sqrt[3]{10}$

That looks irrational.

2 Use your calculator to find an approximation correct to 1 decimal place for the following. Also use these values to show the position of each number on the number line.

a $\sqrt{2}$ b $\sqrt{3}$ c $\sqrt{5}$ d $\sqrt{6}$ e $\sqrt{7}$

f $\sqrt{8}$ g $\sqrt{10}$ h $\sqrt{12}$ i $\sqrt{20}$ j π

3 Between which two consecutive integers does each number below lie?

a $\sqrt{11}$ b $\sqrt{18}$ c $\sqrt{41}$ d $\sqrt{78}$ e $\sqrt{95}$

f $\sqrt{125}$ g $\sqrt{180}$ h $\sqrt{250}$ i $\sqrt{390}$ j $\sqrt{901}$

4 Arrange each set of numbers below in order, from smallest to largest.

a $\sqrt{5}, 2, \sqrt{3}$ b $\sqrt{8}, 3, \pi$ c $\sqrt{10}, \sqrt{12}, 3$

d $7, \sqrt{40}, \sqrt{50}, 6.5$ e $\pi, \sqrt{2}, 2.1, \sqrt{12}$ f $5.6, \sqrt{26}, 6, \sqrt{30}$

g $8.1, \sqrt{65}, 7.9, \sqrt{60}$ h $\sqrt{98}, 10, \sqrt{102}, 10.1$ i $3.1, \pi, \sqrt{9}, 3.2$

j $\sqrt{20}, 4.1, 4.5, \sqrt{21}$ k $20, \sqrt{390}, 21, \sqrt{420}$ l $\sqrt{600}, \sqrt{610}, 24, 25$

5 This diagram shows another construction for locating square roots on the number line.

Use a set square to draw the triangles on graph paper, then use compasses to draw the arcs on the number line.

Extend your diagram to show $\sqrt{6}$.
Check the accuracy of your constructions with your calculator.

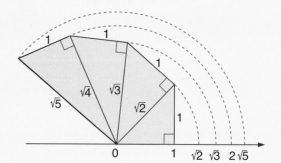

6 To show multiples of a square root on the number line we can use a pair of compasses to mark off equal intervals.

  a Repeat the instructions in question **5** to find the position of $\sqrt{2}$ on the number line. Then use a pair of compasses to mark the position of $2\sqrt{2}$ and $3\sqrt{2}$.

  b Draw a diagram and show the position of $\sqrt{3}$, $2\sqrt{3}$ and $-\sqrt{3}$ on a number line.

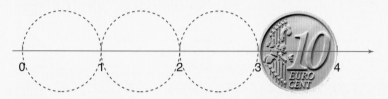

7 The position of π on the number line can be shown by doing the following. Use the diameter of a ten cent coin to mark off units on a number line.

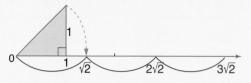
Why is it so?

Then mark a point on the circumference of the coin, align it with zero on the number line, then roll it along the line carefully until the mark meets the number line again. This will show the position of π on the number line.

Reading mathematics 5:06 | Proof that $\sqrt{2}$ is irrational

Let us suppose that $\sqrt{2}$ is rational and, therefore, can be written as a fraction in the form $\dfrac{p}{q}$ where p and q are positive integers **with no common factor.** (This assumption is essential.)

  so $\sqrt{2} = \dfrac{p}{q}$

  then $2 = \dfrac{p^2}{q^2}$ (squaring both sides)

  and $2q^2 = p^2$

These numbers are absurd. They can't be written as an exact decimal.

This last step implies that p^2 must be divisible by 2 (since 2 is prime). Therefore 2 must divide into p exactly.

$\therefore$ p can be expressed in the form $2k$ for some integer k.

$$\therefore 2q^2 = (2k)^2$$
$$2q^2 = 4k^2$$
$$q^2 = 2k^2$$

Perhaps that's why they called them SURDS.

Now, as for p above, it can be argued from this last step that q must be divisible by 2. But p and q were said to have no common factor, hence a contradiction exists. So our original assumption was wrong.

Therefore p and q cannot be found so that $\sqrt{2} = \dfrac{p}{q}$. Hence $\sqrt{2}$ must be irrational.

• Try to use the method above to prove that these are irrational.

1   $\sqrt{3}$ 2 $\sqrt{5}$ 3 $\sqrt{11}$

challenge

5:06

Challenge 5:06 | f-stops and $\sqrt{2}$

Professional photographers have cameras that can alter shutter time and aperture settings using what are called f-stops.

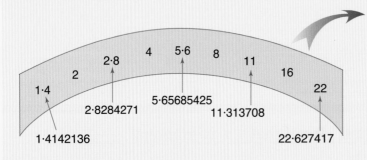

The f-stops 2, 4, 8 and 16 are accurate. More accurate readings for the rest are given below the scale.

• Find the pattern in the accurate f-stops.
  * Try squaring each accurate f-stop number.
  * Try dividing each f-stop number by the one before it.
• Try to discover how f-stops are used.

5:07 | Surds

Find the value of:

1 $\sqrt{16}$ 　　　 2 $\sqrt{9}$ 　　　 3 $\sqrt{36}$ 　　　 4 $\sqrt{16+9}$ 　　　 5 $\sqrt{16} + \sqrt{9}$

6 $\sqrt{16 \times 9}$ 　　 7 $\sqrt{16} \times \sqrt{9}$ 　 8 $\sqrt{\dfrac{36}{9}}$ 　　 9 $\dfrac{\sqrt{36}}{\sqrt{9}}$ 　　 10 $(\sqrt{16})^2$

 Surds are numerical expressions that involve irrational roots. They are irrational numbers.

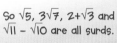 So $\sqrt{5}$, $3\sqrt{7}$, $2+\sqrt{3}$ and $\sqrt{11} - \sqrt{10}$ are all surds.

Surds obey the following rules, which are suggested by Prep Quiz 5:07.

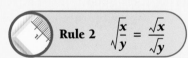 **Rule 1** 　 $\sqrt{xy} = \sqrt{x} \times \sqrt{y}$

worked examples

1 $\sqrt{100} = \sqrt{4} \times \sqrt{25}$
$\quad = 2 \times 5$
$\quad = 10$ (which is true)

2 $\sqrt{27} = \sqrt{9} \times \sqrt{3}$
$\quad = 3 \times \sqrt{3}$
$\quad = 3\sqrt{3}$

3 $\sqrt{5} \times \sqrt{7} = \sqrt{5 \times 7}$
$\quad = \sqrt{35}$

 Rule 2 　 $\sqrt{\dfrac{x}{y}} = \dfrac{\sqrt{x}}{\sqrt{y}}$

■ *Note:* $\sqrt{x}$ means *the positive square root of x when x > 0.*
$\sqrt{x} = 0$ when $x = 0$.

worked examples

1 $\sqrt{\dfrac{16}{4}} = \dfrac{\sqrt{16}}{\sqrt{4}}$
ie $\sqrt{4} = \dfrac{4}{2}$
$\quad = 2$ (which is true)

2 $\sqrt{125} \div \sqrt{5} = \sqrt{125 \div 5}$
$\quad = \sqrt{25}$
$\quad = 5$

3 $\sqrt{30} \div \sqrt{5} = \sqrt{30 \div 5}$
$\quad = \sqrt{6}$

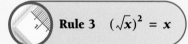 **Rule 3** 　 $(\sqrt{x})^2 = x$

■ *Note:* For $\sqrt{x}$ to exist, x cannot be negative.

worked examples

1 $(\sqrt{25})^2 = (5)^2$
$\quad = 25$

2 $(\sqrt{7})^2 = 7$

3 $(3\sqrt{2})^2 = 3^2 \times (\sqrt{2})^2$
$\quad = 9 \times 2$
$\quad = 18$

A surd is in its simplest form when the number under the square root sign is as small as possible. To simplify a surd we make use of Rule 1 by expressing the square root as the product of two smaller square roots, one being the root of a square number. Examine the examples below.

worked examples

Simplify the following surds.

1. $\sqrt{18} = \sqrt{9} \times \sqrt{2}$
   $= 3 \times \sqrt{2}$
   $= 3\sqrt{2}$

2. $\sqrt{75} = \sqrt{25} \times \sqrt{3}$
   $= 5 \times \sqrt{3}$
   $= 5\sqrt{3}$

3. $5\sqrt{48} = 5 \times \sqrt{16} \times \sqrt{3}$
   $= 5 \times 4 \times \sqrt{3}$
   $= 20\sqrt{3}$

Exercise 5:07

Foundation Worksheet 5:07
Surds
1 Simplify:
  a $\sqrt{6} \times \sqrt{5}$ b $\sqrt{7} \times \sqrt{3}$
2 Simplify:
  a $\sqrt{18}$ b $3\sqrt{8}$

1 Simplify:

a $\sqrt{3} \times \sqrt{5}$ b $\sqrt{5} \times \sqrt{3}$ c $\sqrt{7} \times \sqrt{6}$ d $\sqrt{6} \times \sqrt{7}$

e $\sqrt{10} \times \sqrt{3}$ f $\sqrt{23} \times \sqrt{2}$ g $\sqrt{13} \times \sqrt{5}$ h $\sqrt{11} \times \sqrt{3}$

i $\sqrt{5} \times \sqrt{2}$ j $\sqrt{7} \times \sqrt{2}$ k $\sqrt{11} \times \sqrt{10}$ l $\sqrt{13} \times \sqrt{7}$

m $\sqrt{26} \div \sqrt{2}$ n $\sqrt{55} \div \sqrt{5}$ o $\sqrt{77} \div \sqrt{11}$ p $\sqrt{34} \div \sqrt{17}$

q $\dfrac{\sqrt{38}}{\sqrt{2}}$ r $\dfrac{\sqrt{57}}{\sqrt{3}}$ s $\dfrac{\sqrt{60}}{\sqrt{10}}$ t $\dfrac{\sqrt{22}}{\sqrt{11}}$

2 Square each of the surds below (Rule 3).

a $\sqrt{16}$ b $\sqrt{9}$ c $\sqrt{1}$ d $\sqrt{100}$

e $\sqrt{5}$ f $\sqrt{8}$ g $\sqrt{15}$ h $\sqrt{73}$

i $2\sqrt{2}$ j $3\sqrt{5}$ k $2\sqrt{3}$ l $5\sqrt{3}$

m $7\sqrt{3}$ n $2\sqrt{7}$ o $9\sqrt{11}$ p $6\sqrt{5}$

q $10\sqrt{10}$ r $9\sqrt{20}$ s $6\sqrt{50}$ t $15\sqrt{15}$

3 Simplify each of these surds.

a $\sqrt{8}$ b $\sqrt{20}$ c $\sqrt{12}$ d $\sqrt{50}$

e $\sqrt{24}$ f $\sqrt{32}$ g $\sqrt{45}$ h $\sqrt{54}$

i $\sqrt{28}$ j $\sqrt{90}$ k $\sqrt{56}$ l $\sqrt{63}$

m $\sqrt{44}$ n $\sqrt{52}$ o $\sqrt{108}$ p $\sqrt{40}$

q $\sqrt{99}$ r $\sqrt{60}$ s $\sqrt{96}$ t $\sqrt{76}$

u $\sqrt{68}$ v $\sqrt{126}$ w $\sqrt{200}$ x $\sqrt{162}$

4 Simplify each surd and then, taking $\sqrt{2} = 1.41$ and $\sqrt{3} = 1.73$, give a decimal approximation correct to 1 decimal place.

a $\sqrt{18}$ b $\sqrt{27}$ c $\sqrt{8}$ d $\sqrt{12}$

e $\sqrt{32}$ f $\sqrt{48}$ g $\sqrt{50}$ h $\sqrt{162}$

5 Write each surd below in its simplest form.

a $2\sqrt{12}$ b $3\sqrt{8}$ c $2\sqrt{50}$ d $4\sqrt{18}$

e $5\sqrt{20}$ f $2\sqrt{75}$ g $10\sqrt{27}$ h $3\sqrt{56}$

i $2\sqrt{125}$ j $4\sqrt{45}$ k $3\sqrt{24}$ l $2\sqrt{54}$

m $7\sqrt{56}$ n $3\sqrt{72}$ o $3\sqrt{44}$ p $5\sqrt{90}$

q $6\sqrt{200}$ r $5\sqrt{98}$ s $9\sqrt{108}$ t $5\sqrt{68}$

6 Simplified surds can be written as an entire root by reversing the above process. For example, $4\sqrt{3} = \sqrt{16} \times \sqrt{3} = \sqrt{48}$. Express the following as entire square roots.

a $2\sqrt{3}$ b $3\sqrt{2}$ c $2\sqrt{5}$ d $3\sqrt{6}$

e $4\sqrt{2}$ f $5\sqrt{3}$ g $3\sqrt{7}$ h $5\sqrt{2}$

i $6\sqrt{2}$ j $5\sqrt{6}$ k $3\sqrt{10}$ l $4\sqrt{7}$

m $6\sqrt{7}$ n $5\sqrt{10}$ o $7\sqrt{2}$ p $10\sqrt{2}$

q $9\sqrt{3}$ r $8\sqrt{4}$ s $7\sqrt{9}$ t $12\sqrt{3}$

5:08 | Addition and Subtraction of Surds

Simplify: **1** $\sqrt{12}$ **2** $\sqrt{20}$ **3** $\sqrt{32}$ **4** $\sqrt{50}$

Evaluate: **5** $\sqrt{4} + \sqrt{9}$ **6** $\sqrt{4+9}$ (to 1 decimal place)

         7 $\sqrt{16} - \sqrt{4}$ **8** $\sqrt{16-4}$ (to 1 decimal place)

         9 $\sqrt{25} + \sqrt{36}$ **10** $\sqrt{25+36}$ (to 1 decimal place)

As can be seen from the Prep Quiz, if x and y are two positive numbers,

$\sqrt{x} + \sqrt{y}$ **does not equal** $\sqrt{x+y}$ and

$\sqrt{x} - \sqrt{y}$ **does not equal** $\sqrt{x-y}$

For example:

> $\sqrt{5} + \sqrt{8}$ does not equal $\sqrt{13}$.
>
> $\sqrt{10} - \sqrt{7}$ does not equal $\sqrt{3}$.

Surds are irrational.

Only 'like' surds can be added or subtracted. For example:

$$2\sqrt{3} + 4\sqrt{3} = 6\sqrt{3} \quad \text{and} \quad 5\sqrt{2} - 4\sqrt{2} = \sqrt{2}$$

However, we can only tell whether surds are like or unlike if each is expressed in its simplest form.

Examine the following examples.

I think I'm beginning to like this.

When adding or subtracting surds
- **write each surd in its simplest form**
- **add or subtract *like* surds only.**

■ Remember how in algebra only *like* terms could be added or subtracted.

eg $5x + 3x = 8x$
$7a - 6a = a$

worked examples

Simplify each of the following.

1 $4\sqrt{3} + 7\sqrt{3} - 2\sqrt{3}$
$= 9\sqrt{3}$

2 $8\sqrt{2} + \sqrt{5} - \sqrt{2} + 2\sqrt{5}$
$= 7\sqrt{2} + 3\sqrt{5}$

3 $\sqrt{8} + \sqrt{18}$
$= 2\sqrt{2} + 3\sqrt{2}$
$= 5\sqrt{2}$

4 $\sqrt{75} + \sqrt{27} - 2\sqrt{3}$
$= 5\sqrt{3} + 3\sqrt{3} - 2\sqrt{3}$
$= 6\sqrt{3}$

5 $2\sqrt{12} + 3\sqrt{48}$
$= 2(2\sqrt{3}) + 3(4\sqrt{3})$
$= 4\sqrt{3} + 12\sqrt{3}$
$= 16\sqrt{3}$

6 $2\sqrt{75} - \sqrt{45} + 2\sqrt{20}$
$= 2(5\sqrt{3}) - 3\sqrt{5} + 2(2\sqrt{5})$
$= 10\sqrt{3} - 3\sqrt{5} + 4\sqrt{5}$
$= 10\sqrt{3} + \sqrt{5}$

Exercise 5:08

Foundation Worksheet 5:08

Addition and subtraction of surds

1 Simplify.
  a $3\sqrt{5} + \sqrt{5}$ **b** $2\sqrt{7} - \sqrt{7}$

2 Collect like surds.
  a $5\sqrt{3} + \sqrt{2} + \sqrt{3}$
  b $6\sqrt{5} - 4\sqrt{3} + 7\sqrt{3}$

1 Simplify:

a $3\sqrt{2} + 2\sqrt{2}$ **b** $4\sqrt{3} + 7\sqrt{3}$ **c** $5\sqrt{6} + 2\sqrt{6}$

d $10\sqrt{3} - 7\sqrt{3}$ **e** $9\sqrt{5} - 6\sqrt{5}$ **f** $4\sqrt{2} - 3\sqrt{2}$

g $\sqrt{7} + 4\sqrt{7}$ **h** $5\sqrt{3} + \sqrt{3}$ **i** $9\sqrt{6} - \sqrt{6}$

j $9\sqrt{5} + 2\sqrt{5} + 3\sqrt{5}$ **k** $4\sqrt{10} + 7\sqrt{10} - 2\sqrt{10}$ **l** $4\sqrt{3} - 3\sqrt{3} + 5\sqrt{3}$

m $10\sqrt{2} - 2\sqrt{2} - 5\sqrt{2}$ **n** $\sqrt{3} + 7\sqrt{3} - 5\sqrt{3}$ **o** $2\sqrt{7} + 3\sqrt{7} - 5\sqrt{7}$

2 Simplify by collecting like surds.

a $2\sqrt{5} + 3\sqrt{7} + 4\sqrt{5}$ **b** $\sqrt{7} + 3\sqrt{7} + 2\sqrt{5}$ **c** $2\sqrt{3} + 3\sqrt{5} + 2\sqrt{3} + 5\sqrt{5}$

d $9\sqrt{3} + 2\sqrt{2} - 7\sqrt{3} + 3\sqrt{2}$ **e** $6\sqrt{10} + 5\sqrt{7} - 5\sqrt{10} - \sqrt{7}$ **f** $3\sqrt{3} + 6\sqrt{5} - \sqrt{3} - 4\sqrt{5}$

g $6\sqrt{11} - 2\sqrt{7} + 2\sqrt{11} + 5\sqrt{7}$ **h** $9\sqrt{2} + 3\sqrt{3} + 9\sqrt{3} - 8\sqrt{2}$ **i** $5\sqrt{2} + 4\sqrt{5} - 3\sqrt{5} - 6\sqrt{2}$

j $10\sqrt{7} - 2\sqrt{5} - 8\sqrt{7} - 3\sqrt{5}$

3 Simplify completely:

a $\sqrt{8} + \sqrt{2}$ b $\sqrt{12} + 2\sqrt{3}$ c $2\sqrt{2} + \sqrt{18}$ d $2\sqrt{5} + \sqrt{20}$

e $\sqrt{27} + 2\sqrt{3}$ f $3\sqrt{6} + \sqrt{24}$ g $2\sqrt{8} - \sqrt{2}$ h $3\sqrt{5} - \sqrt{20}$

i $\sqrt{32} - 3\sqrt{2}$ j $\sqrt{18} + \sqrt{32}$ k $\sqrt{20} + \sqrt{45}$ l $2\sqrt{27} - \sqrt{48}$

m $\sqrt{75} - 2\sqrt{12}$ n $\sqrt{98} + 3\sqrt{50}$ o $3\sqrt{50} + 2\sqrt{32}$ p $5\sqrt{28} + 2\sqrt{63}$

q $4\sqrt{45} - 2\sqrt{20}$ r $2\sqrt{75} - 3\sqrt{48}$

4 Simplify:

a $2\sqrt{8} - \sqrt{18} + 3\sqrt{2}$ b $2\sqrt{5} + \sqrt{45} - \sqrt{20}$ c $\sqrt{27} + 2\sqrt{48} - 5\sqrt{3}$

d $5\sqrt{7} - \sqrt{63} + 2\sqrt{28}$ e $5\sqrt{3} + \sqrt{50} - \sqrt{12}$ f $2\sqrt{45} + \sqrt{20} + \sqrt{32}$

g $9\sqrt{8} + 3\sqrt{12} - \sqrt{27}$ h $5\sqrt{18} + \sqrt{72} - \sqrt{75}$

5:09 | Multiplication and Division of Surds

worked examples

Simplify the following.

1 $\sqrt{7} \times \sqrt{3}$

2 $3\sqrt{2} \times 5\sqrt{2}$

3 $5\sqrt{8} \times 3\sqrt{6}$

4 $\sqrt{96} \div \sqrt{12}$

5 $\dfrac{4\sqrt{3} \times \sqrt{18}}{\sqrt{12}}$

6 $\sqrt{3}(2\sqrt{3} - \sqrt{5})$

Using the surd rules, these are easy!

■ 1 $\sqrt{x} \times \sqrt{y} = \sqrt{xy}$
  2 $\sqrt{x} \div \sqrt{y} = \sqrt{x \div y}$

Solutions

1 $\sqrt{7} \times \sqrt{3} = \sqrt{7 \times 3}$
$= \sqrt{21}$

2 $3\sqrt{2} \times 5\sqrt{2} = 3 \times 5 \times \sqrt{2} \times \sqrt{2}, \quad (\sqrt{2} \times \sqrt{2} = 2)$
$= 15 \times 2$
$= 30$

3 $5\sqrt{8} \times 3\sqrt{6}$
$= 5 \times 3 \times \sqrt{8} \times \sqrt{6}$
$= 15 \times \sqrt{48}$
$= 15 \times 4\sqrt{3}$
$= 60\sqrt{3}$

4 $\sqrt{96} \div \sqrt{12} = \sqrt{96 \div 12}$
$= \sqrt{8}$
$= 2\sqrt{2}$

5 $\dfrac{4\sqrt{3} \times \sqrt{18}}{\sqrt{12}} = \dfrac{4\sqrt{3} \times 3\sqrt{2}}{2\sqrt{3}}$
$= \dfrac{4 \times 3 \times \sqrt{3} \times \sqrt{2}}{2\sqrt{3}}$
$= \dfrac{12\sqrt{6}}{2\sqrt{3}}$
$= 6\sqrt{\dfrac{6}{3}}$
$= 6\sqrt{2}$

6 $\sqrt{3}(2\sqrt{3} - \sqrt{5}) = \sqrt{3} \times 2\sqrt{3} - \sqrt{3} \times \sqrt{5}$
$= 2 \times 3 - \sqrt{3 \times 5}$
$= 6 - \sqrt{15}$

■ At this point we could cancel like this:

$\dfrac{^2\cancel{4} \times 3 \times {}^1\cancel{\sqrt{3}} \times \sqrt{2}}{{}^1\cancel{2}\cancel{\sqrt{3}}_1} = 6\sqrt{2}$

Exercise 5:09

Foundation Worksheet 5:09
Multiplication and division
of surds
1 Simplify:
  a $\sqrt{7} \times \sqrt{5}$ b $2\sqrt{3} \times 3\sqrt{2}$
2 Simplify:
  a $\sqrt{20} \div \sqrt{5}$ b $\sqrt{30} \div \sqrt{6}$

1 Simplify these products:

a $\sqrt{2} \times \sqrt{3}$ 　　 b $\sqrt{5} \times \sqrt{7}$ 　　 c $\sqrt{3} \times \sqrt{11}$

d $\sqrt{5} \times \sqrt{2}$ 　　 e $\sqrt{3} \times \sqrt{7}$ 　　 f $\sqrt{10} \times \sqrt{7}$

g $\sqrt{2} \times \sqrt{8}$ 　　 h $\sqrt{3} \times \sqrt{12}$ 　　 i $\sqrt{5} \times \sqrt{20}$

j $\sqrt{3} \times \sqrt{6}$ 　　 k $\sqrt{5} \times \sqrt{10}$ 　　 l $\sqrt{2} \times \sqrt{10}$

m $2\sqrt{3} \times \sqrt{5}$ 　　 n $3\sqrt{2} \times 4\sqrt{5}$ 　　 o $7\sqrt{2} \times 2\sqrt{3}$

p $5\sqrt{2} \times 2\sqrt{2}$ 　　 q $3\sqrt{3} \times 2\sqrt{3}$ 　　 r $4\sqrt{5} \times \sqrt{5}$

s $4\sqrt{2} \times 3\sqrt{10}$ 　　 t $2\sqrt{6} \times \sqrt{8}$ 　　 u $4\sqrt{3} \times 2\sqrt{15}$

v $2\sqrt{x} \times 3\sqrt{x}$ 　　 w $\sqrt{8x} \times \sqrt{2}$ 　　 x $a\sqrt{x} \times a\sqrt{x}$

2 Simplify:

a $\sqrt{10} \div \sqrt{2}$ 　　　　 b $\sqrt{12} \div \sqrt{4}$ 　　　　 c $\sqrt{6} \div \sqrt{3}$

d $\sqrt{27} \div \sqrt{3}$ 　　　　 e $\sqrt{32} \div \sqrt{8}$ 　　　　 f $\sqrt{45} \div \sqrt{5}$

g $5\sqrt{2} \div \sqrt{2}$ 　　　　 h $6\sqrt{5} \div \sqrt{5}$ 　　　　 i $10\sqrt{3} \div 5\sqrt{3}$

j $16\sqrt{8} \div 8$ 　　　　 k $30\sqrt{5} \div 10$ 　　　　 l $24\sqrt{7} \div 24$

m $12\sqrt{10} \div 2\sqrt{5}$ 　　　　 n $9\sqrt{12} \div 3\sqrt{6}$ 　　　　 o $10\sqrt{15} \div 5\sqrt{5}$

p $\sqrt{20} \div 2$ 　　　　 q $\sqrt{75} \div 5$ 　　　　 r $5\sqrt{8} \div 10$

s $\sqrt{2x} \div \sqrt{2}$ 　　　　 t $\sqrt{5a} \div \sqrt{a}$ 　　　　 u $\sqrt{20p} \div 2\sqrt{p}$

3 Simplify fully:

a $\dfrac{2\sqrt{3} \times 2\sqrt{6}}{4}$ 　　　　 b $\dfrac{4\sqrt{5} \times 2\sqrt{6}}{\sqrt{10}}$ 　　　　 c $\dfrac{2\sqrt{5} \times 3\sqrt{8}}{6\sqrt{20}}$

d $\dfrac{\sqrt{15} \times \sqrt{3}}{3\sqrt{5}}$ 　　　　 e $\dfrac{2\sqrt{3} \times \sqrt{6}}{\sqrt{12}}$ 　　　　 f $\dfrac{3\sqrt{7} \times 2\sqrt{6}}{\sqrt{21}}$

g $\dfrac{2\sqrt{6} \times 5\sqrt{5}}{10\sqrt{15}}$ 　　　　 h $\dfrac{6\sqrt{2} \times \sqrt{6}}{4\sqrt{3}}$ 　　　　 i $\dfrac{\sqrt{12} \times \sqrt{27}}{\sqrt{8} \times 2\sqrt{6}}$

4 Expand and simplify:

a $\sqrt{2}(\sqrt{3} + \sqrt{2})$ 　　　 b $\sqrt{5}(\sqrt{5} + \sqrt{2})$ 　　　 c $\sqrt{7}(2\sqrt{7} - \sqrt{2})$

d $\sqrt{3}(5 - \sqrt{3})$ 　　　 e $\sqrt{2}(2\sqrt{3} - 1)$ 　　　 f $\sqrt{10}(5\sqrt{2} - 4)$

g $2\sqrt{2}(\sqrt{2} + 1)$ 　　　 h $3\sqrt{5}(\sqrt{5} + 2)$ 　　　 i $4\sqrt{3}(\sqrt{2} - \sqrt{3})$

j $3\sqrt{6}(\sqrt{5} + \sqrt{6})$ 　　　 k $2\sqrt{7}(\sqrt{7} - \sqrt{2})$ 　　　 l $\sqrt{3}(7 - 3\sqrt{3})$

m $2\sqrt{2}(\sqrt{3} + 2\sqrt{2})$ 　　　 n $4\sqrt{5}(\sqrt{2} - 2\sqrt{5})$ 　　　 o $5\sqrt{6}(2\sqrt{6} - 3\sqrt{2})$

p $\sqrt{a}(\sqrt{a} + 1)$ 　　　 q $\sqrt{x}(2\sqrt{x} + 3)$ 　　　 r $2\sqrt{y}(3\sqrt{y} + 2\sqrt{x})$

5:09 Golden ratio investigations

Investigation 5:09 | Iteration to find square roots

5:09

Iteration is the repetition of a process.
We can use a simple process to find
square roots.

To iterate, repeat the process over and over again.

Example

Find $\sqrt{3}$ correct to 4 decimal places without
using a calculator.

Step 1
Estimate $\sqrt{3}$.

> Let $E = 1 \cdot 6$

(We want E^2 to be close to 3.)

To iterate, repeat the process over and over again.

Step 2
Divide 3 by your estimate.

> $3 \div 1 \cdot 6 = 1 \cdot 875$

Since $1 \cdot 6 \times 1 \cdot 875 = 3$, the correct answer
must lie between $1 \cdot 6$ and $1 \cdot 875$.

Step 3
Average these two numbers to get a better
estimate.

$$\frac{1 \cdot 6 + 1 \cdot 875}{2} = 1 \cdot 7375$$

$$\therefore \sqrt{3} \doteqdot 1 \cdot 7375$$

Can you find other uses for iteration?

- Use $1 \cdot 7375$ as the new estimate and
  repeat the steps above (iterate).

> $E = 1 \cdot 7375$
> $3 \div 1 \cdot 7375 \doteqdot 1 \cdot 72662$

$$\frac{1 \cdot 7375 + 1 \cdot 72662}{2} = 1 \cdot 73206$$

$$\therefore \sqrt{3} \doteqdot 1 \cdot 73206$$

- If we use $1 \cdot 73206$ as our next estimate we get a better approximation (ie $\sqrt{3} \doteqdot 1 \cdot 732051$).
  Since $\sqrt{3}$ lies between $1 \cdot 73206$ and $1 \cdot 732051$ then $\sqrt{3} = 1 \cdot 7321$ correct to 4 decimal places.

1 Use iteration to find, correct to 4 decimal places:

   a $\sqrt{2}$ **b** $\sqrt{5}$ **c** $\sqrt{70}$ **d** $\sqrt{110}$

2 Investigate finding the square root of a number n, using iteration of the formula:

$$\text{New estimate} = \frac{x^2 + n}{2x}$$

where x is your last estimate and we wish to find $\sqrt{n}$.

5:10 | Binomial Products

5:10

prep quiz

Simplify the following:

1 $\sqrt{3} \times \sqrt{5}$ **2** $\sqrt{18} \times \sqrt{2}$ **3** $(\sqrt{5})^2$ **4** $(3\sqrt{2})^2$ **5** $3\sqrt{2} + 7\sqrt{2}$

6 $9\sqrt{3} - \sqrt{3}$ **7** $3\sqrt{3} - 3\sqrt{3}$

Expand and simplify where possible:

8 $5(\sqrt{7} - 4)$ **9** $\sqrt{10}(\sqrt{10} + \sqrt{3})$ **10** $2\sqrt{3}(3\sqrt{2} - \sqrt{3})$

see

4:06

I remember!

In Chapter 4, you saw how to expand a binomial product.

$(a + b)(c + d) = a(c + d) + b(c + d)$
$= ac + ad + bc + bd$

The same procedure is used if some of the terms are not pronumerals, but surds. Examine the following examples.

worked examples

Expand and simplify:

1 a $(\sqrt{2} + 3)(\sqrt{2} - 5)$ **b** $(3\sqrt{2} - \sqrt{5})(2\sqrt{2} + 3\sqrt{5})$

2 a $(2\sqrt{3} + 5)^2$ **b** $(\sqrt{7} - \sqrt{3})^2$

3 a $(\sqrt{5} - \sqrt{2})(\sqrt{5} + \sqrt{2})$ **b** $(5\sqrt{2} - \sqrt{7})(5\sqrt{2} + \sqrt{7})$

Solutions

1 a $(\sqrt{2} + 3)(\sqrt{2} - 5)$
$= \sqrt{2}(\sqrt{2} - 5) + 3(\sqrt{2} - 5)$
$= (\sqrt{2})^2 - 5\sqrt{2} + 3\sqrt{2} - 15$
$= 2 - 2\sqrt{2} - 15$
$= -13 - 2\sqrt{2}$

b $(3\sqrt{2} - \sqrt{5})(2\sqrt{2} + 3\sqrt{5})$
$= 3\sqrt{2}(2\sqrt{2} + 3\sqrt{5}) - \sqrt{5}(2\sqrt{2} + 3\sqrt{5})$
$= 12 + 9\sqrt{10} - 2\sqrt{10} - 15$
$= 7\sqrt{10} - 3$

These are 'perfect squares'.

see

4:07A

2 a $(2\sqrt{3} + 5)^2$
$= (2\sqrt{3})^2 + 2 \times 2\sqrt{3} \times 5 + (5)^2$
$= 12 + 20\sqrt{3} + 25$
$= 37 + 20\sqrt{3}$

b $(\sqrt{7} - \sqrt{3})^2$
$= (\sqrt{7})^2 - 2 \times \sqrt{7} \times \sqrt{3} + (\sqrt{3})^2$
$= 7 - 2\sqrt{21} + 3$
$= 10 - 2\sqrt{21}$

> **Remember!**
> $(a + b)^2 = a^2 + 2ab + b^2$
> $(a - b)^2 = a^2 - 2ab + b^2$

see

4:07B

These give 'the difference of two squares'.

3 a $(\sqrt{5} - \sqrt{2})(\sqrt{5} + \sqrt{2}) = (\sqrt{5})^2 - (\sqrt{2})^2$
$= 5 - 2$
$= 3$

b $(5\sqrt{2} - \sqrt{7})(5\sqrt{2} + \sqrt{7}) = (5\sqrt{2})^2 - (\sqrt{7})^2$
$= 50 - 7$
$= 43$

> **Remember!**
> $(a + b)(a - b) = a^2 - b^2$

Exercise 5:10

Expand and simplify the following:

1 a $(\sqrt{2} + 3)(\sqrt{2} + 1)$

    b $(\sqrt{3} + 5)(\sqrt{3} - 1)$

    c $(\sqrt{7} - 2)(\sqrt{7} - 5)$

    d $(\sqrt{2} + \sqrt{3})(\sqrt{2} + \sqrt{5})$

    e $(\sqrt{7} - \sqrt{2})(\sqrt{5} - \sqrt{2})$

    f $(\sqrt{10} + \sqrt{2})(\sqrt{5} + \sqrt{3})$

    g $(5 + \sqrt{2})(\sqrt{3} + \sqrt{2})$

    h $(2 - \sqrt{3})(2 - \sqrt{5})$

    i $(\sqrt{6} - \sqrt{2})(5 - \sqrt{6})$

    j $(\sqrt{2} + \sqrt{3})(2\sqrt{2} + 1)$

    k $(\sqrt{3} + 2\sqrt{5})(\sqrt{3} + \sqrt{5})$

    l $(2\sqrt{3} + \sqrt{2})(\sqrt{3} + 2\sqrt{2})$

    m $(5\sqrt{2} - \sqrt{7})(\sqrt{7} - 2\sqrt{2})$

    n $(2\sqrt{5} - \sqrt{3})(5\sqrt{3} + \sqrt{5})$

    o $(\sqrt{7} - 5\sqrt{2})(\sqrt{2} - 5\sqrt{7})$

    p $(5\sqrt{3} + 2\sqrt{7})(2\sqrt{3} - 5\sqrt{7})$

    q $(10\sqrt{10} + \sqrt{7})(2\sqrt{7} + \sqrt{10})$

    r $(5\sqrt{3} + 7\sqrt{2})(7\sqrt{3} - 2\sqrt{2})$

    s $(9\sqrt{2} - \sqrt{3})(4\sqrt{2} + 2\sqrt{3})$

    t $(5\sqrt{7} + 4)(2\sqrt{7} - 7)$

    u $(6\sqrt{3} + 5)(7 - 2\sqrt{3})$

    v $(\sqrt{x} + 3)(\sqrt{x} + 2)$

    w $(\sqrt{m} + \sqrt{n})(2\sqrt{m} + \sqrt{n})$

    x $(3\sqrt{a} - 2\sqrt{b})(2\sqrt{a} + 3\sqrt{b})$

2 a $(\sqrt{2} + 1)^2$
  b $(\sqrt{3} - 5)^2$
  c $(\sqrt{5} + 2)^2$

    d $(\sqrt{3} + \sqrt{2})^2$
  e $(\sqrt{5} - \sqrt{2})^2$
  f $(\sqrt{3} + \sqrt{10})^2$

    g $(2\sqrt{3} + 1)^2$
  h $(3\sqrt{2} - 4)^2$
  i $(5 + 2\sqrt{5})^2$

    j $(2\sqrt{2} + \sqrt{7})^2$
  k $(3\sqrt{5} + \sqrt{10})^2$
  l $(\sqrt{7} - 3\sqrt{5})^2$

    m $(5\sqrt{3} + 2\sqrt{2})^2$
  n $(7\sqrt{3} - 2\sqrt{5})^2$
  o $(5\sqrt{10} - 10\sqrt{3})^2$

    p $(\sqrt{x} + \sqrt{y})^2$
  q $(2\sqrt{m} + 5)^2$
  r $(3\sqrt{p} - 2\sqrt{q})^2$

3 a $(\sqrt{2} + 1)(\sqrt{2} - 1)$

    b $(5 + \sqrt{3})(5 - \sqrt{3})$

    c $(\sqrt{10} - 7)(\sqrt{10} + 7)$

    d $(4 - \sqrt{2})(4 + \sqrt{2})$

    e $(\sqrt{2} + \sqrt{3})(\sqrt{2} - \sqrt{3})$

    f $(\sqrt{7} - \sqrt{5})(\sqrt{7} + \sqrt{5})$

    g $(\sqrt{10} - \sqrt{8})(\sqrt{10} + \sqrt{8})$

    h $(\sqrt{11} + \sqrt{7})(\sqrt{11} - \sqrt{7})$

    i $(2\sqrt{3} - 5)(2\sqrt{3} + 5)$

    j $(6 - 3\sqrt{2})(6 + 3\sqrt{2})$

    k $(\sqrt{7} + 2\sqrt{3})(\sqrt{7} - 2\sqrt{3})$

    l $(3\sqrt{5} - \sqrt{3})(3\sqrt{5} + \sqrt{3})$

    m $(5\sqrt{2} - 2\sqrt{3})(5\sqrt{2} + 2\sqrt{3})$

    n $(2\sqrt{3} + 3\sqrt{2})(2\sqrt{3} - 3\sqrt{2})$

    o $(\sqrt{x} + \sqrt{y})(\sqrt{x} - \sqrt{y})$

    p $(2\sqrt{a} + 3\sqrt{b})(2\sqrt{a} - 3\sqrt{b})$

> ▦ *Important notice!*
> The two binomials in each part of question 3 are said to be *conjugate surds*.
> Note that when a binomial surd is multiplied by its 'conjugate', the answer is always a rational number.

5:11 | Rationalising the Denominator

prep quiz

5:11

Simplify the following:

1 $\sqrt{5} \times \sqrt{5}$ **2** $\sqrt{10} \times \sqrt{10}$ **3** $2\sqrt{3} \times \sqrt{3}$ **4** $5\sqrt{2} \times \sqrt{2}$ **5** $2\sqrt{6} \times \sqrt{6}$

6 $(\sqrt{2}+1)(\sqrt{2}-1)$ **7** $(\sqrt{3}-\sqrt{2})(\sqrt{3}+\sqrt{2})$ **8** $(5-\sqrt{2})(5+\sqrt{2})$

9 $(2\sqrt{3}-\sqrt{2})(2\sqrt{3}+\sqrt{2})$ **10** $(5\sqrt{2}-3\sqrt{3})(5\sqrt{2}+3\sqrt{3})$

If a fraction has a surd (ie an irrational number) in its denominator, we generally rewrite the fraction with a 'rational' denominator by using the method shown below.

worked examples

Rewrite with rational denominators:

1 $\dfrac{3}{\sqrt{3}}$ **2** $\dfrac{1}{5\sqrt{2}}$ **3** $\dfrac{\sqrt{5}}{\sqrt{12}}$ **4** $\dfrac{2+\sqrt{3}}{2\sqrt{3}}$

> For these fractions, we multiply top and bottom by the square root in the denominator.

Solutions

1 $\dfrac{3}{\sqrt{3}} = \dfrac{3}{\sqrt{3}} \times \dfrac{\sqrt{3}}{\sqrt{3}}$

$= \dfrac{3\sqrt{3}}{3}$

$= \sqrt{3}$

2 $\dfrac{1}{5\sqrt{2}} = \dfrac{1}{5\sqrt{2}} \times \dfrac{\sqrt{2}}{\sqrt{2}}$

$= \dfrac{\sqrt{2}}{5 \times 2}$

$= \dfrac{\sqrt{2}}{10}$

3 $\dfrac{\sqrt{5}}{\sqrt{12}} = \dfrac{\sqrt{5}}{2\sqrt{3}} \times \dfrac{\sqrt{3}}{\sqrt{3}}$

$= \dfrac{\sqrt{15}}{2 \times 3}$

$= \dfrac{\sqrt{15}}{6}$

> ■ *Note:*
> Multiplying by $\dfrac{\sqrt{3}}{\sqrt{3}}$ is the same as multiplying by 1.

4 $\dfrac{2+\sqrt{3}}{2\sqrt{3}} = \dfrac{2+\sqrt{3}}{2\sqrt{3}} \times \dfrac{\sqrt{3}}{\sqrt{3}}$

$= \dfrac{\sqrt{3}(2+\sqrt{3})}{2 \times 3}$

$= \dfrac{2\sqrt{3}+3}{6}$

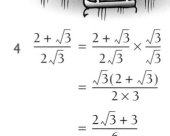

Exercise 5:11

1 Rationalise the denominator for each of the following:

a $\dfrac{1}{\sqrt{2}}$ **b** $\dfrac{1}{\sqrt{5}}$ **c** $\dfrac{2}{\sqrt{3}}$ **d** $\dfrac{5}{\sqrt{10}}$ **e** $\dfrac{3}{\sqrt{2}}$ **f** $\dfrac{6}{\sqrt{3}}$

g $\dfrac{10}{\sqrt{5}}$ **h** $\dfrac{2}{\sqrt{11}}$ **i** $\dfrac{\sqrt{2}}{\sqrt{3}}$ **j** $\dfrac{\sqrt{3}}{\sqrt{5}}$ **k** $\dfrac{\sqrt{5}}{\sqrt{10}}$ **l** $\dfrac{\sqrt{3}}{\sqrt{15}}$

m $\dfrac{1}{2\sqrt{2}}$ **n** $\dfrac{2}{5\sqrt{3}}$ **o** $\dfrac{7}{2\sqrt{5}}$ **p** $\dfrac{10}{2\sqrt{3}}$ **q** $\dfrac{\sqrt{6}}{2\sqrt{3}}$ **r** $\dfrac{\sqrt{5}}{5\sqrt{2}}$

s $\dfrac{2\sqrt{3}}{3\sqrt{2}}$ **t** $\dfrac{5\sqrt{7}}{3\sqrt{5}}$ **u** $\dfrac{2+\sqrt{3}}{\sqrt{3}}$ **v** $\dfrac{1+\sqrt{5}}{\sqrt{2}}$ **w** $\dfrac{\sqrt{7}+\sqrt{3}}{2\sqrt{7}}$ **x** $\dfrac{\sqrt{10}-\sqrt{5}}{5\sqrt{10}}$

2 Evaluate each fraction correct to 3 significant figures (using your calculator). Then rationalise the denominator and evaluate the fraction again. Compare this answer with your first calculation.

a $\dfrac{2}{\sqrt{5}}$ b $\dfrac{3}{\sqrt{7}}$ c $\dfrac{\sqrt{3}}{2\sqrt{2}}$ d $\dfrac{\sqrt{7}}{3\sqrt{5}}$

3 Rationalise each denominator, then express as a single fraction.

a $\dfrac{1}{\sqrt{2}} + \dfrac{1}{\sqrt{3}}$ b $\dfrac{1}{\sqrt{5}} - \dfrac{1}{\sqrt{2}}$ c $\dfrac{1}{\sqrt{6}} + \dfrac{1}{\sqrt{5}}$ d $\dfrac{2}{\sqrt{10}} - \dfrac{3}{\sqrt{5}}$ e $\dfrac{3}{\sqrt{8}} + \dfrac{5}{\sqrt{2}}$

f $\dfrac{2}{2\sqrt{3}} - \dfrac{1}{3\sqrt{2}}$ g $\dfrac{2}{5\sqrt{2}} + \dfrac{5}{\sqrt{10}}$ h $\dfrac{\sqrt{5}}{\sqrt{2}} + \dfrac{\sqrt{5}}{\sqrt{3}}$ i $\dfrac{\sqrt{2}}{\sqrt{5}} - \dfrac{\sqrt{3}}{\sqrt{2}}$

fun spot

5:11

Fun Spot 5:11 | What do Eskimos sing at birthday parties?

Answer each question and put the letter for that question in the box above the correct answer.

A $\dfrac{x}{2} = 5$ E $\dfrac{x}{5} = 3$ E $\dfrac{x}{10} = 1.86$

L $\dfrac{x}{7} = 0.185$ E $\dfrac{x}{5} = 0.5$ O $0.560 = \dfrac{x}{5}$

Simplify:

L $5x - x$ O $5x \div x$ Y $5x \times x$

E $2x \times 3y$ L $x^3 \times x^5$ O $x^6 \div x^2$

F $(2x^5)^3$ G $5x^0 \times 4$ D 35×10^{-2}

E $\sqrt{169}$ F $\sqrt{7} \times \sqrt{7}$ G $(3\sqrt{3})^2$ H $\sqrt{2} + \sqrt{2}$

I $\sqrt{50}$ J $\sqrt{3} \times \sqrt{6}$ L $3\sqrt{7} - \sqrt{7}$ N $\sqrt{50} + \sqrt{18}$

O $5\sqrt{2} \times 3\sqrt{2}$ R $\sqrt{32} \div \sqrt{2}$ S $\sqrt{6} \div \sqrt{2}$ T $\sqrt{3} + 2\sqrt{3}$

Solve:

W $5x + 3 = 21$ Y $\dfrac{14}{x} = 1$ Z $2x - 5 = 7 - 6x$

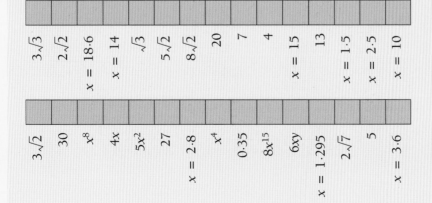

Row 1: $3\sqrt{3}$ | $2\sqrt{2}$ | $x = 18.6$ | $x = 14$ | $\sqrt{3}$ | $5\sqrt{2}$ | $8\sqrt{2}$ | 20 | 7 | 4 | $x = 15$ | 13 | $x = 1.5$ | $x = 2.5$ | $x = 10$

Row 2: $3\sqrt{2}$ | 30 | x^8 | $4x$ | $5x^2$ | 27 | $x = 2.8$ | x^4 | 0.35 | $8x^{15}$ | $6xy$ | $x = 1.295$ | $2\sqrt{7}$ | 5 | $x = 3.6$

Challenge 5:11 | Rationalising binomial denominators

Examples

Rationalise the denominators for each expression.

> For these fractions, we multiply top and bottom by the conjugate of the denominator.

1 $\dfrac{5}{5-\sqrt{2}}$

2 $\dfrac{1}{\sqrt{3}+\sqrt{2}}$

3 $\dfrac{2\sqrt{3}+\sqrt{5}}{2\sqrt{3}-\sqrt{5}}$

Solutions

1
$$\frac{5}{5-\sqrt{2}} = \frac{5}{5-\sqrt{2}} \times \frac{5+\sqrt{2}}{5+\sqrt{2}}$$
$$= \frac{5(5+\sqrt{2})}{25-2}$$
$$= \frac{25+5\sqrt{2}}{23}$$

2
$$\frac{1}{\sqrt{3}+\sqrt{2}} = \frac{1}{\sqrt{3}+\sqrt{2}} \times \frac{\sqrt{3}-\sqrt{2}}{\sqrt{3}-\sqrt{2}}$$
$$= \frac{\sqrt{3}-\sqrt{2}}{3-2}$$
$$= \sqrt{3}-\sqrt{2}$$

3
$$\frac{2\sqrt{3}+\sqrt{5}}{2\sqrt{3}-\sqrt{5}} = \frac{2\sqrt{3}+\sqrt{5}}{2\sqrt{3}-\sqrt{5}} \times \frac{2\sqrt{3}+\sqrt{5}}{2\sqrt{3}+\sqrt{5}}$$
$$= \frac{(2\sqrt{3}+\sqrt{5})^2}{12-5}$$
$$= \frac{17+4\sqrt{15}}{7}$$

> ■ Note:
> The product of a binomial surd and its conjugate is always rational.

Now try these exercises!

1 Express with a rational denominator.

a $\dfrac{1}{1+\sqrt{2}}$ **b** $\dfrac{1}{\sqrt{3}-1}$ **c** $\dfrac{1}{\sqrt{7}-\sqrt{5}}$ **d** $\dfrac{1}{\sqrt{10}+\sqrt{2}}$

e $\dfrac{3}{\sqrt{3}+2}$ **f** $\dfrac{5}{5-\sqrt{2}}$ **g** $\dfrac{10}{\sqrt{5}-\sqrt{2}}$ **h** $\dfrac{12}{\sqrt{7}-\sqrt{3}}$

i $\dfrac{1}{2\sqrt{3}+5}$ **j** $\dfrac{2}{5-2\sqrt{2}}$ **k** $\dfrac{3}{3\sqrt{2}+2\sqrt{3}}$ **l** $\dfrac{1}{4\sqrt{3}-3\sqrt{2}}$

m $\dfrac{5+\sqrt{2}}{5-\sqrt{2}}$ **n** $\dfrac{4+\sqrt{3}}{4-\sqrt{3}}$ **o** $\dfrac{\sqrt{5}-\sqrt{3}}{\sqrt{5}+\sqrt{3}}$ **p** $\dfrac{3\sqrt{2}-\sqrt{3}}{3\sqrt{2}+\sqrt{3}}$

2 Rationalise each denominator, then express as a single fraction.

a $\dfrac{1}{2-\sqrt{3}} + \dfrac{1}{2+\sqrt{3}}$ **b** $\dfrac{1}{\sqrt{5}-\sqrt{3}} - \dfrac{1}{\sqrt{7}+\sqrt{5}}$ **c** $\dfrac{5}{6-\sqrt{3}} + \dfrac{3}{5+\sqrt{3}}$

Mathematical Terms 5

base
- The term which is operated on by the index.
  eg for x^n, x is the base
  for 5^3, 5 is the base.

conjugate
- The binomials that multiply to give the difference of two squares are the 'conjugate' of each other.
  eg $(a - b)$ and $(a + b)$
  $(\sqrt{3} + 5)$ and $(\sqrt{3} - 5)$
  These are conjugate pairs.

exponent
- Another term for a power or index.
- Equations which involve a power are called *exponential* equations.
  eg $3^x = 27$

fractional indices
- Another way of writing the 'root' of a number or term.
- $x^{\frac{1}{2}} = \sqrt{x}$, $x^{\frac{1}{3}} = \sqrt[3]{x}$, $x^{\frac{1}{n}} = \sqrt[n]{x}$

index
- A number indicating how many of a base term need to be multiplied together.
  eg for x^n, n is the index
  $$x^n = \underbrace{x \times x \times x \times x \ldots \ldots x\, x}_{n \text{ factors}}$$
- The plural of index is *indices*.

irrational numbers
- Numbers that *cannot* be expressed in the form $\frac{a}{b}$ where a and b are integers.
- They cannot be given an exact decimal value.
  eg π, $\sqrt{3}$, $3\sqrt{2} + 1$

negative indices
- Indicate the reciprocal of a term.
  eg $x^{-1} = \frac{1}{x}$, $x^{-n} = \frac{1}{x^n}$
  ie $5^{-1} = \frac{1}{5}$, $2^{-3} = \frac{1}{2^3} = \frac{1}{8}$

power
- Another term for an index or exponent.

rational numbers
- Numbers that can be written in the form $\frac{a}{b}$ where a and b are integers ($b \neq 0$).
- They can be expressed as a terminating or repeating decimal.
  eg integers, fractions, percentages

real numbers
- The combination of rational and irrational numbers.

scientific (standard) notation
- A useful way to write very big or very small numbers.
- Numbers are written as the product of a number between 1 and 10 and a power of 10.
  eg $76\,000\,000 = 7{\cdot}6 \times 10^7$
  $0{\cdot}000\,0054 = 5{\cdot}4 \times 10^{-6}$

surds
- Numerical expressions that involve irrational roots.
  eg $\sqrt{3}$, $\sqrt[3]{5}$, $2\sqrt{7} + 5$

zero index
- A term or number with a zero index is equal to 1.
  eg $x^0 = 1$, $4^0 = 1$

Mathematical terms 5

Diagnostic Test 5: | Indices and Surds

- These questions reflect the important skills introduced in this chapter.
- Errors made will indicate areas of weakness.
- Each weakness should be treated by going back to the section listed.

	Section
1 Express in index form: a $3 \times 3 \times 3 \times 3$ b 5×5 c $m \times m \times m$	5:01
2 Evaluate: a 3^2 b 2^4 c 10^3	5:01
3 Simplify: a $3^2 \times 3^5$ b $x^3 \times x^2$ c $6m^2n \times mn^4$	5:01
4 Simplify: a $x^7 \div x^2$ b $15a^5 \div 3a^2$ c $20a^3b^2 \div 10ab$	5:01
5 Simplify: a $(a^4)^2$ b $(x^3)^4$ c $(2a^4)^3$	5:01
6 Simplify: a 7^0 b $5p^0$ c $18x^3 \div 6x^3$	5:01
7 Simplify: a 3^{-2} b 5^{-1} c $(\frac{2}{3})^{-3}$	5:02
8 Simplify, writing answers without negative indices: a $x^7 \times x^{-3}$ b $6x^2 \div 3x^4$ c $(3x^{-1})^2$	5:02
9 Simplify: a $25^{\frac{1}{2}}$ b $27^{\frac{1}{3}}$ c $8^{\frac{1}{3}}$	5:03
10 If $x > 0$ and $m > 0$, simplify: a $3x^{\frac{1}{2}} \times 4x^{\frac{1}{2}}$ b $(49m^6)^{\frac{1}{2}}$ c $(8x^3)^{\frac{1}{3}}$	5:03
11 Express in scientific notation: a 243 b $67\,000$ c $93\,800\,000$	5:04
12 Write as a basic numeral: a $1{\cdot}3 \times 10^2$ b $2{\cdot}431 \times 10^2$ c $4{\cdot}63 \times 10^7$	5:04
13 Express in scientific notation: a $0{\cdot}043$ b $0{\cdot}000\,059\,7$ c $0{\cdot}004$	5:04
14 Write the basic numeral for: a $2{\cdot}9 \times 10^{-2}$ b $9{\cdot}38 \times 10^{-5}$ c $1{\cdot}004 \times 10^{-3}$	5:04

15 Simplify, giving answers in scientific notation:
  a $(3{\cdot}1 \times 10^8)^2$ b $(8{\cdot}4 \times 10^6) + (3{\cdot}8 \times 10^7)$
  c $\sqrt{1{\cdot}96 \times 10^{24}}$ d $\sqrt{1{\cdot}44 \times 10^{-6}}$
	5:05

16 For each, write *rational* or *irrational*.

    a $\sqrt{50}$ **b** $0.\dot{4}$ **c** $\sqrt{2}$ **d** $\sqrt{16}$

    5:06

17 Evaluate correct to 3 decimal places:

    a $\sqrt{5}$ **b** $\sqrt{13}$ **c** $\sqrt{21}$ **d** $\sqrt{47}$

    5:06

18 Simplify each surd.

    a $\sqrt{20}$ **b** $\sqrt{27}$ **c** $3\sqrt{8}$ **d** $2\sqrt{75}$

    5:07

19 Express each of the following as an entire square root.

    a $2\sqrt{5}$ **b** $3\sqrt{2}$ **c** $5\sqrt{7}$ **d** $4\sqrt{5}$

    5:07

20 Simplify completely:

    a $2\sqrt{3}+4\sqrt{3}$ **b** $6\sqrt{5}-\sqrt{5}$ **c** $\sqrt{8}-\sqrt{2}$ **d** $\sqrt{27}+2\sqrt{3}$

    5:08

21 Simplify:

    a $\sqrt{5}\times\sqrt{6}$ **b** $\sqrt{3}\times\sqrt{12}$ **c** $2\sqrt{3}\times\sqrt{5}$ **d** $3\sqrt{8}\times2\sqrt{2}$

    5:09

22 Simplify:

    a $\sqrt{12}\div\sqrt{2}$ **b** $\sqrt{32}\div\sqrt{8}$ **c** $5\sqrt{3}\div\sqrt{3}$ **d** $10\sqrt{10}\div2\sqrt{5}$

    5:09

23 Expand and simplify:

    a $(2+\sqrt{5})(3+\sqrt{5})$ **b** $(2\sqrt{3}+\sqrt{2})(\sqrt{3}-3\sqrt{2})$

    c $(\sqrt{7}+\sqrt{3})^2$ **d** $(5-\sqrt{3})(5+\sqrt{3})$

    5:10

24 Rationalise the denominator of:

    a $\dfrac{3}{\sqrt{2}}$ **b** $\dfrac{5}{\sqrt{5}}$ **c** $\dfrac{\sqrt{3}+1}{2\sqrt{3}}$ **d** $\dfrac{5-\sqrt{2}}{5\sqrt{2}}$

    5:11

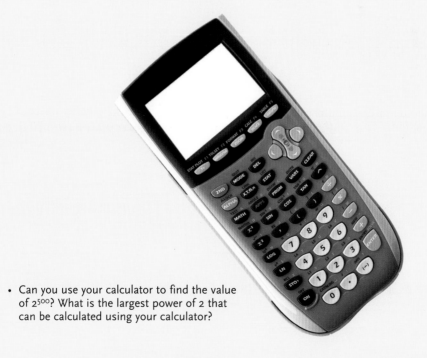

- Can you use your calculator to find the value of 2^{500}? What is the largest power of 2 that can be calculated using your calculator?

Chapter 5 | Revision Assignment

1 Simplify, writing the answers in index form:

a $a^2 \times a^3$ b $3a^2 \times 4a^3$

c $a^2b \times ab$ d $3a^2b \times 4ab^2$

e $3^2 \times 3^3$ f $a^6 \div a^3$

g $7m^2 \div m$ h $12y^6 \div 3y^2$

i $20a^4b^3 \div 10a^2b^2$ j $4^7 \div 4^3$

k $(3^2)^4$ l $(x^2)^3$

m $(a^3)^2 \times a^5$ n $m^7 \div (m^2)^3$

o $\dfrac{12x^2}{6x}$ p $\dfrac{4a^3}{8a}$

2 Express in simplest form:

a $(2x^2)^0$ b $6x^0$ c $(5x^3)^3$

d $(10a^2)^3$ e $(4x^2)^3 \div 8x^5$

3 Write each of the following in standard form (scientific notation).

a $21\,600$ b 125

c $0 \cdot 000\,07$ d $0 \cdot 000\,156$

4 Write each of the following as a basic numeral.

a $8 \cdot 1 \times 10^5$ b $1 \cdot 267 \times 10^3$

c $3 \cdot 5 \times 10^{-2}$ d $1 \cdot 06 \times 10^{-4}$

5 Use your calculator to evaluate:

a 2^{10} b 3^{12}

c $5^5 \times 6^6$ d $7^3 \times 4^5$

6 Find the value of n, if:

a $2^n = 128$ b $3^n = 243$

c $10^n = 100\,000\,000$

7 Simplify and evaluate:

a $3^2 \times 3^5$ b $10^7 \div 10^4$ c $(2^4)^2$

8 Simplify:

a $\dfrac{m^7 \times m^6}{m^{10}}$ b $(2a^3)^3 \times (3a^4)^2$

c $\dfrac{8x^7 \times 9x^4}{6x^6 \times 6x^5}$

9 Noting that $x^{\frac{3}{2}} = (x^3)^{\frac{1}{2}}$, evaluate without using a calculator:

a $4^{\frac{3}{2}}$ b $8^{\frac{2}{3}}$ c $9^{\frac{3}{2}}$ d $1000^{\frac{5}{3}}$

10 Simplify:

a $5x^{\frac{1}{2}} \times 4x^{\frac{1}{2}}$ b $10x^2 \div 5x^4$

c $(36m^4n^6)^{\frac{1}{2}}$

11 Simplify each expression.

a $5\sqrt{20}$ b $\sqrt{28} + 3\sqrt{7}$

c $3\sqrt{8} - 2\sqrt{18}$ d $2\sqrt{7} \times 3\sqrt{2}$

e $2\sqrt{5} \times \sqrt{20}$ f $15\sqrt{12} \div 5\sqrt{3}$

g $\sqrt{3}(\sqrt{3} + \sqrt{15})$ h $(\sqrt{7} + \sqrt{2})^2$

i $(\sqrt{5} + \sqrt{6})(\sqrt{2} + \sqrt{5})$

j $\sqrt{m} \times \sqrt{n}$ k $(\sqrt{m} + \sqrt{n})^2$

l $(\sqrt{m} + \sqrt{n})(\sqrt{m} - \sqrt{n})$

12 Rationalise the denominator of each expression:

a $\dfrac{5}{2\sqrt{5}}$ b $\dfrac{2\sqrt{3}}{3\sqrt{2}}$

c $\dfrac{1}{\sqrt{2}} + \dfrac{1}{\sqrt{3}}$ d $\dfrac{3}{2\sqrt{5}} - \dfrac{2}{3\sqrt{2}}$

Extension

13 Rationalise the denominator of each expression.

a $\dfrac{2}{\sqrt{5} - 1}$ b $\dfrac{1}{\sqrt{7} + \sqrt{2}}$

c $\dfrac{\sqrt{5} - 2}{\sqrt{5} + 2}$ d $\dfrac{\sqrt{2} + \sqrt{3}}{\sqrt{2} - \sqrt{3}}$

14 Simplify each expression, writing your answer with a rational denominator.

a $\dfrac{5}{\sqrt{3}} - \dfrac{2}{\sqrt{3} - 1}$ b $\dfrac{3}{\sqrt{5} + 2} \times \dfrac{2}{\sqrt{5} + 1}$

c $\dfrac{\sqrt{7} + 2}{\sqrt{3} + 1} \div \dfrac{2\sqrt{3} + 1}{2\sqrt{7} - 1}$

Chapter 5 | Working Mathematically

1 Use ID Card 7 on page xix to identify:
  a 5   b 8   c 17   d 18   e 19
  f 20   g 21   h 22   i 23   j 24

2 Use ID Card 6 on page xviii to identify numbers 1 to 12.

3 a How many diagonals can be drawn from one vertex of a regular hexagon? How many vertices has a hexagon?

  b Each diagonal joins two vertices and a diagonal cannot be drawn from a vertex to the two adjacent vertices or to itself. The number of diagonals of a hexagon is $\dfrac{6(6-3)}{2}$. How many diagonals has:
    i a regular octagon?
    ii a regular decagon?
    iii a regular polygon that has 30 sides?

4 Tom was given a cheque for an amount between $31 and $32. The bank teller made a mistake and exchanged dollars and cents on the cheque. Tom took the money without examining it and gave 5 cents to his son. He now found that he had twice the value of the original cheque. If he had no money before entering the bank, what was the amount of the cheque?

$31·62 ...
... $62·31?

5 In the decibel scale, for measuring noise, 10 decibels is a noise that is barely audible. A noise 10 times as intense is 20 decibels, and so on up to 140 decibels, which is the threshold of pain. Study the table and answer the questions below.

Noise	Relative intensity	Decibels
Minimum of audible sound	1	0
Soft wind on leaves	10	10
Whisper at 1 metre	10^2	20
Bush quiet	10^3	30

  a If ordinary conversation has a relative intensity of 10^6, what is its loudness in decibels?
  b If a lawn mower has a relative intensity of 10^{12}, what is its loudness in decibels?
  c By how many times is the relative intensity of the mower greater than that of conversation?
  d By how many times is the relative intensity of heavy traffic (loudness 80 dB) greater than that of bush quiet?
  e From the above it would appear that heavy traffic (80 dB) is four times as noisy as a whisper at 1 metre (20 dB). However, a rise of 10 dB corresponds to a doubling in the subjective loudness to the human ear. How much louder to the human ear is:
    i the average office (50 dB) than bush quiet (30 dB)?
    ii heavy traffic (80 dB) than a whisper at 1 metre (20 dB)?
    iii a rock group (110 dB) than a business office (60 dB)?

Technology Applications
Drag and Drops

1 Index laws
2 Negative indices
3 Fractional indices

4 Simplifying surds
5 Operations with surds

Chapter Review
Questions

6

Equations, Inequations and Formulae

$$\frac{15 + x}{2} = \frac{x + 5}{3}$$
$$3(15 + x) = 2(x + 5)$$
$$45 + 3x = 2x + 10$$
$$45 + x = 10$$
$$x = 10 - 45$$
$$x = -35$$

Rules:
1. Remove fractions
2. Remove grouping symbols
3. Collect like terms
4. Divide out

It's easy when you follow the rules!

That's easy for him to say!

Chapter Contents

Learning Outcomes

Students will be able to:
- Solve linear equations using algebraic techniques.
- Solve simple linear inequalities using algebraic techniques.
- Solve equations involving algebraic fractions.
- Solve literal problems with the use of equations.
- Change the subject of formulae.
- Solve problems using formulae.

Areas of Interaction

Approaches to Learning (Knowledge Acquisition, Problem Solving, Communication, Logical Thinking, Reflection), Human Ingenuity

- Equations are number sentences where one or more of the numbers is missing or unknown. Because it is unknown, the number is represented by a pronumeral.
- When we solve an equation, we are trying to find the numerical value of the pronumeral that makes the sentence true. With some equations it is easy to find this value or solution. With harder equations more work has to be done before the solution is found.
- A solution is correct if it gives a true number sentence when it replaces the pronumeral in the equation. We say that the solution *satisfies* the equation.

 An equation is a number sentence where one or more of the numbers has been replaced by a pronumeral.

6:01 | Equivalent Equations

- Solving equations is like balancing scales. With equations we know that one side of the equation is equal to the other side. We could say that the two sides are *balanced*.
- The solution of the equation is the value of the pronumeral that balances the equation.

The sides are balanced.

$$x + 10 = 15$$

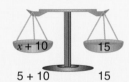

5 + 10   15

$x = 5$ balances the scale.
$x = 5$ is the solution.

$$y - 3 = 8$$

11 − 3   8

$y = 11$ balances the scale.
$y = 11$ is the solution.

- Solving difficult equations requires us to change the equation into a simpler equation. We change equations into simpler equations by performing the same operation on both sides of the equation.
- We may add (+), subtract (−), multiply (×) or divide (÷) by any number, provided we do the same to both sides of the equation.
- If we do not do the same to both sides of the equation, the equation becomes unbalanced and the sides no longer remain equal.
- If we commence with an equation and do the same thing to both sides of the equation, then the sides will remain equal or balanced and the new equation will have the same solution as the original equation.

 If one equation can be changed into another by performing the same operation on both sides, then the equations are said to be equivalent.

We solve equations by making a series of equivalent equations, each one in the series being simpler than the one before it. In this way we reduce a complicated equation to a simple one. We must remember to perform the same operation on both sides of the equation.

worked examples

Examples 1

1 $8a + 6 = 15$
2 $1 - 3b = 7$
3 $5a - 7 = a + 2$
4 $7 - y = 5 - 2y$

Solutions

1 $8a + 6 = 15$
   $\quad -6 \quad -6$ Subtract 6 from
   $\quad 8a = 9$ both sides.
   $\quad \div 8 \quad \div 8$ Divide both sides by 8.
   $$\frac{8a}{8} = \frac{9}{8}$$
   $\therefore a = 1\frac{1}{8}$

2 $1 - 3b = 7$
   $\quad -1 \quad -1$ Subtract 1 from
   $\quad -3b = 6$ both sides.
   $\quad \div -3 \quad \div -3$ Divide both sides by -3.
   $$\frac{-3b}{-3} = \frac{6}{-3}$$
   $\therefore b = -2$

3 $5a - 7 = a + 2$
   $\quad -a = -a$ Subtract a from
   $4a - 7 = 2$ both sides.
   $\quad +7 \quad +7$ Add 7 to both sides.
   $\quad 4a = 9$
   $\quad \div 4 \quad \div 4$ Divide both sides by 4.
   $$\frac{4a}{4} = \frac{9}{4}$$
   $a = 2\frac{1}{4}$

4 $7 - y = 5 - 2y$
   $\quad +2y \quad +2y$ Add $2y$ to
   $7 + y = 5$ both sides.
   $\quad -7 \quad -7$ Subtract 7
   $y = 5 - 7$ from both sides.
   $\therefore y = -2$

Examples 2

Check to see if each given solution is correct by substituting it into the equation.

1 $x + 7 = 2x - 5$
   $x = 12$
2 $5a - 9 = 3 - a$
   $a = 5$

Solutions

1 L.H.S. $= x + 7$ R.H.S. $= 2x - 5$
   $\qquad = 12 + 7$ $\qquad = 2 \times 12 - 5$
   $\qquad = 19$ $\qquad = 19$
   $\therefore$ L.H.S. = R.H.S.
   $\qquad \therefore x = 12$ is correct

2 L.H.S. $= 5a - 9$ R.H.S. $= 3 - a$
   $\qquad = 5 \times 5 - 9$ $\qquad = 3 - 5$
   $\qquad = 16$ $\qquad = -2$
   $\therefore$ L.H.S. $\neq$ R.H.S.
   $\qquad \therefore a = 5$ is incorrect.

Smart people like me always check solutions by substituting.

Exercise 6:01

Foundation Worksheet 6:01

Equivalent equations
1 Solve:
 a $m + 15 = 32$ **b** $n - 12 = 27$
 c $3m = 72$
2 Solve:
 a $2a + 3 = 9$ **b** $4x - 1 = 3$
 c $7n - 6 = 8$

1 Solve the following equations.

  a $x - 125 = 917$ **b** $15·2 + p = 17·1$ **c** $a + 11·3 = 20·1$

  d $h - 1·8 = 6·2$ **e** $b - 3·2 = 1·7$ **f** $16 + y = 3$

  g $x + 7 = 1$ **h** $p - 1 = -3$ **i** $2 - p = 5$

  j $7 - a = 1$ **k** $2·1 + y = 1·4$ **l** $-3 + y = 1·7$

  m $-5 - y = 1$ **n** $5p = 17$ **o** $8x = 2·4$

  p $3·5y = 17·5$ **q** $1·1p = 0·11$ **r** $\dfrac{a}{5} = 1$

  s $\dfrac{b}{3} = 12$ **t** $\dfrac{x}{7} = -2$ **u** $\dfrac{a}{1·1} = 3·2$

2 Find the value of the variable in each of the following.
All solutions are integral.

  a $5b + 1 = 26$ **b** $2m + 9 = 23$

  c $5m + 7 = 82$ **d** $15 = 3p - 57$

  e $15 = 3x + 6$ **f** $1 = 7x - 48$

  g $-3 = 7p - 10$ **h** $12 - 2a = 18$

  i $5y + 17 = 2$ **j** $1 - 3x = 10$

  k $8 - 3b = 20$ **l** $10 - 5b = -30$

Check your answers by substituting into the original equation.

3 Solve the following equations.

  a $3a + 17 = 28$ **b** $4p + 6 = 37$

  c $9y + 15 = 820$ **d** $17 + 3x = 88$

  e $5m - 13 = 42$ **f** $11x - 8 = 52$

  g $17 = 3y - 3$ **h** $28 = 7m - 14$

  i $15 - 4b = 3$ **j** $10 - 2a = 1$ **k** $3a + 15 = 4$

  l $10m - 4 = 8$ **m** $7 = 17 + 7a$ **n** $44 + 6a = 10$

  o $15 - 6a = -10$ **p** $3a + 5 = -10$ **q** $2·5x + 7 = 10$

  r $1·2a - 3·6 = 4·2$ **s** $2·3 - 1·4x = 0·2$ **t** $15 + 0·9a = 17·7$

4 Solve the following equations. (Answers are all integers.)

  a $4x - 5 = 3x - 4$ **b** $4a + 3 = 5a + 4$

  c $4x + 3 = x - 6$ **d** $4x = 3x + 2$

  e $3x - 9 = x - 1$ **f** $5x + 1 = x - 11$

  g $4q + 5 = 3q$ **h** $7m - 1 = 4m + 17$

  i $4p - 4 = 2p + 14$ **j** $2x + 5 = 4x - 5$

  k $3m - 12 = 6m - 6$ **l** $a - 4 = 3a + 10$

  m $5x - 4 = 8x + 20$ **n** $7b + 9 = b - 9$

  o $8t - 9 = 3t - 9$ **p** $3r + 7 = r + 9$

  q $9 - 3b = b + 1$ **r** $7z = 10z - 6$

  s $7g - 12 = 20 - g$ **t** $3x + 9 = 14 - 2x$

  u $8y - 12 = 4y$ **v** $4a + 10 = 5 - a$

  w $5x - 20 = 3x + 30$ **x** $12 - 3d = 2d - 3$

Collect the pronumerals on the side where most are found.

5 Substitute the given solution to see if it is correct.

a $5x + 3 = 7x - 3$
$x = 3$

b $3y - 7 = 5y + 3$
$y = 5$

c $7a + 4 = 2a - 6$
$a = -2$

d $9p + 1 = 10p - 3$
$p = 4$

e $12a - 8 = 10a + 2$
$a = 5$

f $m - 8 = 2m + 3$
$m = -5$

g $3x - 1 = x - 5$
$x = -2$

h $4g + 2 = 16 - 3g$
$g = 2$

i $7x + 1 = 3x - 3$
$x = -1$

j $4x + 9 = 5x$
$x = 9$

k $9h - 4 = 10 + 1$
$h = -3$

l $15y - 5 = 11y - 11$
$y = 4$

6 Solve these equations.

a $6a + 3 = 2a - 5$

b $5m + 3 = 2m + 10$

c $4x - 5 = 2 - x$

d $3y + 6 = 5 - 2y$

e $8 + 5t = 3t - 2$

f $6x = 2x - 20$

g $12x - 9 = x + 1$

h $10 - 3d = 2d + 5$

i $9t = 3t + 5$

j $5m - 3 = 9$

k $2x - 3 + 4x = 5 - x$

l $4y = 2y - 9 + 7y$

m $4a + 9 = 2a - 4$

n $12 = 5 - 6b$

o $18 - 5s = 4s + 27$

p $21 + 4x = 3x - 5 - x$

q $21 - 7g = 3 - g$

r $32 + \frac{1}{2}x = 20 - x$

s $\frac{3}{4}x - 5 = 1 - \frac{1}{4}x$

t $5 - 8y = 2y + 5$

u $12 + 4d = 5 - 3d$

6:01 Flowcharts

6:02 | Equations with Grouping Symbols

6:02

Rewrite these expressions without grouping symbols.

1 $7(x + 4)$
2 $2(a - 3)$
3 $5(4a + 9)$
4 $6(2p - 7)$
5 $-3(x - 4)$

Solve these one-step equations.

6 $x + 9 = 4$
7 $x - 8 = -2$
8 $3p = -27$
9 $10p = 5$
10 $6 + x = -1$

If you remember how to 'expand' grouping symbols, these equations are no harder than the ones you have already seen. Look at these worked examples.

worked examples

1 Expand the grouping symbols and then solve the equation.

a
$$2(x + 3) = 8$$
$$2x + 6 = 8$$
$$-6 \quad -6$$
$$2x = 2$$
$$\div 2 \quad \div 2$$
$$\therefore x = 1$$

b
$$5(a - 3) = 3$$
$$5a - 15 = 3$$
$$+15 \quad +15$$
$$5a = 18$$
$$\div 5 \quad \div 5$$
$$\therefore a = \frac{18}{5} \text{ or } 3\frac{3}{5}$$

c
$$3(2m - 4) = 4m - 6$$
$$6m - 12 = 4m - 6$$
$$-4m \quad -4m$$
$$2m - 12 = -6$$
$$+12 \quad +12$$
$$2m = 6$$
$$\div 2 \quad \div 2$$
$$\therefore m = 3$$

2 Expand each set of grouping symbols and then solve the equations.

a $3(a + 7) = 4(a - 2)$
$3a + 21 = 4a - 8$
$\quad -3a \quad -3a$
$\quad 21 = a - 8$
$\quad +8 \quad +8$
$\quad 29 = a$
$\quad \therefore a = 29$

b $3(x + 4) + 2(x + 5) = 4$
$3x + 12 + 2x + 10 = 4$
Collect like terms.
$\quad 5x + 22 = 4$
$\quad -22 \quad -22$
$\quad 5x = -18$
$\quad \div 5 \quad \div 5$
$\quad \therefore x = -3\tfrac{3}{5}$

Just take it one step at a time.

Exercise 6:02

Foundation Worksheet 6:02

Equations with grouping symbols
1 Expand these grouping symbols.
  a $5(x + 3)$ **b** $7(a - 4)$ **c** $9(2y + 3)$
2 Solve these equations.
  a $2(a + 3) = 8$ **b** $5(m - 1) = 10$ **c** $7(2n + 1) = 21$

1 Expand the grouping symbols and then solve each equation. (Answers are all integers.)

a $4(x + 1) = 20$
b $8(a - 3) = 56$
c $6(y - 3) = 18$
d $3(2x + 1) = 21$
e $5(3 - 4m) = 75$
f $7(2b + 3) = 12b - 9$
g $a + 1 = 3(5 - 2a)$
h $9(2x + 3) = 3(7x - 1)$
i $14 + 4(2x - 1) = 2(5x - 2)$
j $3(5x - 2) + 2(5x - 2) = 5x + 10$

2 Solve each equation using the worked examples as a guide.

a $4(x - 3) = 5(x + 1)$
b $7(a + 5) = 3(5 - a)$
c $6(5 - y) = 3(y + 1)$
d $4(t - 1) = 2(t + 3)$
e $3(2x - 1) = 7(x - 5)$
f $7(x + 1) = 2(2x - 3)$
g $9(x - 5) = 4(3x - 1) + 9$
h $2(4m - 3) = 5m + 5(2m + 1)$
i $4(2a + 7) + 3a - 6 = 0$
j $3t + 2(6 - 5t) - 4 = 9 - 10t$
k $5(2a - 1) + 3(2a - 1) = 10$
l $3(5 - 3y) + 12(y + 5) = 90$
m $4(3a - 1) + 2(5a + 6) = 10$
n $6(5 - 3n) + 5(3n + 1) = 5$
o $2(2y - 9) + (y + 8) = 5$
p $5x + 5(x + 5) - 9 = 0$
q $7(1 - 2t) + 5(t - 8) + 5 = 0$
r $4(4 + 3a) + 3(2 - a) = 7$

3 Solve each equation. Use Worked Example 2(b) as a guide.

a $3(a + 2) + a + 5 = 15$
b $5(m - 1) + 2m = 2$
c $2(m + 3) + 5(m + 2) = 23$
d $3(x + 2) + 2(x - 3) = 10$
e $5(p + 1) + 2(p + 4) = 20$
f $4(t - 2) + 2(t + 5) = 14$
g $4(2a + 3) + 2(a - 5) = 22$
h $2(2m + 3) + 3(m - 5) = 5$
i $5(a - 3) + 3(2 + 3a) = 19$

4 Solve these equations, but first read the warning sign!

a $3(x - 2) - 5(x + 2) = 0$
b $7(2a + 3) - 3(a - 5) = 12$
c $9(2t - 3) - (t + 5) = 2$
d $5(3y - 5) - 6(1 - y) = 11$
e $4(6 - 3b) - 2(7b - 1) = 26$
f $9(3q + 7) - 6(2q + 5) = 14$
g $2(3w + 1) - 3(5 - 4w) = 4(2w + 3)$
h $17 - 6(2x - 5) = 17$
i $\frac{1}{2}(4x + 3) - 2(2x - 1) = 7$
j $\frac{3}{4}(8x - 9) - \frac{1}{4}(8x - 9) = 15$

5 Try solving these equations, but first read the warning sign!

a $3(a + 2) - 2(a + 1) = 6$
b $5(m + 3) - 4(m + 2) = 10$
c $5(n + 4) - 3(n - 2) = 30$
d $6(a + 2) - 4(a - 1) = 20$
e $4(a + 3) - (a + 2) = 13$
f $2{\cdot}4(p + 5) - (p + 3{\cdot}8) = 11$

▓ **Warning!**
Remember how to expand with a negative term:
$-2(x + 4) = -2x - 8$
or
$-3(a - 1) = -3a + 3$

Investigation 6:02 | Solving equations using a spreadsheet

A spreadsheet such as Excel can be used to solve equations using the 'formula bar'. To solve an equation such as $2x + 5 = 11$ we need to enter the numbers into the appropriate 'cells' and tell the spreadsheet how to arrive at the answer for x.

- The equation $2x + 5 = 11$ is of the form $ax + b = c$.

- Enter the letters a, x, b and c in the first row as shown. These will act as headings.

B2	▼	fx =(D2–C2)/A2 ◄

	A	B	C	D	E
1	a	x	b	c	
2		2	3	5	11	
3					
4					

- The numbers 2, 5 and 11 are then placed in cells A2, C2 and D2.

- To solve $2x + 5 = 11$ we would need to complete these steps:
$$2x + 5 = 11$$
$$2x = 11 - 5$$
$$x = \frac{11 - 5}{2}$$

- Matching the 'cells' with these numbers we would have:
$$x = \frac{D2 - C2}{A2}$$

- In cell B2 we type '=(D2 – C2)/A2'. This also shows in the formula bar.

	A	B	C	D
1	a	x	b	c
2		2	3	5	11
3				
4				

- When we press ENTER the answer 3 appears in cell B2.

We can now change any of the values for a, b or c and the value for x, ie the answer will automatically change.

Try entering other values including negative numbers and decimals.

6:03 | Equations with Fractions (1)

 Remove the fractions by multiplying by the denominator of the fraction.

worked examples

Find the value of the pronumeral in each of the following equations.

1 $3 - \dfrac{a}{5} = 2$

2 $\dfrac{x - 7}{3} = 5$

3 $\dfrac{2 - 3x}{4} = 5$

Solutions

1
$$3 - \frac{a}{5} = 2$$
$$\times 5 \quad \times 5$$
$$5\left(3 - \frac{a}{5}\right) = 2 \times 5$$
$$15 - \frac{5a}{5} = 10$$
$$15 - a = 10$$
$$-a = -5$$
$$\therefore a = 5$$

2
$$\frac{x - 7}{3} = 5$$
$$\times 3 \quad \times 3$$
$$\frac{3(x - 7)}{3} = 5 \times 3$$
$$x - 7 = 15$$
$$\therefore x = 22$$

3
$$\frac{2 - 3x}{4} = 5$$
$$\times 4 \quad \times 4$$
$$\frac{4(2 - 3x)}{4} = 5 \times 4$$
$$2 - 3x = 20$$
$$-3x = 18$$
$$\therefore x = -6$$

Can you think of an alternative way of solving example 1?

1 Make sure you multiply both sides of the equation by the same number.
2 Make sure you remove the parentheses correctly.
$$4(3 + 2) = 4 \times 3 + 4 \times 2$$
so
$$4(x + 2) = 4 \times x + 4 \times 2$$
$$= 4x + 8$$

Exercise 6:03

1 Solve the following equations.

a $\dfrac{m}{4} + 3 = 6$ b $9 - \dfrac{a}{5} = 12$

c $8 = \dfrac{t}{4} - 1$ d $5 = 3 - \dfrac{1}{3}x$

e $\dfrac{3p}{5} = 9$ f $-6 = \dfrac{5m}{7}$

g $\dfrac{3y - 4}{5} = 6$ h $\dfrac{3 + 5b}{2} = 18$

i $\dfrac{6x - 5}{7} = -1$ j $\dfrac{2}{5}(2q - 1) = 6$

The denominator is the bottom number of a fraction.

2 Check to see if the given solution is correct or incorrect.

a $\quad 3 + \dfrac{a}{2} = 5$

$\quad\quad a = -1$

b $\quad 9 - \dfrac{t}{3} = 7$

$\quad\quad t = 6$

c $\quad \dfrac{5 + 3c}{4} = 8$

$\quad\quad c = 9$

d $\quad \dfrac{4m - 6}{5} = 7$

$\quad\quad m = 10\frac{1}{4}$

e $\quad \dfrac{6 - 5x}{3} = 18$

$\quad\quad x = 0$

f $\quad \dfrac{2 + 5y}{3} = 9$

$\quad\quad y = 4\frac{1}{5}$

3 In each of the following, check to see if the solution is correct or incorrect. If it is incorrect, write down the letter of the first incorrect line.

a $\quad \dfrac{3k}{5} - 1 = 7$

$\quad 5\left(\dfrac{3k}{5} - 1\right) = 7 \times 5 \quad$ A

$\quad \dfrac{15k}{5} - 1 = 35 \quad$ B

$\quad 3k - 1 = 35 \quad$ C

$\quad 3k = 36 \quad$ D

$\quad k = 12 \quad$ E

b $\quad \dfrac{2x + 1}{3} = 5$

$\quad \dfrac{3(2x + 1)}{3} = 5 \quad$ A

$\quad 2x + 1 = 5 \quad$ B

$\quad 2x = 4 \quad$ C

$\quad x = 2 \quad$ D

c $\quad \dfrac{5x - 7}{2} = 9$

$\quad \dfrac{2(5x - 7)}{2} = 9 \times 2 \quad$ A

$\quad 5x - 7 = 18 \quad$ B

$\quad 5x = 25 \quad$ C

$\quad x = 5 \quad$ D

4 Solve these equations which have variables on both sides.

a $\quad \dfrac{3m}{2} - 4 = m$

b $\quad \dfrac{3x}{7} + 1 = 2x$

c $\quad q - 3 = \dfrac{2q}{3}$

d $\quad a = \dfrac{3a + 4}{5}$

e $\quad \dfrac{2p + 7}{3} = 2p - 3$

f $\quad 2t - 5 = \dfrac{6t - 1}{9}$

g $\quad \dfrac{5y}{3} - 6 = \dfrac{4y - 5}{3}$

h $\quad \dfrac{1}{4}(3x - 11) = 2x + 1$

i $\quad \dfrac{5 - 4d}{6} = d + 5$

j $\quad 1 - y = \dfrac{7 - 9y}{6}$

> Remember:
> $\dfrac{1}{3}(2y + 3)$
> $= \dfrac{2y + 3}{3}$

6:04 | Equations with Fractions (2)

What are the first three multiples of:

1 2?   **2** 5?

What is the lowest common multiple of:

3 2 and 6?   **4** 3, 4 and 5?   **5** x and $3x$?

Simplify:

6 $5 \times \dfrac{a}{5}$ **7** $10 \times \dfrac{3x}{2}$ **8** $\dfrac{3(2x+1)}{3}$ **9** $\dfrac{4(2x-1)}{2}$ **10** $5 \times 3\left(\dfrac{2x-1}{5}\right)$

In the last set, the equations only had a single denominator. The equations in this set have more than one denominator. To simplify these equations we must multiply by the lowest common multiple of all the denominators. (Or, in other words, we must multiply by some number that will cancel out every denominator.)

worked examples

Solve:

1 $\dfrac{3x}{5} - \dfrac{x}{4} = 1$ **2** $\dfrac{a}{5} - 1 = \dfrac{3a-1}{2} + 4$ **3** $\dfrac{m+2}{3} - \dfrac{m-5}{4} = 6$

Solutions

1 $\dfrac{3x}{5} - \dfrac{x}{4} = 1$

Multiply both sides by 20.

$\therefore 20\left(\dfrac{3x}{5} - \dfrac{x}{4}\right) = 1 \times 20$

$\therefore \dfrac{60x}{5} - \dfrac{20x}{4} = 20$

$\therefore 12x - 5x = 20$

$\therefore 7x = 20$

$\therefore x = \dfrac{20}{7}$

$\therefore x = 2\dfrac{6}{7}$

2 $\dfrac{a}{5} - 1 = \dfrac{3a-1}{2} + 4$

$\therefore \dfrac{a}{5} = \dfrac{3a-1}{2} + 5$

Multiply both sides by 10.

$\therefore \dfrac{{}^2\cancel{10}a}{\cancel{5}_1} = \dfrac{\cancel{10}^5(3a-1)}{\cancel{2}_1} + 50$

$\therefore 2a = 5(3a-1) + 50$

$\therefore 2a = 15a - 5 + 50$

$\therefore -13a = 45$

$\therefore a = \dfrac{45}{-13}$

$\therefore a = -3\dfrac{6}{13}$

3 $\dfrac{m+2}{3} - \dfrac{m-5}{4} = 6$

Multiply both sides by 12.

$\therefore 12\left(\dfrac{m+2}{3} - \dfrac{m-5}{4}\right) = 6 \times 12$

$\therefore 4(m+2) - 3(m-5) = 72$

$\therefore 4m + 8 - 3m + 15 = 72$

$\therefore m + 23 = 72$

$\therefore m = 49$

Exercise 6:04

Foundation Worksheet 6:04

Equations with fractions (2)

1 Simplify:

a $5 \times \left[\dfrac{2a+1}{5} \right]$ b $6 \times \left[\dfrac{4m-1}{3} \right]$

2 Simplify:

a $6 \times \left[\dfrac{x}{2} + \dfrac{x}{3} \right]$ b $12 \times \left[\dfrac{x+2}{3} - \dfrac{x+3}{4} \right]$

1 Solve the following equations. All solutions are integers. You should check all solutions by substituting your solution into the equation.

a $\dfrac{x}{2} + \dfrac{x}{3} = 5$ b $\dfrac{p}{6} + \dfrac{p}{2} = 8$

c $\dfrac{m}{4} + \dfrac{m}{6} = 20$ d $\dfrac{y}{2} - \dfrac{y}{4} = 3$ e $\dfrac{m}{4} - \dfrac{m}{5} = 1$

f $\dfrac{x}{3} - \dfrac{x}{5} = 4$ g $\dfrac{3k}{2} + \dfrac{k}{4} = 14$ h $\dfrac{5x}{3} + \dfrac{4x}{5} = 37$

i $\dfrac{3p}{2} + \dfrac{p}{3} = 11$ j $\dfrac{x}{2} - \dfrac{2x}{5} = 3$ k $\dfrac{5m}{6} - \dfrac{m}{4} = 7$

l $4a - \dfrac{2a}{5} = 18$ m $\dfrac{m}{4} = \dfrac{m}{3} - 2$ n $\dfrac{3p}{10} - 4 = \dfrac{p}{2} - 8$

o $\dfrac{x}{2} + \dfrac{x}{10} = \dfrac{2x}{5} + 4$ p $\dfrac{b+4}{2} = \dfrac{b+10}{3}$

q $\dfrac{m+6}{3} = \dfrac{2m+4}{4}$ r $\dfrac{k-1}{4} = \dfrac{k-5}{2}$

2 Solve:

a $\dfrac{(x+3)}{2} + \dfrac{(x+5)}{5} = 8$ b $\dfrac{(a+1)}{3} + \dfrac{(a+1)}{4} = 9$

c $\dfrac{p-3}{3} + \dfrac{p-2}{4} = 7$ d $\dfrac{2b-3}{4} + \dfrac{1+3b}{2} = 6$

e $\dfrac{2p-3}{2} + \dfrac{p+4}{3} = 1$ f $1 - p = \dfrac{p+6}{10}$

g $\dfrac{1}{3}(x+2) - \dfrac{1}{5}(2x-1) = 5$ h $\dfrac{2(a+1)}{3} - \dfrac{3(1+a)}{4} = a$

i $\dfrac{2a+3}{2} - \dfrac{a-2}{3} = \dfrac{a-1}{4}$

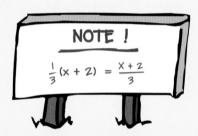

NOTE !

$\dfrac{1}{3}(x+2) = \dfrac{x+2}{3}$

Challenge 6:04 | Equations with pronumerals in the denominator

Some equations may have pronumerals in the denominators. Examine the following examples
and then attempt the following questions.

Examples

Solve each equation:

1
$$\frac{3}{2b} + 1 = 4$$
$$\times 2b \qquad \times 2b$$
$$\therefore\ 2b\left(\frac{3}{2b} + 1\right) = 4 \times 2b$$
$$\therefore\ \frac{6b}{2b} + 2b = 8b$$
$$\therefore\ 3 + 2b = 8b$$
$$\therefore\ 3 = 6b$$
$$\therefore\ b = \tfrac{1}{2}$$

2
$$\frac{a}{a-3} = 4$$
$$\times (a-3) \quad \times (a-3)$$
$$\therefore\ \cancel{(a-3)} \times \frac{a}{\cancel{(a-3)}} = 4 \times (a-3)$$
$$\therefore\ a = 4a - 12$$
$$\therefore\ -3a = -12$$
$$\therefore\ a = 4$$

3
$$\frac{3}{x+1} = \frac{2}{x+4}$$

Multiply both sides by $(x+1)(x+4)$
$$\therefore\ \frac{3\cancel{(x+1)}(x+4)}{\cancel{(x+1)}} = \frac{2(x+1)\cancel{(x+4)}}{\cancel{(x+4)}}$$
$$\therefore\ 3(x+4) = 2(x+1)$$
$$\therefore\ 3x + 12 = 2x + 2$$
$$\therefore\ x + 12 = 2$$
$$\therefore\ x = -10$$

> ▇ Remove the fraction by
> multiplying by the denominator
> of the fraction.

1 Solve the following equations.

a $\dfrac{4}{x} = 2$ **b** $\dfrac{3}{a} = 18$ **c** $\dfrac{3}{2x} = 4$ **d** $\dfrac{3}{p} + 1 = 12$

e $\dfrac{4}{3a} - 4 = 3$ **f** $5 + \dfrac{3}{x} = 2$ **g** $10 - \dfrac{1}{p} = 3$ **h** $\dfrac{1}{x-3} = 4$

i $\dfrac{2}{a+5} = 6$ **j** $\dfrac{4}{y-3} + 2 = 1$ **k** $\dfrac{a}{2a+1} - 1 = 6$ **l** $20 - \dfrac{x}{2x-1} = 4$

2 Solve:

a $\dfrac{1}{x-3} = \dfrac{1}{2x+1}$ **b** $\dfrac{4}{x} + \dfrac{1}{2x} = \dfrac{9}{4}$ **c** $\dfrac{3}{2k} - \dfrac{2}{3k} = \dfrac{5}{18}$ **d** $\dfrac{3}{2k-1} = 0{\cdot}2$

e $\dfrac{3}{a} - \dfrac{1}{a-2} = 0$ **f** $2\left(\dfrac{1}{a} + 2\right) = 5 - \dfrac{2}{a}$ **g** $\dfrac{4}{x} - \dfrac{1}{2x} = 3$ **h** $\dfrac{x}{2x+7} = 3$

i $\dfrac{2b-5}{b-2} = 5$ **j** $\dfrac{3}{2a} + \dfrac{1}{a} = 4 - \dfrac{5}{3a}$ **k** $\dfrac{x}{2x+1} - 3 = 1$ **l** $\dfrac{1}{1-x} - 1 = 3$

6:05 | Solving Problems Using Equations

What is the sum of:

1 3 and 4?   　　　　2 x and 3?   　　　　3 x and y?

What is the product of:

4 3 and 4?   　　　　5 x and 3?   　　　　6 x and y?

7 I have $50. I spend $$x$. How much do I have left?

8 There are x books and each one costs $5. What is the total cost of the books?

9 There are x cars with y people in each car. How many people are there altogether?

10 A man is x years old. How old will he be in 5 years time?

Consider the following simple problem.

'I think of a number. If I add 7 to the number the result is 22. What is the number?'

- This problem can be solved by forming an equation. If the missing number is represented by the pronumeral x, then the equation $x + 7 = 22$ represents the information given in the problem. Solving the equation then yields the answer to the original problem.

worked examples

Translate the following into number sentences.
In all cases use the 'x' to represent the unknown number.

> We often use 'x'
> to represent an
> unknown number.

1 I multiply a number by 2 and the result is 50.
2 If I add 6 to a number the answer is 11.
3 I subtract a number from 6 and the answer is 2.
4 A certain number is multiplied by 3 then 6 is
   added and the result is 17.

Solutions

1 I multiply a number by 2 and the result is 50.

$$\underbrace{2 \times x} \qquad \underset{=50}{\downarrow \downarrow}$$

The equation is $2x = 50$.

2 If I add 6 to a number the answer is 11.

$$\underbrace{6 + x} \qquad \underset{=11}{\downarrow \downarrow}$$

The equation is $6 + x = 11$.

3 I subtract a number from 6 and the answer is 2.

$$\underbrace{6 - x} \qquad \underset{=2}{\downarrow \downarrow}$$

The equation is $6 - x = 2$.

'is' means
'equals'.

4 A certain number is multiplied by 3, then 6 is added and the result is 17.

$$\underbrace{x \times 3} \quad , \quad \underbrace{+ 6} \qquad \underset{=17}{\downarrow \downarrow}$$

The equation is $3x + 6 = 17$.

To use equations to solve problems we must be able to analyse a written problem, translate it into an equation and then solve it.

Approach

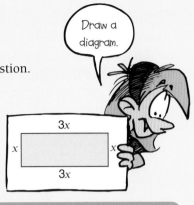

- Read the problem carefully, examining the wording of the question.
- Establish what is to be found and what information is given.
- Ask yourself whether any other information can be assumed, eg that a pack of cards mentioned is a standard pack.
- Try to connect the given information to form an equation. This will often require a knowledge of a formula or the meaning of mathematical terms.

worked examples

Example 1

A rectangle is three times longer than it is wide. If it has a perimeter of 192 m, what are its dimensions?

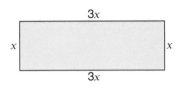

Solution 1

Let the width be x metres.

$\therefore$ The length $= 3 \times x$ metres

$\qquad = 3x$ metres

Now perimeter means the sum of the lengths of the sides (or the distance around the outside of the figure).

$\therefore 3x + x + 3x + x = 192$

$\therefore 8x = 192$

$\therefore x = 24$

$\therefore$ The width $= 24$ m

and the length $= 3 \times 24$ m

$\qquad = 72$ m

▮ In the first line of each solution, indicate what the pronumeral represents.

Example 2

My father was 28 years old when I was born. If he is now three times as old as I am, what are our present ages?

Solution 2

Let my present age be x years.

$\therefore$ My father's present age is $3 \times x$ years.

When I was born my father was 28.

$\therefore$ The difference in our ages is 28 years.

$\therefore$ Father's age − my age always equals 28 years.

$\therefore 3x - x = 28$

$\qquad 2x = 28$

$\qquad x = 14$

$\therefore$ I am 14 years old and my father is 42 years old (ie 3×14 years).

Example 3

Car A left London for Manchester at 6:00 am and travelled at an average speed of 80 km/h. At 7:30 am car B left London for Manchester. If car B travels at an average speed of 100 km/h, at what time will it catch car A?

continued ➔➔➔

Solution 3

Car B will catch car A when both have travelled the same distance *and* distance travelled = average speed × time.

Now *let car B catch up to car A t hours after car B starts.*

∴ Car B has been travelling for t hours.

∴ Car A has been travelling for $(t + 1\frac{1}{2})$ hours (since it started at 6 am).

∴ Distance travelled by car A   Distance travelled by car B
$$= 80 \times (t + 1\tfrac{1}{2})$$ $$= 100 \times t$$

$$\therefore\ 80(t + 1\tfrac{1}{2}) = 100t$$
$$\therefore\ 80t + 80 \times 1\tfrac{1}{2} = 100t$$
$$\therefore\ 120 = 20t$$
$$\therefore\ t = 6$$

∴ Car B catches car A 6 hours after it starts, ie at 1:30 am.

CAR A
Speed = 80 km/h
Starts at 6:00 am
Travels for $(t + 1\frac{1}{2})$ hours
Distance travelled = $80(t + 1\frac{1}{2})$

CAR B
Speed = 100 km/h
Starts at 7:30 am
Travels for t hours
Distance travelled = $100t$

Exercise 6:05

I   Translate the following sentences into equations, using the pronumeral 'x' to represent the unknown number. Then solve the equation to find the value of the unknown number.

   ■ 'I subtract 3 from a certain number' translates to $x - 3$.

   'I subtract a certain number from 3' translates to $3 - x$.

   Also $x - 3$ is not the same as $3 - x$.

a   If 5 is added to a number the answer is 22.
b   If I subtract 3 from a certain number the result is 10.
c   I multiply a number by 8 and the result is 32.
d   Dividing a certain number by 8 gives an answer of 7.
e   A number is multiplied by 2, then 6 is added and the result is 14.
f   Three times a certain number is added to 5 and the result is 20.
g   A certain number is multiplied by 5, then 8 is subtracted and the result is 22.
h   If 5 is added to a certain number and the result is multiplied by 4 the answer is 56.
i   When 5 is subtracted from half of a number the result is 3.

2 For each of the following problems form an equation and then solve it.

   a I think of a number, double it, add 3 and the result is 33. What is the number?

   b I think of a number and multiply it by 4. If I then subtract 3, the answer is 25.
Find the number.

   c I think of a number, add 3 and then double that result. If the answer is 22, find the number.

   d I think of a number. After dividing it by 4 and subtracting 7 the result is 1.
What is the number?

   e I think of a number. If I add 4 and then divide by 3 the result is 8. Find the number.

3 Solve each of the following problems by first forming an equation.

   a If 5 is added to 3 times a certain number the result is 38. What is the number?

   b If I subtract 6 from 5 times a certain number the result is 29. What is the number?

   c If 5 is subtracted from a certain number and that result is then halved, the answer is 6.
What is the number?

   d A number is doubled and then 5 is added. When this is divided by 3 the result is 7.
What is the number?

4 **a** My father is three times as old as I am. If he is 26 years older than I, what are our ages?

   b Two men have $560 between them. If one man has six times as much money as the other,
how much has each man?

   c Jalena has $7 less than Mina. Together they have $43. How much does each girl have?

   d Prizemoney of $500 is divided between Alex and Zarko so that Alex receives $170 more
than Zarko. How much does each receive?

   e If a father is five times as old as his son at present, how old is he if he was 32 years old
when his son was born?

5 **a** In a class of 32 students, it is known that there are
6 more boys than girls. How many girls are there
in the class?

   b A rectangle is 6 cm longer than it is wide. Find its
dimensions if its perimeter is 64 cm.

   c If a quarter of the weight of a leg of lamb is lost in
roasting, what weight of lamb should be bought
in order to have 3 kg of roasted meat?

   d A town B is between towns A and C. B is five times
as far from C as it is from A. The distance from
A to C is 144 km. How far is it from A to B?

6 a Six kilograms of an inferior tea is mixed with 3 kilograms of tea that costs $2 a kilogram more. The total price of the mixture is $24.
What was the price of the inferior tea?

b Two bike riders X and Y both start at 2 pm riding towards each other from 40 km apart. X rides at 30 km/h, Y at 20 km/h. If they meet after t hours, find when and where they meet.

c A man is twice as old as his son. If 9 years ago the sum of their ages was 66 years, find their present ages.

d A man notices that a tank is half full. After emptying 600 litres from the tank, he observes that it is now one-third full. How much does the tank hold when it is full?

7 a Franco is 25 years older than Alejandro and, in 5 years, he will be twice as old as Alejandro. Find their present ages.

I'm not as old as I look …

b A bank teller notices that he has 50 coins all of which are 5c or 10c pieces. He finds that the value of the coins is $4.20. How many of each must he have?

c A tennis player has won 36 out of 54 matches. His sponsor says that he must win 60% of his total number of matches to qualify for a bonus. If there are 26 matches remaining on the tour, how many more must he win to collect his bonus?

d One tank holds 300 litres more than another. If the smaller is two-thirds full, it holds as much as the larger when it is half full. What is the capacity of each?

e A certain journey took 40 min to complete. If half the distance was travelled at an average speed of 100 km/h and the other half at an average speed of 60 km/h, what was the length of the journey?

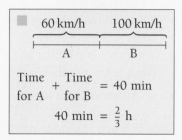

$$\frac{\text{Time}}{\text{for A}} + \frac{\text{Time}}{\text{for B}} = 40 \text{ min}$$
$$40 \text{ min} = \frac{2}{3} \text{ h}$$

8 a Pump A delivers water at twice the rate of pump B. If both pumps operate together, a tank of 18 000 litres capacity can be filled in 30 minutes. Find the pumping rate of each pump, in litres per minute.

b A car travels between A and B at an average speed of 60 km/h. If the car increased its average speed to 100 km/h it would take 10 minutes less to make the trip. How far is it between the towns?

c Car A is travelling along a freeway at 100 km/h when it is passed by car B. If both cars maintain a constant speed and the end of the freeway is 10 km away, find the speed at which car B must travel to beat car A to the end of the freeway by 1 minute.

d A sum of money is divided between A, B and C in the ratio $1:2:3$. However, before the money is divided C dies and it is decided to divide his share between A and B in the ratio $1:3$. If After C's share is divided B has $2000 more than A, how much money was there altogether?

e Rectangles A and B are both four times as long as they are wide and the length of rectangle A is three times the length of rectangle B. If the difference in the perimeters is 16 cm, find the dimensions of each rectangle.

6:06 | Inequations

An inequation is a number sentence where the 'equals' sign has been replaced by an inequality sign. The most common inequality signs are:

'is greater than'   'is less than'   'is greater than or equal to'   'is less than or equal to'

Inequations, unlike equations, usually have more than one solution. For instance:
- the equation $x + 6 = 10$ has one solution, namely $x = 4$.
- the inequation $x + 6 > 10$ has an infinite number of solutions. The numbers $4\frac{1}{2}$, 8, 9·5, 30 are some solutions. The full set of solutions is written as $x > 4$.

The solutions of inequations are often graphed on a number line.

worked examples

1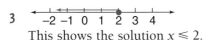
This shows the solution $x = 2$.

2
This shows the solution $x \geqslant 2$.

3
This shows the solution $x \leqslant 2$.

4
This shows the solution $x < 2$.

5
This shows the solution $x > 2$.

'2' is not included in the solution set.   '2' is included in the solution set.

Investigation 6:06 | Solutions to inequations

$x - 1 > 3$ is an *inequation* because it has an *inequality sign* rather than an equal sign.

Complete the table below to investigate some solutions to this inequation.

$x =$	$x - 1 =$	$x - 1 > 3$?
4	3	No
5	4	Yes
6		
7		
8		
9		

This would suggest that x could take any value bigger than or equal to 5. Can you find any values between 4 and 5 that also satisfy this inequation?

Try to write an expression that includes **all** the solutions to this inequation. Do the same with the inequation $x + 3 < 5$ with the following values of x.

$x =$	$x + 3$	$x + 3 < 5$?
4		
3		
2		
1		
0		
−1		

By examining values of x close to your last 'No' answer, try to write an expression that includes **all** the solutions to this inequation.

Try to work out a method for the solution of these inequations using algebra, rather than trial and error. Explain your method in full using examples.

Does your new method work for the following inequations? Prove this by substitution:

$$2x < 8, \; 2x + 3 \geq 11, \; 5 + 3x \leq 14$$

Now fully investigate solutions to the following inequations in the same way. Outline the algebraic steps you are taking to solve each inequation, the answers you get and whether or not they satisfy the inequation.

$$5 - x < 3, \; 5 - x > 3, \; 3 - 2x \geq 13$$

Write down any patterns you notice in the answers when the coefficient of x is negative. Try to work out a method for the solution of inequations in which the coefficient of x is a negative.

I was taller than John last year. . .

. . .and we both grew 4 cm.

Then you're still taller than John!

From the investigation, you should have noticed that solving inequations is exactly the same as solving equations except that if you need to multiply (or divide) by a negative the inequality sign needs to be reversed.

 When multiplying or dividing an inequation by a negative numeral, the inequality sign must be reversed to obtain an equivalent inequality.

$-x \leq 1$ is the same as $x \geq -1$.

Solve the following inequations.

1 $2x - 3 > 7$ **2** $\dfrac{y}{5} + 2 \leqslant 7$ **3** $7 - 3a \geqslant 28$

4 $3 - (4 + 2t) > 5$

Solutions

1 $2x - 3 > 7$
$ + 3 + 3$
$\therefore 2x > 10$
$ \div 2 \div 2$
$\therefore x > 5$

2 $\dfrac{y}{5} + 2 \leqslant 7$
$\phantom{\dfrac{y}{5}} - 2 - 2$
$\therefore \dfrac{y}{5} \leqslant 5$
$\phantom{\dfrac{y}{5}} \times 5 \times 5$
$\therefore y \leqslant 25$

3 $7 - 3a \geqslant 28$
$ - 7 - 7$
$-3a \geqslant 21$
$\div (-3) \div (-3)$
(reverse sign)
$a \leqslant -7$

4 $3 - (4 + 2t) > 5$
$3 - 4 - 2t > 5$
$-1 - 2t > 5$
$ + 1 + 1$
$-2t > 6$
$\div (-2) \div (-2)$
(reverse sign)
$t < -3$

$-1 \leq x$ is the same as $x \geq -1$.

Exercise 6:06

Foundation Worksheet 6:06

Solving inequations
1 Show on a number line:
  a $x > 3$ **b** $x \leqslant 2$ **c** $x < -1$
2 Solve:
  a $x + 3 > 5$ **b** $m - 2 \leqslant 6$ **c** $n + 7 < 4$

1 Solve the following inequations.

  a $4x - 1 < 7$ **b** $3y + 5 \geqslant 3$

  c $6 + 5a > 21$ **d** $\dfrac{t}{7} \leqslant 14$

  e $12 + 5q < 2$ **f** $8 > 2n - 5$ **g** $5m - 8 \geqslant 3m$

  h $\dfrac{w - 4}{3} < 5$ **i** $\dfrac{3y}{5} > 15$ **j** $3 \leqslant \dfrac{q - 9}{4}$

2 Solve the following inequations.

  a $3a + 7 < a - 2$ **b** $2x + 8 \geqslant 5x - 2$ **c** $3(5 - 2b) > 27$

  d $7 \leqslant 3y + 13$ **e** $5(x - 3) - 2(2x + 1) \leqslant 5$ **f** $16 - 3(m - 6) > 1$

  g $3t - 8 \geqslant 5t + 2$ **h** $19 > 7 - 3(n + 2)$ **i** $6 - (x + 1) \leqslant -3$

  j $3(2x + 5) + x > -6$

3 Find the solution to each of the following inequations.

  a $\dfrac{x - 9}{4} < 1$ **b** $\dfrac{8 - a}{5} \geqslant 2$ **c** $\dfrac{t}{3} - 6 > 1$

  d $\dfrac{2w}{3} - \dfrac{3w}{2} \leqslant 5$ **e** $6 - \dfrac{w}{3} > 9$ **f** $\dfrac{5d}{3} - 2 \leqslant 3$

  g $7 - \dfrac{3q}{5} \geqslant 1$ **h** $3 < 4 - \dfrac{b}{6}$ **i** $z < 6 - \dfrac{z}{5}$

  j $\dfrac{3 - 2y}{5} < 7$ **k** $\dfrac{3 - 5x}{4} \geqslant -3$ **l** $\dfrac{m}{3} - 2 \leqslant \dfrac{1}{2}$

4 Solve the following inequations and sketch a graph of the result.

a $3m > 21$ b $6p \leq 42$
c $12m < 24$ d $5y \geq -42$
e $15 > 4x$ f $-20 < 10x$
g $\dfrac{x}{3} < 5$ h $\dfrac{y}{2} > 6$

i $\dfrac{m}{4} \geq 1$ j $\dfrac{x}{5} < -10$

k $3 > \dfrac{x}{2}$ l $-4 < \dfrac{x}{3}$

Draw only the part of the line that you need.

5 Solve the following inequations and sketch a graph of the result.

a $-3m < 24$ b $-4x > 16$
c $-5p \leq 20$ d $-6x < -12$
e $15 < -6x$ f $10 \geq -3x$
g $-x > 4$ h $-x < 3$
i $5 \geq -x$ j $-\dfrac{1}{2}x > 3$

k $-\dfrac{1}{5}x > 1$ l $-\dfrac{1}{4}x \geq 2$

m $\dfrac{x}{-2} < 1$ n $\dfrac{x}{-3} > 2$

o $-\dfrac{x}{4} > 3$

Remember: Change '<' to '>', or vice versa, if you multiply or divide by a negative.

6 Solve:

a $2x + 5 > 11$ b $4m + 3 < 19$
c $2p + 1 \geq 7$ d $10 + 3p \leq 7$
e $4 + 5p \geq 10$ f $13 + 2x < 6$
g $3x - 8 \leq 4$ h $5p - 1 \geq 9$
i $4y - 3 < 2$ j $12 > 5x - 3$
k $3 < 2x - 1$ l $3 \geq 8x - 9$
m $2(x + 3) < 14$ n $3(m + 2) > 15$
o $3(2x - 5) \leq 6$ p $4(x - 3) \geq 5$
q $4 < 2(2m - 3)$ r $2(5p - 4) > 22$

Set them out just like equations!

7 Solve:

a $5 - 3m > 11$ b $10 - 2y < 14$
c $12 \leq 6 - 4x$ d $10 - x \leq 12$
e $2 - m \geq -4$ f $17 - 2m \leq 1$
g $9 - 4p < 7$ h $2(1 - x) < 6$
i $3(4 - y) > 15$ j $3(4 - 2x) \geq 18$
k $2(3 - 5y) \leq -4$ l $2(3 - 2p) > 8$
m $4 \geq 3(1 - 2x)$ n $2(5 - 2a) \leq -5$
o $3(1 - 2x) > 2$

8 Find the solution of each of the following inequations.

a $5x + 6 > x + 18$

b $3x - 5 < x + 6$

c $m + 3 \geqslant 2m - 7$

d $3 - a \leqslant 5 - 2a$

e $12 - b \geqslant 2b + 21$

f $3(m + 4) < 2(m + 6)$

g $\dfrac{x}{2} + 1 < 6$

h $\dfrac{p}{3} - 1 > 4$

i $\dfrac{3x}{4} - 5 > 1$

j $5 - \dfrac{2y}{3} < 6$

k $\dfrac{p - 1}{4} < 2$

l $\dfrac{2p + 3}{2} > 7$

m $\dfrac{4 - x}{3} > 1$

n $\dfrac{x}{2} + \dfrac{x}{3} > 5$

o $\dfrac{a}{4} + \dfrac{a}{2} < 6$

p $3b - \dfrac{2b}{3} < 5$

q $\dfrac{x}{2} - \dfrac{2x}{3} < 3$

r $\dfrac{y}{2} - 3y > 4$

s $1 - \dfrac{3a}{2} > -3$

t $\dfrac{1 - 2x}{3} < 6$

u $\dfrac{1 - 3x}{4} < \dfrac{2(1 - x)}{3}$

9 Write an inequation for each of the following problems, *then* solve it.

a Three times a number is always smaller than eight. What could the number be?

b Four less than twice a number is greater than nine. What values could the number take?

c When four times a number is subtracted from one hundred the answer must be less than twenty five. What is the smallest integer that satisfies this condition?

d Donella has scored 94 points in the last six basketball games. If she earns two points per basket, how many baskets must she shoot in the next six games for her average points per game to be greater than 16?

e Jacky sells ice creams at the football. If she gets 25 cents for each ice cream she sells, how many must she sell to have at least $20, after she has given her brother Aaron the $5.40 she owed him?

Reading mathematics 6:06 | **Read carefully (and think)!**

Answer each problem below.

1 Which weighs more: 3 kg of lead or 3 kg of feathers?

2 A company has 5943 employees. All but 742 of them attended the company picnic. How many did not attend?

3 There are 27 students in Mr Han's class, of which 18 were boys. How many were not girls?

4 Mrs Glumicic left for work at 7:45 am, half an hour earlier than normal. She arrived at work at 6:25 am, worked for 8 hours and then went home. The trip home took 10 minutes longer than the trip to work. What time did Mrs Glumicic usually leave for work in the morning.

Be careful, now!

6:06

6:07 | Formulae: Evaluating the Subject

Formulae are special equations that represent relationships between quantities. For example $A = L \times W$ is a formula that represents the relationship between the area of a rectangle and its length and width.

A formula has more than one variable. To find the value of one variable, you must know the value of all the others in the formula.

The 'subject' of a formula is the pronumeral by itself, on the left-hand side.

Did you know that?

---

worked examples

1 Given that $v = u + at$ find v when $u = 6$, $a = 10$ and $t = 5$.

2 If $A = \dfrac{lw}{2}$, find A if $w = 9$ and $l = 5$.

3 Given that $d = \sqrt{h^2 + 2rh}$, find d when $h = 0.00175$ and $r = 6400$.

4 If $V = \dfrac{4}{3}\pi r^3$, find V when $r = 6$ (use the π value from your calculator).

Solutions

1 $u = 6$, $a = 10$ and $t = 5$

$v = u + at$

$v = 6 + 10 \times 5$

$v = 56$

2 $w = 9$ and $l = 5$

$A = \dfrac{lw}{2}$

$A = \dfrac{9 \times 5}{2}$

$A = 22\frac{1}{2}$

3 $h = 0.00175$ and $r = 6400$

$d = \sqrt{h^2 + 2rh}$

$d = \sqrt{(0.00175)^2 + 2 \times 6400 \times 0.00175}$

$d = 4.73$ (correct to 2 decimal places)

4 V when $r = 6$

$V = \dfrac{4}{3}\pi r^3$

$V = \dfrac{4}{3} \times \pi \times 6^3$

$V = 904.78$ (correct to 2 decimal places)

■ *Remember:*
• Replace the pronumerals with the given numerals.
• To find the value of one of the pronumerals you must be given the value of every other pronumeral.

Exercise 6:07

1 **a** If $\dfrac{x^2}{4a}$, evaluate y when $x = 12$ and $a = 4$.

b $T = a + (n - 1)d$. Find the value of T when $a = 7$, $d = 6$ and $n = 36$.

c Given that $A = P\left(1 + \dfrac{r}{100}\right)^n$, evaluate A to the nearest whole number if $P = 2500$, $r = 0.07$ and $n = 10$.

d If $T = ar^{n-1}$, find the value of T if $a = -3$, $r = 3$ and $n = 10$.

e $T = 2m\sqrt{\dfrac{l}{g}}$. Find the value of T if $m = 4.8$, $L = 3.6$ and $g = 0.1$.

f Given that $S = \dfrac{n}{2}(2a + (n - 1)d)$, find the value of S if $a = 7$, $d = 6$ and $n = 36$.

g If $x = \dfrac{-b + \sqrt{b^2 - 4ac}}{2a}$, evaluate x when $a = 2$, $b = -5$ and $c = -3$.

h $m = \dfrac{y_2 - y_1}{x_2 - x_1}$. Evaluate m when $x_1 = 3$, $x_2 = 5$, $y_1 = 4$ and $y_2 = 12$.

2 If the sides of a non-right angle triangle are given, the area can be calculated using the formula $A = \sqrt{s(s - a)(s - b)(s - c)}$, where a, b and c are the lengths of the sides of the triangle and $s = \dfrac{a + b + c}{2}$.

If the lengths of the sides of a triangle are 5 cm, 6 cm and 7 cm
  a Find the value of s for this triangle.
  b Find the area of the triangle correct to 1 decimal place.

3 **a** Sofia works out that the formula for the surface area, S, of the square pyramid shown is:

$$S = x^2 + x\sqrt{4h^2 + x^2}$$

Use Sofia's formula to find S when $x = 6$ and $h = 12$.

b Heron's formula states that the area of a triangle with sides of lengths a, b and c and semi-perimeter s is

$$A = \sqrt{s(s - a)(s - b)(s - c)}$$

Find A when $a = 7$, $b = 8$, $c = 11$ and $s = 13$.

c Given that $M = (X - Y)(X^2 + XY + Y^2)$ and $N = (X + Y)(X^2 - XY + Y^2)$ find M and N when $X = 8$ and $Y = -3$.

d Given $S = (X + Y + Z)^4 - 3(XY + XZ + YZ)^3 + (XYZ)^2$ find S when $X = -3$, $Y = -4$ and $Z = 5$.

• Formulae are used in many occupations when solving everyday problems.

6:08 | Formulae: Equations Arising from Substitution

Consider some of the formulae from the previous section:

$$v = u + at \qquad d = \sqrt{h^2 + 2rh} \qquad A = P\left(1 + \frac{r}{100}\right)^n \qquad T = 2m\sqrt{\frac{l}{g}}$$

The variable that is on the left-hand side of each of these formulae (on the own side of the equals sign) is called the **subject** of the formula. In the exercises so far, you have been asked to evaluate the subject of the formula.

Often the value of the subject is known and one of the other variables has to be evaluated. To do this, the known values are substituted which results in an equation that has to be solved.

worked examples

1 Given that $v = u + at$, evaluate a, when $v = 48$, $u = 16$ and $t = 4$.

2 $S = \frac{n}{2}(a + l)$. Find the value of a if $S = 144$, $n = 12$ and $l = 2$.

3 If $T = 2m\sqrt{\frac{l}{g}}$, find the value of l if $T = 72$, $m = 3$ and $g = 10$.

Solutions

1 $v = 48$, $u = 16$ and $t = 4$

$$v = u + at$$
$$48 = 16 + 4a$$
$$32 = 4a$$
$$\therefore a = 8$$

Remember:
Substitute then
solve the
equation.

Caution!
Equation
solving ability
needed here.

2 $S = 144$, $n = 12$ and $l = 2$

$$S = \frac{n}{2}(a + l)$$
$$144 = \frac{12}{2}(a + 2)$$
$$144 = 6(a + 2)$$
$$144 = 6a + 12$$
$$132 = 6a$$
$$\therefore a = 22$$

3 $T = 72$, $m = 3$ and $g = 10$

$$T = 2m\sqrt{\frac{l}{g}}$$
$$72 = 2 \times 3\sqrt{\frac{l}{10}}$$
$$12 = \sqrt{\frac{l}{10}}$$
$$144 = \frac{l}{10}$$
$$\therefore l = 1440$$

1 If $u = v - at$, find:

    a v when $u = 16$, $a = 3$, $t = 5$ **b** a when $u = 24$, $v = 3$, $t = 7$

    c v when $u = 8$, $a = 5$, $t = 2$ **d** t when $u = 0$, $v = 6$, $a = 3$

    e a when $u = -10$, $v = -6$, $t = 8$ **f** t when $u = 6$, $v = 15$, $a = \frac{1}{4}$

2 If $A = \dfrac{h}{2}(a + b)$, find:

    a h when $A = 36$, $a = 2$, $b = 4$ **b** h when $A = 48$, $a = 9$, $t = 6$

    c a when $A = 9$, $h = 6$, $b = 3$ **d** a when $A = 21$, $h = 5$, $b = 6$

    e b when $A = 60$, $h = 8$, $a = 8$ **f** b when $A = 49$, $h = 7$, $a = 9$

3 If $F = \dfrac{mv^2}{r}$, find:

    a m when $F = 20$, $v = 2$, $r = 5$ **b** m when $F = 35$, $v = 5$, $r = 8$

    c r when $F = 50$, $m = 10$, $v = 15$ **d** r when $F = 10$, $m = 3$, $v = 7$

    e v when $F = 18$, $m = 9$, $r = 8$ **f** v when $F = 32$, $m = 8$, $r = 9$

4 **a** If $V = IR$, find the value of R when $V = 30$ and $I = 7$.

    b If $F = \dfrac{gm_1 m_2}{r^2}$, find the value of g if $F = 60$, $m_1 = 12$, $m_2 = 8$ and $r = 4$.

    c $S = \dfrac{a}{1 - r}$. Find A when $S = 8$ and $r = 0.5$.

    d $V = \sqrt{\dfrac{3RT}{M}}$. Find the value of T if $V = 4$, $R = 2$ and $M = 5$.

    e Given that $F = 32 + \frac{9}{5}C$, evaluate C if $F = 95$.

5 **a** Given that $\dfrac{1}{A} = \dfrac{1}{B} + \dfrac{1}{C}$, evaluate B when $A = 3$ and $C = 5$.

    b $m = \dfrac{y_2 - y_1}{x_2 - x_1}$. Evaluate x_2 if $m = 2$, $y_2 = 6$, $y_1 = 4$ and $x_1 = 2$.

    c If $x^2 + y^2 = r^2$, find the value of x if $y = 15$ and $r = 17$.

    d $E = mgh + \frac{1}{2}mv^2$. Evaluate m if $E = 336$, $g = 10$, $h = 4$ and $v = 2$.

    e Given that $A = P\left(1 + \dfrac{r}{100}\right)^n$, find the value of P if $A = 3993$, $r = 10$ and $n = 3$.

6 **a** Given that $d = \dfrac{Ax + By}{A + B}$, find A given that $d = 12$, $B = 3$, $x = 9$ and $y = 2$.

    b If $X = \dfrac{x + ky}{1 + k}$, evaluate K when $X = 2\frac{1}{2}$, $x = -2$ and $y = 4$.

    c $D = \dfrac{T - a}{n - 1}$. Find the value of n if $T = 6 \cdot 1$, $a = 1 \cdot 6$ and $D = 0.3$.

    d Given that $R = \dfrac{S}{2\pi(L + H)}$, evaluate H if $R = 7 \cdot 2$, $S = 600$, $\pi = 3 \cdot 14$ and $L = 10 \cdot 6$.

    e $y = \dfrac{x + 3}{x - 2}$. Find the value of x when $y = 0 \cdot 8$.

6:09 | Solving Literal Equations (1)

prep quiz

Complete the following:

1 $x + 25 = 93$
∴ $x = 93 - ?$

2 $x + a = b$
∴ $x = b - ?$

3 $x - 27 = 53$
∴ $x = 53 + ?$

4 $x - m = n$
∴ $x = n + ?$

5 $5x = 70$
∴ $x = 70 \div ?$

6 $ax = b$
∴ $x = b \div ?$

7 $\dfrac{x}{5} = 3$
∴ $x = 3 \times ?$

8 $\dfrac{x}{m} = n$
∴ $x = n \times ?$

Solve:

9 $2a + 15 = 17$

10 $3(x - 5) = 10$

A formula such as $A = lb$ is written with A as its subject. This means that we can quite easily calculate A if we know the values of l and b. Sometimes, however, we need to rearrange the formula so that one of the other pronumerals is the subject. To do this, the same procedures as for solving equations are used.

In the examples, compare the solving of each equation with the changing of the subject of the formula to x, on the right.

■ *Remember:*
'+' is the opposite of '−'
'−' is the opposite of '+'
'×' is the opposite of '÷'
'÷' is the opposite of '×'

■ Another name for a formula is a 'literal equation'.

worked examples

1 Solve for x.

a $3x + 1 = 13$ −1 both sides
    $3x = 12$ ÷3 both sides
    $x = 4$

b $5 - 2x = 1$ +2x both sides
    $5 = 1 + 2x$ −1 both sides
    $4 = 2x$ ÷2 both sides
    $2 = x$
   ie $x = 2$

2 Make x the subject.

a $ax + b = c$ −b both sides
    $ax = c - b$ ÷a both sides
    $x = \dfrac{c - b}{a}$

b $m - nx = p$ +nx both sides
    $m = p + nx$ −p both sides
    $m - p = nx$ ÷n both sides
    $\dfrac{m - p}{n} = x$
   ie $x = \dfrac{m - p}{n}$

■ *Note:*
Another way of saying 'make x the subject of this formula' is: 'solve this literal equation for x'.

c $3(x + 2) = 5$ Expand

$3x + 6 = 5$ −6 both sides

$3x = -1$ ÷3 both sides

$x = \dfrac{-1}{3}$

c $a(x + b) = c$ Expand

$ax + ab = c$ −ab both sides

$ax = c - ab$ ÷a both sides

$x = \dfrac{c - ab}{a}$

3 Each formula below has had its subject changed to the capital letter.
The operation done to each side is shown for each step.

a $v = u + aT$ −u both sides

$v - u = aT$ ÷a both sides

$\dfrac{v - u}{a} = T$

$\therefore T = \dfrac{v - u}{a}$

b $m = \frac{1}{2}(x + Y)$ ×2 both sides

$2m = x + Y$ −x both sides

$2m - x = Y$

$\therefore Y = 2m - x$

c $t = a + (N - 1)d$ Expand

$t = a + Nd - d$ −a both sides

$t - a = Nd - d$ +d both sides

$t - a + d = Nd$ ÷d both sides

$\dfrac{t - a + d}{d} = N$

$\therefore N = \dfrac{t - a + d}{d}$

d $a = 2\pi r(r + H)$ Expand

$a = 2\pi r^2 + 2\pi rH$ −2πr² both sides

$a - 2\pi r^2 = 2\pi rH$ ÷2πr both sides

$\dfrac{a - 2\pi r^2}{2\pi r} = H$

$\therefore H = \dfrac{a - 2\pi r^2}{2\pi r}$

To change the subject of a formula (solve a literal equation):
1   **Expand parentheses if applicable.**
2   **By using inverse operations, isolate the pronumeral required to be the subject.**

Exercise 6:09

Foundation Worksheet 6:09

Solving literal equations
1 Make x the subject of:
   a $x - a = y$ **b** $2x = a$
2 Solve for x:
   a $2x + m = n$ **b** $\dfrac{x + a}{3} = y$

1   Make x the subject of each formula.

   a $p = x + m$ **b** $m = x + np$ **c** $n = pq - x$

   d $ax = b$ **e** $3x = y$ **f** $a^2x = b + c$

   g $b - ax = 2d$ **h** $ax - b = c$ **i** $c - 2b = ax + b$

   j $y = \dfrac{x}{a}$ **k** $y = \dfrac{a}{x}$ **l** $\dfrac{x}{y} = b$

   m $a = \dfrac{25}{x}$ **n** $\dfrac{ax}{b} = c$ **o** $p = \dfrac{2x}{L}$

2   After first expanding the grouping symbols, solve each literal equation for x.

   a $a = 2(x + y)$ **b** $p = 5(t + x)$ **c** $y = 3(x - 7)$

   d $p = q(x - r)$ **e** $6(a - x) = b$ **f** $w = t(v - x)$

   g $R = 2r(x + 2)$ **h** $p = 5q(x - y)$ **i** $A = \pi r(r - x)$

3 Solve each literal equation for the pronumeral shown in the brackets.

a $A = x + y$ [y]   b $P = 2L + 2B$ [L]   c $C = \pi d$ [d]

d $v = u + at$ [u]   e $v = u + at$ [a]   f $E = mc^2$ [m]

g $S = \dfrac{D}{T}$ [D]   h $R = \dfrac{V}{I}$ [V]   i $I = \dfrac{PRT}{100}$ [P]

j $P = RI^2$ [R]   k $v^2 = u^2 + 2as$ [s]   l $F = ac + p$ [a]

m $P = a(m + n)$ [n]   n $x = 2a(p + q)$ [p]   o $K = \frac{1}{2}mV^2$ [m]

p $P = m(v - u)$ [u]   q $V = \dfrac{AH}{3}$ [H]   r $V = \dfrac{\pi r^2 h}{3}$ [h]

s $S = \pi r^2 + \pi rh$ [h]   t $E = mgh + \frac{1}{2}mv^2$ [h]   u $P = 2ab - 2ak$ [k]

v $A = \dfrac{a + b}{2}$ [a]   w $A = \dfrac{h(a + b)}{2}$ [b]   x $F = \dfrac{q_2 q_2}{r}$ [r]

y $T = a + (n - 1)d$ [d]   z $S = \dfrac{a(r^n - 1)}{r - 1}$ [a]

6:10 | Solving Literal Equations (2)

Solve the equations:

1 $\dfrac{x}{5} = 3$ 2 $\dfrac{x}{8} = \dfrac{3}{4}$ 3 $\dfrac{x + 2}{3} = 5$ 4 $x^2 = 9$

5 $\sqrt{x} = 5$ 6 $(x + 3)^2 = 25$ 7 $\sqrt{x - 3} = 2$

Factorise fully:

8 $3x + 12$ 9 $x^2 - 2x$ 10 $5a^2 + 10ab$

In this section the formulae may also contain a squared term or a square root sign, or the pronumeral to become the subject may appear more than once.

■ Remember!
$\sqrt{}$ is the opposite of $(\ )^2$.
$(\ )^2$ is the opposite of $\sqrt{}$.

worked examples

Change the subject of the formula to the letter indicated in brackets.

1 $E = mc^2$ [c]   2 $v^2 = u^2 - 2as$ [u]   3 $r = \sqrt{\dfrac{A}{\pi}}$ [A]

4 $a = 6 - \dfrac{12}{R}$ [R]   5 $y = \dfrac{A}{A + 2}$ [A]

Solutions

1 $E = mc^2$ ÷ m both sides

$\dfrac{E}{m} = c^2$ $\sqrt{\ }$ both sides

$\therefore\ c = \pm\sqrt{\dfrac{E}{m}}$

2 $v^2 = u^2 - 2as$ $+\,2as$ both sides

$v^2 + 2as = u^2$ $\sqrt{\ }$ both sides

$\pm\sqrt{v^2 + 2as} = u$

$\therefore\ u = \pm\sqrt{v^2 + 2as}$

3 $r = \sqrt{\dfrac{A}{\pi}}$ Square both sides

$r^2 = \dfrac{A}{\pi}$ $\times\,\pi$ both sides

$\pi r^2 = A$

$\therefore\ A = \pi r^2$

4 $a = 6 - \dfrac{12}{R}$ $\times\,R$ both sides

$aR = 6R - 12$ $-\,6R$ both sides

$aR - 6R = -12$ Factorise L.H.S.

$R(a - 6) = -12$ $\div\,(a - 6)$ both sides

$\therefore\ R = \dfrac{-12}{a - 6}$

5 $y = \dfrac{A}{A + 2}$ $\times\,(A + 2)$ both sides

$y(A + 2) = A$ Expand L.H.S.

$Ay + 2y = A$ $-Ay$ both sides

$2y = A - Ay$ Factorise R.H.S.

$2y = A(1 - y)$ $\div\,(1 - y)$ both sides

$\dfrac{2y}{1 - y} = A$

$\therefore\ A = \dfrac{2y}{1 - y}$

> ▦ Remember!
> Sometimes formulae are called *literal equations*. When literal equations are 'solved' for a certain pronumeral, it is the same as changing the subject of the formula to that pronumeral.

 If the pronumeral that is to be the subject appears in more than one term in the formula, gather the terms together and factorise as in examples 4 and 5.

Exercise 6:10

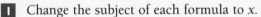

1   Change the subject of each formula to x.

   a $mx^2 = n$ **b** $a = bx^2$ **c** $x^2 - a = b$ **d** $h = k - x^2$

   e $\dfrac{x^2}{a} = y$ **f** $m = \dfrac{nx^2}{3}$ **g** $L = x^2 - y^2$ **h** $A = \dfrac{B}{x^2}$

2   Make a the subject of each formula.

   a $\sqrt{ab} = c$ **b** $u = \sqrt{3a}$ **c** $c = \sqrt{a - b}$ **d** $c = \sqrt{a} - b$

   e $P = L + M\sqrt{a}$ **f** $M - N\sqrt{a} = L$ **g** $\sqrt{3a - 1} = L$ **h** $P = \sqrt{b - 2a}$

3 Make N the subject of each formula after first multiplying each term by the lowest common denominator.

a $a = \dfrac{3N}{2}$

b $a = L - \dfrac{3N}{2}$

c $\dfrac{x}{3} = \dfrac{N}{2} - 1$

d $L = \dfrac{N}{2} + \dfrac{M}{3}$

e $x = \dfrac{N + a}{3}$

f $x = \dfrac{N - 1}{2} + \dfrac{M + 1}{3}$

g $\dfrac{N + u}{3} = \dfrac{m + u}{4}$

h $\dfrac{N - a}{b} = \dfrac{L + b}{a}$

4 Solve each literal equation for x.

a $a + x = b - x$

b $ax = px + q$

c $x + a = ax + b$

d $m - nx = n - mx$

e $px^2 = qx^2 + 2$

f $L = Ax + (1 + B)x$

g $\dfrac{x}{5} + \dfrac{x}{3} = a$

h $a = \dfrac{x}{x + 2}$

i $y = \dfrac{x}{x - 5}$

j $m = \dfrac{x + 3}{1 + x}$

k $A = \dfrac{a + bx}{1 + x}$

l $B = \dfrac{x + a}{x - a}$

5 Solve each equation for the letter shown in brackets.

A		B		C	
a $A = LB$	[B]	$A = X - Y$	[X]	$V = u + at$	[t]
b $D = \dfrac{M}{V}$	[V]	$D = \dfrac{S}{T}$	[S]	$P = RI^2$	[I]
c $V = \dfrac{Ah}{3}$	[h]	$V = \frac{1}{3}\pi r^2 h$	[r]	$S = 4\pi r^2$	[r]
d $M = \dfrac{a + b}{2}$	[b]	$A = \frac{1}{2}h(x + y)$	[y]	$v^2 = u^2 + 2as$	[s]
e $x^2 = ay - y^2$	[a]	$S = 2\pi r(r + h)$	[h]	$T = \dfrac{n}{2}[2a + (n - 1)d]$	[d]
f $a = \sqrt{bc}$	[c]	$Y = a\sqrt{X}$	[X]	$X = 2\sqrt{a - b}$	[a]
g $X = \sqrt{\dfrac{Y}{a}}$	[Y]	$R = \sqrt{\dfrac{ax}{b}}$	[x]	$m = \sqrt{\dfrac{a + b}{n}}$	[b]
h $T = 2\pi\sqrt{\dfrac{l}{g}}$	[l]	$A = 2x\sqrt{\dfrac{t}{u}}$	[u]	$u = \sqrt{v^2 - 2as}$	[s]
i $y = \dfrac{a}{3} + \dfrac{b}{2}$	[a]	$Z = \dfrac{X}{4} + \dfrac{Y}{3}$	[X]	$A = \dfrac{b - c}{5}$	[c]
j $\dfrac{A + x}{3} = \dfrac{A + y}{2}$	[A]	$L = \dfrac{N - 1}{2} + \dfrac{N + 1}{3}$	[N]	$\dfrac{X}{a} = \dfrac{X - a}{b}$	[X]
k $h = \dfrac{k}{2k + 1}$	[k]	$y = \dfrac{a}{a + 2}$	[a]	$z = \dfrac{x}{x - 3}$	[x]

6:11 | Solving Problems with Formulae

Often the solution of a problem requires the use of a formula. You have met formulae before in other areas of mathematics, such as finding the area and volume of shapes and solids.

In this section you will be asked to solve problems which involve formulae. Sometimes they are given, while at other times you will have to recall the relevant formula yourself.

worked examples

1   The density of a solid, D, in grams per cm^3 is given by the formula $D = \dfrac{M}{V}$, where M is the mass in grams and V is the volume in cm^3. Find:
   a   the density of a 92 gram block of steel if it has a volume of 9·6 cm^3
   b   the volume of a block of iron that has a density of 7·5 g/cm^3 and a mass of 450 grams.

2   The time, T, taken by a pendulum for one swing is given by the formula $T = 2\pi\sqrt{\dfrac{l}{g}}$ where $g = 9\cdot8$ m/s^2 and l is the length of the string in metres.

   a   Express the formula with l as the subject.
   b   If the time for one swing is 3·5 s, what must be the length of the pendulum, to the nearest cm?

Solutions

1   $$D = \frac{M}{V}$$

   a   If $M = 92$ g and $V = 9\cdot6$ cm^3

      then $D = \dfrac{92}{9\cdot6}$

         $= 9\cdot58$ g/cm^3 (to 2 dec. pl.)

   b   If $D = 7\cdot5$ g/cm^3 and $M = 450$ g

      then $7\cdot5 = \dfrac{450}{V}$

      ie $V = \dfrac{450}{7\cdot5}$

      so $V = 60$ cm^3

2   $$T = 2\pi\sqrt{\frac{l}{g}}$$

   a   Rearranging this formula gives:

      $$T = 2\pi\sqrt{\frac{l}{g}}$$

      $$\frac{T}{2\pi} = \sqrt{\frac{l}{g}}$$

      $$\left(\frac{T}{2\pi}\right)^2 = \frac{l}{g}$$

      so $l = g\left(\dfrac{T}{2\pi}\right)^2$

   b $$l = g\left(\frac{T}{2\pi}\right)^2$$

      If $g = 9\cdot8$ and $T = 3\cdot5$

      then $l = 9\cdot8\left(\dfrac{3\cdot5}{2\pi}\right)^2$

      Using a calculator:

         $l = 3\cdot04$ m

Note: If the solving of a problem requires the evaluation of a pronumeral that is *not* the subject, we may do it in two ways.
1   **Substitute the given values into the formula and solve the resulting equation; or**
2   **Change the subject of the formula before substituting the given values.**

Exercise 6:11

1 **a** If the perimeter of a square is 16·8 m, what is its area?
  b Calculate the area of a rectangle that has a perimeter of 150 cm if its width is 25 cm.

2 **a** Write down the formula for the area of a circle.
  b Determine the diameter of a circle, to the nearest cm, if its area is 38·5 cm².

3 The temperature in degrees Fahrenheit (F) is related to the Celsius measure (C) by the formula: $F = \frac{9}{5}C + 32$
  a If the temperature is 65°C, what is it in degrees Fahrenheit?
  b If the temperature is 104°F, what is it in degrees Celsius?

4 The volume of a cube is given by the formula $V = x^3$, where x is the side length of the cube. Find the side length of the cube if the volume is 1728 cm³.

5 The volume of a cone is given by the formula $V = \dfrac{\pi r^2 h}{3}$, where h is the height of the cone and r is the radius of the cone. If the volume of a cone is 12·6 m³, find, to the nearest cm:
  a the height, if the radius is 1·4 m
  b the radius, if the height is 2·2 m

6 Find the radius of a sphere, correct to 2 significant figures, if its surface area is 45 cm². The surface area, S, is given by the formula $S = 4\pi r^2$, where r is the radius.

7 The diagram shows an oval made up of a rectangle with two semicircular ends. Calculate a formula for the perimeter, P, in terms of D and x. Calculate the value of D needed to give a perimeter of 400 m if:
  a $x = 80$ m   **b** $x = 100$ m

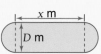

8 If a body has an initial velocity of u m/s and it accelerates at a rate of a m/s² for a time period of t seconds, its velocity v is given by the formula:
    $v = u + at$
  If the final velocity, v, of a certain body is 25 m/s, find:
  a its initial velocity, u, if $a = 5\cdot6$ m/s² and $t = 3\cdot2$ seconds
  b its acceleration, a, if $u = 13$ m/s and $t = 2\cdot5$ seconds
  c the time, t, taken if $u = 14\cdot6$ m/s and $a = 1\cdot6$ m/s²

9 The kinetic energy K (in joules) of a particle of mass m kg, moving with a velocity of v m/s, is given by the formula:

$$K = \tfrac{1}{2}mv^2$$

If the kinetic energy of a particle is 4·6 joules, find:

a its mass, if the velocity is 1·9 m/s

b its velocity, if the mass is 1·26 kg

(Give answers correct to 1 decimal place.)

10 A cylindrical tank holds 1200 litres of water. Its radius is 0·8 metres, what is the depth of the water? (*Note:* 1 cubic metre = 1000 litres.) Give your answer correct to the nearest centimetre.

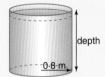

11 The formula for compound interest is:

$$A = P\left(1 + \frac{r}{100}\right)^n$$

where A is the amount accumulated after investing P dollars for n years at a rate of $r\%$ pa. Find:

a the amount A after investing $2000 for 8 years at 11% pa.

b the original investment, P, if it accumulated to $11 886 in 12 years at $9\tfrac{1}{2}\%$ pa. (Answer correct to the nearest dollar.)

c At what rate must $10 000 be invested to accumulate to $19 254 in 5 years? Answer correct to 2 significant figures.

12 **a** Construct a formula for the area of this annulus.

b If $R = 6·9$ cm and $r = 4·1$ cm, find its area.

c If its area is 45 cm² and $R = 5·2$ cm, find r.

d If its area is 75 cm² and $r = 3·9$ cm, find R.

(Give answers correct to 1 decimal place.)

13 **a** Construct a formula for the volume of this solid.

b Find its volume if $r = 2·6$ m and $h = 5·1$ m.

c Find h if its volume is 290 m² and $r = 3·2$ m.

(Give answers correct to 3 significant figures.)

(Volume of sphere $= \tfrac{4}{3}\pi r^3$)

14 The formula $V = \dfrac{q}{4\pi\varepsilon_0 r}$ gives the potential V volts, at a distance r metres from a point charge of q coulombs.

a Find V if $q = 1·0 \times 10^{-8}$ coulombs, $r = 0·2$ m and $4\pi\varepsilon_0 = 9·0 \times 10^9$.

b Find r if $q = 3·0 \times 10^{-7}$ coulombs, $V = 54\,000$ volts and $4\pi\varepsilon_0 = 9·0 \times 10^9$.

15 The formula $F = \dfrac{Kq_1 q_2}{r^2}$ gives the force between two point charges of q_1 and q_2 coulombs that are r metres apart. If two equally charged balls are placed 0·1 m apart and the force between the balls is $9·8 \times 10^{-4}$ newtons, calculate the charge on each ball. $K = 9·0 \times 10^9$.

Mathematical Terms 6

equation
- A number sentence where one or more of the numbers is missing or unknown.
- The unknown number is represented by a pronumeral.

 eg $x + 5 = 8$, $\dfrac{3x + 1}{7} = \dfrac{x - 5}{2}$

expression
- An algebraic expression consists of one or more terms joined together by operation signs.

 eg $a + 5$, $x^2 - x + 4$, $\dfrac{3m - 1}{7}$

- An expression does *not* have an 'equals' sign like an equation.

formula (plural: formulae)
- A formula represents a relationship between physical quantities.
- It will always have more than one pronumeral.

 eg $A = L \times B$ represents the relationship between the area (A) of a rectangle and its length (L) and breadth (B).

grouping symbols
- The most common types are:

 parentheses ( )
 brackets [ ]
 braces { }

- Used to 'group' a number of terms together in an expression.

 eg $5(x + 3)$

inequality signs
- $>$ greater than, $<$ less than
- $\geqslant$ greater than or equal to, $\leqslant$ less than or equal to

 eg $x + 3 < 4$ means that
  $x + 3$ *is less than 4*

inequation
- An *equation* where the 'equals' sign has been replaced by an inequality sign.

 eg $4x - 1 > 5$ or $\dfrac{x}{3} \leqslant 4$

inverse operation
- The operation that will reverse or 'undo' a previous operation.

 eg addition is the inverse operation of subtraction; division is the inverse operation of multiplication

pronumeral
- A symbol used to represent a number.
- Usually a letter such as x.

solution
- Method of finding the answer to a problem
 OR
 the answer to a problem.
- The solution to an equation is the number or numbers that satisfy the equation or make it a true sentence.

 eg $x = 3$ is the solution to $x + 2 = 5$

solve
- Find the *solution* or answer to a problem or equation.

subject
- The subject of a formula is the pronumeral by itself, on the left-hand side.

 eg in the formula $v = u + at$ the subject is v.

substitution
- The replacing of a pronumeral with a numeral in a formula or expression.

 eg to substitute 3 for a in the expression $4a - 2$ would give:
  $4(3) - 2$
  $= 12 - 2$
  $= 10$

Mathematical terms 6

Diagnostic Test 6: | Equations, Inequations and Formulae

- Each part of this test has similar items which test a certain type of question.
- Failure in more than one item will identify an area of weakness.
- Each weakness should be treated by going back to the section listed.

	Section
1 Solve: a $4p + 3 = 31$ b $2m - 7 = 17$ c $25 = 5 - 2m$	6:01
2 Solve: a $3x + 5 = 2x + 1$ b $5a - 7 = 3a - 1$ c $4b + 7 = b - 8$	6:01
3 Solve: a $3(x + 1) = 9$ b $4(a - 3) = 24$ c $6(x - 3) + 4x = 8$	6:02

4 Solve:
  a $3(x + 4) = 2(x - 3)$ b $3(a - 1) + 5(a + 3) = 20$
  c $2(2m + 3) - 3(m - 5) = 7$
	6:02

5 Solve: a $\dfrac{y}{2} + 1 = 7$ b $\dfrac{m}{2} - 1 = 5$ c $4 = 13 - \dfrac{p}{2}$ d $\dfrac{3m}{5} = 6$	6:03
6 Solve: a $\dfrac{m + 3}{4} = 2$ b $\dfrac{m - 6}{3} = 1$ c $\dfrac{3p - 7}{2} = 7$ d $\dfrac{5 + 3x}{5} = 5$	6:03
7 Solve: a $\dfrac{m}{5} + 2 = m$ b $2x + 1 = \dfrac{3x}{2}$ c $\dfrac{n + 7}{4} = 2n$ d $\dfrac{5a - 2}{3} = 3 - a$	6:03
8 Solve: a $\dfrac{a}{3} + \dfrac{a}{2} = 10$ b $\dfrac{2m}{3} - \dfrac{m}{2} = 4$ c $\dfrac{x}{4} = \dfrac{x}{5} - 3$ d $\dfrac{2y + 1}{4} = \dfrac{3y - 4}{3}$	6:04

9 Form an equation from the given data for each of these.
(In each case let a represent the unknown number.)
  a I think of a number, multiply it by 2, add 7 and the result is 10.
  b I think of a number, divide it by 3, subtract 4 and the result is 4.
  c I think of a number, add 6, then multiply by 3 and the result is 32.
	6:05

10 Form an equation for each question. (Let the unknown quantity be x.)
  a The sum of a brother's and sister's ages is 57 years. If the brother is 5 years older than his sister, find their ages.
  b A rectangle is three times longer than it is wide. If its perimeter is 48 cm, find its length and width.
  c A father is presently three times as old as his son. In 10 years he will be twice as old as his son. Find their present ages.
	6:05

11 Graph the following on a number line. a $x > 3$ b $x \leqslant -1$ c $x \geqslant 0$ d $x < 5$	6:06

12 Solve:

   a $2x + 5 \geqslant 6$ **b** $\dfrac{2x - 1}{3} < 6$ **c** $3x - 7 > x + 3$

13 Solve:

   a $5 - 3x > 11$ **b** $-\frac{1}{3}x > 21$ **c** $3 - 4a > 2 - a$

14 **a** If $v = u + at$, find v when $u = 6.8$, $a = 9.8$ and $t = 3$.

   b If $C = 2\pi r^2$, find C when $\pi = \frac{22}{7}$ and $r = 0.77$.

   c Given $A = \frac{1}{2}h(a + b)$, find A when $h = 2.6$, $a = 9.4$ and $b = 16.4$.

15 **a** If $M = 2m + 3n$, find m when $M = 17.5$ and $n = 0.5$.

   b If $V = \dfrac{AH}{3}$, find H when $V = 6.03$ and $A = 1.2$.

   c Given that $V = 4\pi r^2$, find r when $\pi = 3.14$ and $V = 153.86$.

16 Change the subject of each formula to a.

   a $x = 3a - 2b$ **b** $V^2 = u^2 + 2as$ **c** $A = \dfrac{D(a + b)}{h}$

17 Change the subject of each formula to y.

   a $ay^2 = x$ **b** $T = A\sqrt{\dfrac{B}{y}}$ **c** $P = \dfrac{y}{1 + y}$

• Many equations need to be solved in the design and construction of aircraft.

Chapter 6 | Revision Assignment

1 Solve:
   a $5m - 7 = 8$ b $3y + 7 = 4$
   c $6m - 1 = 17$ d $4n + 10 = 2$
   e $3x + 7 = 5x - 4$ f $x - 5 = 6x + 3$
   g $10 + 4x = 3x - 1$ h $8 - 3x = 7 + 2x$
   i $12 - 5x = 10 - 3x$

2 Solve these equations which involve grouping symbols.
   a $5(x + 7) = 30$ b $7(a - 3) = 21$
   c $8(m - 1) = 4$ d $4(x + 3) = 3(x + 2)$
   e $5(n - 2) = 3(n + 4)$
   f $10(x - 7) = 7(x - 10)$
   g $4(2a + 3) + 3(a - 3) = 5$
   h $5(3n + 4) + 2(5 - 2n) = 7$
   i $6(m + 4) - 5(m + 3) = 6$
   j $7(4x + 3) - 3(8x - 5) = 0$

3 Solve:
   a $\dfrac{x}{4} + 3 = 5$ b $\dfrac{m}{5} - 2 = 1$

   c $\dfrac{2x}{3} - 4 = 2$ d $\dfrac{a + 7}{4} = 6$

   e $\dfrac{y - 5}{3} = 1$ f $\dfrac{3p + 1}{5} = 2$

   g $\dfrac{2m}{3} - 1 = m$ h $\dfrac{5m - 1}{4} = 2m$

   i $2n + 5 = \dfrac{n - 1}{3}$ j $\dfrac{x + 5}{2} = \dfrac{x - 3}{4}$

   k $\dfrac{a}{5} - \dfrac{a}{2} = 7$ l $\dfrac{5q + 1}{2} = \dfrac{q}{3} - \dfrac{q}{4}$

4 Solve and graph each solution on a number line.
   a $m + 7 = 5$ b $2x - 1 < 7$
   c $5n + 1 > 3$ d $3x + 7 \leqslant x + 10$
   e $y - 5 > 3y - 8$ f $4n + 7 \geqslant 7n - 4$
   g $6 - 2x > 14$ h $-\dfrac{2x}{3} \geqslant 6$
   i $10 - 3a \leqslant 7 - a$

5 Write an equation for each of the following and then solve it.
   a A number is multiplied by 3, then 7 is added and the result is 15.
   b Nine is subtracted from a number and the result is multiplied by five to equal thirty.

   c Eight times a certain number plus ten is equal to twelve times the same number minus seven.
   d A boy is 12 years older than his sister. If in 4 years time he will be twice her age, what are their present ages?
   e Two sisters are presently 2 years old and 12 years old respectively. How many years will have to pass before the elder sister is $1\frac{1}{2}$ times the age of the younger sister?

6 a Given that $S = ut + \frac{1}{2}at^2$, find S when $u = 7$, $t = 3$, $a = 10$.
   b If $C = 2mr$, find m when $C = 17 \cdot 6$ and $r = 1 \cdot 1$.
   c If $P = \dfrac{1}{a} + \dfrac{1}{b}$, find P when $a = 0 \cdot 4$ and $b = 0 \cdot 625$.

7 a If $D = \dfrac{M}{V}$, find V when $D = 1 \cdot 5$ and $M = 0 \cdot 5$.
   b If $E = \dfrac{Ab}{A + b}$, find b when $E = 15$ and $A = 0 \cdot 4$.
   c Given that $M = \dfrac{X}{a} + \dfrac{X}{b}$, find a when $M = 27 \cdot 5$, $X = 15$, $b = 3$.

8 Rearrange each formula to make P the subject.
   a $A = \dfrac{PRT}{100}$ b $V = RP^2$

   c $T = \sqrt{\dfrac{3P}{R}}$ d $X = \dfrac{1}{P} - \dfrac{1}{Q}$

9 **Challenge question**
   Solve the following equations.
   a $\dfrac{3}{x} = 5$ b $\dfrac{2}{x - 1} = 3$

   c $\dfrac{x}{x + 1} = 4$ d $\dfrac{4}{3x} - \dfrac{2}{x} = 5$

   e $\dfrac{x}{2x - 1} - 3 = \dfrac{1}{4}$ f $\dfrac{1}{3} - \dfrac{1}{p - 1} = 3$

Chapter 6 | Working Mathematically

1 Use ID Card 7 on page xix to identify:

   a 13   **b** 14   **c** 15   **d** 16   **e** 19

   f 20   **g** 21   **h** 22   **i** 23   **j** 24

2 Use the Algebra Card on page xx to:

   a multiply column H by column J   **b** multiply column N by column A

   c square column G   **d** multiply column O by column H

3 Ten students lined up at a tap to get a drink. Each person took one minute to drink.

   a How long did it take before the last student finished drinking?

   b What was the total time spent by all ten students in waiting and drinking?

4 Find the basic numeral for:

$$(1 - \tfrac{1}{2}) + (\tfrac{1}{2} - \tfrac{1}{3}) + (\tfrac{1}{3} - \tfrac{1}{4}) + (\tfrac{1}{4} - \tfrac{1}{5}) + (\tfrac{1}{5} - \tfrac{1}{6}) + (\tfrac{1}{6} - \tfrac{1}{7}) + (\tfrac{1}{7} - \tfrac{1}{8}) + (\tfrac{1}{8} - \tfrac{1}{9}) + (\tfrac{1}{9} - \tfrac{1}{10})$$

5 In computing, the units kilobyte, megabyte and gigabyte are used. Because computers use the binary system, which is based on powers of 2, each prefix is given the value of the power of 2 nearest to its true value.

   For example:

      kilo = 1000

      $2^{10} = 1024$

   This is the power of 2 nearest to 1000.

   So 1 kilobyte = 1024 bytes.

   a Find what power of 2 is closest in value to: **b** How many bytes are there in:

      i 1 000 000   **ii** 1 000 000 000   **i** a megabyte?   **ii** a gigabyte?

6 **a** How long does it take the water to reach a temperature of 80°C?

   b What is the temperature of the water after 10 min?

   c What is the temperature of the water after 20 min?

   d From the graph it can be seen that the water doesn't cool at a constant rate.

      The dotted line represents a constant cooling rate. If the water had cooled at a constant rate, what would its temperature have been after 10 min?

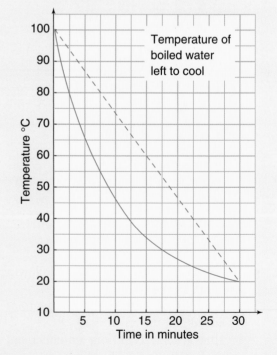

Temperature of boiled water left to cool

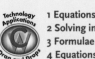
Technology Applications

1 Equations with fractions

2 Solving inequations

3 Formulae

Drag and Drops

4 Equations from formulae

5 Solving literal equations

Chapter Review

Questions

7

Factorising Algebraic Expressions

Can you crack the code, Mr. x?

$3x + 12 = 7x$
$(a+3)(a+4)$
$\sqrt{9y^2}$
$\dfrac{x}{2}$

Chapter Contents

Learning Outcomes

Students will be able to:

- Factorise using common factors.
- Factorise by grouping in pairs.
- Factorise using the difference of two squares.
- Factorise quadratic trinomials.
- Simplify algebraic fractions by factorising.
- Perform operations with algebraic fractions.

Areas of Interaction

Approaches to Learning (Knowledge Acquisition, Problem Solving, Logical Thinking, Reflection), Human Ingenuity

In Chapter 4, Algebraic Expressions, you were shown how to expand various algebraic products that were written in a factorised form; that is, each product had to be rewritten without grouping symbols.

For example:

$$3a(5 - 2a) \rightarrow 15a - 6a^2$$
$$(a - 2)(a + 7) \rightarrow a^2 + 5a - 14$$
$$(x + 5)^2 \rightarrow x^2 + 10x + 25$$
$$(m + 2)(m - 2) \rightarrow m^2 - 4$$

This chapter will show you how to reverse this process. You will learn how to factorise various algebraic expressions.

7:01 | Factorising Using Common Factors

To factorise an algebraic expression, we must determine the highest common factor (HCF) of the terms and insert grouping symbols, usually parentheses.

If we expand the expression $5a(a - 2)$ we obtain $5a^2 - 10a$.
To factorise $5a^2 - 10a$ we simply reverse the process. We notice that $5a$ is the HCF of $5a^2$ and 2, so $5a$ is written outside the brackets and the remainder is written inside the brackets: $5a^2 - 10a = 5a(a - 2)$.

> ■ A factor of a given number is another number that will divide into the given number with no remainder.
> eg {1, 2, 3, 6, 9, 18} is the set of factors of 18.

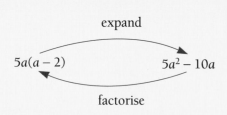

expand

$5a(a - 2)$ $5a^2 - 10a$

factorise

'Gnidnapxe' is the reverse of 'expanding'.

It's 'factorising', you dummy!

worked examples

1   $5y + 15 = 5 \times y + 5 \times 3$ (HCF is 5)
         $= 5(y + 3)$

2   $21x - 24y = 3 \times 7x - 3 \times 8y$ (HCF is 3)
           $= 3(7x - 8y)$

3   $12ab + 18a = 6a \times b + 6a \times 3$ (HCF is $6a$)
           $= 6a(b + 3)$

4   $5x^2 - 30x = 5x \times x - 5x \times 6$ (HCF is $5x$)
           $= 5x(x - 6)$

5   $-12x^2 - 3x = -3x \times 4x - 3x \times 1$ (HCF is $-3x$)
           $= -3x(4x + 1)$

6   $3a^2b - 9ab^2 + 15ab = 3ab \times a - 3ab \times b + 3ab \times 5$
                    $= 3ab(a - b + 5)$

$ab + ac = a(b + c)$

Exercise 7:01

1 Factorise the following completely.

a $5x + 15y$ b $-3m - m^2$

c $6xy - 2x$ d $15p - 20q$

e $15pq - 20q$ f $12st^2 + 15st$

g $-18xy - 6x$ h $at - at^2$

i $7x^2y + xy$ j $a^2 + ab$

2 Factorise each of the following.

a $a^2 + ab + 3a$ b $xy - 3x^2 + 2x$

c $12st - 4t^3 + 8t$ d $36 - 12ab + 18b$

e $3ab - 9a^2b + 12ab^2 + a^2b^2$ f $4m - 8n - 12mn$

g $3 + 5m - 2n$ h $-3n - 5mn + 2n^2$

i $12x^2 + 8x - 4$ j $12x^2y^2 + 8xy^2 - 4y^2$

3 Examine this example

$x(x + 1) - 2(x + 1)$ has a common factor of $(x + 1)$ so it can be taken out as a common factor

so $x(x + 1) - 2(x + 1) = (x + 1)(x - 2)$

Now factorise these similar types.

a $x(x + 4) + y(x + 4)$ b $4(a + 2) - b(a + 2)$

c $m(m - 1) - 3(m - 1)$ d $2(s - 3) + s(s - 3)$

e $2a(a - 1) - (a - 1)$ f $3m(9 - 2m) + 2(9 - 2m)$

g $x(x - 5) + 2(3x - 15)$ h $y(y + 5) + 2(-y - 5)$

i $x(3 - x) + 5(x - 3)$ j $ab(9 - a) - 2(a - 9)$

> ■ Note:
> $(x + 1)(x - 2) = (x - 2)(x + 1)$

4 Factorise fully the following algebraic expressions.

a $9x + 6$ b $10 + 15a$ c $4m - 6n$

d $x^2 + 7x$ e $2a^2 - 3a$ f $12y - 6y^2$

g $ab - bx$ h $st - s$ i $4ab + 10bc$

j $-4m + 6n$ k $-x^2 - 3x$ l $-15a + 5ab$

m $3x + x^2 - ax$ n $ax + ay + az$ o $4m - 8n + 6p$

p $2(a + x) + b(a + x)$ q $x(3 + b) + 2(3 + b)$ r $y(x - 1) - 3(x - 1)$

s $5ab - 15ac + 10ad$ t $x^2 - 7x + xy$ u $a(a + 3) - (a + 3)$

Factorise these expressions.	**1** $3a + 18$	**2** $5x + ax$	**3** $pq - px$	
	4 $3ax - 9bx$	**5** $x^2 - 2x$	**6** $a^3 + a^2$	
	7 $9 - 3a$	**8** $-5m - 10$		
	9 $9(a + 1) + x(a + 1)$			
	10 $x(x + y) - 1(x + y)$			

For some algebraic expressions, there may not be a factor common to every term. For example, there is no factor common to every term in the expression:

$3x + 3 + mx + m$

But the first two terms have a common factor of 3 and the remaining terms have a common factor of m. So:

$3x + 3 + mx + m = 3(x + 1) + m(x + 1)$

Now it can be seen that $(x + 1)$ is a common factor for each term.

$3(x + 1) + m(x + 1) = (x + 1)(3 + m)$

Therefore:

$3x + 3 + mx + m = (x + 1)(3 + m)$

The original expression has been factorised by grouping the terms in pairs.

worked examples

1
$$2x + 2y + ax + ay = 2(x + y) + a(x + y)$$
$$= (x + y)(2 + a)$$

2
$$a^2 + 3a + ax + 3x = a(a + 3) + x(a + 3)$$
$$= (a + 3)(a + x)$$

3
$$ax - bx + am - bm = x(a - b) + m(a - b)$$
$$= (a - b)(x + m)$$

4
$$ab + b^2 - a - b = b(a + b) - 1(a + b)$$
$$= (a + b)(b - 1)$$

5
$$5x + 2y + xy + 10 = 5x + 10 + 2y + xy$$
$$= 5(x + 2) + y(2 + x)$$
$$= (x + 2)(5 + y)$$

> *Note:* Terms had to be rearranged to pair those with common factors.

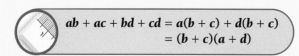
$$ab + ac + bd + cd = a(b + c) + d(b + c)$$
$$= (b + c)(a + d)$$

Exercise 7:02

Foundation Worksheet 7:02

Grouping in pairs
1 Complete the factorising.
   a $3(x + 2) + a(x + 2)$
2 Factorise.
   a $am + 5a + 2m + 10$

1 Complete the factorisation of each expression below.

a $2(a + b) + x(a + b)$ b $a(x + 7) + p(x + 7)$

c $m(x - y) + n(x - y)$ d $x(m + n) - y(m + n)$

e $a^2(2 - x) + 7(2 - x)$ f $q(q - 2) - 2(q - 2)$

g $(x + y) + a(x + y)$ h $x(1 - 3y) - 2(1 - 3y)$

2 Factorise these expressions.

a $pa + pb + qa + qb$ b $3a + 3b + ax + bx$ c $mn + 3np + 5m + 15p$

d $a^2 + ab + ac + bc$ e $9x^2 - 12x + 3xy - 4y$ f $12p^2 - 16p + 3pq - 4q$

g $ab + 3c + 3a + bc$ h $xy + y + 4x + 4$ i $a^3 + a^2 + a + 1$

j $pq + 5r + 5p + qr$ k $xy - x + y - 1$ l $8a - 2 + 4ay - y$

m $mn + m + n + 1$ n $x^2 + my + xy + mx$ o $x^2 - xy + xw - yw$

p $x^2 + yz + xz + xy$ q $11a + 4c + 44 + ac$ r $a^3 - a^2 + a - 1$

3 Factorise the following.

a $xy + xz - wy - wz$ b $ab + bc - ad - cd$ c $5a + 15 - ab - 3b$

d $6x - 24 - xy + 4y$ e $11y + 22 - xy - 2x$ f $ax^2 - ax - x + 1$

• This is an exercise you can sink your teeth into!

7:03 | Factorising Using the Difference of Two Squares

Simplify: **1** $\sqrt{16}$ **2** $\sqrt{49}$ **3** $\sqrt{121}$

If x is positive, simplify: **4** $\sqrt{x^2}$ **5** $\sqrt{9x^2}$ **6** $\sqrt{64x^2}$

Expand and simplify: **7** $(x-2)(x+2)$ **8** $(x+5)(x-5)$

    9 $(7-a)(7+a)$ **10** $(3m+2n)(3m-2n)$

If the expression we want to factorise is the difference of two squares, we can simply reverse the procedure seen in section 3:07B.

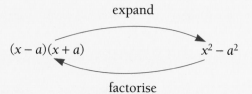

expand

$(x-a)(x+a)$ $x^2 - a^2$

factorise

worked examples

1 $x^2 - 9 = x^2 - 3^2$
          $= (x-3)(x+3)$

2 $25a^2 - b^2 = (5a)^2 - b^2$
              $= (5a - b)(5a + b)$

3 $a^4 - 64 = (a^2)^2 - 8^2$
          $= (a^2 - 8)(a^2 + 8)$

4 $36m^2 - 49n^2 = (6m)^2 - (7n)^2$
                 $= (6m - 7n)(6m + 7n)$

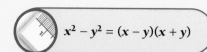 $x^2 - y^2 = (x-y)(x+y)$

■ *Note:* $(x-y)(x+y) = (x+y)(x-y)$

Exercise 7:03

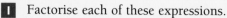

1   Factorise each of these expressions.

a $x^2 - 4$	**b** $a^2 - 16$	**c** $m^2 - 25$	**d** $p^2 - 81$
e $y^2 - 100$	**f** $x^2 - 121$	**g** $9 - x^2$	**h** $1 - n^2$
i $49 - y^2$	**j** $a^2 - b^2$	**k** $x^2 - a^2$	**l** $y^2 - a^2$
m $9a^2 - 4$	**n** $16x^2 - 1$	**o** $25p^2 - 9$	**p** $49 - 4a^2$
q $25p^2 - a^2$	**r** $m^2 - 81n^2$	**s** $100a^2 - 9b^2$	**t** $81x^2 - 121y^2$

2   Factorise by first taking out a common factor.

a $2x^2 - 32$	**b** $3x^2 - 108$
c $4a^2 - 100$	**d** $5y^2 - 20$
e $24a^2 - 6b^2$	**f** $3x^2 - 27y^2$
g $8y^2 - 128$	**h** $80p^2 - 5q^2$
i $4x^2 - 64$	**j** $3x^2 - 3$
k $72p^2 - 2$	**l** $2 - 18x^2$
m $8a^2 - 18m^2$	**n** $125 - 20a^2$
o $200x^2 - 18y^2$	**p** $98m^2 - 8n^2$

worked example

$18x^2 - 50 = 2(9x^2 - 25)$
            $= 2([3x]^2 - 5^2)$
            $= 2(3x - 5)(3x + 5)$

Challenge 7:03 | The difference of two cubes (Extension)

- The large cube has a volume of a^3 cubic units
  It is made up of four smaller parts
  (a cube and three rectangular prisms).
  Our aim is to find an expression for the
  difference of two cubes ($a^3 - b^3$).

1 Complete the table below.

2 Write an expression for the volume of the large
  cube (a^3) in terms of the volumes of the four
  smaller parts.
  ie $a^3 = V_① + V_② + V_③ + V_④$

3 Use your answer to question **2** to write an
  expression for $a^3 - b^3$.

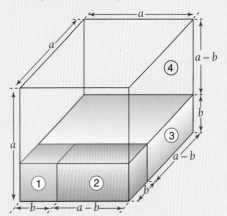

Volume of part ①	Volume of part ②	Volume of part ③	Volume of part ④
$b \times b \times b$			

Express each volume as a product of its factors.

> ▆ Note: $a^3 - b^3 = (a - b)(a^2 + ab + b^2)$

Applying this to algebraic expressions, we could factorise a difference of two cubes:

eg $x^3 - 8 = x^3 - 2^3$
$\qquad = (x - 2)(x^2 + 2x + 4)$

Exercises

Factorise these expressions using the formula above.

1 $m^3 - n^3$ 2 $x^3 - y^3$

3 $a^3 - 8$ 4 $m^3 - 27$

5 $x^3 - 1000$ 6 $y^3 - 125$

7 $64 - n^3$ 8 $27 - k^3$

9 $8m^3 - 27$ 10 $64x^3 - 125y^3$

11 $125x^3 - 8y^3$ 12 $27m^3 - 343n^3$

prep quiz

Expand:

1 $(x + 2)(x + 3)$ 2 $(a - 1)(a + 3)$ 3 $(m - 7)(m - 2)$

4 $(x + 5)^2$ 5 $(a - 2)^2$

Find two numbers a and b where:

6 $a + b = 5$ and $ab = 6$ 7 $a + b = 9$ and $ab = 20$

8 $a + b = -2$ and $ab = -15$ 9 $a + b = 3$ and $ab = -4$

10 $a + b = 7$ and $ab = -18$

- An expression with three terms is called a *trinomial*.
- Expressions like $x^2 + 3x - 4$ are called *quadratic trinomials*. The highest power of the variable is 2.
- Factorising is the reverse of expanding.

$$(x + a)(x + b) = x^2 + ax + bx + ab$$
$$= x^2 + (a + b)x + ab$$

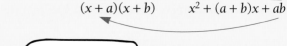

$(x + a)(x + b) \qquad x^2 + (a + b)x + ab$

Using this result, to factorise $x^2 + 5x + 6$ we look for two values a and b, where $a + b = 5$ and $ab = 6$.

These numbers are 2 and 3, so:
$x^2 + 5x + 6 = (x + 2)(x + 3)$

2 and 3 add to give 5 and multiply to give 6.

worked examples

Factorise:

1 $x^2 + 7x + 10$ 2 $m^2 - 6m + 8$ 3 $y^2 + y - 12$ 4 $x^2 - 9x - 36$ 5 $3y^2 + 15y - 72$

If $x^2 + 7x + 10 = (x + a)(x + b)$ then $a + b = 7$ and $ab = 10$.

Solutions

1
$2 + 5 = 7$
$2 \times 5 = 10$

$\therefore x^2 + 7x + 10$
$= (x + 2)(x + 5)$

2
$(-2) + (-4) = -6$
$(-2) \times (-4) = 8$

$\therefore m^2 - 6m + 8$
$= (m - 2)(m - 4)$

3
$(-3) + 4 = 1$
$(-3) \times 4 = -12$

$\therefore y^2 + y - 12$
$= (y - 3)(y + 4)$

4
$3 + (-12) = -9$
$3 \times (-12) = -36$

$\therefore x^2 - 9x - 36$
$= (x + 3)(x - 12)$

5 $3y^2 + 15y - 72$
$= 3(y^2 + 5y - 24)$

$(-3) + 8 = 5$
$(-3) \times 8 = -24$

$\therefore 3(y^2 + 5y - 24)$
$= 3(y - 3)(y + 8)$

Step 1:
Take out any common factor.

Exercise 7:04

Foundation Worksheet 7:04

Factorising trinomials
1 Which two integers:
  a add to   **b** multiply to
  give 4?   give 5?
2 Factorise:
  a $m^2 + 8m + 9$ **b** $n^2 - 3n + 2$

1 Factorise each of these trinomials.

a $x^2 + 4x + 3$	**b** $x^2 + 3x + 2$	
c $x^2 + 6x + 5$	**d** $x^2 + 7x + 6$	
e $x^2 + 9x + 20$	**f** $x^2 + 10x + 25$	
g $x^2 + 12x + 36$	**h** $x^2 + 10x + 21$	**i** $x^2 + 9x + 18$
j $x^2 + 14x + 40$	**k** $x^2 + 15x + 54$	**l** $x^2 + 13x + 36$
m $x^2 - 4x + 4$	**n** $x^2 - 12x + 36$	**o** $x^2 - 7x + 12$
p $x^2 - 9x + 20$	**q** $x^2 + 2x - 3$	**r** $x^2 + x - 12$
s $x^2 + 4x - 12$	**t** $x^2 + 7x - 30$	**u** $x^2 - x - 2$
v $x^2 - 10x - 24$	**w** $x^2 - 7x - 30$	**x** $x^2 - x - 56$

2 Factorise:

a $a^2 + 6a + 8$	**b** $m^2 + 9m + 18$	**c** $y^2 + 13y + 42$
d $p^2 + 7p + 12$	**e** $x^2 + 12x + 20$	**f** $n^2 + 17n + 42$
g $s^2 + 21s + 54$	**h** $a^2 + 18a + 56$	**i** $x^2 - 3x - 4$
j $a^2 - 2a - 8$	**k** $p^2 - 5p - 24$	**l** $y^2 + y - 6$
m $x^2 + 7x - 8$	**n** $q^2 + 5q - 24$	**o** $m^2 + 12m - 45$
p $a^2 + 18a - 63$	**q** $y^2 + 6y - 55$	**r** $x^2 - 2x + 1$
s $k^2 - 5k + 6$	**t** $x^2 - 13x + 36$	**u** $a^2 - 22a + 72$
v $p^2 + 22p + 96$	**w** $q^2 - 12q - 45$	**x** $m^2 - 4m - 77$

3 Factorise by first taking out a common factor (see example 5).

a $2x^2 + 6x + 4$	**b** $3x^2 - 6x - 9$	**c** $5x^2 - 10x - 40$
d $2x^2 + 16x + 32$	**e** $3x^2 - 30x - 33$	**f** $3x^2 + 21x + 36$
g $4a^2 - 12a - 40$	**h** $2n^2 + 8n + 6$	**i** $5x^2 - 30x + 40$
j $3x^2 - 21x + 36$	**k** $3a^2 - 15a - 108$	**l** $5x^2 + 15x - 350$

Fun Spot 7:04 | How much logic do you have?

See if you can solve the three problems below.

1 What is the next letter in this sequence?
O, T, T, F, F, S, S, ?

2 A man passing a beggar in the street exclaimed,
'I am that beggar's father!' But the beggar was
not the man's son. How can this be?

3 Two guards are guarding two sacks.
One guard always tells the truth, but the
other guard always lies, but you do not
know which guard is which. One of the
sacks is full of gold; the other is full of
peanuts. You are permitted to take one
of the sacks but you are not sure which one contains the gold.
You are also allowed to ask one of the guards just one question.

What question should you ask to ensure you get the sack of gold?

7:05 | Factorising Further Quadratic Trinomials

- In all quadratic trinomials factorised so far, the *coefficient* of x^2 has been 1. We will now consider cases where the *coefficient* of x^2 is not 1.

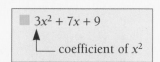

$3x^2 + 7x + 9$

└── coefficient of x^2

- To **expand** $(5x - 1)(x + 3)$ we can use a cross diagram.

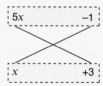

$5x^2$ is the product of the two left terms.
-3 is the product of the two right terms.
$14x$ is the sum of the products along the cross, ie $15x + (-x)$.

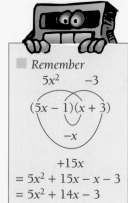

■ Remember

$$5x^2 \qquad -3$$
$$(5x - 1)(x + 3)$$
$$-x$$
$$+15x$$
$$= 5x^2 + 15x - x - 3$$
$$= 5x^2 + 14x - 3$$

$\therefore (5x - 1)(x + 3) = 5x^2 + 14x - 3$

- One method used to factorise trinomials like $5x^2 + 14x - 3$ is called the cross method.

Cross method

To factorise $5x^2 + 14x - 3$, we need to reverse the expanding process.
We need to choose two factors of $5x^2$ and two factors of -3 to write on the cross.

Try:
$\begin{cases} 5x \\ x \end{cases}$ and $\begin{cases} -3 \\ +1 \end{cases}$

- If $(5x - 3)$ and $(x + 1)$ are the factors of $5x^2 + 14x - 3$, then the products of numbers on the ends of each arm will have a sum of $+14x$.

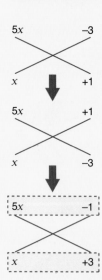

- When we add the cross products here, we get:
$(5x) + (-3x) = 2x$
This does not give the correct middle term of $14x$,
so $(5x - 3)$ and $(x + 1)$ are **not** factors.

- Vary the terms on the cross.

Try: $\begin{cases} 5x \\ x \end{cases}$ and $\begin{cases} +1 \\ -3 \end{cases}$

Cross product $= (-15x) + (x) = -14x$

Keep trying.

- Try: $\begin{cases} 5x \\ x \end{cases}$ and $\begin{cases} -1 \\ +3 \end{cases}$

Cross product $= (15x) + (-x) = 14x$
$\therefore$ This must be the correct combination.
$\therefore 5x^2 + 14x - 3 = (5x - 1)(x + 3)$

Examine the examples below. Make sure you understand the method.

worked examples

Find the factors of:

1 $3x^2 - 19x + 6$ **2** $4x^2 - x - 3$ **3** $2x^2 + 25x + 12$

Solutions

1

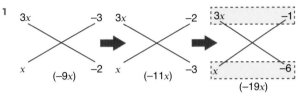

This cross product gives the correct middle term of $-19x$, so:

$3x^2 - 19x + 6 = (3x - 1)(x - 6)$

Note: The factors of $+6$ had to be both negative to give a negative middle term.

2

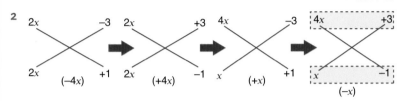

$$\therefore 4x^2 - x - 3$$
$$= (4x + 3)(x - 1)$$

3 In practice, we would not draw a separate cross for each new set of factors. We simply cross out the factors that don't work and try a new set.

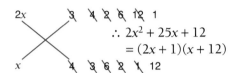

$$\therefore 2x^2 + 25x + 12$$
$$= (2x + 1)(x + 12)$$

> ▨ To factorise a quadratic trinomial, $ax^2 + bx + c$, when a (the coefficient of x^2) is not 1, use the cross method.

Note: Another method for factorising these trinomials is shown in Challenge 7:05 on page 187.

Exercise 7:05

1 **a** Which diagram will give the factors of $2x^2 + 13x + 6$?

i   **ii**   **iii**   **iv**

b Which diagram will give the factors of $9x^2 - 9x - 4$?

i   **ii**   **iii**   **iv**

c Which diagram will give the factors of $5x^2 - 19x + 12$?

   i $5x$ -3 ii $5x$ -4 iii $5x$ -2 iv $5x$ -6

   x -4 x -3 x -6 x -2

d Which diagram will give the factors of $12x^2 + 7x - 10$?

  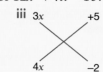

   i $6x$ $+10$ ii $12x$ -10 iii $3x$ $+5$ iv $4x$ $+5$

   $2x$ -1 x $+1$ $4x$ -2 $3x$ -2

2 Factorise these expressions.

a $2x^2 + 7x + 3$
b $3x^2 + 8x + 4$
c $2x^2 + 7x + 6$
d $2x^2 + 11x + 5$
e $3x^2 + 5x + 2$
f $2x^2 + 11x + 15$
g $4x^2 + 13x + 3$
h $5x^2 + 17x + 6$
i $2x^2 + 13x + 15$
j $2x^2 - 5x + 2$
k $3x^2 - 11x + 6$
l $5x^2 - 17x + 6$
m $4x^2 - 11x + 6$
n $10x^2 - 21x + 9$
o $5x^2 - 22x + 21$
p $2x^2 + x - 10$
q $3x^2 + 4x - 15$
r $4x^2 + 11x - 3$
s $2x^2 - x - 6$
t $2x^2 - 5x - 3$
u $3x^2 - x - 30$
v $6x^2 - 5x - 21$
w $2x^2 - 5x - 12$
x $4x^2 - x - 18$

3 Find the factors of the following:

a $12x^2 + 7x + 1$
b $6a^2 + 5a + 1$
c $6p^2 + 7p + 2$
d $10y^2 - 9y + 2$
e $12x^2 - 7x + 1$
f $9a^2 - 21a + 10$
g $8m^2 + 18m - 5$
h $6n^2 - 7n - 3$
i $21q^2 - 20q + 4$
j $20x^2 - x - 1$
k $8m^2 - 2m - 15$
l $18y^2 - 3y - 10$
m $6a^2 + 5a - 6$
n $15k^2 + 26k + 8$
o $8x^2 + 18x + 9$
p $4 - 3a - a^2$
q $2 + m - 10m^2$
r $6 + 7x - 3x^2$
s $6 - 7x - 3x^2$
t $15 - x - 28x^2$
u $2 + 9n - 35n^2$
v $3x^2 + 10xy + 8y^2$
w $2x^2 - 5xy + 2y^2$
x $5m^2 - 2mn - 7n^2$

4 Factorise by first taking out the common factor.

a $6x^2 + 10x - 4$
b $6a^2 - 2a - 4$
c $6a^2 + 9a - 27$
d $8x^2 + 12x - 36$
e $6x^2 + 28x + 16$
f $12p^2 + 12p - 9$
g $30q^2 + 55q - 35$
h $10m^2 - 46m + 24$
i $50a^2 + 15a - 5$
j $4 - 6x - 10x^2$
k $36 - 3t - 3t^2$
l $9 + 24x + 12x^2$

5 Complete each in as many ways as possible by writing positive whole numbers in the boxes and inserting operation signs.

a $(x \ldots \square)(x \ldots \square) = x^2 \ldots \square x \ldots 15$

b $(x \ldots \square)(x \ldots \square) = x^2 \ldots \square x - 12$

c $(x \ldots \square)(x \ldots \square) = x^2 \ldots 5x + \square$

d $(5x \ldots \square)(x \ldots \square) = 5x^2 \ldots \square x \ldots 2$

Challenge 7:05 | Another factorising method for harder trinomials

Example

Factorise $3x^2 + 14x - 5$.

$$(3x\qquad)(3x\qquad)$$
$$\underline{\qquad\qquad\qquad\qquad} \; 3$$

- Put '$3x$' in both sets of parentheses and divide by '3'.

Follow this carefully.

$$\overset{-15}{\text{Now: } 3x^2 + 14x - 5}$$

- Multiply $3 \times (-5)$ and write the answer above -5.

- Then find the two numbers that multiply to give -15 and add to give $+14$ (ie $+15$ and -1).

- Now place these numbers in the parentheses.

$$\frac{(3x + 15)(3x - 1)}{3}$$

- Then divide the '3' into the product above.

$$\frac{(\cancel{3}^1 x + \cancel{15}^5)(3x - 1)}{\cancel{3}_1}$$

- The solution is: $(x + 5)(3x - 1)$

Now check out this second factorisation.

Example

Factorise $10x^2 - 19x + 6$.

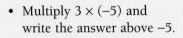

$$(10x\qquad)(10x\qquad)$$
$$\underline{\qquad\qquad\qquad\qquad} \; 10$$

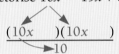

$$\begin{array}{l}(-15) \times (-4) = 60 \\ (-15) + (-4) = -19\end{array}$$

$$\overset{60}{= 10x^2 - 19x + 6}$$

$$= \frac{(10x - 15)(10x - 4)}{10}$$

$$= \frac{(\cancel{10}^2 x - \cancel{15}^3)(\cancel{10}^5 x - \cancel{4}^2)}{\cancel{10}_1}$$

The solution is: $(2x - 3)(5x - 2)$.

Note: the '10' in the denominator cancelled partly with each set of

Try the method with these trinomials.

1 $2x^2 + 7x + 6$	**2** $4x^2 - 19x - 5$	**3** $3x^2 - 13x + 12$
4 $6x^2 + 7x + 2$	**5** $5x^2 + 9x - 2$	**6** $12x^2 - 25x + 12$

7:06 | Factorising: Miscellaneous Types

When factorising any algebraic expressions, remember this checklist . . .

> ■ *First:*
> Always take out any common factor.
> *Then:*
> If there are two terms, is it a difference of two squares, $a^2 - b^2$?
> If there are three terms, is it a quadratic trinomial, $ax^2 + bx + c$?
> If there are four terms, can it be factorised by grouping the terms into pairs?

worked examples

1 $4x^2 - 36$
   $= 4(x^2 - 9)$ common factor
   $= 4(x - 3)(x + 3)$ diff. of 2 squares

2 $15x^2y - 20xy + 10xy^2$
   $= 5xy(3x - 4 + 2y)$ common factor

3 $8x^2 - 40x + 32$
   $= 8(x^2 - 5x + 4)$ common factor
   $= 8(x - 4)(x - 1)$ quadratic trinomial

4 $12 - a - 6a^2$
   $= (3 + 2a)(4 - 3a)$ quadratic trinomial

   3 6 $-6a$ a $-3a$ $2a$
   4 2   a $-6a$ $2a$ $-3a$

5 $ap - aq - 3p + 3q$
   $= a(p - q) - 3(p - q)$ grouping terms into pairs
   $= (p - q)(a - 3)$

Exercise 7:06

1 Factorise each of these expressions:

a $x^2 - 6x + 5$ b $x^2 - 9$ c $xy + 2y + 9x + 18$ d $a^2 - 9a$

e $a^2 - 6a + 9$ f $4x^2 - 1$ g $12x^2 - x - 35$ h $a^2 - 13a + 40$

i $5a^2b - 10ab^3$ j $p^2 - q^2$ k $pq - 3p + 10q - 30$ l $7x^2 + 11x - 6$

m $a^2 + 3a - ab$ n $16 - 25a^2$ o $1 - 2a - 24a^2$ p $4m + 4n - am - an$

q $5ay - 10y + 15xy$ r $15x^2 - x - 28$ s $x^2y^2 - 1$ t $x^2 - x - 56$

u $2mn + 3np + 4m + 6p$ v $100a^2 - 49x^2$

w $2 - 5x - 3x^2$ x $k^2 + 2k - 48$

2 Factorise completely:

a $2 - 8x^2$ b $5x^2 - 10x - 5xy + 10y$ c $2a^2 - 22a + 48$

d $3m^2 - 18m + 27$ e $x^4 - 1$ f $p^3 - 4p^2 - p + 4$

g $4x^2 - 36$ h $a^3 - a$ i $3a^2 - 39a + 120$

j $9 - 9p^2$ k $3k^2 + 3k - 18$ l $24a^2 - 42a + 9$

m $ax^2 + axy + 3ax + 3ay$ n $(x + y)^2 + 3(x + y)$ o $5xy^2 - 20xz^2$

p $6ax^2 + 5ax - 6a$ q $x^2 - y^2 + 5x - 5y$ r $3x^2 - 12x + 12$

s $63x^2 - 28y^2$ t $a^4 - 16$ u $(a - 2)^2 - 4$

v $1 + p + p^2 + p^3$ w $8t^2 - 28t - 60$ x $8 - 8x - 6x^2$

Answer each question and put the letter for that question in the box above the correct answer.

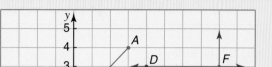

For the number plane on the right, find:
E the equation of the *x*-axis
E the distance BC
E the midpoint of AB
E the equation of AB
F the gradient of DF
H the intersection of DF and EF
I the distance of F from the origin
G the equation of the *y*-axis
E the distance AB
G the gradient of AB

E the *y*-intercept of DF
H the equation of DF
I the intersection of AB and BC

Simplify:
I $10x^2 + x^2$ **L** $10x^2 - x^2$ **L** $10x^2 \times x^2$
M $10x^2 \div x^2$ **N** $\frac{1}{4}$ of $8x^4$ **N** 5% of $40x$
N $(2x^2)^3$ **N** $\frac{x}{2} + \frac{x}{2}$

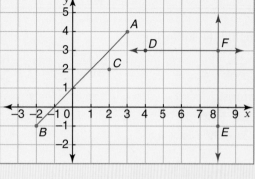

A playing card is chosen at random from a standard pack. Find the probability that it is:
O the Ace of spades   **P** a heart
R a King   **S** a picture card
T a red card greater than 3 but less than 9

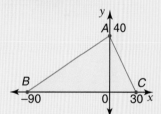

Expand and simplify:
O $(x + 1)(x + 7)$ **O** $(a - b)(a + b)$
S $(a + b)^2$ **T** $(a - b)^2$

On this number plane, what is the length of:
T OC?   **U** OA?   **U** AC?
V BC?   **W** OB?   **Y** AB?
O What is the area of △ABC?

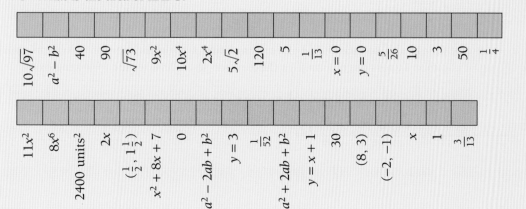

$10\sqrt{97}$	$a^2 - b^2$	40	90	$\sqrt{73}$	$9x^2$	$10x^4$	$2x^4$	$5\sqrt{2}$	120	5	$\frac{1}{13}$	$x = 0$	$y = 0$	$\frac{5}{26}$	10	3	50	$\frac{1}{4}$

$11x^2$	$8x^6$	2400 units²	$2x$	$(\frac{1}{2}, 1\frac{1}{2})$	$x^2 + 8x + 7$	0	$a^2 - 2ab + b^2$	$y = 3$	$\frac{1}{52}$	$a^2 + 2ab + b^2$	$y = x + 1$	30	$(8, 3)$	$(-2, -1)$	x	1	$\frac{3}{13}$

7:07 | Simplifying Algebraic Fractions: Multiplication and Division

Simplify the following:

1 $\dfrac{5a^2}{10a}$ 2 $\dfrac{12xy^2}{8x^2y}$ 3 $\dfrac{2x}{3} \times \dfrac{6}{x}$ 4 $\dfrac{2x}{3} \div \dfrac{4x}{9}$

Factorise:

5 $6x^2 + 9x$ 6 $x^2 + 7x + 12$ 7 $x^2 - 49$ 8 $3x^2 + 6x + 3$

9 $3x + 3y + ax + ay$ 10 $2x^2 + 9x - 5$

Just as numerical fractions can be simplified by cancelling common factors in the numerator and the denominator, so algebraic fractions can often be simplified in the same way after first factorising where possible. Look at the examples below.

worked examples

1 $\dfrac{2x - 2}{3x - 3} = \dfrac{2(x-1)^1}{3(x-1)_1}$

     $= \dfrac{2}{3}$

2 $\dfrac{x^2 + 7x + 12}{x^2 - 9} = \dfrac{(x+4)(x+3)^1}{(x-3)(x+3)^1}$

     $= \dfrac{x+4}{x-3}$

3 $\dfrac{6 - 6a^2}{3 + 3a + x + ax} = \dfrac{6(1-a)(1+a)^1}{(3+x)(1+a)^1}$

     $= \dfrac{6(1-a)}{3+x}$

4 $\dfrac{3x^2 - 9x}{3x^2 - 27} = \dfrac{{}^1 3x(x-3)^1}{3_1(x-3)_1(x+3)}$

     $= \dfrac{x}{x+3}$

Simplifying looks simple.

Algebraic fractions should also be factorised before completing a multiplication or a division since the cancelling of common factors often simplifies these processes. Consider the following examples.

worked examples

1 $\dfrac{5x + 15}{x + 1} \times \dfrac{2x + 2}{5} = \dfrac{5^1(x+3)}{(x+1)_1} \times \dfrac{2(x+1)^1}{5_1}$

     $= 2(x + 3)$

2 $\dfrac{x^2 - 9}{x^2 + 5x + 6} \times \dfrac{3x + 6}{x^2 - 2x - 3} = \dfrac{\overset{1}{\cancel{(x-3)}}\overset{1}{\cancel{(x+3)}}}{\cancel{(x+2)}\cancel{(x+3)}} \times \dfrac{3\overset{1}{\cancel{(x+2)}}}{\cancel{(x-3)}(x+1)}$

$$= \dfrac{3}{x+1}$$

3 $\dfrac{6x - 14}{3x - 9} \div \dfrac{3x - 7}{5x - 15} = \dfrac{2\overset{1}{\cancel{(3x-7)}}}{3\cancel{(x-3)}} \times \dfrac{5\overset{1}{\cancel{(x-3)}}}{\cancel{(3x-7)}}$

$$= \dfrac{10}{3}$$

4 $\dfrac{a^2 - 16}{a^2 - 25} \div \dfrac{a^2 - 2a - 8}{a^2 + 10a + 25} = \dfrac{\overset{1}{\cancel{(a-4)}}(a+4)}{(a-5)\cancel{(a+5)}} \times \dfrac{\overset{1}{\cancel{(a+5)}}(a+5)}{\cancel{(a-4)}(a+2)}$

$$= \dfrac{(a+4)(a+5)}{(a-5)(a+2)}$$

 To simplify algebraic fractions, factorise both numerator and denominator, where possible, and then cancel.

Exercise 7:07

1 Factorise and simplify:

a $\dfrac{5x + 10}{5}$ **b** $\dfrac{4}{2x + 6}$ **c** $\dfrac{12}{3x - 9}$

d $\dfrac{2x - 10}{x - 5}$ **e** $\dfrac{x + 7}{3x + 21}$ **f** $\dfrac{5a - 5}{8a - 8}$

g $\dfrac{3a + 9}{6a + 18}$ **h** $\dfrac{7m - 28}{3m - 12}$ **i** $\dfrac{x^2 + x}{x^2 - x}$

j $\dfrac{x^2 - 4}{x - 2}$ **k** $\dfrac{a + 1}{a^2 - 1}$ **l** $\dfrac{4y^2 - 9}{4y + 6}$

m $\dfrac{a^2 - 4a}{3a - a^2}$ **n** $\dfrac{2x^2 - 2}{2x - 2}$ **o** $\dfrac{x^2 - 36}{3x - 18}$

p $\dfrac{a^2 - 3a - 4}{a + 1}$ **q** $\dfrac{x^2 - 6x + 9}{x - 3}$ **r** $\dfrac{x^2 - 4}{x^2 + 3x + 2}$

s $\dfrac{x^2 + 3x + 2}{x^2 + 5x + 6}$ **t** $\dfrac{m^2 + 5m - 24}{m^2 - 7m + 12}$ **u** $\dfrac{t^2 + 7t + 12}{t^2 - 9}$

v $\dfrac{a^2 - x^2}{a^2 + 3a + ax + 3x}$ **w** $\dfrac{2x^2 - x - 1}{4x^2 - 1}$ **x** $\dfrac{18a^2 - 8}{6a^2 + a - 2}$

2 Simplify the following:

a $\dfrac{2x+4}{3} \times \dfrac{6x}{x+2}$

b $\dfrac{5y-15}{2y+8} \times \dfrac{y+4}{10}$

c $\dfrac{2x-4}{3x-9} \times \dfrac{5x-15}{7x-14}$

d $\dfrac{5n+10}{n+3} \times \dfrac{6n+18}{4n+8}$

e $\dfrac{7y+28}{21} \times \dfrac{6}{6y+24}$

f $\dfrac{1+2a}{10+30a} \times \dfrac{6+18a}{1-2a}$

g $\dfrac{y^2+y}{2y+8} \times \dfrac{4y+6}{3y+3}$

h $\dfrac{x^2-3x}{x^2} \times \dfrac{2x^2+5x}{9x-27}$

i $\dfrac{x+3}{x^2-9} \times \dfrac{x-3}{x+1}$

j $\dfrac{3x+15}{x^2-25} \times \dfrac{x^2-49}{3x-21}$

k $\dfrac{a^2+5a+6}{a^2-4} \times \dfrac{a^2-a-2}{a^2-1}$

l $\dfrac{y^2+3y+2}{y^2+5y+6} \times \dfrac{y^2+7y+12}{y^2+5y+4}$

m $\dfrac{x^2+6x+5}{x^2+5x+4} \times \dfrac{x^2+7x+12}{x^2+12x+35}$

n $\dfrac{m^2-1}{m^2-6m+5} \times \dfrac{m^2-10m+25}{m^2-25}$

o $\dfrac{a^2-4}{a^2+3a-4} \times \dfrac{a^2-16}{a^2+2a-8}$

p $\dfrac{2x^2+4x+2}{x^2-1} \times \dfrac{x^2+3x-4}{4x+4}$

q $\dfrac{3x^2+5x+2}{x^2-x-2} \times \dfrac{x^2+x-6}{3x^2+11x+6}$

r $\dfrac{5a^2+16a+3}{25a^2-1} \times \dfrac{5a^2-a}{2a^2+5a-3}$

s $\dfrac{x^2-y^2+x-y}{x^2-2xy+y^2} \times \dfrac{10x-10y}{5x+5y+5}$

t $\dfrac{(a+b)^2-c^2}{a^2+ab+ac+bc} \times \dfrac{a^2+ab-ac-bc}{a+b+c}$

3 Simplify:

a $\dfrac{3a+6}{2} \div \dfrac{a+2}{4}$

b $\dfrac{x+2}{5x} \div \dfrac{7x+4}{10x}$

c $\dfrac{5m-10}{m+1} \div \dfrac{3m-6}{3m+3}$

d $\dfrac{6m+9}{2m-8} \div \dfrac{2m+3}{3m-12}$

e $\dfrac{3x}{5x+15} \div \dfrac{x^2+x}{x+3}$

f $\dfrac{24y-16}{4y+6} \div \dfrac{3y-2}{8y+12}$

g $\dfrac{5m-20}{4m+6} \div \dfrac{5m-20}{2m^2+3m}$

h $\dfrac{25k+15}{3k-3} \div \dfrac{5k+3}{3k}$

i $\dfrac{n^2-9}{2n+4} \div \dfrac{n+3}{2}$

j $\dfrac{y+7}{y-7} \div \dfrac{y^2-49}{y^2-7y}$

k $\dfrac{a^2+5a+4}{a^2-16} \div \dfrac{a^2-9}{a^2-a-12}$

l $\dfrac{x^2+6x+9}{x^2+8x+15} \div \dfrac{x^2+5x+6}{x^2+7x+10}$

m $\dfrac{x^2-4}{x^2-7x+10} \div \dfrac{x^2-x-6}{x^2-3x-10}$

n $\dfrac{p^2+7p+10}{p^2-2p-8} \div \dfrac{p^2+2p-15}{p^2+p-12}$

o $\dfrac{n^2-49}{n^2-9} \div \dfrac{n^2+14n+49}{n^2-6n+9}$

p $\dfrac{2x^2-8x-42}{x^2+6x+9} \div \dfrac{x^2-9x+14}{x^2+x-6}$

q $\dfrac{3x^2-48}{x^2-3x-4} \div \dfrac{x^2+4x}{x^3-x}$

r $\dfrac{2a^2-a-1}{a^2-1} \div \dfrac{6a^2+a-1}{3a^2+2a-1}$

s $\dfrac{x+y+x^2-y^2}{x^2+2xy+y^2} \div \dfrac{1+x-y}{2x+2y}$

t $\dfrac{p^2-(q+r)^2}{p^2+pq-pr-qr} \div \dfrac{p-q-r}{p^2-pq-pr+qr}$

7:08 | Addition and Subtraction of Algebraic Fractions

prep quiz

7:08

Simplify:

1. $\dfrac{1}{2} + \dfrac{3}{5}$

2. $\dfrac{3}{4} + \dfrac{3}{8}$

3. $\dfrac{9}{10} - \dfrac{3}{5}$

4. $\dfrac{7}{15} - \dfrac{3}{20}$

5. $\dfrac{5}{x} + \dfrac{7}{x}$

6. $\dfrac{2}{a} + \dfrac{1}{2a}$

7. $\dfrac{2}{3a} + \dfrac{3}{2a}$

8. $\dfrac{1}{x} - \dfrac{1}{4x}$

9. $\dfrac{a}{2x} + \dfrac{2a}{x}$

10. $\dfrac{5m}{2n} - \dfrac{4m}{3n}$

The Prep Quiz above should have reminded you that, when adding or subtracting fractions, the lowest common denominator needs to be found. If the denominators involve two or more terms, factorising first may help in finding the lowest common denominator. For example:

$$\frac{2}{x^2 - 9} + \frac{5}{x^2 + 5x + 6} = \frac{2}{(x-3)(x+3)} + \frac{5}{(x+3)(x+2)}$$

LCD stands for lowest common denominator.

■ Here the LCD = $(x - 3)(x + 3)(x + 2)$. Note that the factors of each denominator are present without repeating any factor common to both. Each numerator is then multiplied by each factor not present in its original denominator.

$$= \frac{2(x + 2) + 5(x - 3)}{(x - 3)(x + 3)(x + 2)}$$

$$= \frac{2x + 4 + 5x - 15}{(x - 3)(x + 3)(x + 2)}$$

$$= \frac{7x - 11}{(x - 3)(x + 3)(x + 2)}$$

 When adding or subtracting fractions:
- **factorise the denominator of each fraction**
- **find the lowest common denominator**
- **rewrite each fraction with this common denominator and simplify.**

1 $\dfrac{2}{x+2} + \dfrac{1}{x+3} = \dfrac{2(x+3) + 1(x+2)}{(x+2)(x+3)}$

$\qquad\qquad\qquad = \dfrac{2x+6+x+2}{(x+2)(x+3)}$

$\qquad\qquad\qquad = \dfrac{3x+8}{(x+2)(x+3)}$

■ No factorising was needed in these first two examples.

2 $\dfrac{3}{2x+1} - \dfrac{4}{3x-1} = \dfrac{3(3x-1) - 4(2x+1)}{(2x+1)(3x-1)}$

$\qquad\qquad\qquad = \dfrac{9x-3-8x-4}{(2x+1)(3x-1)}$

$\qquad\qquad\qquad = \dfrac{x-7}{(2x+1)(3x-1)}$

3 $\dfrac{1}{x^2+5x+6} + \dfrac{2}{x+3}$

$\quad = \dfrac{1}{(x+2)(x+3)} + \dfrac{2}{(x+3)}$

$\quad = \dfrac{1+2(x+2)}{(x+2)(x+3)}$

$\quad = \dfrac{1+2x+4}{(x+2)(x+3)}$

$\quad = \dfrac{2x+5}{(x+2)(x+3)}$

4 $\dfrac{4}{x^2+x} - \dfrac{3}{x^2-1}$

$\quad = \dfrac{4}{x(x+1)} - \dfrac{3}{(x-1)(x+1)}$

$\quad = \dfrac{4(x-1) - 3x}{x(x+1)(x-1)}$

$\quad = \dfrac{4x-4-3x}{x(x+1)(x-1)}$

$\quad = \dfrac{x-4}{x(x+1)(x-1)}$

5 $\dfrac{x+3}{x^2+2x+1} - \dfrac{x-1}{x^2-x-2}$

$\quad = \dfrac{x+3}{(x+1)(x+1)} - \dfrac{x-1}{(x+1)(x-2)}$

$\quad = \dfrac{(x+3)(x-2) - (x-1)(x+1)}{(x+1)(x+1)(x-2)}$

$\quad = \dfrac{x^2+x-6-(x^2-1)}{(x+1)(x+1)(x-2)}$

$\quad = \dfrac{x-5}{(x+1)^2(x-2)}$

Factorise first.

Exercise 7:08

Foundation Worksheet 7:08

Addition and subtraction of algebraic fractions

1 Simplify:

  a $\dfrac{2}{x} + \dfrac{5}{x}$ **b** $\dfrac{3}{x} - \dfrac{1}{x+1}$

2 Simplify:

  a $\dfrac{6}{5a} - \dfrac{3}{2a}$ **b** $\dfrac{1}{x^2-1} + \dfrac{2}{x-1}$

1 Simplify each of the following. (*Note*: No factorising is needed.)

a $\dfrac{1}{x+1} + \dfrac{1}{x-1}$ **b** $\dfrac{1}{a+5} + \dfrac{1}{a+3}$ **c** $\dfrac{1}{y-7} - \dfrac{1}{y+1}$

d $\dfrac{2}{x+3} + \dfrac{3}{x+5}$ **e** $\dfrac{5}{m+1} - \dfrac{3}{m-2}$ **f** $\dfrac{6}{t+10} - \dfrac{3}{t+2}$

g $\dfrac{1}{2x-1} + \dfrac{3}{x-1}$ **h** $\dfrac{9}{3x+2} - \dfrac{7}{2x+5}$ **i** $\dfrac{8}{5x-1} + \dfrac{7}{3x+1}$

j $\dfrac{3}{2x} + \dfrac{5}{x+7}$ **k** $\dfrac{9}{2x+5} - \dfrac{5}{3x}$ **l** $\dfrac{1}{2a} - \dfrac{3}{2a+1}$

m $\dfrac{x}{x+3} + \dfrac{x}{x+1}$ **n** $\dfrac{a}{2a+1} - \dfrac{2a}{4a-1}$ **o** $\dfrac{x+1}{x+2} + \dfrac{x+2}{x+1}$

2 Simplify. (*Note:* The denominators are already factorised.)

a $\dfrac{1}{(x+1)(x+2)} + \dfrac{1}{x+1}$

b $\dfrac{1}{x(x+2)} + \dfrac{1}{x+2}$

c $\dfrac{1}{x+3} - \dfrac{1}{x(x+3)}$

d $\dfrac{1}{x-5} - \dfrac{1}{(x-5)(x+2)}$

e $\dfrac{3}{(x+2)(x+3)} + \dfrac{4}{x+2}$

f $\dfrac{5}{x+4} - \dfrac{3}{(x+1)(x+4)}$

g $\dfrac{1}{(x+1)(x+2)} + \dfrac{1}{(x+2)(x+3)}$

h $\dfrac{2}{(x-3)(x+3)} + \dfrac{4}{(x+3)(x+1)}$

i $\dfrac{3}{(x+7)(x-1)} + \dfrac{5}{(x+7)(x+1)}$

j $\dfrac{9}{(x+9)(x+3)} - \dfrac{7}{(x+3)(x-1)}$

k $\dfrac{1}{(2x+1)(x+5)} + \dfrac{3}{(x+5)(x+2)}$

l $\dfrac{5}{(2x-1)(3x+2)} - \dfrac{6}{x(2x-1)}$

m $\dfrac{x-1}{(x+3)(x+1)} + \dfrac{x+1}{(x+3)(x-1)}$

n $\dfrac{x+2}{x(x+3)} - \dfrac{x-1}{x(x+2)}$

3 Simplify, by first factorising each denominator where possible.

a $\dfrac{1}{x^2+x} + \dfrac{1}{x+1}$

b $\dfrac{1}{3x+9} - \dfrac{1}{x+3}$

c $\dfrac{2}{2x+3} + \dfrac{3}{4x+6}$

d $\dfrac{5}{x^2-1} + \dfrac{3}{x-1}$

e $\dfrac{1}{x^2-9} + \dfrac{1}{2x-6}$

f $\dfrac{1}{x^2+x} - \dfrac{1}{x^2-1}$

g $\dfrac{1}{x^2+2x+1} + \dfrac{1}{x^2-1}$

h $\dfrac{1}{x^2+7x+12} + \dfrac{1}{x^2+8x+16}$

i $\dfrac{2}{x^2+6x+8} + \dfrac{4}{x^2+5x+6}$

j $\dfrac{2}{x^2+7x+12} + \dfrac{4}{x^2+5x+4}$

k $\dfrac{3}{x^2-x-2} - \dfrac{4}{x^2-2x-3}$

l $\dfrac{3}{x^2-x-6} - \dfrac{2}{x^2-2x-3}$

m $\dfrac{5}{x^2-3x-4} - \dfrac{3}{x^2-x-2}$

n $\dfrac{3}{2x^2+7x-4} - \dfrac{4}{3x^2+14x+8}$

o $\dfrac{2}{x^2-49} + \dfrac{4}{x^2-4x-21}$

p $\dfrac{4}{2x^2+x-1} - \dfrac{1}{x^2-1}$

q $\dfrac{x+1}{x^2+5x+6} + \dfrac{x-1}{x^2-9}$

r $\dfrac{x+3}{x^2-16} - \dfrac{x+2}{x^2-4x}$

s $\dfrac{2x}{5x^2-20} + \dfrac{x+1}{x^2+4x+4}$

t $\dfrac{5x+2}{2x^2-5x-3} + \dfrac{3x-1}{4x^2-1}$

Mathematical Terms 7

binomial
- An algebraic expression consisting of two terms.
  eg $2x + 4$, $3x - 2y$

coefficient
- The number that multiplies a pronumeral in an algebraic expression.
  eg In $3x - 5y$,
  - the coefficient of x is 3
  - the coefficient of y is -5

expand
- To remove grouping symbols by multiplying each term inside grouping symbols by the term or terms outside.

factorise
- To write an expression as a product of its factors.
- The reverse of expanding.

product
- The result of multiplying terms or expressions together.

quadratic trinomial
- Expressions such as $x^2 + 4x + 3$, which can be factorised as $(x + 3)(x + 1)$.
- The highest power of the variable is 2.

trinomial
- An algebraic expression consisting of three terms.

Mathematical terms 7

1 Factorising using common factors
2 Grouping in pairs
3 Factorising trinomials 1
4 Factorising trinomials 2
5 Mixed factorisations

- This spiral or helix is a mathematical shape.
- Discover how it can be drawn.
- Investigate its links to the golden rectangle.

Diagnostic Test 7: | Factorising Algebraic Expressions

- Each part of this test has similar items that test a particular skill.
- Errors made will indicate areas of weakness.
- Each weakness should be treated by going back to the section listed.

	Section
1 Factorise by taking out a common factor. **a** $3x - 12$ **b** $ax + ay$ **c** $-2x - 6$ **d** $ax + bx - cx$	7:01

2 Factorise by grouping the terms into pairs.
  a $ax + bx + 2a + 2b$ **b** $6m + 6n + am + an$
  c $xy - x + y - 1$ **d** $ab + 4c + 4a + bc$
	7:02

3 Factorise these 'differences of two squares'. **a** $x^2 - 25$ **b** $a^2 - x^2$ **c** $4 - m^2$ **d** $9x^2 - 1$	7:03
4 Factorise these trinomials. **a** $x^2 + 7x + 12$ **b** $x^2 - 5x + 6$ **c** $x^2 - 3x - 10$ **d** $x^2 + x - 20$	7:04

5 Factorise:
  a $2x^2 + 11x + 5$ **b** $3x^2 - 11x + 6$
  c $4x^2 - x - 18$ **d** $6x^2 + 5x + 1$
	7:05

6 Simplify, by first factorising where possible. **a** $\dfrac{6x + 12}{6}$ **b** $\dfrac{12a - 18}{14a - 21}$ **c** $\dfrac{x^2 + 5x}{ax + 5a}$ **d** $\dfrac{x^2 + 3x - 10}{x^2 - 4}$	7:07

7 Simplify:
  a $\dfrac{3x + 6}{4} \times \dfrac{8x}{x + 2}$ **b** $\dfrac{a^2 + 5a + 6}{a^2 - 9} \times \dfrac{a^2 - 1}{a^2 + 3a + 2}$
 	
  c $\dfrac{3m - 6}{m + 3} \div \dfrac{5m - 10}{3m + 9}$ **d** $\dfrac{x^2 - 3x - 10}{x^2 - x - 6} \div \dfrac{x^2 - 7x + 10}{x^2 - 4}$
	7:07

8 Simplify:
  a $\dfrac{2}{x + 3} + \dfrac{1}{x - 1}$ **b** $\dfrac{1}{x(x + 2)} - \dfrac{1}{(x + 2)(x + 1)}$
 	
  c $\dfrac{5}{x^2 - 9} + \dfrac{3}{2x - 6}$ **d** $\dfrac{x}{x^2 + 7x + 12} - \dfrac{x + 2}{x^2 + 2x - 3}$
	7:08

Chapter 7 | Revision Assignment

1 Factorise the following expressions:
   a $a^2 + 9a + 20$
   b $2p - 4q$
   c $m^2 - 4m - 45$
   d $5x^3 + 10x^2 + x + 2$
   e $4x^2 - 1$
   f $x^2y - xy$
   g $6a^2 - 13a + 5$
   h $x^2 + x - 30$
   i $3a^2 - 4a - 15$
   j $xy + xz + py + pz$
   k $2x^2 + x - 1$
   l $x^3 - 3x^2 + 2x - 6$
   m $-5ab - 10a^2b^2$
   n $x^2 - y^2 + 2x - 2y$
   o $2 - 3x - 9x^2$

2 Factorise fully:
   a $2y^2 - 18$
   b $3r^2 + 9r - 84$
   c $4x^3 + 6x + 4x^2 + 6$
   d $2 - 18x^2$
   e $a^3 + a^2 - 72a$
   f $33 + 36a + 3a^2$
   g $(x - y)^2 + x - y$
   h $(x - 2)^2 - 4$

3 Simplify each of the following:
   a $\dfrac{x^2 + 9x - 36}{x^2 - 9}$

   b $\dfrac{20x^2 - 5}{2x^2 + 5x - 3}$

   c $\dfrac{3}{x + 2} + \dfrac{2}{x + 3}$

   d $\dfrac{x}{x - 1} - \dfrac{2x}{x - 2}$

   e $\dfrac{x^2 - 1}{5x} \times \dfrac{x^2 + x}{x^2 + 2 + 1}$

   f $\dfrac{x - 1}{x^2 - 4} \div \dfrac{x^2 - 4x + 3}{x^2 - x - 6}$

   g $\dfrac{x + 1}{x + 2} - \dfrac{x + 2}{x + 1}$

   h $\dfrac{2}{3x - 1} + \dfrac{1}{(3x - 1)^2}$

   i $\dfrac{4}{3 + 2x} - \dfrac{3}{2x + 3}$

   j $\dfrac{x^2 + 5x - 14}{5x^2 - 20} \times \dfrac{x^2 + 4x + 4}{x^2 - 49}$

Chapter Review
Questions

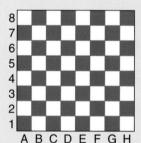

- In Chess, a Knight can move 3 squares from its starting position to its finishing position. The squares must form an 'L' shape in any direction. Some possible moves are shown below.

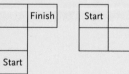

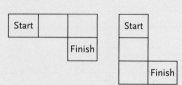

- Which squares can the Knight in the photo move to? If the Knight was standing on the square C1 what squares could it move to? Give a sequence of squares showing how the Knight could move from A1 to B1 to C1 to ... H1.
- Chess is played on an 8 by 8 square grid. Each square is named using a letter and a number. The Knight pictured is standing on the square A1.

Chapter 7 | Working Mathematically

1 Use ID Card 5 on page xvii to identify:
a 5   b 12   c 14   d 16   e 17   f 20   g 21   h 22   i 23   j 24

7B

2 Use ID Card 6 on page xviii to identify:
a 4   b 12   c 13   d 14   e 15   f 17   g 21   h 22   i 23   j 24

3 If the exterior angles $x°$, $y°$ and $z°$ of a triangle are in the ratio $4:5:6$, what is the ratio of the interior angles $a°$, $b°$ and $c°$?

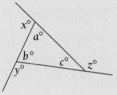

4 The average of five numbers is 11. A sixth number is added and the new average is 12. What is the sixth number?

5 This sector graph shows the method of travelling to work for all persons.
a What percentage of the workforce caught a train to work?
b What percentage of the workforce was driven to work?
c What is the size of the sector angle for 'other' means of transport? Do not use a protractor.
d What percentage of the workforce used a car to get to work?

6 a From the data in the graph below, who has the greater chance of having heart disease:
a 60-year-old woman or a 60-year-old man?
b Who has the greater chance of having cancer: a 50-year-old woman or a 50-year-old man?
c Which of the three diseases reveals the greatest gender difference for the 20-to-50-year-old range?
d Would the number of 80-year-old men suffering from heart disease be greater or less than the number of 80-year-old women suffering from heart disease? Give a reason for your answer.

Health risks

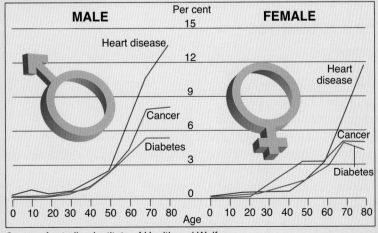

Source: Australian Institute of Health and Welfare

8

Coordinate Geometry

Negative gradients:
$m < 0$

Positive gradients:
$m > 0$

Chapter Contents

Learning Outcomes

Students will be able to:
- Find the distance between two points.
- Find the midpoint of an interval.
- Find the gradient of an interval.
- Graph straight lines on the Cartesian plane.
- Use the gradient-intercept form of a straight line.
- Find the equation of a straight line given a point and the gradient, or two points on the line.
- Identify parallel and perpendicular lines.
- Graph linear inequalities on the Cartesian plane.

Areas of Interaction

Approaches to Learning (Knowledge Acquisition, Problem Solving, Communication, Logical Thinking, IT Skills, Reflection), Human Ingenuity

The French mathematician René Descartes first introduced the number plane. He realised that using two sets of lines to form a square grid allowed the position of a point in the plane to be recorded using a pair of numbers or coordinates.

Coordinate geometry is a powerful mathematical technique that allows algebraic methods to be used in the solution of geometrical problems.

In this chapter, we will look at the basic ideas of:
- the distance between two points on the number plane
- the midpoint of an interval
- gradient (or slope)
- the relationship between a straight line and its equation.

We shall then see how these can be used to solve problems.

8:01 | The Distance Between Two Points

The number plane is the basis of coordinate geometry, an important branch of mathematics. In this chapter, we will look at some of the basic ideas of coordinate geometry and how they can be used to solve problems.

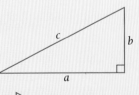

1   Which of the following is the correct statement of Pythagoras' theorem for the triangle shown?

   A $a^2 = b^2 + c^2$ **B** $b^2 = a^2 + c^2$ **C** $c^2 = a^2 + b^2$

For questions 2 to 4, use Pythagoras' theorem to find the value of d.

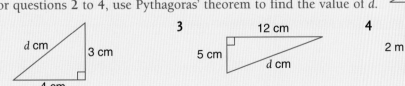

2   d cm, 3 cm, 4 cm

3   12 cm, 5 cm, d cm

4   2 m, d m, 4 m

8:01

5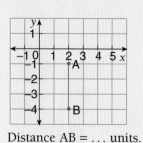

Distance AB = ... units.

6 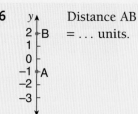 Distance AB = ... units.

7 Distance AB = ... units.

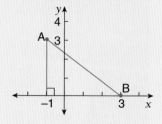

8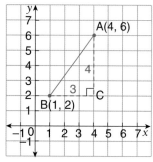

Distance AB = ... units.

9 Find the distance AB.

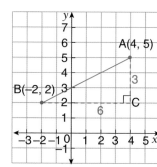

10 Find the distance AB.

Pythagoras' theorem can be used to find the distance between two points on the number plane.

worked examples

1. Find the distance between the points (1, 2) and (4, 6).
2. If A is (−2, 2) and B is (4, 5) find the length of AB.

Solutions

1

$$c^2 = a^2 + b^2$$
$$AB^2 = AC^2 + BC^2$$
$$= 4^2 + 3^2$$
$$= 16 + 9$$
$$= 25$$
$$\therefore AB = \sqrt{25}$$

∴ the length of AB is 5 units.

2

$$c^2 = a^2 + b^2$$
$$AB^2 = AC^2 + BC^2$$
$$= 3^2 + 6^2$$
$$= 9 + 36$$
$$= 45$$
$$\therefore AB = \sqrt{45}$$

∴ the length of AB is $\sqrt{45}$ unit.

$\sqrt{45}$ is a surd. We simplify surds if they are perfect squares.

By drawing a right-angled triangle we can use Pythagoras' theorem to find the distance between any two points on the number plane.

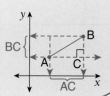

Distance formula

A formula for finding the distance between two points, $A(x_1, y_1)$ and $B(x_2, y_2)$, can be found using Pythagoras' theorem. We wish to find the length of interval AB.

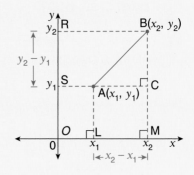

Now $LM = x_2 - x_1$ (since LM = MO − LO)

    $\therefore$ $\boxed{AC = x_2 - x_1}$ (ACML is a rectangle)

and $RS = y_2 - y_1$ (since RS = RO − SO)

    $\therefore$ $\boxed{BC = y_2 - y_1}$ (BCSR is a rectangle)

Now $AB^2 = AC^2 + BC^2$ (Pythagoras' theorem)

    $= (x_2 - x_1)^2 + (y_2 - y_1)^2$

    $\therefore AB = \sqrt{(x_2 - x_1)^2 + (y_2 - y_1)^2}$

The distance AB between $A(x_1, y_1)$ and $B(x_2, y_2)$ is given by:

$$d = \sqrt{(x_2 - x_1)^2 + (y_2 - y_1)^2}$$

worked examples

1 Find the distance between the points (3, 8) and (5, 4).

2 Find the distance between the points (−2, 0) and (8, −5)

Solutions

1 Distance $= \sqrt{(x_2 - x_1)^2 + (y_2 - y_1)^2}$

    $(x_1, y_1) = (3, 8)$ and $(x_2, y_2) = (5, 4)$

    $\therefore d = \sqrt{(5 - 3)^2 + (4 - 8)^2}$

        $= \sqrt{(2)^2 + (-4)^2}$

        $= \sqrt{4 + 16}$

        $= \sqrt{20}$

  $\therefore$ Distance $\doteqdot 4 \cdot 47$ (using a calculator to answer to 2 decimal places).

2 Distance $= \sqrt{(x_2 - x_1)^2 + (y_2 - y_1)^2}$

    $(x_1, y_1) = (-2, 0)$ and $(x_2, y_2) = (8, -5)$

    $\therefore d = \sqrt{(8 - -2)^2 + (-5 - 0)^2}$

        $= \sqrt{(10)^2 + (-5)^2}$

        $= \sqrt{100 + 25}$

        $= \sqrt{125}$

  $\therefore$ Distance $\doteqdot 11 \cdot 18$ (using a calculator to answer to 2 decimal places).

- You should check that the formula will still give the same answer if the coordinates are named in the reverse way. Hence, in example 1, if we call $(x_1, y_1) = (5, 4)$ and $(x_2, y_2) = (3, 8)$, we would produce the same answer.

Exercise 8:01

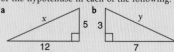
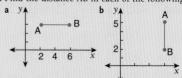
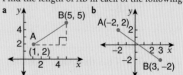
1 Use Pythagoras' theorem to find the length of each of the following. (Leave your answer as a surd, where necessary.)

a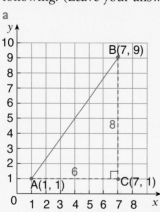

b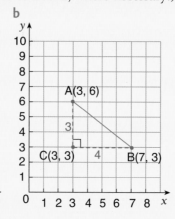

c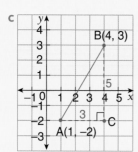

d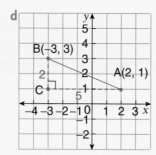

e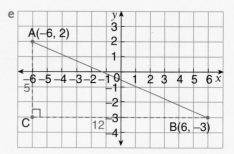

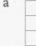

2 Find the lengths BC and AC and use these to find the lengths of AB. (Leave your answers in surd form.)

a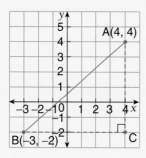

b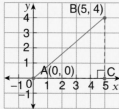

c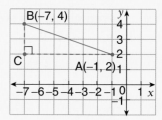

d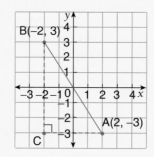

e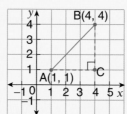

f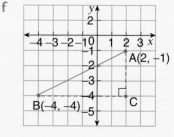

3 Use Pythagoras' theorem to find the length of interval AB in each of the following. (Leave answers in surd form.)

a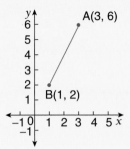

b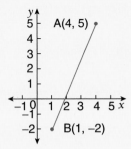

c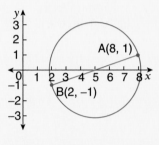

d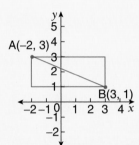

e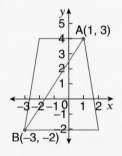

f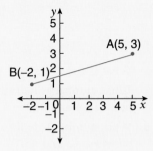

4 Use the formula $d = \sqrt{(x_2 - x_1)^2 + (y_2 - y_1)^2}$ to find the distance between the points:

a (4, 2) and (7, 6)   **b** (0, 1) and (8, 7)   **c** (−6, 4) and (−2, 1)
d (−2, −4) and (4, 4)   **e** (−6, 2) and (6, 7)   **f** (4, 9) and (−1, −3)
g (3, 0) and (5, −4)   **h** (8, 2) and (7, 0)   **i** (6, −1) and (−2, 4)
j (−3, 2) and (−7, 3)   **k** (6, 2) and (1, 1)   **l** (4, 4) and (3, 3)

5 **a** Find the distance from the point (4, 2) to the origin.
     b Which of the points (−1, 2) or (3, 5) is closer to the point (3, 0)?
     c Find the distance from the point (−2, 4) to the point (3, −5).
     d Which of the points (7, 2) or (−4, −4) is further from (0, 0)?

Making a sketch will help.

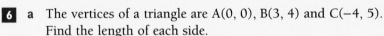

6 **a** The vertices of a triangle are A(0, 0), B(3, 4) and C(−4, 5). Find the length of each side.
     b ABCD is a parallelogram where A is the point (2, 3), B is (5, 5), C is (4, 3) and D is (1, 1). Show that the opposite sides of the parallelogram are equal.
     c Find the length of the two diagonals of the parallelogram in part **b**.
     d EFGH is a quadrilateral, where E is the point (0, 1), F is (3, 2), G is (2, −1) and H is (−1, −2). Prove that EFGH is a rhombus. (The sides of a rhombus are equal.)
     e (3, 2) is the centre of a circle. (6, 6) is a point on the circumference. What is the radius of the circle?
     f Prove that the triangle ABC is isosceles if A is (−2, −1), B is (4, 1) and C is (2, −5). (Isosceles triangles have two sides equal.)
     g A is the point (−13, 7) and B is (11, −3). M is halfway between A and B. How far is M from B?

8:02 | The Midpoint of an Interval

8:02

prep quiz

1 $\dfrac{4+10}{2}$

2 $\dfrac{-2+4}{2}$

3 What is the average of 4 and 10?

4 What is the average of −2 and 4?

5 What number is halfway between 4 and 10?

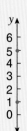

1 2 3 4 5 6 7 8 9 10 11 12 x

6 What number is halfway between −2 and 4?

−4 −3 −2 −1 0 1 2 3 4 5 6 7 x

7 What number is halfway between 1 and 5?

8 $\dfrac{1+5}{2}$ = ?

9 What number is halfway between −1 and 3?

10 $\dfrac{-1+3}{2}$ = ?

- The midpoint of an interval is the halfway position. If M is the midpoint of AB then it will be halfway between A and B.

If M is the midpoint of AB then AM = MB.

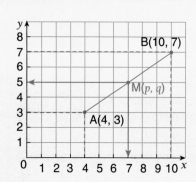

Consider the x-coordinates.

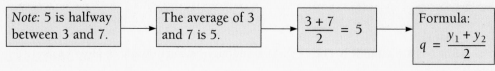

Note: 7 is halfway between 4 and 10.	The average of 4 and 10 is 7.	$\dfrac{4+10}{2} = 7$	Formula: $p = \dfrac{x_1 + x_2}{2}$

Consider the y-coordinates.

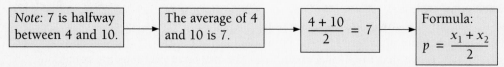

Note: 5 is halfway between 3 and 7.	The average of 3 and 7 is 5.	$\dfrac{3+7}{2} = 5$	Formula: $q = \dfrac{y_1 + y_2}{2}$

Midpoint formula

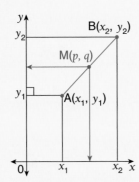

$$M = \left(\frac{x_1 + x_2}{2}, \frac{y_1 + y_2}{2}\right)$$

Could you please say that in English, Miss?

The midpoint, **M**, of interval **AB**, where **A** is (x_1, y_1) and **B** is (x_2, y_2), is given by:

$$M = \left(\frac{x_1 + x_2}{2}, \frac{y_1 + y_2}{2}\right).$$

worked examples

1 Find the midpoint of the interval joining $(2, 6)$ and $(8, 10)$.

2 Find the midpoint of interval AB, if A is the point $(-3, 5)$ and B is $(4, -2)$.

Solutions

1 Midpoint $= \left(\dfrac{x_1 + x_2}{2}, \dfrac{y_1 + y_2}{2}\right)$

$= \left(\dfrac{2 + 8}{2}, \dfrac{6 + 10}{2}\right)$

$= (5, 8)$

2 Midpoint $= \left(\dfrac{x_1 + x_2}{2}, \dfrac{y_1 + y_2}{2}\right)$

$= \left(\dfrac{-3 + 4}{2}, \dfrac{5 + -2}{2}\right)$

$= (\tfrac{1}{2}, \tfrac{3}{2})$ or $(\tfrac{1}{2}, 1\tfrac{1}{2})$

Exercise 8:02

Foundation Worksheet 8:02

Midpoint
1 Read the midpoint of the interval AB from the graph
2 Find the midpoint of the interval that joins:
  a (3, 4) to (10, 8)   b ...
3 Find the midpoint of the interval that joins:
  a (−4, 6) to (−3, −5)   b ...

1 Use the graph to find the midpoint of each interval.

a

b

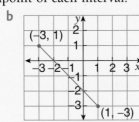

c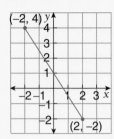

d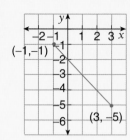

e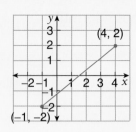

2 Use the graph to find the midpoints of the intervals:

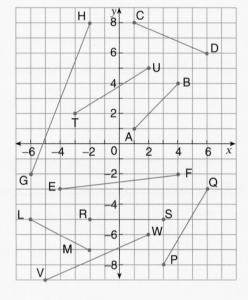

a AB   b CD   c GH
d EF   e LM   f PQ
g RS   h TU   i VW

3 Find the midpoint of each interval AB if:

a A is (2, 4), B is (6, 10)   b A is (1, 8), B is (5, 6)   c A is (4, 1), B is (8, 7)
d A is (0, 0), B is (−4, 2)   e A is (−1, 0), B is (5, 4)   f A is (−2, −6), B is (4, 2)
g A is (−8, −6), B is (0, −10)   h A is (−2, 4), B is (−4, −6)   i A is (−2, −4), B is (−6, −7)

4 Find the midpoint of the interval joining:

a (−3, −3) and (2, −3)   b (8, −1) and (7, −1)   c (5, 5) and (5, −5)
d (6, −7) and (−7, 6)   e (0, −4) and (−4, 0)   f (6, −6) and (5, −5)
g (111, 98) and (63, 42)   h (68, −23) and (72, −29)   i (400, 52) and (124, 100)

5 a   i Find the midpoint of AC.
     ii Find the midpoint of BD.
     iii Are the answers for i and ii the same?
     iv What property of a rectangle does this result demonstrate?

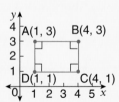

b If (4, 6) and (2, 10) are points at opposite ends of a diameter of a circle, what are the coordinates of the centre?

c **i** Find the midpoint of AC.
ii Find the midpoint of BD.
iii Are the answers for **i** and **ii** the same?
iv What property of a parallelogram does this result demonstrate?

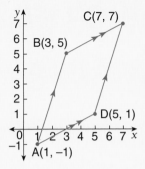

6 **a** If the midpoint of (3, k) and (13, 6) is (8, 3), find the value of k.
b The midpoint of AB is (7, −3). Find the value of d and e if A is the point (d, 0) and B is (−1, e).
c The midpoint of AB is (−6, 2). If A is the point (4, 4), what are the coordinates of B?
d A circle with centre (3, 4) has a diameter of AB. If A is the point (−1, 6) what are the coordinates of B?

7 **a** If A is the point (1, 4) and B is the point (15, 10), what are the coordinates of the points C, D and E?
b If A is the point (1, 4) and D is the point (15, 10), what are the coordinates of the points B, C and E?

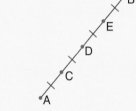

8 **a** Use coordinate geometry to show that the points A(−12, 10), B(8, 0), C(4, −6) and D(−16, 4) form a parallelogram.
b Use coordinate geometry to show that the points (−3, 2), (5, −2), (4, −4) and (−4, 0) form a rectangle.

Roger has 4 different pizza toppings. How many different pizzas could be made using:
• 1 topping?
• 2 toppings?
• any number of toppings?

8:03 | The Gradient of a Line

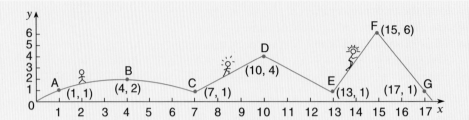

1 Which is steepest, AB or EF?

2 3 and **4** If I travel from left to right, between which 3 pairs of letters am I travelling upwards?

5 6 and **7** Between which 3 pairs of letters am I travelling downwards?

Say whether the hill is sloping up, down, or not at all, at the points

8 A   **9** G   **10** F

The **gradient** or **slope** of a line is a measure of *how steep* it is.

Negative gradient   Positive gradient   A higher positive gradient

* If we move from left to right the line going down is said to have a *negative* gradient (or slope). The line going up is said to have a *positive* gradient (or slope).
* If the line is horizontal (not going up or down) its gradient is *zero*.
* We find the gradient of a line by comparing its rise (change in *y*) with its run (change in *x*).

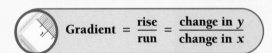

$$\text{Gradient} = \frac{\text{rise}}{\text{run}} = \frac{\text{change in } y}{\text{change in } x}$$

* So a gradient of $\frac{1}{2}$ means that for every run of 2 there is a rise of 1 (or for every 2 that you go across you go up 1).

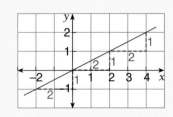

Finding the gradient of a line

1   Select any two points on the line.

2   Join the points and form a right-angled triangle by drawing a
    vertical line from the higher point and a horizontal side from
    the lower point.

3   Find the change in the *y*-coordinates (rise) and the change
    in the *x*-coordinates (run).

4   Use the formula above to find the gradient.

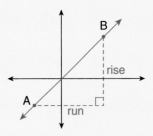

worked examples

Use the points A and B to find the gradient of the line AB in each case.

1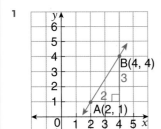

2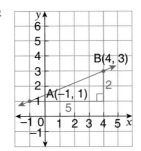

3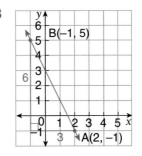

Solutions

1   Gradient

$$= \frac{\text{change in } y}{\text{change in } x}$$

$$= \frac{\text{up } 3}{\text{across } 2}$$

$$= \frac{3}{2}$$

2   $m = \dfrac{\text{change in } y}{\text{change in } x}$

$$= \frac{\text{up } 2}{\text{across } 5}$$

$$= \frac{2}{5}$$

3   $m = \dfrac{\text{change in } y}{\text{change in } x}$

$$= \frac{\text{down } 6}{\text{across } 3}$$

$$= -\frac{6}{3}$$

$$= -2$$

▪ *m* is used
for 'gradient'

▪ Gradient is
generally left as an
improper fraction
instead of a mixed
numeral. So we write
$\frac{3}{2}$ instead of $1\frac{1}{2}$.

• Architectural design often
requires an understanding
of gradients (slopes).

Gradient formula

We wish to find a formula for the gradient of a line AB where A is (x_1, y_1) and B is (x_2, y_2).

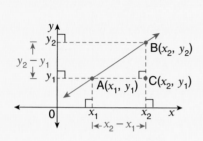

Gradient of AB $= \dfrac{\text{rise}}{\text{run}}$

$= \dfrac{\text{change in } y}{\text{change in } x}$

$= \dfrac{BC}{AC}$

$\therefore m = \dfrac{y_2 - y_1}{x_2 - x_1}$ (opposite sides of a rectangle are equal)

m is used for 'gradient'

The gradient of the line that passes through the points $A(x_1, y_1)$ and $B(x_2, y_2)$ is given by the formula:

$$m = \frac{y_2 - y_1}{x_2 - x_1}$$

worked examples

Find the gradient of the straight line passing through the following points.

1 (1, 3) and (4, 7)   **2** (6, −2) and (2, −1)

Solutions

1 Let (x_1, y_1) be (1, 3) and (x_2, y_2) be (4, 7).

Gradient $= \dfrac{y_2 - y_1}{x_2 - x_1}$

$= \dfrac{7 - 3}{4 - 1}$

$= \dfrac{4}{3}$

$\therefore$ The gradient is $1\frac{1}{3}$.

2 Let (x_1, y_1) be (6, −2) and (x_2, y_2) be (2, −1).

$m = \dfrac{y_2 - y_1}{x_2 - x_1}$

$= \dfrac{-1 - (-2)}{2 - 6}$

$= \dfrac{1}{-4}$

$\therefore$ The gradient is $-\frac{1}{4}$.

It doesn't matter which point is called (x_1, y_1).

Exercise 8:03

1 For each of the following, state if the line has a positive or negative gradient.

a

b
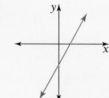

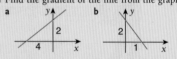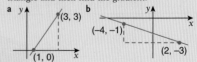

c

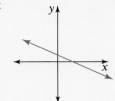

d

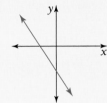

e

2 Using Gradient = $\dfrac{\quad}{\text{Run}}$ find the gradient of AB in each of the following:

a

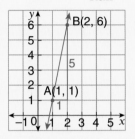

b

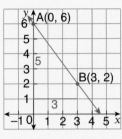

c

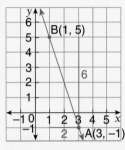

d A(2, 9), B(−1, 0)   **e** A(0, 5), B(5, 0)   **f** A(−3, −8), B(1, 8)

3   **a**   Calculate the gradients of the four lines.
     b   Which lines have the same gradients?
     c   Which lines are parallel?

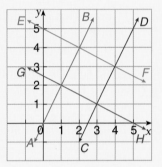

4 On the same number plane, draw:
     a   a line through (0, 0) with a gradient of −2
     b   a line through (1, 1) which is parallel to the line in **a**.
     c   Do the lines in **a** and **b** have the same gradient?

> ■ If two lines have the same gradient they are *parallel*.

5 Use the formula $m = \dfrac{y_2 - y_1}{x_2 - x_1}$ to find the gradient of the straight line passing through the points:

     a   (2, 6) and (5, 7)   **b**   (4, 2) and (5, 6)
     c   (3, 1) and (7, 3)   **d**   (0, 0) and (5, 2)
     e   (0, 5) and (6, 6)   **f**   (3, 0) and (5, 6)
     g   (6, 2) and (2, 1)   **h**   (7, 7) and (5, 6)
     i   (9, 12) and (3, 7)   **j**   (−4, 3) and (1, 4)
     k   (−3, −2) and (0, 6)   **l**   (4, −1) and (3, 3)
     m   (2, 3) and (−4, 9)   **n**   (−4, 1) and (−2, −4)
     o   (5, 2) and (7, −6)   **p**   (−3, −1) and (−6, −7)
     q   (4, −2) and (−4, −2)   **r**   (−6, 3) and (1, 3)

> If a line has no slope m = 0.

6 a Find the gradient of the line that passes through A(3, 1) and B(5, 11).

b Find the slope of the line that passes through O(0, 0) and B(−1, −2).

c On the graph shown, all of the points A, B, C and D lie on the same straight line, $x + 2y = 6$.
Find the gradient of the line using the points:

  i A and B   **ii** C and D
  iii A and D   **iv** B and C

Conclusion: Any two points on a straight line can be used to find the gradient of that line.
A straight line has only one gradient.

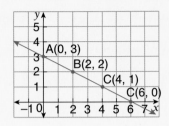

d Use the gradient of an interval to show that the points (−2, 5), (2, 13) and (6, 21) are collinear (ie, lie on the same straight line).

7 a **i** Find the gradient of BC and of AD.
    ii Find the gradient of AB and of DC.
    iii What kind of quadrilateral is ABCD?
       Give a reason for your answer.

b Prove that a quadrilateral that has vertices A(2, 3), B(9, 5), C(4, 0) and D(−3, −2) is a parallelogram. (It will be necessary to prove that opposite sides are parallel.)

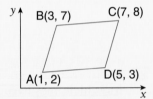

8 Use the fact that *a rhombus is a parallelogram with a pair of adjacent sides equal* to prove that the points A(−1, 1), B(11, 4), C(8, −8) and D(−4, −11) form the vertices of a rhombus.

8:04 | Graphing Straight Lines

A straight line is made up of a set of points, each with its own pair of coordinates.

- Coordinate geometry uses an equation to describe the relationship between the x- and y-coordinates of any point on the line.

  In the diagram, the equation of the line is $x + y = 3$. From the points shown, it is clear that the relationship is that the sum of each point's coordinates is 3.

- A point can only lie on a line if its coordinates satisfy the equation of the line. For the points $(-3, 2)$ and $(2, 3)$, it is clear that the sum of the coordinates is not equal to 3. So they do not lie on the line.

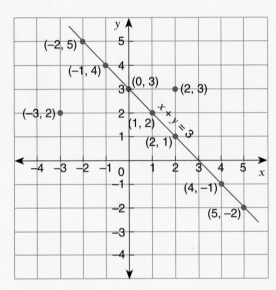

The x and y in the equation are the point's coordinates.

$x + y = 3$

To graph a straight line we need:
- an equation to allow us to calculate the x- and y-coordinates for each point on the line
- a table to store at least two sets of coordinates
- a number plane on which to plot the points.

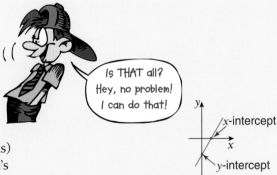

Is THAT all? Hey, no problem! I can do that!

Two important points on a line are:
- the x-intercept (where the line crosses the x-axis)
  This is found by substituting $y = 0$ into the line's equation and then solving for x.
- the y-intercept (where the line crosses the y-axis)
  This is found by substituting $x = 0$ into the line's equation and then solving for y.

Horizontal and vertical lines

The line shown on the graph on the right is vertical.
- Below, we have put the points on the line into a table.

x	2	2	2	2	2	2
y	−2	−1	0	1	2	3

- There seems to be no connection between x and y.
  However, x is always 2. So the equation is $x = 2$.

Vertical lines have equations of the form $x = a$ where a is where the line cuts the x-axis.

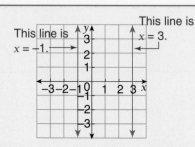

This line is $x = -1$.

This line is $x = 3$.

They cut the x-axis at −1 and 3.

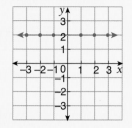

The line on the right is horizontal.
- Below, we have put the points on the line, into a table.

x	−2	−1	0	1	2	3
y	2	2	2	2	2	2

- There seems to be no connection between x and y.
  However, y is always 2. So the equation is $y = 2$.

Horizontal lines have equations of the form $y = b$ where b is where the line cuts the y-axis.

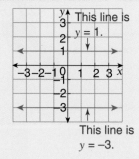

This line is $y = 1$.

This line is $y = -3$.

They cut the y-axis at −3 and 1.

Draw the graph of each straight line.

1 $y = 3x - 5$ **2** $3x + y = 5$ **3** $2x + 3y = 6$ **4** $3x - 4y + 12 = 0$

Solutions

1 $y = 3x - 5$

x	0	1	2
y	−5	−2	1

when $x = 0$, $y = 3 \times 0 - 5$
                  $y = -5$

when $x = 1$, $y = 3 \times 1 - 5$
                  $y = -2$

when $x = 2$, $y = 3 \times 2 - 5$
                  $y = 1$

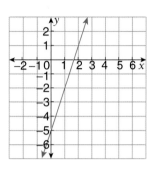

2 $3x + y = 5$

x	0	1	2
y	5	2	−1

when $x = 0$, $3 \times 0 + y = 5$
                 $0 + y = 5$
                     $y = 5$

when $x = 1$, $3 \times 1 + y = 5$
                 $3 + y = 5$
                     $y = 2$

when $x = 2$, $3 \times 2 + y = 5$
                 $6 + y = 5$
                     $y = -1$

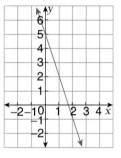

3 $2x + 3y = 6$

x	0	1	2
y	2	$1\frac{1}{3}$	$\frac{2}{3}$

when $x = 0$, $2 \times 0 + 3y = 6$
                 $0 + 3y = 6$
                    $y = 2$

when $x = 1$, $2 \times 1 + 3y = 6$
                 $2 + 3y = 6$
                    $3y = 4$
                    $y = 1\frac{1}{3}$

when $x = 2$, $2 \times 2 + 3y = 6$
                 $4 + 3y = 6$
                    $3y = 2$
                    $y = \frac{2}{3}$

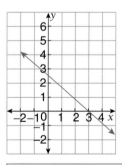

Since it is difficult to plot fractions, an intercept method would be better here:

At the x axis, $y = 0$
$\therefore 2x + 3 \times 0 = 6$
            $2x = 6$
              $x = 3$

At the y axis, $x = 0$
$\therefore 2 \times 0 + 3y = 6$
            $3y = 6$
             $y = 2$

continued ➜➜➜

4 $3x - 4y + 12 = 0$

It can be seen that if a table of values is used here fractions will result. The intercept method is better again.

Rewrite the equation as $3x - 4y = -12$

At the x axis, $y = 0$
$\therefore 2x - 4 \times 0 = -12$
$\qquad 2x = -12$
$\qquad x = -6$

At the y axis, $x = 0$
$\therefore 2 \times 0 + 4y = -12$
$\qquad 4y = -12$
$\qquad y = -3$

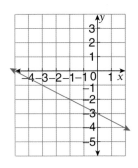

Exercise 8:04

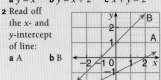
1 Using separate axes labelled from −4 to 6, draw the graph of the following lines using any of the above methods.
  a $y = 2x - 3$ **b** $y = 4 - 3x$
  c $2x + y = 5$ **d** $y + 3x = 3$

2 Graph the lines represented by these equations using an appropriate method.
  a $x + 2y = 4$ **b** $y = 5 - x$ **c** $y = 3x + 2$ **d** $2y - 5x = 10$
  e $x + 3y + 9 = 0$ **f** $3 - 2x = y$ **g** $3y = 2x + 6$ **h** $y - 2 = 4x$

3 On which of the following lines does the point (−2, 3) lie?
  a $y = 2x + 1$ **b** $2x + y + 1 = 0$ **c** $x = 2y - 8$ **d** $y - 2x = -1$
  e $3x - 2y = 0$ **f** $2y - 3x = 0$

4 The line $2x - 5y + 6 = 0$ passes through which of the following points?
  a (2, 2)   **b** (7, 4)   **c** (−2, 2)   **d** (−3, 0)   **e** (8, 2)   **f** (3, 0)

5 For each number plane, write down the equations of the lines Ⓐ to Ⓕ.
  a

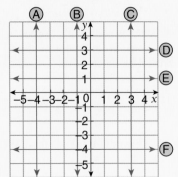

  b

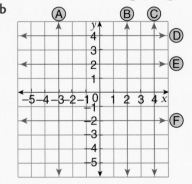

6 Using values from −5 to 5 on each axis, draw the graphs of the following straight lines. Use a new diagram for each part.

a $y = 4$, $x = 5$, $y = -1$, $x = 0$ b $x = 1$, $y = 0$, $x = 2$, $y = 3$

c $y = 4$, $x = 2$, $y = -2$, $x = -4$ d $x = 5$, $y = -5$, $x = 2$, $y = 2$

e $y = -2$, $y = 0$, $x = 0$, $x = 3$

Which of these encloses a square region?

7 Match each of the graphs A to F with one of the following equations:

$y = 2x$ $y = x - 2$ $2x + y = 0$

$y = x$ $x + y = 3$ $2x + y = 2$

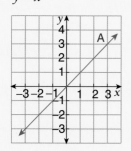 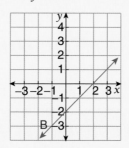 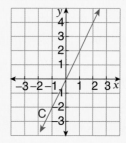

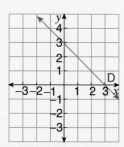 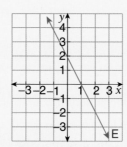 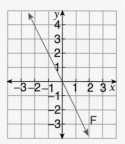

8 Which of the lines A, B, C or D could be described by the following equation.

a $x - y = 2$ b $x + y = 4$

c $2x + y + 2 = 0$ d $x - 2y + 2 = 0$

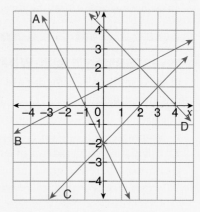

9 Use the intercept method to graph the following lines.

a $2x + y = 2$ b $3x + y = 6$ c $2x + y = 4$

d $2x - y = 4$ e $3x - y = 3$ f $4x - y = 2$

10 Draw the graph of each equation.

a $y = \dfrac{3x}{2}$ b $y = \dfrac{x + 1}{2}$ c $y = \dfrac{x - 1}{2}$

d $3x + 2y = 7$ e $5x - 2y - 6 = 0$ f $2x - 3y - 5 = 0$

8:05 | The Gradient–Intercept Form of a Straight Line: $y = mx + c$

If $x = 0$, what is the value of:

1 $2x$ **2** $mx + c$

If $x = 0$, what is the value of y when:

3 $y = 3x + 2$ **4** $y = 4x - 1$

What is the gradient of:

5 line A   **6** line B

What are the coordinates of the y-intercept of:

7 line A   **8** line B

9 Does every point on the y-axis have an x-coordinate of 0?

10 Can the y-intercept of a line be found by putting $x = 0$.

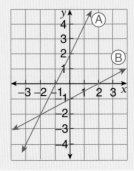

As you learnt in Book 3:

- The equation of a line can be written in several ways. For instance,
  $x - y - 4 = 0$, $y = x - 4$ and $x - y = 4$
  are different ways of writing the same equation.

- When the equation is written in the form $x - y - 4 = 0$, it is said to be in general form.

- The form $y = x - 4$ is a particularly useful way of writing the equation of a line. It allows us to get information about the line directly from the equation.

Investigation 8:05 | What does $y = mx + c$ tell us?

Please use the Assessment Grid on the page 222 to help you understand what is required for this Investigation.

For each of the following equations complete the table by:

1 graphing each line on a Cartesian grid

2 calculating the gradient of each line (use any two points that the line passes through), and

3 noting where the graph crosses the y axis (y-intercept).

Line	Equation	Gradient	y-intercept
1	$y = 3x - 4$		
2	$y = 5 - 2x$		
3	$y = \frac{1}{2}x + 1$		
4	$y = x$		
5	$y = 3 - 2x$		

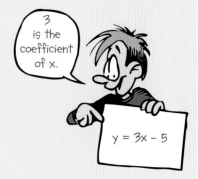

3 is the coefficient of x.

y = 3x − 5

Are there any patterns you can find connecting the gradients and the *y*-intercepts and the numbers in the equations of the lines? Explain these patterns or connections.

Try to write a rule that will help you write down the gradient and *y*-intercept for a line without drawing the line.

4 Using your rule, write down the equations of the lines shown in the Cartesian grid below.

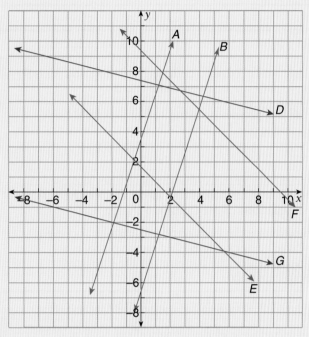

5 By making a table of values for your equations, check that your equations represent the lines given.

6 Do you notice anything special about the lines that have the same colour?

7 Can you discuss some possible real life applications of straight lines and their equations?

- **When an equation of a line is written in the form $y = mx + c$,**
  m **gives the gradient of the line and**
  c **gives the *y*-intercept of the line.**
- **Clearly, lines with the same gradient are parallel.**
- **When an equation of a line is written in the form $ax + by + c = 0$, where *a*, *b* and *c* are integers and $a > 0$, it is said to be in general form.**

Assessment Grid for Investigation 8:05 | What does $y = mx + c$ tell us?

The following is a sample assessment grid for this investigation. You should carefully read the criteria *before* beginning the investigation so that you know what is required.

			Assessment Criteria (B, C, D) for this investigation		Achieved ✓
Criterion B Investigating Patterns	a		None of the following descriptors has been achieved.	0	
	b		Some help was needed to complete the table and identify the simple patterns in questions 2 and 3.	1	
				2	
	c		Mathematical problem-solving techniques have been selected and applied to accurately graph the lines required and complete the table, with some suggestion of emerging patterns.	3	
				4	
	d		The student has graphed the required lines and used the patterns evident in the table to find a connecting rule to give the equations of the lines in question 4.	5	
				6	
	e		The patterns evident between the equations and their graphs have been explained and summarised as a mathematical rule. The patterns for the lines in part 6 have been explained.	7	
				8	
Criterion C Communication in Mathematics	a		None of the following descriptors has been achieved.	0	
	b		There is a basic use of mathematical language and representation. Lines of reasoning are insufficient.	1	
				2	
	c		There is satisfactory use of mathematical language and representation. Graphs, tables and explanations are clear but not always logical or complete.	3	
				4	
	d		A good use of mathematical language and representation. Graphs are accurate, to scale and fully labelled. Explanations and answers are complete and concise.	5	
				6	
Criterion D Reflection in Mathematics	a		None of the following descriptors has been achieved.	0	
	b		An attempt has been made to explain whether the results make sense, with connection to possible real-life applications.	1	
				2	
	c		There is a correct but brief explanation of whether results make sense and how they were found. A description of the important aspects of the graphs is given and the relation to their equations.	3	
				4	
	d		There is a critical explanation of the graphs obtained and their related equations. All results are fully explained and justified, and specific reference to real-life applications of lines is given.	5	
				6	

1 Write down the gradient and y-intercepts of these lines.

a $y = 4x - 2$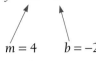

$m = 4$ $b = -2$

Gradient $= 4$

y-intercept $= -2$

b $y = 3 - 5x$

$b = 3$ $m = -5$

Gradient $= -5$

y-intercept $= 3$

c $2x + 3y = 12$

$3y = -2x + 12$

$y = -\frac{2}{3}x + 4$

$m = -\frac{2}{3}$ $b = 4$

Gradient $= -\frac{2}{3}$

y-intercept $= 4$

2 From the graph of the line shown, write down the gradient and y-intercept of the line and hence its equation.

From the graph:

The y-intercept $(c) = -1$

The gradient $(m) = \dfrac{4}{2} = 2$

$\therefore$ the equation $y = mx + c$
becomes $y = 2x - 1$

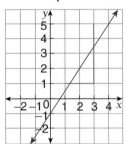

This line is 'rising', so, the gradient is positive.

3 Use the y-intercept and the gradient to graph the following lines:

a $y = 4x - 3$

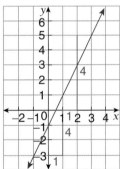

Start at the y-intercept of $(c) = -3$.

Gradient $= \dfrac{\text{Rise}}{\text{Run}} = 4 = \dfrac{4}{1}$ and is positive so for every

1 unit across there is a rise of 4 units.

b $5x + 2y = 6$

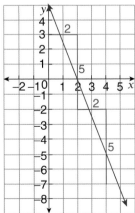

First, rearrange the equation in the form $y = mx + c$.

$5x + 2y = 6$

$2y = -5x + 6$

$y = -\dfrac{5}{2}x + 3$.

Start at the y-intercept $(c) = 3$

Gradient $= \dfrac{\text{Rise}}{\text{Run}} = -\dfrac{5}{2}$

and is negative so for every 2 units across there is a fall of 5 units.

Remember! A negative gradient always slopes down to the right.

Exercise 8:05

Foundation Worksheet 8:05

Gradient–intercept form
1 For each line find from the graph its:
   a y-intercept   **b** gradient
2 What is $y = mx + b$ when:
   a $m = 4$ and $b = 3$ **b** $m = -3$ and $b = -1$
3 Find the equation of a line with:
   a a gradient of 2 and y-intercept of 2

1 Write the gradient and y-intercept of the following lines:

  a $y = 4x - 5$ **b** $y = 3x + 2$ **c** $y = 9 - x$

  d $y = 3 + \frac{5}{7}x$ **e** $2y = 3x - 5$

2 By first rearranging the equation in the form $y = mx + c$
write the gradient and y-intercept of the following lines:

  a $2y = 6x + 8$ **b** $y - 5 = 3x$ **c** $3x + 4y = 10$ **d** $2x = 6 - 3y$

  e $3 - 2y = x$ **f** $2y + 4x - 10 = 0$ **g** $5x - 3y = -1$ **h** $3y - 4 = 6x$

  i $x - y - 1 = 0$ **j** $6 - 5x = y$

3 Use the graph to find the gradient and
y-intercept of each line and hence
write the equation of each line in the
general form. (The general form of a
line is $ax + by + c = 0$, where a, b and c
are whole numbers and a is positive.)

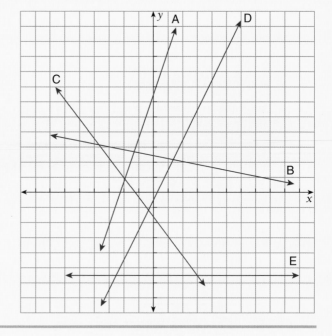

4 Draw the graphs of the following using
only the gradient and y-intercept
(follow example 3).

  a $y = x - 6$

  b $y = 3 - 2x$

  c $2y = 3x - 6$

  d $3x - 4y = 8$

  e $x + 2y - 4 = 0$

  f $2x + y + 4 = 0$

  g $y + 6 = 0$

  h $3x - 2y = -12$

Technology
Applications

Activities

8:05 Equation grapher

'Slope' is another name
for 'gradient'.

8:06 | The Equation of a Straight Line, Given Point and Gradient

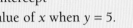
A line has the equation $y = 3x + 5$. Find:

1 its gradient

2 its y-intercept

3 the value of y when $x = 2$

4 the value of x when $y = 5$.

If $y = mx + c$, find the value of c if:

5 $m = 2, x = 0, y = 4$

6 $m = -2, x = 1, y = 3$

7 $m = 3, x = -1, y = -2$

8 $m = -2, x = -4, y = 10$

9 $m = 0, x = 2, y = 3$

10 $m = 1, x = 2, y = 2$

Through a given point, any number of lines can be drawn. Each of these lines has a different gradient, so the equation of a straight line can be found if we know its gradient and a point through which it passes.

The equation of a line through $(1, 2)$ having a gradient of 3 can be found by beginning with the formula $y = mx + b$. We know that $m = 3$, but we must also find the value of b. To do this, we substitute the coordinates of $(1, 2)$ into the equation, as a point on the line must satisfy its equation.

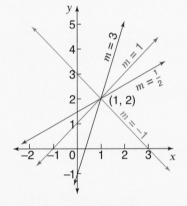

Working:
$$y = mx + c \quad \text{(formula)}$$
$$\therefore y = 3x + c \quad (m = 3 \text{ is given})$$
$$2 = 3(1) + c \quad [(1, 2) \text{ lies on the line}]$$
$$2 = 3 + c$$
$$\therefore c = -1$$

$\therefore$ The equation of the line is $y = 3x - 1$.

To find the equation of a straight line that has a gradient of 2 and passes through $(7, 5)$:

(1) Substitute $m = 2$, $x = 7$ and $y = 5$ into the formula $y = mx + c$ to find the value of c.

(2) Rewrite $y = mx + c$ replacing m and c with their numerical values.

We can use the method above to discover a formula that could be used instead.

Question: What is the equation of a line that has a gradient m and passes through the point (x_1, y_1)?

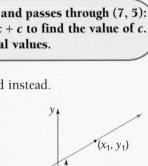

Working:
$$y = mx + c \quad \text{(formula; gradient is } m)$$
$$\therefore y_1 = mx_1 + c \quad [(x_1, y_1) \text{ lies on the line}]$$
$$\therefore c = y_1 - mx_1$$
$\therefore$ The equation of the line is
$$y = mx + (y_1 - mx_1)$$
ie $y - y_1 = mx - mx_1$
$$\therefore y - y_1 = mx(x - x_1)$$

This last form of the answer is the easiest to remember as it could be written as $\dfrac{y - y_1}{x - x_1} = m$.

The equation of a line with gradient m, that passes through the point (x_1, y_1) is given by:

$$y - y_1 = m(x - x_1) \quad \text{or} \quad \frac{y - y_1}{x - x_1} = m.$$

worked examples

1 Find the equation of the line that passes through $(1, 4)$ and has gradient 2.

2 A straight line has gradient $-\frac{1}{2}$ and passes through the point $(1, 3)$. Find the equation of this line.

You can use either formula.

$$\blacksquare \; y - y_1 = m(x - x_1)$$
or
$$y = mx + c$$

Solutions

1 Let the equation of the line be:
$$y = mx + c$$
$$\therefore y = 2x + c \qquad (m = 2 \text{ is given})$$
$$4 = 2(1) + c \quad [(1, 4) \text{ lies on the line}]$$
$$4 = 2 + c$$
$$\therefore c = 2$$
$$\therefore \text{ The equation is } y = 2x + 2.$$

or

1 $y - y_1 = m(x - x_1)$
(x_1, y_1) is $(1, 4)$, $m = 2$
$$\therefore y - 4 = 2(x - 1)$$
$$y - 4 = 2x - 2$$
$$\therefore y = 2x + 2 \text{ is the}$$
equation of the line.

2 Let the equation be:
$$y = mx + c$$
$$\therefore y = -\frac{1}{2}x + c \quad (m = -\frac{1}{2} \text{ is given})$$
$$3 = -\frac{1}{2}(1) + c \quad [(1, 3) \text{ is on the line}]$$
$$3 = -\frac{1}{2} + c$$
$$\therefore c = 3\frac{1}{2}$$
$$\therefore \text{ The equation is } y = -\frac{1}{2}x + 3\frac{1}{2}.$$

or

2 $y - y_1 = m(x - x_1)$
(x_1, y_1) is $(1, 3)$, $m = -\frac{1}{2}$
$$\therefore y - 3 = -\frac{1}{2}(x - 1)$$
$$y - 3 = -\frac{1}{2}x + \frac{1}{2}$$
$$\therefore y = -\frac{1}{2}x + 3\frac{1}{2} \text{ is the}$$
equation of the line.

Exercise 8:06

Foundation Worksheet 8:06

Point–gradient form
Use $y - y_1 = m(x - x_1)$
to find the equation of
a line when:
1 $m = 2$, $(x_1, y_1) = (1, 4)$
2 $m = -2$, $(x_1, y_1) = (-1, 3)$

1 For each part, find c if the given point lies on the given line.

    a $(1, 3)$, $y = 2x + c$ **c** $(2, 10)$, $y = 4x + c$ **c** $(-1, 3)$, $y = 2x + c$

    d $(5, 5)$, $y = 2x + c$ **e** $(3, 1)$, $y = x + c$ **f** $(-1, -9)$, $y = -2x + c$

2 Find the equation of the straight line (giving answers in the form $y = mx + c$) if it has:

    a gradient 2 and passes through the point $(1, 3)$

    b gradient 5 and passes through the point $(0, 0)$

    c gradient 3 and passes through the point $(2, 2)$

    d slope 4 and passes through the point $(-1, 6)$

e gradient −1 and passes through the point (−2, 8)

f gradient −2 and passes through the point (0, 7)

g slope −5 and passes through the point (1, 0)

h gradient $\frac{1}{2}$ and passes through the point (4, 5)

i gradient $\frac{1}{4}$ and passes through the point $(6, 3\frac{1}{2})$

j slope $-\frac{1}{2}$ and passes through the point (−4, −1)

'Slope' is another name for 'gradient'.

3 **a** A straight line has a gradient of 2 and passes through the point (3, 2). Find the equation of the line.

b A straight line has a gradient of −1. If the line passes through the point (2, 1), find the equation of the line.

c What is the equation of a straight line that passes through the point (−2, 0) and has a gradient of 3?

d A straight line that passes through the point (1, −2) has a gradient of −3. What is the equation of this line?

e A straight line that has a gradient of 3 passes through the origin. What is the equation of this line?

f Find the equation of the straight line that has a gradient of 4 and passes through the point (−1, −2).

g (2, 8) is on a line that has a gradient of 4. Find the equation of this line.

h The point (−6, 4) lies on a straight line that has a gradient of −2. What is the equation of this line?

i Find the equation of the straight line that has a gradient of 2 and passes through the midpoint of the interval joining (1, 3) and (5, 5).

j A straight line passes through the midpoint of the interval joining (0, 0) and (−6, 4). Find the equation of the line if its gradient is $\frac{1}{2}$.

8:07 | The Equation of a Straight Line, Given Two Points

Only one straight line can be drawn through two points. Given two points on a straight line, we can always find the equation of that line.

Consider the line passing through (1, 1) and (2, 4). Let the equation of the line be:

$$y = mx + c \text{ (formula)}$$

First find the gradient using the two points.

$$m = \frac{y_2 - y_1}{x_2 - x_1}$$

$(x_1, y_1) = (1, 1)$
$(x_2, y_2) = (2, 4)$

$$= \frac{4-1}{2-1}$$

$$= 3$$

$\therefore y = 3x + c$ (since $m = 3$)

$4 = 3(2 + c)$ [(2, 4) lies on the line]

$\therefore c = -2$

$\therefore$ The equation of the line is $y = 3x - 2$.

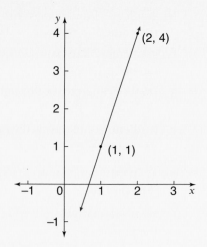

To find the equation of a straight line that passes through the two points $(1, 2)$ and $(3, 6)$:
1   Find the value of the gradient m, using the given points.
2   For $y = mx + c$, find the value of c by substituting the value of m and the coordinates of one of the given points.
3   Rewrite $y = mx + c$ replacing m and c with their numerical values.

Another method is to use the formula:

$$y - y_1 = \frac{y_2 - y_1}{x_2 - x_1}(x - x_1)$$

where (x_1, y_1) and (x_2, y_2) are points on the line.

worked example

Find the equation of the line that passes through the points $(-1, 2)$ and $(2, 8)$.

Solution

Let the equation of the line be:

$y = mx + c$

Now $m = \dfrac{y_2 - y_1}{x_2 - x_1}$

$(x_1, y_1) = (-1, 2)$
$(x_2, y_2) = (2, 8)$

$$= \frac{8-2}{2-(-1)}$$

$$= \frac{6}{3}$$

$\therefore m = 2$

$\therefore y = 2x + c$ (since $m = 2$)

$(2, 8)$ lies on the line.

$\therefore 8 = 2(2) + c$

$\therefore c = 4$

$\therefore$ The equation is $y = 2x + 4$.

or

$$y - y_1 = \frac{y_2 - y_1}{x_2 - x_1}(x - x_1)$$

(x_1, y_1) is $(-1, 2)$, (x_2, y_2) is $(2, 8)$

$$\therefore y - 2 = \frac{8-2}{2-(-1)}[x - (-1)]$$

$$y - 2 = \frac{6}{3}(x + 1)$$

$$y - 2 = 2(x + 1)$$

$$y - 2 = 2x + 2$$

$$\therefore y = 2x + 4 \text{ is the equation of the line.}$$

1 Find the gradient of the line that passes through the points:

a (2, 0) and (3, 4)   b (−1, 3) and (2, 6)
c (3, 1) and (1, 5)   d (−2, −1) and (0, 9)
e (−2, 1) and (2, 2)   f (5, 2) and (4, 3)
g (0, 0) and (1, 3)   h (1, 1) and (4, 4)
i (−1, 8) and (1, −2)   j (0, 0) and (1, −3)

2 Use your answers for question **1** to find the equations of the lines passing through the pairs of points in question **1**.

3 a Find the equation of the line that passes through the points (−2, −2) and (1, 4).
  b The points A(4, 3) and B(5, 0) lie on the line AB. What is the equation of AB?
  c What is the equation of the line AB if A is the point (−2, −4) and B is (2, 12)?
  d Find the equation of the line that passes through the points (1, 6) and (2, 8). By substitution in this equation, show that (3, 10) also lies on this line.
  e What is the equation of the line CD if C is the point (2, 3) and D is the point (4, 5)?

4 A is the point (−2, 1), B is the point (1, 4) and C is the point (3, −2).
  a Find the gradient of each side of △ABC.
  b Find the equation of each of the lines AB, BC and AC.
  c Find the y-intercept of each of the lines AB, BC and AC.
  d Find the equation of the line passing through point A and the midpoint of interval BC.
  e Find the gradient and y-intercept of the line passing through point A and the midpoint of interval BC.

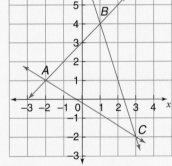

5 a Find the equation of the line joining A(1, 2) and B(5, −6). Hence show that C(3, −2) also lies on this line.
  b A(−2, 2), B(1, −4) and C(3, −8) are points on the number plane. Show that they are collinear.
  c Show that the points (−2, −11), (3, 4) and (4, 7) are collinear.

Recipe for question 5a
1. Find the equation of AB
2. Substitute C into this equation.

Collinear points lie on the same straight line.

6 Find the equation of the lines in general form that pass through the points:
  a (3, −2) and (−4, 1)
  b (−2, −4) and (3, 2)
  c (1·3, −2·6) and (4, −7·3)
  d $(1\frac{1}{2}, -\frac{2}{3})$ and $(-2\frac{1}{3}, \frac{1}{2})$

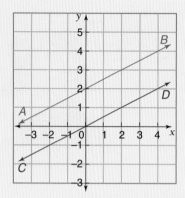

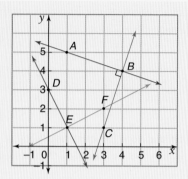

In the diagram, AB is perpendicular to BC, and DE is perpendicular to EF.

1 What is the gradient of each line?
2 Are the lines parallel?
3 If EF was drawn parallel to AB, what would its gradient be?
4 Is it possible for two lines with with different gradients to be parallel?

5 Find the gradient of AB. Call this m_1.
6 Find the gradient of BC. Call this m_2.
7 Using your answers to 5 and 6, find the product of the gradients, m_1m_2.
8 Find the gradient of DE. Call this m_3.
9 Find the gradient of EF. Call this m_4.
10 Using your answers to 8 and 9, find the product of the gradients, m_3m_4.

Questions 1 to 4 in the Prep Quiz remind us that:
• two straight lines are parallel if their gradients are equal
• the gradients of two lines are equal if the lines are parallel.
Questions 5 to 10 of the Prep Quiz suggest that a condition for two lines to be perpendicular might be that the product of their gradients is equal to −1.
We do not intend to prove this here, but let us look at several pairs of lines where the product of the gradient is −1 to see if the angle between the lines is 90°.

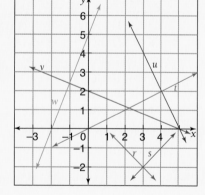

A Line r has gradient −1.   ∴ $m_1 = -1$
   Line s has gradient 1.   ∴ $m_2 = 1$
   Note that $m_1m_2 = -1$.
B Line t has gradient $\frac{1}{2}$.   ∴ $m_1 = \frac{1}{2}$
   Line u has gradient −2.   ∴ $m_2 = -2$
   Note that $m_1m_2 = -1$.
C Line v has gradient $-\frac{2}{5}$.   ∴ $m_1 = -\frac{2}{5}$
   Line w has gradient $\frac{5}{2}$.   ∴ $m_2 = \frac{5}{2}$
   Note that $m_1m_2 = -1$.
• By measurement, or use of Pythagoras' theorem, we can show that the angle between each pair of lines is 90°.
• If two lines are perpendicular, then the product of their gradients is −1.
• $m_1m_2 = -1$ (where neither gradient is zero).

- If the product of the gradients of two lines is −1, then the lines are perpendicular.

Two lines with gradients of m_1 and m_2 are:
- **parallel if $m_1 = m_2$**
- **perpendicular if $m_1m_2 = -1$**

(or $m_1 = \dfrac{-1}{m_2}$) where neither m_1 nor m_2 can equal zero.

worked examples

1 Which of the lines $y = 4x$, $y = 3x + 2$ and $y = x$ is perpendicular to $x + 4y + 2 = 0$?

2 Find the equation of the line that passes through the point (2, 4) and is perpendicular to $y = 3x - 2$.

3 Find the equation of the line that passes through the point (1, 4) and is parallel to $y = 3x - 2$.

Solutions

1 Step 1: Find the gradient of $x + 4y + 2 = 0$.

Writing this in gradient form gives:

$y = -\frac{1}{4}x - 2$

∴ The gradient of this line is $-\frac{1}{4}$.

Step 2: Find the gradients of the other lines.

The gradient of $y = 4x$ is 4.

The gradient of $y = 3x + 2$ is 3.

The gradient of $y = x$ is 1.

Step 3: Find which gradient in step **2** will multiply $-\frac{1}{4}$ to give −1.

Conclusion: $-\frac{1}{4} \times 4 = -1$

∴ $x + 4y + 2 = 0$ is perpendicular to $y = 4x$.

If $m_1m_2 = -1$,

then $m_1 = \dfrac{-1}{m_2}$

2 Let the equation of the line be $y = mx + b$. Now the gradient of $y = 3x - 2$ is 3.

∴ $m = -\frac{1}{3}$ (since $-\frac{1}{3} \times 3 = -1$)

∴ $y = -\frac{1}{3}x + c$

$4 = -\frac{1}{3}(2) + c$ [since (2, 4) lies on line]

$4 = -\frac{2}{3} + c$

∴ $c = 4\frac{2}{3}$

∴ The equation of the line is $y = -\frac{1}{3}x + 4\frac{2}{3}$.

3 Let the equation of the line be $y = mx + c$.

$y = 3x - 2$ has gradient 3.

∴ $m = 3$ (Parallel lines have equal gradients.)

∴ $y = 3x + c$

$4 = 3(1) + c$,   [(1, 4) lies on the line]

∴ $c = 1$

∴ The equation of the line is $y = 3x + 1$.

Foundation Worksheet 8:08

Parallel and
perpendicular lines
1 Use $y = mx + c$ to find the
  slope of the lines in columns
  A and B.
2 Which lines in columns
  A and B are:
  a parallel? b perpendicular?

1 Are the following pairs of lines parallel or not?
   a $y = 3x + 2$ and $y = 3x - 1$
   b $y = 5x - 2$ and $y = 2x - 5$
   c $y = x + 7$ and $y = x + 1$
   d $y = x - 3$ and $y = 1x + 2$
   e $y = 3x + 2$ and $2y = 6x - 3$
   f $y = 2x + 1$ and $2x - y + 3 = 0$
   g $3x + y - 5 = 0$ and $3x + y + 1 = 0$
   h $x + y = 6$ and $x + y = 8$

2 Are the following pairs of lines perpendicular or not?
   a $y = \frac{1}{5}x + 3$, $y = -5x + 1$
   b $y = 3x - 2$, $y = -\frac{1}{3}x + 7$
   c $y = 2x - 1$, $y = -\frac{1}{2}x + 3$
   d $y = \frac{2}{3}x + 4$, $y = -\frac{3}{2}x - 5$
   e $y = 4x$, $y = \frac{1}{4}x - 3$
   f $y = \frac{3}{4}x - 1$, $y = -\frac{4}{3}x$
   g $y = 3x - 1$, $x + 3y + 4 = 0$
   h $x + y = 6$, $x - y - 3 = 0$

3 a Which of the following lines are parallel to $y = 2x + 3$?
      $y = 3x + 2$ $2x - y + 6 = 0$ $2y = x + 3$ $y = 2x - 3$
   b Two of the following lines are parallel. Which are they?
      $y = x - 3$ $x + y = 3$ $y = 3x$ $3y = x$ $y = -x + 8$
   c A is the point $(1, 3)$, B is $(3, 4)$, C is $(6, 7)$ and D is $(8, 8)$.
      Which of the lines AB, BC, CD and DA are parallel?

4 a Which of the following lines are perpendicular to $y = 2x$?
      $y = 3x$ $y = 2x - 3$ $x + 2y = 4$ $y = -0.5x + 5$
   b Two of the following lines are perpendicular. Which are they?
      $y = -1\frac{1}{2}x + 2$ $y = \frac{1}{2}x - 1$ $y = \frac{2}{3}x$
   c A is the point $(2, -1)$, B is the point $(3, -2)$ and C is $(4, -1)$. Prove that AB $\perp$ BC.

5 a Find the equation of the line that has y-intercept 3 and is parallel to $y = 5x - 1$.
   b Line AB is parallel to $y = 3x - 4$. Find the equation of AB if its y-intercept is -1.
   c Line EF is parallel to $y = x + 5$. Its y-intercept is 3. What is the equation of EF?
   d A line has a y-intercept of 10 and is parallel to the line $x + y = 4$. What is the equation
      of this line?

6 a Find the equation of the line that has y-intercept 5 and is perpendicular to $y = -\frac{1}{3}x + 1$.
   b The line AB is perpendicular to $y = -x + 4$. Its y-intercept is 3. What is the equation of AB?
   c Find the equation of CD if CD is perpendicular to the line $y = -\frac{1}{2}x$ and has a y-intercept of 0.
   d A line has a y-intercept of 1.5 and is perpendicular to the line $y = -2x + 1$. Find the
      equation of the line.

7 **a** AB is a line which passes through the point (2, 3). What is the equation of AB if it is parallel to $y = 5x + 2$?

b Find the equation of the line that passes through (1, 0) and is parallel to $y = -3x - 1$.

c A is the point (0, 0) and B is the point (1, 3). Find the equation of the line that has y-intercept 5 and is parallel to AB.

d Find the equation of the line that has y-intercept -3 and is parallel to the x-axis.

e What is the equation of the line that is parallel to the x-axis and passes through the point (−2, −3)?

8 **a** If AB passes through the point (2, 3) and is perpendicular to $y = 2x - 7$, find the equation of AB in general form.

b Find the equation of the line that passes through (1, 0) and is perpendicular to $y = -3x - 1$. Write your answer in general form.

c A is the point (0, 0) and B is the point (1, 3). Find the equation of the line that has y-intercept 5 and is perpendicular to AB. Give the answer in general form.

d Find the equation of the line that has y-intercept -3 and is perpendicular to the y-axis.

e What is the equation of a line that is perpendicular to the x-axis and passes through (3, −2)?

9 **a** Find the equation of the line that is parallel to the line $2x - 3y + 6 = 0$ and passes through the point (3, −4). Give the answer in general form.

b A line is drawn through (−1, 2), perpendicular to the line $4x + 3y - 6 = 0$. Find its equation in general form.

c A line is drawn through the point (−1, −1), parallel to the line $2x - 3y + 9 = 0$. Where will it cross the x-axis?

d A line is drawn parallel to $4x - 3y + 1 = 0$, through the points (1, 3) and (6, a). What is the value of a?

10 In the diagram, the line $5x + 2y + 5 = 0$ cuts the x-axis and y-axis at E and C respectively. BD is the line $x = 2$, AB is parallel to the x-axis and BE and CD are perpendicular to AC. Find the coordinates of the points A, B, C, D and E.

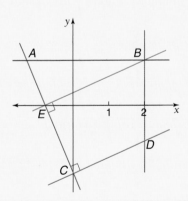

8:09 | Graphing Inequalities on the Number Plane

prep quiz

8:09

For each number line graph, write down the appropriate equation or inequation.

1 0 1 2 3 4 5 6 x

2 0 1 2 3 4 5 6 x

3 0 1 2 3 4 5 6 x

4 −2 −1 0 1 2 3 4 x

5 −2 −1 0 1 2 3 4 x

6 −2 −1 0 1 2 3 4 x

7 −5 −4 −3 −2 −1 0 1 x

8 −5 −4 −3 −2 −1 0 1 x

9 −5 −4 −3 −2 −1 0 1 x

10 On a number line, draw the graph of $x < -2$ where x is a real number.

In Prep Quiz 8:09 questions **1**, **2** and **3**, we see that, once $x = 3$ is graphed on the number line, all points satisfying the inequation $x > 3$ lie on one side of the point and all points satisfying the inequation $x < 3$ lie on the other side.

On the number plane, all points satisfying the equation $y = 2x + 1$ lie on one straight line.

All points satisfying the inequation $y < 2x + 1$ will lie on one side of the line.

All points satisfying the inequation $y > 2x + 1$ will lie on the other side of the line.

A $y = 2x + 1$

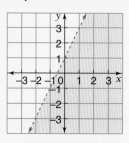

B $y < 2x + 1$

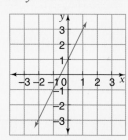

Note:
- Inequations **B**, **C** and **D** are often called 'half planes'.
- In **D**, the line is part of the solution set. In **B** and **C**, the line acts as a boundary only, and so is shown as a broken line.
- Choose points at random in each of the half planes in **B**, **C** and **D** to confirm that all points in each half plane satisfy the appropriate inequation.

C $y > 2x + 1$

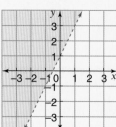

D $y \leqslant 2x + 1$

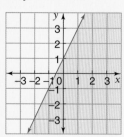

> Points that lie on broken lines are not part of the solution.

worked examples

1 Graph the region $3x + 2y > 6$ on the number plane.

2 Graph **a** the union and **b** the intersection of the half planes representing the solutions of $x + 2y \geqslant 2$ and $y < 3x - 1$.

continued ➜➜➜

Solutions

1 Graph the boundary line $3x + 2y = 6$ as a broken line since it is not part of $3x + 2y > 6$.

$3x + 2y = 6$

x	0	1	2
y	3	1·5	0

> ■ Points that lie on broken lines are not part of the solution.

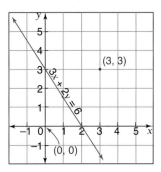

Discover which half plane satisfies the inequation $3x + 2y > 6$ by substituting a point from each side of the boundary into $3x + 2y > 6$.

$(0, 0)$ is obviously to the left of $3x + 2y = 6$.
∴ substitute $(0, 0)$ into $3x + 2y > 6$.
  $3(0) + 2(0) > 6$, which is false.
∴ $(0, 0)$ does not lie in the half plane.

$(3, 3)$ is obviously to the right of $3x + 2y = 6$.
∴ substitute $(3, 3)$ into $3x + 2y > 6$.
  $3(3) + 2(3) > 6$, which is true.
∴ $(3, 3)$ lies in the half plane $3x + 2y > 6$.
Shade in the half plane on the (3, 3) side.

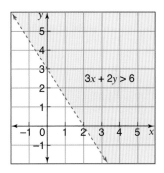

2 Graph the two half planes using the method above.

$x + 2y = 6$

x	0	1	2
y	1	0·5	0

$y = 3x - 1$

x	0	1	2
y	−1	2	5

Points above the boundary line satisfy $x + 2y \geqslant 2$.

Points to the right of the boundary satisfy $y < 3x - 1$.

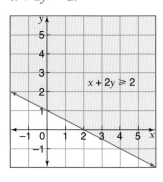

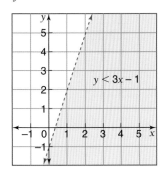

continued ➜➜➜

a The union of the two half planes is the region that is part of one or the other or both graphs.

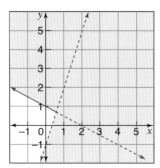

The union is written:
$\{(x, y): x + 2y \geqslant 2 \cup y < 3x - 1\}$

b The intersection is the region that belongs to both half planes. It is the part that the graphs have in common.

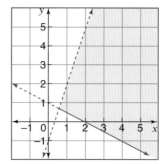

The intersection is written:
$\{(x, y): x + 2y \geqslant 2 \cap y < 3x - 1\}$

Note: • Initially draw the boundary lines as broken lines.
• Part of each region has a part of the boundary broken and a part unbroken.

Exercise 8:09

Foundation Worksheet 8:09

Graphing inequalities
1 Write down the inequality that describes each region.
a   **b**

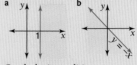

2 Graph the inequalities:
  a $y < 2$ **b** $y \geqslant x - 2$

1 By testing a point from each side of the line, write down the inequation for each solution set graphed below.

a

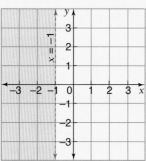

b

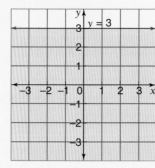

c

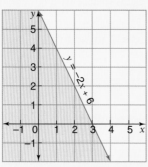

d

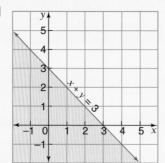

e

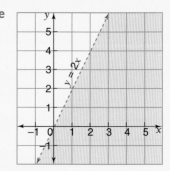

2 On separate number plane diagrams, draw the graph of:

a $x \geqslant 1$ b $y > x$ c $y < 2$ d $x + y \leqslant 4$

e $y < -x + 5$ f $y \geqslant 2x - 2$ g $2x + 3y - 6 \leqslant 0$ h $y > 0$

3 Draw a separate diagram to show the part of the number plane where:

a $x \geqslant 0$ and $y \geqslant 0$, ie $\{(x, y): x \geqslant 0 \cap y \geqslant 0\}$

b $x \geqslant 0$ and $y \leqslant 0$, ie $\{(x, y): x \geqslant 0 \cap y \leqslant 0\}$

c $x \leqslant 0$ and/or $y \geqslant 0$, ie $\{(x, y): x \leqslant 0 \cup y \geqslant 0\}$

d $x \leqslant 0$ and/or $y \leqslant 0$, ie $\{(x, y): x \leqslant 0 \cup y \leqslant 0\}$

'∩' means intersection;
'∪' means union.

4 Use question 1 of this exercise to sketch the region described by the intersection of:

a $x < -1$ and $y \leqslant 3$ b $y \leqslant 3$ and $y < 2x$

c $y \leqslant -2x + 6$ and $y \leqslant 3$ d $x + y \leqslant 3$ and $y < 2x$

e $y \leqslant -2x + 6$ and $x + y \leqslant 3$ f $y \leqslant -2x + 6$ and $y < 2x$

$\{(x, y):...\}$ means:
'the set of points such that...'

5 Use question 1 of this exercise to sketch the region described by the union of:

a $x < -1$ and $y \leqslant 3$ b $x + y \leqslant 3$ and $y < 2x$

c $x + y \leqslant 3$ and $y \leqslant 3$ d $y \leqslant -2x + 6$ and $y < 2x$

6 Describe, in terms of the union or intersection of inequations, the regions drawn below.

a

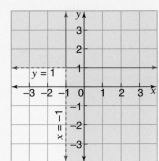

b

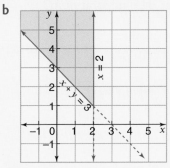

c

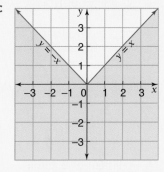

7 Sketch the regions described below.

a the intersection of $y \geqslant 2x$ and $x + y \leqslant 3$

b the union of $y < 1$ and $y < x - 2$

c the intersection of $y < 2x + 1$ and $5x + 4y < 20$

d the union of $y \geqslant 2$ and $y < x$

☐ Fill in only that part of the boundary which is part of the answer.

8 Graph the regions which satisfy all of the following inequalities:

a $x \geqslant 1, x \leqslant 4, y \geqslant 0, y \leqslant 4$ b $y \geqslant 0, y \leqslant 2x, x + y \leqslant 6$

9 Write down the inequalities that describe each region.

a
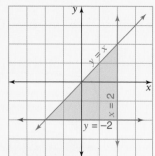

b
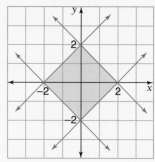

c
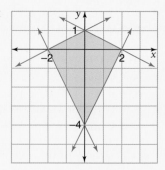

8:09

Fun Spot 8:09 | Why did the banana go out with a fig?

Answer each question and put the letter for that question in the box above the correct answer.

For the points A(2, 5), B(−1, 3), C(4, 2), D(0, 6), find:

E distance AC	**E** distance CD	**E** distance BD
A slope of AB	**A** slope of AD	**T** slope of BC
T midpoint of DC	**N** midpoint of AC	**I** midpoint of AB

What is the gradient of the following lines:

C $y = 2x − 1$ **U** $2y = x − 5$ **G** $2x + y + 1 = 0$

What is the y-intercept of the following lines.

D $y = 2x − 1$ **T** $2y = x − 5$ **L** $2x + y − 1 = 0$

Find the equation of the line with:

C gradient of 2 and a *y*-intercept of −1   **O** slope of 3 and a *y*-intercept of 5

T *y*-intercept of 4 and a slope of −2   **S** *y*-intercept of −2 and a slope of 4

Write in the form y = mx + b:
B $2x − y − 5 = 0$ **E** $2x − y + 5 = 0$ **A** $x = \frac{1}{2}y − 2$

In the diagram find:

D slope of AB   **U** coordinates of C

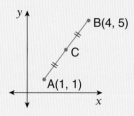

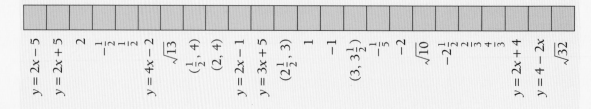

| $y = 2x − 5$ | $y = 2x + 5$ | 2 | $-\frac{1}{2}$ $-\frac{1}{2}$ | $\sqrt{13}$ | $(\frac{1}{2}, 4)$ (2, 4) | $y = 2x − 1$ | $y = 3x + 5$ | $(2\frac{1}{2}, 3)$ | 1 | −1 | $(3, 3\frac{1}{2})$ $-\frac{1}{5}$ | −2 | $\sqrt{10}$ | $-2\frac{1}{2}$ $2\frac{2}{3}$ $\frac{4}{3}$ | $y = 2x + 4$ | $y = 4 − 2x$ | $\sqrt{32}$ |

Mathematical Terms 8

coordinates
- A pair of numbers that gives the position of a point in a number plane relative to the origin.
- The first of the coordinates is the x-coordinate. It tells how far right (or left) the point is from the origin.
- The second of the coordinates is called the y-coordinate. It tells how far the point is above (or below) the origin.

distance formula
- Gives the distance between the points (x_1, y_1) and (x_2, y_2).

$$d = \sqrt{(x_2 - x_1)^2 + (y_2 - y_1)^2}$$

general form
- A way of writing the equation of a line.
- The equation is written in the form $ax + by + c = 0$.
  where a, b, c are integers and $a > 0$.

gradient
- The slope of a line or interval. It can be measured using the formula:

$$\text{Gradient} = \frac{\text{rise}}{\text{run}}$$

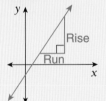

gradient formula
- Gives the gradient of the interval joining (x_1, y_1) to (x_2, y_2).

$$m = \frac{y_2 - y_1}{x_2 - x_1}$$

gradient–intercept form
- A way of writing the equation of a line.
  eg $y = 2x - 5$, $y = \frac{1}{2}x + 2$

  When an equation is rearranged and written in the form $y = mx + c$ then m is the gradient and c is the y-intercept.

graph (a line)
- All the points on a line.
- To plot the points that lie on a line.

interval
- The part of a line between two points.

midpoint
- Point marking the middle of an interval.

midpoint formula
- Gives the midpoint of the interval joining (x_1, y_1) to (x_2, y_2).

$$\text{Midpoint} = \left(\frac{x_1 + x_2}{2}, \frac{y_1 + y_2}{2} \right)$$

number plane
- A rectangular grid that allows the position of points in a plane to be identified by an ordered pair of numbers.

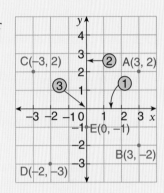

origin
- The point where the x-axis and y-axis intersect, $(0, 0)$. See ③ under **number plane**.

plot
- To mark the position of a point on the number plane.

x-axis
- The horizontal number line in a number plane. See ① under **number plane**.

x-intercept
- The point where a line crosses the x-axis.

y-axis
- The vertical number line in a number plane. See ② under **number plane**.

y-intercept
- The point where a line crosses the y-axis.

Technology Applications

Mathematical terms 8

Drag and Drops

Diagnostic Test 8: | Coordinate Geometry

- These questions reflect the important skills introduced in this chapter.
- Errors made will indicate areas of weakness.
- Each weakness should be treated by going back to the section listed.

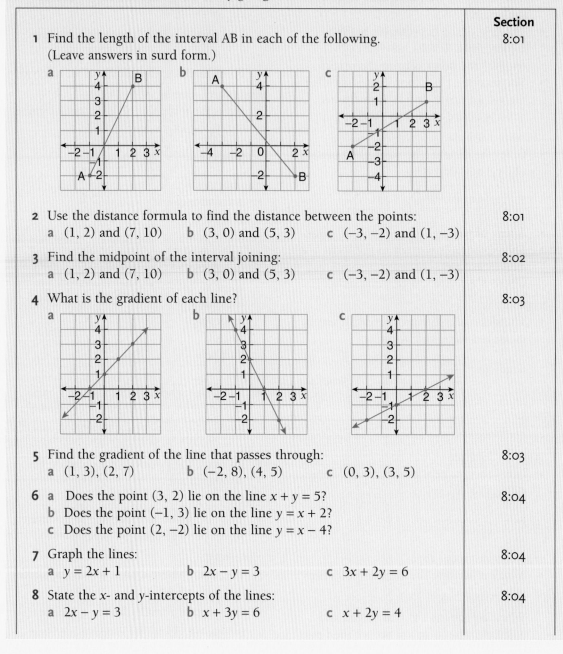

Section

1 Find the length of the interval AB in each of the following.
   (Leave answers in surd form.)   8:01

2 Use the distance formula to find the distance between the points: 8:01
   a (1, 2) and (7, 10)   b (3, 0) and (5, 3)   c (−3, −2) and (1, −3)

3 Find the midpoint of the interval joining: 8:02
   a (1, 2) and (7, 10)   b (3, 0) and (5, 3)   c (−3, −2) and (1, −3)

4 What is the gradient of each line?   8:03

5 Find the gradient of the line that passes through: 8:03
   a (1, 3), (2, 7)   b (−2, 8), (4, 5)   c (0, 3), (3, 5)

6 a Does the point (3, 2) lie on the line $x + y = 5$?   8:04
   b Does the point (−1, 3) lie on the line $y = x + 2$?
   c Does the point (2, −2) lie on the line $y = x − 4$?

7 Graph the lines: 8:04
   a $y = 2x + 1$ b $2x − y = 3$ c $3x + 2y = 6$

8 State the x- and y-intercepts of the lines: 8:04
   a $2x − y = 3$ b $x + 3y = 6$ c $x + 2y = 4$

9 Graph the lines: 8:04
   a $x = 2$ **b** $y = -1$ **c** $x = -2$

10 Write down the equation of the line which has: 8:05
   a a gradient of 3 and a y-intercept of 2
   b a gradient of $\frac{1}{2}$ and a y-intercept of -3
   c a y-intercept of 3 and a gradient of -1

11 Write each of the answers to question **10** in general form. 8:05

12 What is the gradient and y-intercept of the lines: 8:05
   a $y = 2x + 3$?   **b** $y = 3 - 2x$?   **c** $y = -x + 4$?

13 Rearrange these equations into gradient–intercept form. 8:05
   a $4x - y + 6 = 0$ **b** $2x + 3y - 3 = 0$ **c** $5x + 2y + 1 = 0$

14 Find the equation of the line that: 8:06
   a passes through $(1, 4)$ and has a gradient of 2
   b has a gradient of -3 and passes through $(1, 3)$
   c has a gradient of $\frac{1}{2}$ and passes through $(-2, 0)$

15 Find the equation of the line that: 8:07
   a passes through the points $(1, 1)$ and $(2, 3)$
   b passes through the points $(-1, 2)$ and $(1, -4)$
   c passes through the origin and $(3, 4)$

16 Find the equation of the line that: 8:08
   a has a y-intercept of 2 and is parallel to $y = 4x - 1$
   b passes through $(1, 7)$ and is parallel to $y = -3x + 4$
   c is perpendicular to $y = \frac{2}{3}x + 1$ and passes through $(-1, 4)$
   d is perpendicular to $y = 1 - 2x$ and passes through $(-1, 4)$

17 Write down the inequation for each region. 8:09
   a   **b**   **c**

18 Graph **a** the union and **b** the intersection of the half planes representing 8:09
the solutions of $x + 2y \geqslant 2$ and $y < 3x - 1$.

Chapter 8 | Revision Assignment

8A

1 Find:
  a the length AB as a surd
  b the slope of AB
  c the midpoint of AB.

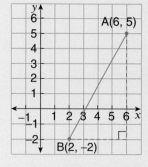

2 A is the point (2, 5) and B is the point (7, 17).
  a What is the length AB (as a surd)?
  b What is the slope of AB?
  c What is the midpoint of AB?

3 A is the point (6, 5) and B is the point (2, −2).
  a What is the equation of the line AB?
  b The line AB passes through the point (100, b). What is the value of b?
  c AC is perpendicular to AB. Find its equation in general form.

4 a A line has an x-intercept of 3 and a gradient of 1. Find where the line crosses the y-axis and hence write down its equation.

b A line has a slope of $-\frac{1}{2}$ and a y-intercept of 6. What is its equation? What is its x-intercept?
  c A line has an x-intercept of 3 and a y-intercept of 6. What is its equation?

5 The points X(2, 2), Y(−2, 4) and Z(−4, 0) form a triangle. Show that the triangle is both isosceles and right-angled.

6 A line is drawn perpendicular to the line $2x − 3y + 4 = 0$ through its y-intercept. What is the equation of the line? Give the answer in general form.

7 A median of a triangle is a line drawn from a vertex to the midpoint of the opposite side. Find the equation of the median through A of the triangle formed by the points A(3, 4), B(−2, −4) and C(−6, 8).

8 What inequalities describe the region shown?

Technology Applications
Drag and Drops

1 *x* and *y* intercept and graphs
2 Using $y = mx + c$ to find the gradient
3 General form of a line
4 Parallel and perpendicular lines
5 Inequalities and regions

Technology Applications
Animations

Linear graphs and equations

Chapter Review
Questions

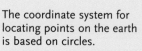
The coordinate system for locating points on the earth is based on circles.

Chapter 8 | Working Mathematically

1 The diagram shows a 4-minute timer.

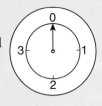

a If this timer was started with the pointer on zero, what number would it be pointing to after 17 minutes?

b At what time between 30 minutes and 1 hour will the pointer be pointing at number 3?

2 The faces of a cube are divided into 4 squares. If each square on each face is to be painted, what is the minimum number of colours needed if no squares that share an edge can be the same colour?

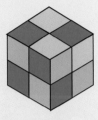

3 Brendan and Warwick wish to use a photocopier to reduce drawings.

a Brendan's drawing is 15 cm high but must be reduced to 8 cm to fit into the space he has left in his project. What percentage setting must he choose on the photocopier to achieve the required reduction?

b Warwick thinks the machine is malfunctioning so he decides to check it by reducing his drawing, which is 20 cm long. He chooses the 60% setting. If the machine is functioning properly, what would you expect the length of his picture to be?

c The setting button jams on 68%. What sized copies are possible by repeated use of this button? (Give all answers above 20%.)

4 Four friends decide to play tennis. Find out how many different:

a singles matches can be played. (A singles match is one player against another player.)

b doubles matches can be played. (A doubles match is two players against two players.)

5 What is the smallest whole number that, if you multiply by 7, will give you an answer consisting entirely of 8s?

6 A 4 × 4 grid is drawn and the numbers 1, 2, 3 and 4 are placed in the grid so that every number occurs only once in each row and only once in each column.

1	2	3	
	4		2
4			

a Find the missing numbers in the grid shown.

b Now place the numbers in a 4 × 4 grid, following the rules above, so that the sums of the diagonals are 16 and 4.

9

Simultaneous Equations

$3x + 5y = 14$ .... (1)
$7x - 2y = 19$ .... (2)

$x = 3$
$y = 1$

MATHS
CALCULUS
TRIG.

Chapter Contents

Investigation: Solving problems by 'guess and check'
9:01 The graphical method of solution
Investigation: Solving simultaneous equations using a graphics calculator
Fun Spot: What did the book say to the librarian?

9:02 The algebraic method of solution
A Substitution method
B Elimination method
9:03 Using simultaneous equations to solve problems
Reading Mathematics: Breakfast time
Mathematical Terms, Diagnostic Test, Revision Assignment, Working Mathematically

Learning Outcomes

Students will be able to:
• Solve linear simultaneous equations using graphs.
• Solve linear simultaneous equations using algebraic methods.
• Use simultaneous equations to solve problems.

Areas of Interaction

Approaches to Learning (Knowledge Acquisition, Problem Solving, Communication, Logical Thinking, IT Skills, Reflection), Human Ingenuity

Investigation 9:01A | Solving problems by 'guess and check'

Consider the following problem.

> A zoo enclosure contains wombats and emus. If there are 50 eyes and 80 legs, find the number of each type of animal.

Knowing that each animal has two eyes but a wombat has 4 legs and an emu has two legs, we could try to solve this problem by guessing a solution and then checking it.

Solution

If each animal has two eyes, then, because there are 50 eyes, I know there must be 25 animals.

If my first guess is 13 wombats and 12 emus, then the number of legs would be $13 \times 4 + 12 \times 2 = 76$.

Since there are more legs than 76, I need to increase the number of wombats to increase the number of legs to 80.

I would eventually arrive at the correct solution of 15 wombats and 10 emus, which gives the correct number of legs ($15 \times 4 + 10 \times 2 = 80$).

Try solving these problems by guessing and then checking various solutions.

1   Two numbers add to give 86 and subtract to give 18. What are the numbers?

2   At the school disco, there were 52 more girls than boys. If the total attendance was 420, how many boys and how many girls attended?

3   In scoring 200 runs, Max hit a total of 128 runs as boundaries. (A boundary is either 4 runs or 6 runs.) If he scored 29 boundaries in total, how many boundaries of each type did he score?

4   Sharon spent $5158 buying either BHP shares or ICI shares. These were valued at $10.50 and $6.80 respectively. If she bought 641 shares in total, how many of each did she buy?

In this chapter, you will learn how to solve problems like those in Investigation 9:01A more systematically. Problems like these have two pieces of information that can be represented by two equations. These can then be solved to find the common or 'simultaneous' solution.

9:01 | The Graphical Method of Solution

If $y = 2x - 1$, find y when:

1	$x = 1$	**2**	$x = 0$
3	$x = -1$	**4**	$x = -5$

If $x - 2y = 5$, find y when:

5	$x = 0$	**6**	$x = 1$
7	$x = 2$	**8**	$x = -4$

9 If $3x - y = 2$, complete the table below.

x	0	1	2
y			

10 Copy this number plane and graph the line $3x - y = 2$.

There are many real-life situations in which we wish to find when or where two conditions come or occur together. The following example illustrates this.

worked example

A runner set off from a point and maintained a speed of 9 km/h. Another runner left the same point 10 minutes later, followed the same course, and maintained a speed of 12 km/h. When, and after what distance travelled, would the second runner have caught up to the first runner?

We have chosen to solve this question graphically.

First runner

t	0	30	40	60
d	0	4·5	6	9

Second runner

t	10	30	40	70
d	0	4	6	12

From these tables we can see that the runners meet after 6 km and 40 minutes.

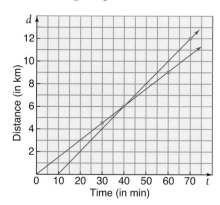

t = time in minutes after the first runner begins
d = distance travelled in kilometres

* From the graph, we can see that the lines cross at (40, 6).

* The simultaneous solution is $t = 40$, $d = 6$.

* The second runner caught the first runner 40 minutes after the first runner had started and when both runners had travelled 6 kilometres.

After the second runner has run for 30 minutes, $t = 40$.

Often, in questions, the information has to be written in the form of equations. The equations are then graphed using a table of values (as shown above). The point of intersection of the graphs tells us when and where the two conditions occur together.

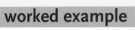

'Simultaneous' means 'at the same time'.

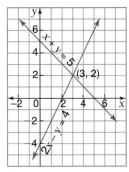

worked example

Solve the following equations simultaneously.
$x + y = 5$
$2x - y = 4$

Solution

You will remember from your earlier work on coordinate geometry that, when the solutions to an equation such as $x + y = 5$ are graphed on a number plane, they form a straight line.

Hence, to solve the equations $x + y = 5$ and $2x - y = 4$ simultaneously, we could simply graph each line and find the point of intersection. Since this point lies on both lines, its coordinates give the solution.

$x + y = 5$

x	0	1	2
y	5	4	2

$2x - y = 4$

x	0	1	2
y	−4	−2	0

- The lines $x + y = 5$ and $2x - y = 4$ intersect at (3, 2).
  Therefore the solution is:
  $x = 3$
  $y = 2$

 To solve a pair of simultaneous equations graphically, we graph each line. The solution is given by the coordinates of the point of intersection of the lines.

It is sometimes difficult to graph accurately either or both lines, and it is often difficult to read accurately the coordinates of the point of intersection.

Despite these problems, the graphical method remains an extremely useful technique for solving simultaneous equations.

Exercise 9:01

Foundation Worksheet 9:01

Graphical method
of solution

1 Graph these lines on the
same number plane and find
where they intersect.
  a $y = x + 2$ and $x + y = 2$
  b $y = 2x$ and $y = x + 1$

1 Use the graph to write down the solutions to the
following pairs of simultaneous equations.

  a $y = x + 1$ b $y = x + 1$
     $x + y = 3$ $x + 2y = -4$

  c $y = x + 3$ d $y = x + 3$
     $3x + 5y = 7$ $x + y = 3$

  e $x + y = 3$ f $3x - 2y = 9$
     $3x + 5y = 7$ $x + y = 3$

  g $y = x + 3$ h $y = x + 1$
     $y = x + 1$ $2y = 2x + 2$

Explain why
(g) and (h)
above are
unusual.

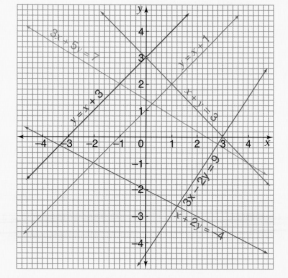

2 Use the graph in question **1** to estimate, correct to one decimal place, the solutions of the
following simultaneous equations.

  a $y = x + 1$ b $y = x + 3$ c $3x - 2y = 9$ d $3x - 2y = 9$
       $3x + 5y = 7$ $x + 2y = -4$ $x + 2y = -4$ $3x + 5y = 7$

3 Solve each of the following pairs of equations by graphical means. All solutions are integral
(ie they are whole numbers).

  a $x + y = 1$ b $2x + y = 3$ c $x - y = 3$ d $3x - y - 2 = 0$
     $2x - y = 5$ $x + y = 1$ $2x + y = 0$ $x - y + 2 = 0$

  e $3a - 2b = 1$ f $p + 2q = 2$ g $3a + 2b = 5$ h $p = 6$
     $a - b = 1$ $p - q = -4$ $a = 1$ $p - q = 4$

4 Solve each pair of simultaneous equations by the graphical
method. (Use a scale of 1 cm to 1 unit on each axis.)

  a $y = 4x$ b $3x - y = 1$ c $x = 4y$
       $x + y = 3$ $x - y = 2$ $x + y = 1$

The graphical method
doesn't always give exact
answers.

5 Estimate the solution to each of the following pairs of
simultaneous equations by graphing each, using a scale
of 1 cm to 1 unit on each axis. Give the answers correct
to 1 decimal place.

  a $4x + 3y = 3$ b $x - y = 2$ c $4a - 6b = 1$
     $x - 2y = 1$ $8x + 4y = 7$ $4a + 3b = 4$

6 A car passed a point on a course at exactly 12 noon and maintained a speed of 60 km/h. A second car passed the same point 1 hour later, followed the same course, and maintained a speed of 100 km/h. When, and after what distance from this point, would the second car have caught up to the first car? (*Hint:* Use the method shown in the worked example on page 438 but leave the time in hours.)

7 Mary's salary consisted of a retainer of $480 a week plus $100 for each machine sold in that week. Bob worked for the same company, had no retainer, but was paid $180 for each machine sold. Study the tables below, graph the lines, and use them to find the number, N, of machines Bob would have to sell to have a wage equal to Mary (assuming they both sell the same number of machines). What salary, S, would each receive for this number of sales?

Mary

N	0	4	8
S	480	880	1280

Bob

N	0	4	8
S	0	720	1440

N = number of machines
S = salary

8 No Frills Car Rental offers new cars for rent at €38 per day and 50c for every 10 km travelled in excess of 100 km per day. Prestige Car Rental offers the same type of car for €30 per day plus €1 for every 10 km travelled in excess of 100 km per day.

Draw a graph of each case on axes like those shown, and determine what distance would need to be travelled in a day so that the rentals charged by each company would be the same.

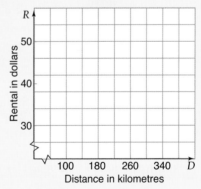

9 Star Car Rental offers new cars for rent at $38 per day and $1 for every 10 km travelled in excess of 100 km per day. Safety Car Rental offers the same type of car for $30 per day plus 50c for every 10 km travelled in excess of 100 km per day.

Draw a graph of each on axes like those in question **8**, and discuss the results.

Investigation 9:01B | Solving simultaneous equations using a graphics calculator

Using the graphing program on a graphics calculator complete the following tasks.

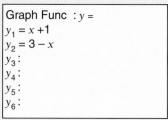

Graph Func : $y =$
$y_1 = x + 1$
$y_2 = 3 - x$
y_3 :
y_4 :
y_5 :
y_6 :

- Enter the equations of the two lines $y = x + 1$ and $y = 3 - x$. The screen should look like the one shown.

- Draw these graphs and you should have two straight lines intersecting at (1, 2).

- Using the **G-Solv** key, find the point of intersection by pressing the **F5** key labelled **ISCT**.

- At the bottom of the screen, it should show $x = 1$, $y = 2$.

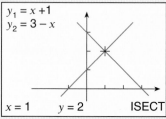

$y_1 = x + 1$
$y_2 = 3 - x$

$x = 1$ $y = 2$ ISECT

Now press **EXIT** and go back to enter other pairs of equations of straight lines and find their point of intersection.

Note: You can change the scale on the axes using the **V-Window** option.

Fun Spot 9:01 | What did the book say to the librarian?

Work out the answer to each part and put the letter for that part in the box that is above the correct answer.

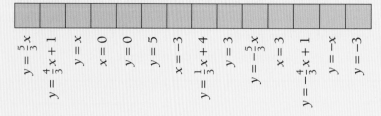

Write the equation of:

A line AB   **C** line OB
U line BF   **A** line EB
I the y-axis   **O** line AF
U line OF   **K** line AE
E line CB   **T** the x-axis
T line EF   **N** line OD
Y line CD   **O** line OA

$y = \frac{5}{3}x$ $y = \frac{4}{3}x + 1$ $y = x$ $x = 0$ $y = 0$ $y = 5$ $x = -3$ $y = \frac{1}{3}x + 4$ $y = 3$ $y = -\frac{5}{3}x$ $x = 3$ $y = -\frac{4}{3}x + 1$ $y = -x$ $y = -3$

9:02 | The Algebraic Method of Solution

We found in the last section that the graphical method of solution lacked accuracy for many questions. Because of this, we need a method that gives the exact solution. There are two such algebraic methods — the substitution method and the elimination method.

9:02A Substitution method

worked examples

Solve the simultaneous equations:

1   $2x + y = 12$ and $y = 5x - 2$
2   $3a + 2b = 7, 4a - 3b = 2$

In this method one pronumeral is replaced by an equivalent expression involving the other pronumeral.

Solutions

When solving simultaneous equations, first 'number' the equations involved.

1   $2x + y = 12$ .... ①

      $y = 5x - 2$ .... ②

Now from ② we can see that $5x - 2$ is equal to y. If we substitute this for y in equation ①, we have:

$$2x + (5x - 2) = 12$$
$$7x - 2 = 12$$
$$7x = 14$$
$$x = 2$$

So the value of x is 2. This value for x can now be substituted into either equation ① or equation ② to find the value for y:

In ①: In ②:
$2(2) + y = 12$ $y = 5(2) - 2$
$4 + y = 12$ $= 10 - 2$
$y = 8$ $= 8$

So, the total solution is:
$x = 2, y = 8$.

> ▢ To check this answer substitute into equations ① and ②.

continued ➔➔➔

2 $3a + 2b = 7$ .... ①

$4a - 3b = 2$ .... ②

Making a the subject of ② gives:

$$a = \frac{2 + 3b}{4}$$

If we substitute this expression for a into equation ①, we get:

Multiply both sides by 4.

$$3\left(\frac{2 + 3b}{4}\right) + 2b = 7$$

$$3(2 + 3b) + 8b = 28$$

$$6 + 9b + 8b = 28$$

$$17b = 22$$

$$b = \frac{22}{17}$$

Substituting this value for b into, say, equation ② gives:

$$4a - 3\left(\frac{22}{17}\right) = 2$$

$$4a - \frac{66}{17} = \frac{34}{17}$$

$$4a = \frac{100}{17}$$

$$a = \frac{25}{17}$$

So the total solution is:

$$a = \frac{25}{17}, b = \frac{22}{17}.$$

> ■ To check your answer, substitute $a = \frac{25}{17}$, $b = \frac{22}{17}$ in equations ① and ②.

Check each step!

Exercise 9:02A

Foundation Worksheet 9:02A

The substitution method
1 Solve these equations:
   a $x + (x + 4) = 6$ **b** $2x - (x + 3) = 5$
2 Substitute $y = x + 2$ for y in the equation $x + y = 10$.

1   Solve the following pairs of equations using the substitution method.
Check all solutions.

a $x + y = 3$ and $y = 4$
b $x + y = 7$ and $y = x + 3$
c $x + y = -3$ and $y = x + 1$
d $x - y = 5$ and $y = 1 - x$
e $2x + y = 9$ and $y = x - 3$
f $2x + y = 8$ and $y = x - 4$
g $2x - y = 10$ and $y = 10 - 3x$
h $x + 2y = 9$ and $y = 2x - 3$
i $2x + y = 14$ and $x = 6$
j $2x + y = 7$ and $x = y - 4$

2 Use one of each pair of equations to express y in terms of x. Then use the method of substitution to solve the equations. Check all solutions.

a $x + 2y = 4$
   $x - y = 7$

b $2x - 3y = 4$
   $2x + y = 6$

c $x + 2y = 8$
   $x + y = -2$

d $x - y = 2$
   $x + 2y = 11$

e $2x - y = -8$
   $2x + y = 0$

f $x + y = 5$
   $2x + y = 7$

g $x + 2y = 11$
   $2x - y = 2$

h $3x + y = 13$
   $x + 2y = 1$

i $3x + 2y = 2$
   $2x - y = -8$

3 Solve the following simultaneous equations using the substitution method.

a $2x - y = 1$
   $4x + 2y = 5$

b $3a + b = 6$
   $9a + 2b = 1$

c $m - 2n = 3$
   $5m + 2n = 2$

d $4x - 2y = 1$
   $x + 3y = -1$

Questions 3 and 4 involve harder substitutions and arithmetic.

4 Solve the following pairs of simultaneous equations.

a $2a - 3b = 1$
   $4a + 2b = 5$

b $7x - 2y = 2$
   $3x + 4y = 8$

c $3m - 4n = 1$
   $2m + 3n = 4$

d $2x - 3y = 10$
   $5x - 3y = 3$

9:02B Elimination method

---

worked examples

Solve each pair of simultaneous equations:

1 $5x - 3y = 20$
   $2x + 3y = 15$

2 $x + 5y = 14$
   $x - 3y = 6$

3 $2x + 3y = 21$
   $5x + 2y = 3$

> ▪ In this method, one of the pronumerals is eliminated by adding or subtracting the equations.

Solutions

First, number each equation.

1 $5x - 3y = 20$ .... ①

   $2x + 3y = 15$ .... ②

> ▪ You add or subtract the equations, depending upon which operation will eliminate one of the pronumerals.

Now if these equations are 'added', the y terms will be eliminated, giving:

$$7x = 35$$
ie $x = 5$

Substituting this value into equation ① we get:
$$5(5) - 3y = 20$$
$$25 - 3y = 20$$
$$3y = 5$$
$$y = \frac{5}{3} \text{ or } 1\frac{2}{3}.$$

continued ➜➜➜

So the total solution is:

$x = 5, y = 1\frac{2}{3}$.

Check in ①: $5(5) - 3(1\frac{2}{3}) = 20$ (true).

Check in ②: $2(5) + 3(1\frac{2}{3}) = 15$ (true).

Check that the values satisfy both original equations.

2    $x + 5y = 14$ .... ①

     $x - 3y = 6$ .... ②

Now if equation ② is 'subtracted' from equation ①, the x terms are eliminated and we get:

     $8y = 8$

ie $y = 1$

Substituting this value into ① gives:

$x + 5(1) = 14$

   $x + 5 = 14$

      $x = 9$

∴ The solution is:

$x = 9, y = 1$.

Check in ①: $9 + 5(1) = 14$ (true).

Check in ②: $9 - 3(1) = 6$ (true).

3    $2x + 3y = 21$ .... ①

     $5x + 2y = 3$ .... ②

Multiply equation ① by 2

and equation ② by 3.

This gives:

   $4x + 6y = 42$ .... ①*

$15x + 6y = 9$ .... ②*

Now if ②* is subtracted from ①* the y terms are eliminated and we get:

     $-11x = 33$

So $x = -3$

Take one step at a time.

■ *Notice*
To eliminate a pronumeral, the size of the coefficients in each equation must be made the same by multiplying one or both equations by a constant.

Substituting this value into ① gives:

$$2(-3) + 3y = 21$$
$$-6 + 3y = 21$$
$$3y = 27$$
$$y = 9$$

So the solution is $x = -3$, $y = 9$

Check in ①: $2(-3) + 3(9) = 21$ (true).

Check in ②: $5(-3) + 2(9) = 3$ (true).

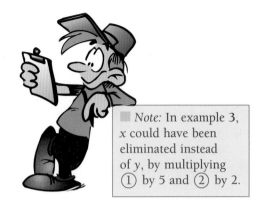

■ *Note:* In example 3, x could have been eliminated instead of y, by multiplying ① by 5 and ② by 2.

Exercise 9:02B

1 Use the elimination method to solve simultaneously each pair of equations by first adding the equations together.

a $x + y = 9$
   $x - y = 1$

b $x + y = 14$
   $2x - y = 1$

c $2x + y = 7$
   $x - y = 2$

d $x + 2y = 3$
   $x - 2y = 7$

e $3x - 2y = 5$
   $x + 2y = 7$

f $5x - 2y = 1$
   $3x + 2y = 7$

g $x + 3y = 10$
   $-x + y = 6$

h $-x + 2y = 12$
   $x + 2y = -4$

i $3x + y = 11$
   $-3x + 2y = 10$

j $2x + 7y = 5$
   $x - 7y = 16$

k $5x - 2y = 0$
   $4x + 2y = 9$

l $7x + 5y = -3$
   $2x - 5y = 21$

2 By first subtracting to eliminate a pronumeral, solve each pair of equations.

a $2x + y = 5$
   $x + y = 3$

b $5x + y = 7$
   $3x + y = 1$

c $10x + 2y = 2$
   $7x + 2y = -1$

d $3x - 2y = 0$
   $x - 2y = 4$

e $5x - y = 14$
   $2x - y = 2$

f $x - 3y = 1$
   $2x - 3y = 5$

g $2x + y = 10$
   $x + y = 7$

h $2x + 5y = 7$
   $2x + y = 5$

i $5x - y = 16$
   $5x - 3y = 8$

j $6x + y = 13$
   $6x - y = 11$

k $2x + 5y = 20$
   $3x + 5y = 17$

l $7x - 2y = 1$
   $4x - 2y = 4$

3 Solve these simultaneous equations by the elimination method.

a $2x + y = 7$
   $x - y = -4$

b $x + y = 5$
   $2x - y = 1$

c $x - y = 12$
   $2x + y = 3$

d $3x + 2y = 2$
   $x - 2y = -10$

e $2x + 3y = 13$
   $4x - 3y = -1$

f $3x + 4y = -1$
   $3x - 2y = -10$

g $5x + 2y = 1$
   $3x - 2y = 7$

h $7x - 3y = 31$
   $7x + y = -1$

i $8x - 2y = 34$
   $8x + 4y = 4$

4 After multiplying either, or both of the equations by a constant, use the elimination method to solve each pair of equations.

a $x + y = 7$
$2x + 3y = 17$

b $2x + y = 7$
$x + 2y = 11$

c $5x + y = 12$
$3x + 2y = 10$

d $4x - y = 10$
$x + 3y = 9$

e $4x - y = 6$
$3x + 2y = -1$

f $5x - 2y = -16$
$x + 3y = 7$

g $12x - 3y = 18$
$4x + 2y = 0$

h $3x - 7y = 2$
$9x + 5y = 32$

i $2x + 3y = 8$
$3x + 2y = 7$

j $5x + 2y = 10$
$4x + 3y = 15$

k $5x + 2y = 28$
$3x + 5y = 51$

l $2x + 2y = -2$
$3x - 5y = -19$

m $7x + 3y = 4$
$5x + 2y = 3$

n $2x - 4y = -2$
$3x + 5y = 45$

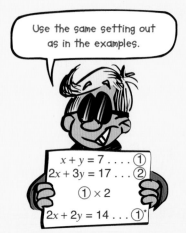

Use the same setting out as in the examples.

$x + y = 7 \ldots$ ①
$2x + 3y = 17 \ldots$ ②
① $\times 2$
$2x + 2y = 14 \ldots$ ①*

9:03 | Using Simultaneous Equations to Solve Problems

In Chapter 6, we saw how equations could be used to solve problems. Simultaneous equations can also be used to solve problems, often in a much easier way than with only one equation. The same techniques that were met in Chapter 6 also apply here.

These clues will help you solve the problem!

Remember:
• Read the question carefully.
• Work out what the problem wants you to find.
  (These things will be represented by pronumerals.)
• Translate the words of the question into mathematical expressions.
• Form equations by showing how different mathematical expressions are related.
• Solve the equations.
• Finish off with a sentence stating the value of the quantity or quantities that were found.

worked example

Adam is 6 years older than his sister, Bronwyn.
If the sum of their ages is 56 years, find their ages.

This is a fairly easy problem, but you must set it out just like the harder ones.

Solution

Let Adam's age be x years.

Let Bronwyn's age be y years.

Now, Adam is 6 years older than Bronwyn

$\therefore x = y + 6$ .... ①

Also, the sum of their ages is 56 years.

$\therefore x + y = 56$................... ②

Solving these simultaneously gives:

$x = 31$ and $y = 25$.

$\therefore$ Adam is 31 years old and Bronwyn is 25 years old.

Exercise 9:03

Foundation Worksheet 9:03

Using simultaneous equations to solve problems

1 If two numbers are x and y, write sentences for:

  a the sum of two numbers equals 7

  b twice one number minus another number equals 12.

2 Write equations for:

  a Six times x plus five times y is equal to 28.

1 Form pairs of simultaneous equations and solve the following problems. Let the numbers be x and y.

  a The sum of two numbers is 25 and their difference is 11. Find the numbers.

  b The sum of two numbers is 97 and their difference is 33. Find the numbers.

  c The sum of two numbers is 12, and one of the numbers is three times the other. Find the numbers.

  d The difference between two numbers is 9 and the smaller number plus twice the larger number is equal to 24. Find the numbers.

  e The larger of two numbers is equal to 3 times the smaller number plus 7. Also, twice the larger number plus 5 times the smaller is equal to 69. Find the numbers.

2 In each problem below there are two unknown quantities, and two pieces of information. Form two simultaneous equations and solve each problem.

  a The length of a rectangle is 5 cm more than the width. If the perimeter of the rectangle is 22 cm, find the length and the width.

  b One pen and one pencil cost 57c. Two pens and three pencils cost $1.36. Find the cost of each.

  c If a student's maths mark exceeded her science mark by 15, and the total marks for both tests was 129, find each mark.

    d Six chocolates and three drinks cost $2.85 while three chocolates and two drinks cost $1.65. Find the price of each.

    e Bill has twice as much money as Jim. If I give Jim $2.50, he will have three times as much as Bill. How much did Bill and Jim have originally?

3 Form two equations from the information on each figure to find values for x and y.

a

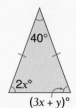
2x + y
x + y
7
12

b

5x − 2y
7
x + 2y
11

c

3x°
(x + y)°

d

40°
2x°
(3x + y)°

e

x + 2y
3x − 5y
11

f

2x + 3
3x + y
3y + 16
9 − y

4 a A rectangle is 4 cm longer than it is wide. If both the length and breadth are increased by 1 cm, the area would be increased by 18 cm². Find the length and breadth of the rectangle.

    b A truck is loaded with two different types of boxes. If 150 of box A and 115 of box B are loaded onto the truck, its capacity of 10 tonnes is reached. If 300 of box A are loaded, then the truck can only take 30 of box B before the capacity of 10 tonnes is reached. Find the weight of each box.

    c A theatre has 2100 seats. All of the rows of seats in the theatre have either 45 seats or 40 seats. If there are three times as many rows with 45 seats than those with 40 seats, how many rows are there?

    d A firm has five times as many junior workers as it does senior workers. If the weekly wage for a senior is $620 and for a junior is $460, find how many of each are employed if the total weekly wage bill is $43 800.

5 Use graphical methods to solve these.

    a Esther can buy aprons for €6 each. She bought a roll of material for €20 and gave it to a dressmaker, who then charged €3.50 for each apron purchased. How many aprons would Esther need to purchase for the cost to be the same as buying them for €6 each.

    b Star Bicycles had produced 3000 bicycles and were producing 200 more per week. Prince Bicycles had produced 2500 bicycles and were producing 300 more each week. After how many weeks would they have produced the same number of bicycles?

 Technology Applications 9:03 Break-even analysis   Challenge worksheet 9:03 Simultaneous equations with 3 variables

Activities

Reading mathematics 9:03 | Breakfast time

A certain breakfast cereal has printed on the box the information shown here. Examine the figures and answer the questions below.

	30 g alone contains approx.	With $\frac{1}{2}$ cup whole milk contains approx.
Kilojoules	477	837
Calories	114	200
Protein	6·0 g	10·2 g
Fat	0·1 g	5·0 g
Starch and related carbohydrates	17·2 g	17·2 g
Sucrose and other sugars	4·7 g	10·6 g
Total carbohydrate	21·9 g	27·8 g

1 How many grams of this cereal contains 477 kilojoules?

2 How many kilojoules is equivalent to 200 calories?

3 How much milk must be added to give 27·8 g of carbohydrate with 30 g of cereal?

	60 g alone contains		With 1 cup whole milk contains	
	by weight	% of daily allowance	by weight	% of daily allowance
Protein	12·0 g	17	20·4 g	29
Thiamine	0·55 mg	50	0·65 mg	59
Riboflavin	0·8 mg	50	1·2 mg	75
Niacin	5·5 mg	50	5·7 mg	52
Iron	5·0 mg	50	5·1 mg	51
Calcium	38 mg	5	334 mg	48
Phosphorus	94 mg	9	340 mg	34

4 What must be the fat content of $\frac{1}{2}$ cup of milk?

5 How many milligrams of niacin are contained in 60 g of cereal?

6 When 60 g of cereal is added to 1 cup of milk, which mineral has 48% of a person's daily allowance provided?

7 How many milligrams is the total daily allowance of
 a riboflavin?   b calcium?

8 How many grams of cereal alone would be needed to provide 30 g of protein?

Mathematical Terms 9

elimination method
- Solving simultaneous equations by adding or subtracting the equations together to 'eliminate' one pronumeral.

graphical solution
- The solution obtained by graphing two equations in the number plane and observing the point of intersection.
- If the point of intersection is $(3, -2)$, then the solution is $x = 3$ and $y = -2$.

guess and check
- A method of solving problems by guessing a solution and then checking to see if it works. Solutions are modified until the correct solution is found.

simultaneous equations
- When two (or more) pieces of information about a problem can be represented by two (or more) equations.
- These are then solved to find the common or simultaneous solution
  eg The equations $x + y = 10$ and $x - y = 6$ have many solutions but the only simultaneous solution is $x = 8$ and $y = 2$.

substitution method
- Solving simultaneous equations by substituting an equivalent expression for one pronumeral in terms of another, obtained from another equation.
  eg If $y = x + 3$ and $x + y = 7$, then the second equation could be written as $x + (x + 3) = 7$ by substituting for y using the first equation.

Diagnostic Test 9: | Simultaneous Equations

- These questions reflect the important skills introduced in this chapter.
- Errors made will indicate areas of weakness.
- Each weakness should be treated by going back to the section listed.

	Section
1 Use the graph to solve the following simultaneous equations. 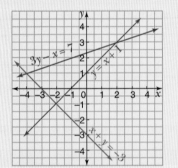 **a** $x + y = -3$ $y = x + 1$ **b** $y = x + 1$ $3y - x = 7$ **c** $3y - x = 7$ $x + y = -3$	9:01
2 Solve the following simultaneous equations by the substitution method. **a** $y = x - 2$　　**b** $x - y = 5$　　**c** $4a - b = 3$ 　　$2x + y = 7$　　　　$2x + 3y = 2$　　　　$2a + 3b = 11$	9:02A
3 Solve the following simultaneous equations by the elimination method. **a** $2x - y = 3$　　**b** $4x - 3y = 11$　　**c** $2a - 3b = 4$ 　　$3x + y = 7$　　　$2x + y = 5$　　　　$3a - 2b = 6$	9:02B

Chapter 9 | Revision Assignment

1   Solve the following simultaneous equations by the most suitable method.

    a $x + y = 3$ **b** $4x - y = 3$
        $2x - y = 6$ $2x + y = 5$

    c $4a + b = 6$ **d** $6a - 3b = 4$
        $5a - 7b = 9$ $4a - 3b = 8$

    e $a - 3b = 5$ **f** $2x - 3y = 6$
        $5a + b = 6$ $3x - 2y = 5$

    g $p = 2q - 7$ **h** $4x - y = 3$
        $4p + 3q = 5$ $4x - 3y = 7$

    i $7m - 4n - 6 = 0$
          $3m + n = 4$

2   A man is three times as old as his daughter. If the difference in their ages is 36 years, find the age of father and daughter.

3   A theatre can hold 200 people. If the price of admission was \$5 per adult and \$2 per child, find the number of each present if the theatre was full and the takings were \$577.

4   A man has 100 shares of stock A and 200 shares of stock B. The total value of the stock is \$420. If he sells 50 shares of stock A and buys 60 shares of stock B, the value of his stock is \$402. Find the price of each share.

5   Rectangle A is 3 times longer than rectangle B and twice as wide. If the perimeters of the two are 50 cm and 20 cm respectively, find the dimensions of the larger rectangle.

6   A rectangle has a perimeter of 40 cm. If the length is reduced by 5 cm and 5 cm is added to the width, it becomes a square. Find the dimensions of the rectangle.

7   A canoeist paddles at 16 km/h with the current and 8 km/h against the current. Find the velocity of the current.

Chapter 9 | Working Mathematically

1 You need to replace the wire in your clothes-line. Discuss how you would estimate the length of wire required.

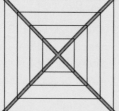

  a On what measurements would you base your estimate?

  b Is it better to overestimate or underestimate?

  c What level of accuracy do you feel is necessary? The diagram shows the arrangement of the wire.

2 What is the last digit of the number 3^{2004}?

3 Two smaller isosceles triangles are joined to form a larger isosceles triangle as shown in the diagram. What is the value of x?

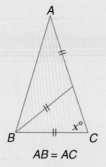

$AB = AC$

4 In a round-robin competition each team plays every other team. How many games would be played in a round-robin competition that had:

  a three teams?   b four teams?

  c five teams?   d eight teams?

5 How many different ways are there of selecting three chocolates from five?

6 A school swimming coach has to pick a medley relay team. The team must have 4 swimmers, each of whom must swim one of the four strokes. From the information in the table choose the fastest combination of swimmers.

Name	Back	Breast	Fly	Free
Dixon	37·00	44·91	34·66	30·18
Wynn	37·17	41·98	36·59	31·10
Goad	38·88			
Nguyen	41·15	49·05	39·07	34·13
McCully		43·01		32·70
Grover		43·17		
Harris			37·34	34·44

• What is the fastest medley relay?

Graphs of Physical Phenomena

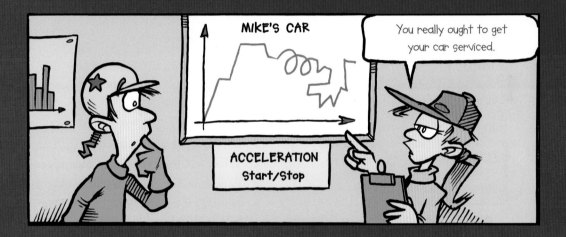

Chapter Contents

Learning Outcomes

Students will be able to:

• Interpret and construct both linear and non-linear distance/time graphs.
• Relate and interpret graphs of physical phenomena.

Areas of Interaction

Approaches to Learning (Knowledge Acquisition, Problem Solving, Communication, Logical Thinking, Reflection), Human Ingenuity, Environments

10:01 | Distance/Time Graphs

10:01A Review of linear graphs

As covered in Book 3:

- A distance–time graph (or travel graph) can be a type of line graph used to describe one or more trips or journeys.

- The vertical axis represents distance from a certain point, while the horizontal axis represents time.

- The formulae that connect distance travelled (D), time taken (T) and average speed (S) are given below.

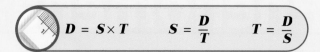

$$D = S \times T \qquad S = \frac{D}{T} \qquad T = \frac{D}{S}$$

worked examples

Example 1

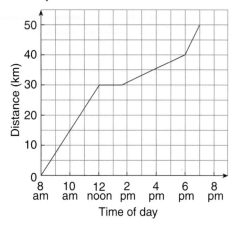

The travel graph shows the journey made by a cyclist.

a How many hours was the journey?

b How far did the cyclist travel?

c What was the cyclist's average speed?

d Between what times did the cyclist stop to rest?

e Between what times was the cyclist travelling fastest?

Solution 1

a The cyclist began at 8 am and finished at 7 pm. That is a total of 11 hours.

b He travelled a total of 45 km.

c Average speed = Total distance travelled ÷ the time taken
$$= 45 \div 11$$
$$= 4\frac{1}{11} \text{ km/h}$$

d Between 12 am and 1:30 pm the line is flat which means no distance was travelled during that time. This must have been the rest period.

e When the graph is at its steepest, more distance is being covered per unit of time. So this is when the cyclist is travelling fastest. This would be from 6 pm to 7 pm.

Example 2

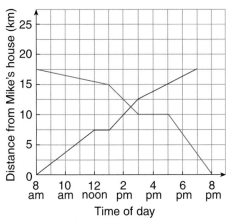

The graph shows the journeys of two friends, Mike and Mal.

They each leave their own house at 8 am and walk to the other's house to see who can walk the fastest.

a Which graph shows Mike's journey?

b When do the two friends pass one another?

c Who has the longest rest?

d What is the speed of each friend?

e Who walks the fastest at any time in their journey?

Solution 2

a Because the graph shows the distance from Mike's house, the person who starts 0 km from there must be Mike. Therefore the blue graph is Mike and the red graph is Mal.

b They pass one another when they are the same distance from Mike's house. So they pass one another where the graphs cross — at 2:15 pm.

c Mike rests for 1 hour, Mal rests for 2 hours (where the graphs are flat) so Mal has the longest rest.

d Mike's speed = $\dfrac{17 \cdot 5}{7}$ Mal's speed = $\dfrac{17 \cdot 5}{8}$

    = $2 \cdot 5$ km/h   = $2 \cdot 1875$ km/h

e Mal walks the fastest from 5 pm to 8 pm as the gradient is the steepest of all.

Gradient = $\dfrac{4}{3}$. At no other time is the gradient steeper than this.

Exercise 10:01A

1

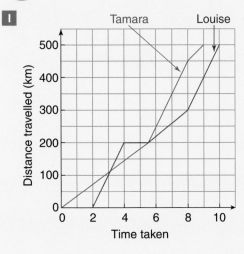

Two women, Tamara and Louise, are travelling along the same road. Their progress is shown on the graph.

a Who started first?

b Who stopped for a rest?

c Who had the fastest average speed?

d When did they meet on the road?

e What was the fastest speed for either of them?

2 The graph shows the journey taken by Max as he went for a training run on his bicycle.

a When was Max travelling fastest? What was the speed at this time?

b Did he stop? If so, for how long?

c How many kilometres did Max cycle?

d What was his average speed for the entire trip?

e Max's brother Thilo did the same trip, but cycled at a constant speed all the way and did not stop. Show his journey on the same graph.

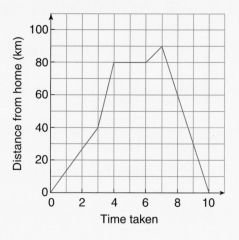

3 A family left Hamburg by car at 9 am. They drove 200 km in the first 2 hours then stopped for half an hour for lunch. Then they drove 150 km along the autobahn in the next hour. They then left the autobahn in the next hour. They then left the autobahn and drove at an average speed of 50 km/h for the last 1·5 hours of their journey.

a Draw a graph showing their journey.

b What was their average speed for the whole trip?

4 The graph shows the progress of a group of bushwalkers hiking in bush over a number of days. It shows their distance from the start of the hike which is at the ranger's station.

a How far did they hike?

b Did they hike every day? If not, on which day did they rest?

c On which day did they hike the least distance?

d On average, how far did they hike per day?

e How much more than the average did they hike on the last day?

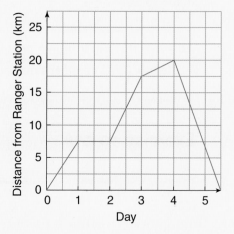

5

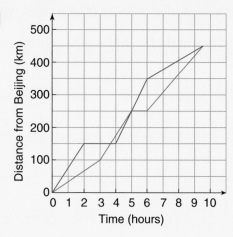

The graph shows the journey taken by two motorists — one represented in blue and the other in red.

a If the speed limit on all the roads travelled is 80 km/h, did either motorist break the speed limit? If so which one?

b Apart from when they stopped, what was the slowest speed for each motorist?

c Which motorist drove most consistently?

d What can be said about the average speed of the two motorists?

e If both motorists were in the same make of car, and the fuel consumption is 8 L/100 km under 70 km/h and 10 L/100 km over 70 km/h, which motorists will use the least fuel?

10:01

Investigation 10:01 | Graphing coins

By rolling a coin along a wooden ruler it is possible to graph the position of a coloured mark as the coin moves. The mark on the coin is highest when it is at the top. The mark is actually touching the ground when it is at the bottom.

• The greatest height is equal to the diameter of the coin.

• The smallest height is zero, which occurs when the mark is on the ground. Because the coin is rolling, the height of the mark will oscillate between these two positions as the distance rolled increases.

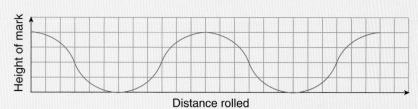

1 Choose three coins of different sizes. Produce a separate graph for each, similar to the one above.

2 Superimpose the three graphs onto one, using a different colour for each graph.

10:01B Non-linear graphs

- The distance–time graphs in 10:01A were all composed of straight line segments. In reality, these might only be an average representation of the motion.

- Consider this simple graph which shows a car's journey from A to B.

- The straight red line shows the car arriving at B, 5 km away, in 5 minutes. The average speed of 1 km/min is shown by this line.

- However, the curved green line would more accurately represent the motion of the car during its journey.

- At A and B, the curve is flat, or horizontal, showing that its speed is zero, since the car has stopped at these points.

- At point C, the car would be going fastest as the curve is steepest at this point.

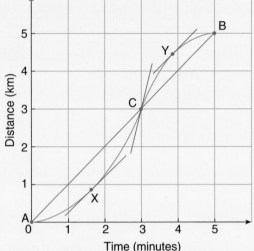

- An indication of the speed at any point on the curve can be worked out by noting the slope of the tangent to the curve at this point. Three tangents have been drawn in blue at points X, Y and C. Since the slope of the tangents at X and Y is the same as the red line, the speed of the car at X and Y would be 1 km/min.

- Can you see that the speed of the car between X and Y would be greater than 1 km/min since the curve is steeper in this section?

- Can you see that from A to X and from Y to B the car's speed would be less than 1 km/min?

worked examples

Example 1

1 A ball is thrown from ground level and lands on a roof.
   a To what height did the ball rise and how high was the roof?
   b What was the average speed of the ball until it reached its maximum height?
   c What was the speed of the ball at its maximum height?
   d When was the ball travelling at its fastest speed?
   e When was the height decreasing?

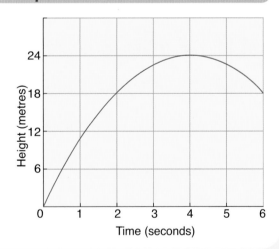

Solution 1

a The maximum height (H) is 24 m. The height of the roof (R) is 18 m.

b The average speed from the ground G to H is indicated by the straight red line. The ball travelled 24 m in 4 seconds, so the average speed was 6 m/s.

c The speed of the ball at H is zero because the graph is flat at this point. That is, the slope of the tangent to the curve is zero.

d The fastest speed was at G, when the ball was first thrown. After that, the ball was slowing down. Its height was increasing, but at a decreasing rate. (It goes up, but the same increase will take a longer time.)

e The height was obviously decreasing after 4 seconds. This is shown on the graph by the line going down or decreasing. The slope of the tangent at any point between H and R would be negative.

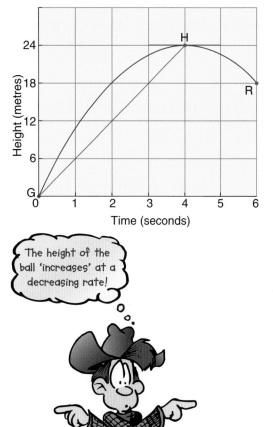

The height of the ball 'increases' at a decreasing rate!

and then it 'decreases' at an increasing rate!

Example 2

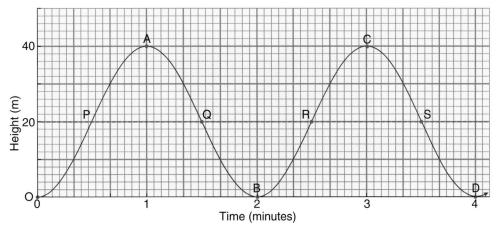

This graph shows the height of a particular seat on a ferris wheel as it rotates to a height of 40 m.

continued ➜➜➜

a   At what point is the rate of change in the height zero?
b   When is the seat rising at its fastest speed?
c   When is the seat falling at its fastest speed?
d   Describe the rate of change in height of the seat from O to A.

Solution 2

a   At the top and bottom of each rotation, the rate of change in height is zero; ie at points O, A, B, C, D on the graph.
b   The seat is rising its fastest when the graph is increasing at the greatest rate. This is at points P and R, where the slope of the curve is steepest; ie at a height of 20 metres.
c   The seat is also falling at its fastest rate when the height is 20 m, but at points Q and S, where the slope of the curve is negative.
d   The height of the seat increases from zero at O at an increasing rate until it reaches point P. The height continues to increase, but at a decreasing rate, until it reaches its maximum height at point A, where the rate of change is zero.

Exercise 10:01B

1   Amanda cycled from her home (H) to her friend's house (F), 30 km away. The black curved line shows her actual distance from H at any time.

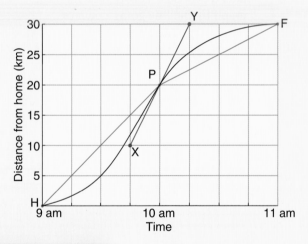

a   What is her average speed for the whole ride?
b   What is the average speed from H to point P?
c   What is the average speed from P to F?
d   If the blue line XY is the tangent to the curve at point P, what is Amanda's actual speed at point P?

2 Jono drove from O to S as shown by this graph, in $3\frac{1}{2}$ hours. His speed varied due to traffic and road conditions.

a What was Jono's average speed from O to Q?

b Was Jono driving faster at point P or point Q?

c Was Jono driving faster at point Q or point R?

d Use the blue tangent drawn through point P to determine the speed at which Jono was travelling at this time.

e Similarly calculate Jono's speed at point R.

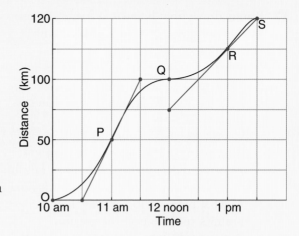

3 This graph shows Benny's journey in blue and Robyn's journey in red as they made their way from A to B via different routes. They both arrived at the same time.

a What was their average speed for the journey?

b At 2 pm they were both 40 km from A, but who was travelling at the greater speed at this point?

c When they were each 10 km from B, who was travelling at the greater speed?

d At approximately what two times during their journeys was Benny's and Robyn's speed the same?

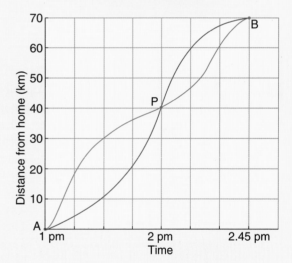

4 Briony drove from home to a friend's house 100 km away. After staying a short while, she then drove home.

a What was Briony's average speed from home to her friend's house?

b Is Briony's speed greater or less than this average speed at:
  i point A?   ii point B?

c After point D, the slope of the graph is negative, indicating that Briony is travelling in the opposite direction, ie towards home. At what point on the journey home does Briony's speed appear the greatest?

d Between which two points on the journey to Briony's friend's house was Briony's distance from home increasing at a decreasing rate?

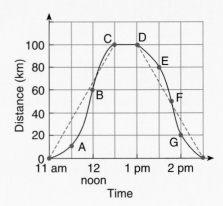

'Wow! I was increasing at a decreasing rate.'

5

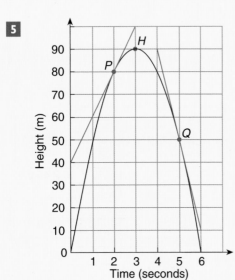

A projectile was fired 90 metres into the air and returned to the ground after 6 seconds.

a What was the average speed of the projectile from the start to its maximum height H?

b Determine the speed of the projectile at point P, when the height was 80 m.

c Determine the speed at point Q, when the projectile was at a height of 50 m on its return journey.

d The projectile's height increased for the first 3 seconds. Did it do so at an increasing or decreasing rate?

e The height then decreased until the projectile reached the ground. Did it do so at an increasing or decreasing rate?

6 Grain is poured into a conical-shaped silo. The graph shows the height of grain as the grain is poured in after t minutes.

The equation for this graph is

$h = 1{\cdot}56\sqrt[3]{100}\, t$ (that is, $1{\cdot}56 \times \sqrt[3]{100}\, t$)

a Determine the height of grain in the silo when the elapsed time is:
  i 10 min   **ii** 2 min

b Describe the rate of change of the height as the silo is filled.

c By drawing tangents to the curve, estimate the rate of change in the height of the grain in metres/min when:
  i $t = 1$ **ii** $t = 2$

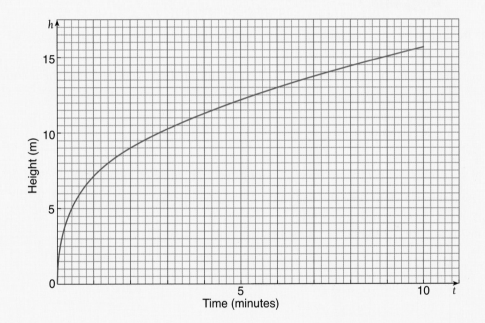

Challenge 10:01 | Rolling down an inclined plane

10:01

- When an object is dropped, the force of gravity causes
  it to increase its speed by about 9·8 m/s every second;
  ie acceleration due to gravity ≑ 9·8 m/s per second.
- When a ball rolls down an inclined plane the
  acceleration will be much less.

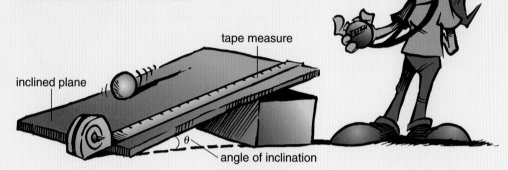

tape measure

inclined plane

θ

angle of inclination

This investigation involves finding the acceleration of a ball (shot put or marble) as it rolls
down an inclined plane of your choice.

If the ball starts from rest (ie speed = 0), then the formula $s = \frac{1}{2}at^2$ describes the motion.

Here: s is distance travelled,
  t is time taken,
  a is acceleration

Steps

1 Make a long inclined plane (over 2 m long) with an angle of inclination of about 10°.

2 Use a stop watch to time the ball as it
   rolls 0·5, 1, 1·5 and 2 m down the
   inclined plane. Complete the table below
   as you go.

s	0·5	1	1·5	2
t				
t^2				

3 Plot s against t and draw the curve of best fit.

4 Plot s against t^2 (ie the value of s on the
   vertical axis and the value of t^2 on the
   horizontal axis).

5 Draw the line of best fit. The gradient of
   this line (rise divided by run) will be an
   approximation to $\frac{1}{2}a$. Double the gradient
   to find a. (If friction were not present,
   9·8 sin θ would be the acceleration of the
   ball, where θ is the angle of inclination
   of the inclined plane.)

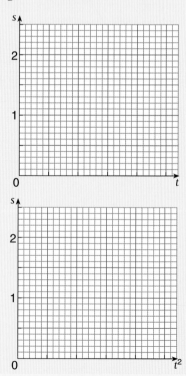

10:02 | Relating Graphs to Physical Phenomena

Much of a mathematician's work is concerned with finding a relationship between two quantities that can change or vary their values.

For example, we could study a person's height at different times of their life. As one quantity changes (eg time), the other changes or varies (eg height). The features that change, and the pronumerals used to represent them, are called *variables*.

Graphs provide an excellent means of exploring the relationship between variables.

They give an immediate 'picture' of the relationship, from which we can see such things as:
- whether a variable is increasing or decreasing with respect to the other variable
- when a variable has its highest or lowest value
- whether a variable is increasing quickly or slowly with respect to the other variable.

Graphs can be used to show relationships between data such as:
- temperature and time of day (or year)
- height and weight
- water level before, during and after a bath
- distance and speed
- light brightness and proximity
- tidal movements over time, and many more.

In the graphs on the right, in which graph does:

1 M increase as *t* increases?
2 M decrease as *t* increases?
3 M stay unchanged?

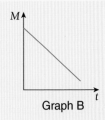
Graph A

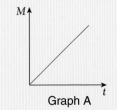
Graph B

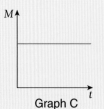
Graph C

4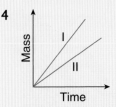
Time

5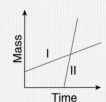
Time

In each diagram on the left, for which line is the mass increasing more quickly, I or II?

In which part of this graph does:
6 the height increase slowly?
7 the height increase quickly?

Time

In which of the graphs does:

8 M increase slowly at first and then quickly?
9 M increase quickly at first, then slowly?
10 M increase at the same rate?

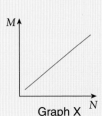
Graph X

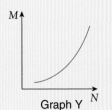
Graph Y

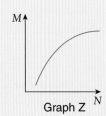
Graph Z

Example 1

A person is driving a car at a certain speed and then increases that speed.
Which graph represents this?

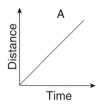
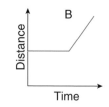
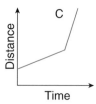

Solution 1

Since two speeds are involved, the second one greater than the first, the graph must have two sections, one for each speed. Graph A is unsuitable because it consists of only one section. Graph B is unsuitable because the first section is a horizontal section, which indicates that the car was not moving. But the question indicates that the car was moving and then changed its speed. Graph C best illustrates the information given.

Example 2

Water is added to the tank shown at a steady rate. Which graph best represents the increase in the water level h?

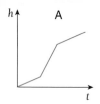
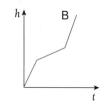
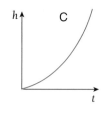

The skinny one will fill up faster than the wide one.

Solution 2

Looking at the tank we notice that the middle part is skinnier than the other parts. Therefore, if water is poured in at a steady rate it will fill up faster in the middle part than in the other two sections. Hence in our graph the water level, h, will increase more quickly for this section of the tank than for the others. Hence the correct graph must consist of three sections, with the steepest section in the middle. Hence graph A is the best representation.

Example 3

A point A is on the circumference of a wheel. If this wheel is rolled, make a graph to show the height of this point above the ground.

Once around is called a 'revolution'.

Solution 3

The highest point on the wheel above the ground is when it is at the top of the wheel. Therefore the greatest height above the ground is the diameter of the wheel.

The smallest height above the ground is zero, which occurs when the point is actually on the ground.

Because the wheel is rolling, the height of point A will oscillate between these positions.

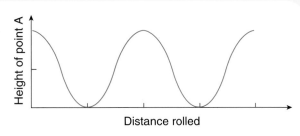

Example 4

An automatic pump is used to fill a cylindrical tank. The tank, which is empty to start with, is filled at a steady rate.

The tank remains full for a period before it is emptied at a steady rate. If it is emptied faster than it is filled, make a sketch which shows the variation in water level in the tank for one complete pumping cycle.

Solution 4

At the start of the cycle the tank is empty and so the water level is zero.

The tank is then filled at a steady rate, which means that the water level will rise at a steady rate.

After it is filled, the tank remains full for a period. For this period, the water level remains the same.

The tank is then emptied at a steady rate but one which is faster than the rate at which it was filled. This means that the line in this section of the graph must be steeper than the line in the first section.

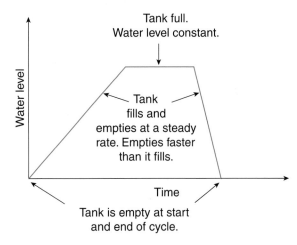

It is also important to be able to describe and interpret information presented in graphs.

Example 5

Describe what this graph is showing.

Solution 5

A flat basketball was inflated, probably with a motorised pump. It was then used for a while before a puncture developed.

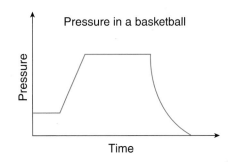

1

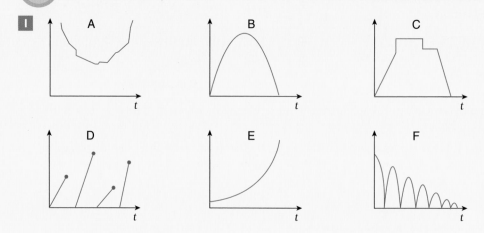

Choose the graph above that best represents each situation below.

a   Population growth as time passes.
b   The number of people waiting for a train on a station as time passes.
c   The maximum daily temperature in Sydney throughout a year.
d   The depth of water in a bath as time passes as it is filled, a person gets in, has a bath, the person gets out and then the water is let out.
e   The height of a ball as time passes as it is dropped from a window and continues to bounce.
f   The height of a stone as time passes if the stone is thrown into the air.

2   A lady in a car drives for three hours averaging 80 km/h, 60 km/h and 90 km/h respectively in each hour. Which graph best represents her trip?

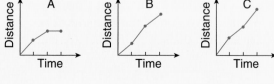

3   A boy rode his bike down the road. He said he rode quickly at the start and then slowed down. Which graph best represents his journey?

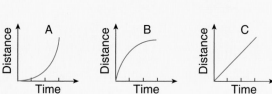

4   The diagram on the right shows the water level of a tank which is filled and emptied periodically.

Give an interpretation of this graph by describing what happens in the first 120 minutes.

Water level in a tank

5 Give a reasonable story or explanation for the information shown in each graph below.

a

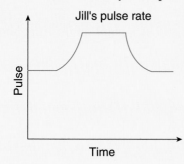
Jill's pulse rate

b

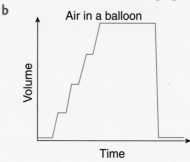
Air in a balloon

c

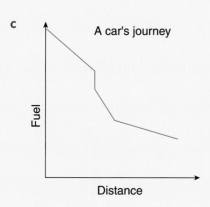
A car's journey

d

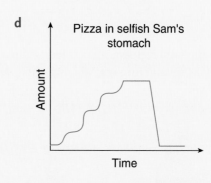
Pizza in selfish Sam's stomach

6 X is a point on the circumference of a roller, as shown in the diagram. The roller can be moved in either a clockwise or an anticlockwise direction.

The graphs below give the height of X above the ground. Which graph represents the clockwise rotation?

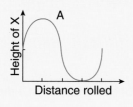

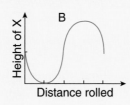

7 Shock absorbers in a car are designed to reduce the bouncing up and down that is caused when the car hits a bump in the road.

The following three graphs show the vertical distance moved by a point on the front bonnet of the car, after hitting a bump.

Which graph best represents a well-designed shock absorber?

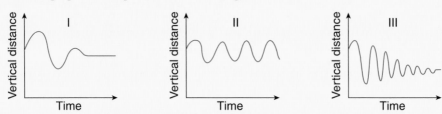

8 Each of the four containers pictured is filled with water at a steady rate. When the level of water in each container was plotted, the graphs I to IV were obtained. Match each container to its graph.

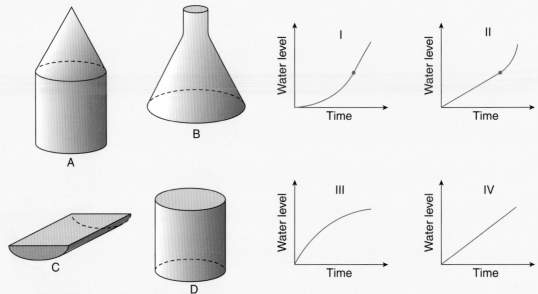

9 The following is known about the solubility of four chemical salts.

Salt A: As the temperature increases the solubility increases, slowly at first and then at a much faster rate.

Salt B: Shows very little increase in solubility as the temperature increases.

Salt C: Increases its solubility at a steady rate as the temperature increases.

Salt D: As the temperature increases the solubility decreases and then increases.

Match each salt to the graphs I to IV.

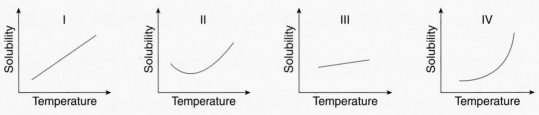

10 A point A is on the circumference of a wheel. The wheel completes one revolution where the starting position of A can be at any of the points 1, 2, 3 or 4 marked on the diagram on the right.

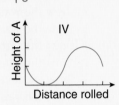

Which one of the graphs below best represents the height of A above the ground when A starts at:

a position 1?   **b** position 3?   **c** position 2?

You will need to know that the wheel is rolled from left to right.

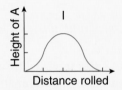

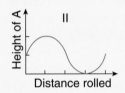

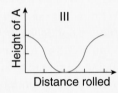

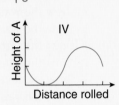

11 Two boys are riding on a see-saw. Make a sketch representing the height of a boy above the ground as time passes if he starts on the ground and goes up and down twice.

12 When boiling water is allowed to cool, it is known that it loses heat quickly at the start and, as time goes on, it loses heat at a slower rate.

Make a sketch to show the shape of a graph which would support this information. Show water temperature on the vertical axis and time on the horizontal axis.

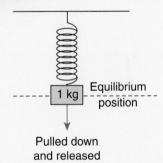

13 A mass of 1 kg is hanging from a vertical spring as shown in the diagram. If this mass is pulled downwards and then released, the mass will move.

Make a sketch to show how the position of the mass will vary from its equilibrium position as time passes.

14 Sketch a line graph to represent each of the following situations. Choose axis labels wisely. Time, when mentioned, should always appear on the horizontal axis.

a how water level varies in a bath as it is being filled

b the relationship between speed and time when a car travels at a constant speed

c the relationship between speed and time when a car travelling at a constant speed brakes slowly before coming to a halt

d a similar relationship as in part **c**, but the car brakes quickly

e how the brightness of a red traffic light varies against time

f how the water level in a bath varies against time when you take a bath

g how the water level in a leaking tank varies against time just after the leak starts

h how the temperature of boiled water varies against time as it cools

i how the fluid level in a cup of tea varies against time as it is consumed

j how the level of fuel in a fuel tank varies against the number of kilometres travelled by a car

k how the water level in a glass containing water and floating ice changes as the ice melts

l how your excitement level changes as you work through this exercise

15 A parachutist jumps from a plane. Before she opens her chute, her speed increases at a constant rate. On opening her chute her speed falls rapidly, approaching a constant terminal value. Make a sketch showing how her speed varies with time.

16 A car is approaching a set of traffic lights at a constant speed when the driver sees the lights change and immediately applies the brakes. The car comes to a stop. After waiting for the lights to change the car accelerates away until it reaches the same constant speed at which it had approached the lights. Make a sketch showing:

a how the car's speed relates to time

b how the distance travelled by the car relates to time

17 A person walking in the desert attempts to walk in a straight line. However, her legs are not exactly the same length and so she walks in a circle.

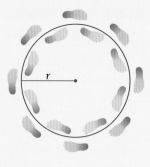

The table below shows the relationship between the difference (*d*) between the right and left leg in regards to length of step and the radius (*r*) of the circle in which the person walks.

Difference in millimetres, *d*	1	2	3	4	5
Radius of circle in metres, *r*	180	90	60	45	36

a If her left leg is longer than her right leg, would she turn to the left or to the right?
b As the difference between the lengths of steps increases, what happens to the radius of the circle?
c Plot the information in the table onto the number plane to the right. Draw a curve joining these points.
d Write a formula to describe this relationship.
e If the difference in steps is 1·5 mm, what would be the radius of the circle in which she walked?
f What happens when there is no difference in steps?

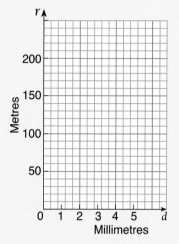

18 Gary discovered that, when draining his pool, the volume of water (*V* litres) remaining in the pool is related to the time (*t* minutes) that the water has been draining.
The formula relating *V* and *t* is:

$$V = 20(30 - t)^2.$$

a When $t = 0$ (initially), the pool was full.
   What volume of water can the pool hold?
b Copy and complete this table using the formula.

t	0	5	10	20	25	30
V	18 000					

c Graph the relationship using the axes shown.
d How long does it take to drain 9000 L from the pool?
e Does the water drain from the pool at a steady rate? Explain your answer.

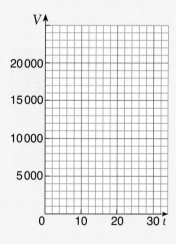

10:02 Filling tanks

Technology Applications

Activities

Investigation 10:02 | Spreadsheet graphs

The data contained in a spreadsheet can be presented in the form of a graph or chart.

A baby's weight in grams was recorded every two weeks. The results for the first ten weeks were entered on a spreadsheet as shown.

This data was then displayed as a graph by 'inserting a chart' on the spreadsheet. Three different samples are shown here.

- Which graph do you think shows the data most clearly?

- Investigate the 'chart' option in a spreadsheet program such as Excel by using this data or other data of your own.

	F14	▼	fx		
	A	B	C	D	E
1	age	weight			
2	0w	3000			
3	2w	4000			
4	4w	4500			
5	6w	5200			
6	8w	6100			
7	10w	7400			
8					
9					

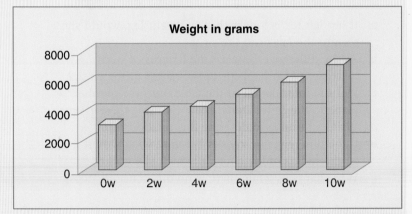

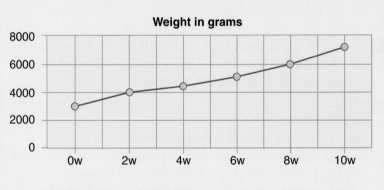

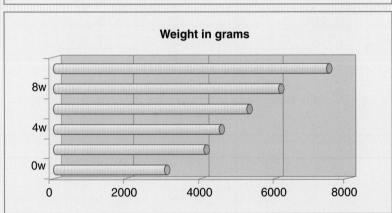

Fun Spot 10:02 | Make words with your calculator

Use the sums and the clues below to complete the crossword. You read the answers to the sums by turning your calculator around and looking at the numbers upside down. (Ignore any decimal points.)

Across

1 A light worker (4231×9)

5 Santa sound $(2 \div 5)$

6 Dirty stuff (45×1269)

8 Not the stinging type (9.5×4)

9 Water tube $(12 \times 4 \times 73)$

11 Some people open theirs too much $(1970 - 43 \times 27)$

12 A fowl animal $(210 \times 165 + 359)$

13 One of these is always right $(11.62 - 2.25)$

14 Not profitable $(92.1 - 37.03)$

19 Peas or the sea $(278^2 + 61)$

21 Good to duck $(\sqrt{5329} + 4.18)$

23 Spots $(97 \times 5 \times 11)$

24 Don't buy! $(7103 + 829 - 197)$

25 Grain store (0.5×1.43)

26 Top person $(9634 - 4126)$

28 More of 12 across $(40\,000 - 4661)$

Down

1 Yukky muck (0.3^2)

2 Give it the O.K. (2768.9×20)

3 Don't stand around! $(2.37 - 1.47)$

4 Exists $(47.3 - 28.6 + 32.3)$

6 Come in pairs $(10\,609 \times 5)$

7 This word is slack $(190^2 - 1093)$

8 A shocking sound $(1.7 - 1.62)$

9 What a pig! (8×113)

10 A bit fishy $(100.6 - 93.27)$

12 Set substance $(752 - \sqrt{169})$

15 Slippery stuff $(7.1 \times 25 \times 4)$

16 Cry, etc (35×23)

17 A manly title $(\sqrt{1296} - 2)$

18 'Well?' – 'Not exactly.' $(800 - 29)$

20 Was it an adder? $(6325 + 1607 - 2418)$

22 Ice house $(0.6903 - 0.6112)$

23 Opposite to 17 down (15×23)

24 Only one of these (2470×1.5)

27 Therefore $(2.451 + 1.63 - 3.581)$

Challenge 10:02 | Curves and stopping distances

The approximate stopping distance of a car is given by the formula:

$$d = v + 0.073v^2$$

while the approximate stopping distance of a truck is given by the formula:

$$d = v + 0.146v^2$$

- For both formulae, d is measured in metres and v is measured in metres per second.

- This table relates stopping distance and the speed of a **car** for various speeds.

$$d = v + 0.073v^2$$

v	0 km/h (0 m/s)	30 km/h (8·3 m/s)	60 km/h (16·7 m/s)	80 km/h (22·2 m/s)	100 km/h (27·8 m/s)
d	0 m	13·4 m	36·9 m	58·3 m	84·1 m

1   Complete the table below, which relates stopping distance and the speed of a **truck** for various speeds.

$$d = v + 0.146v^2$$

v	0 km/h (0 m/s)	30 km/h (8·3 m/s)	60 km/h (16·7 m/s)	80 km/h (22·2 m/s)	100 km/h (27·8 m/s)
d					

2   The graph below is a model of the distance between cars after stopping. The cars are 100 m apart, heading towards one another, when the drivers sense danger. The drivers brake at the same instant.
   - The right axes and graph refer to the car coming from the right. The left axes and graph refer to the car coming from the left.
   - In the first table above, the reading on the vertical axis (speed) is mentioned first.

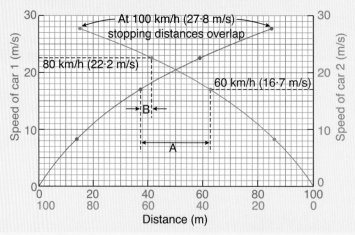

Examples

- If both cars are travelling at 60 km/h (16·7 m/s), the interval A gives the distance apart when they stop.
  From the graph, this is 26 m.
- If the stopping distances of the cars have overlapped, then a collision has occurred.
  At 100 km/h (27·8 m/s) the readings on the distance axis have overlapped, indicating a collision.
- If the red car is travelling at 60 km/h (16·7 m/s) and the green car at 80 km/h (22·2 m/s), the interval B gives the distance apart when they stop.
  From the graph, this is about 4 m.

1   **a**   Do the cars collide if they are both travelling at 80 km/h?
      At what speed (in m/s) would a collision just be avoided if the cars are travelling at the same speed?

   b   What would be the distance between the cars after stopping, if they had both been travelling at:
      i 10 m/s?   **ii** 20 m/s?

   c   At what speed would both cars be travelling if they stop:
      i 20 m apart?   **ii** 60 m apart?

   d   What would be the distance between the cars after stopping, if the speeds of the cars were:
       i red, 10 m/s; green, 27 m/s?
       ii red, 23 m/s; green, 12 m/s?

2   Draw a graph, similar to the one above, to model the distance between vehicles after stopping if the vehicles are the car and the truck referred to in the tables on page 521.
   - Use the questions in **1** above as a guide to list similar findings using your new graph.

Mathematical Terms 10 | Graphs of physical phenomena

axis (pl. axes)
- Each graph has two axes, a horizontal axis and a vertical axis, which show the two quantities that are being compared on the graph.

graph
- A representation of numerical data in the form of a diagram.
- A graph provides a quick way of analysing patterns in numerical data.

phenomenon (pl. phenomena)
- An object or occurrence that is observed.
- A physical phenomenon is one that can be measured.

scale
- Set of marks at measured distances on an axis.
- Used in measuring or making proportional reductions or enlargements.

speed
- Relative rate of motion or action.
- Defined as: $\dfrac{\text{distance}}{\text{time}}$
- Measuring in units such as km/h or m/s.

travel graph
- A line graph where distance travelled is plotted against time taken.
- The gradient (or slope) of the line is an indication of the speed of the motion.

10

Diagnostic Test 10: | Graphs of physical phenomena

- Each part of this test has similar items that test a certain question type.
- Errors made will indicate areas of weakness.
- Each weakness should be treated by going back to the section listed.

Section

1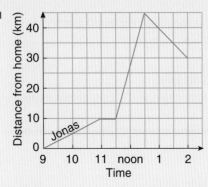

a At what time is Ms Jonas 5 km from home?

b How far from home is Ms Jonas at 1:30 pm?

c What is the furthest distance from home?

d At what time did she rest? For how long?

e How far has she travelled on her trip?

10:01A

2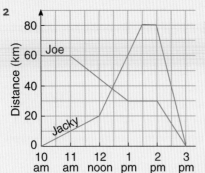

This graph shows the distance of two brothers, Joe and Jacky, from home.

a How far does Joe start from home?

b What is Jacky's average speed from:
  i 10 am to 12 noon?
  ii 12 noon to 1:30 pm?
  iii 2 pm to 3 pm?

c What is Joe's average speed for the entire journey from 10 am to 3 pm?

d What is Joe's greatest speed and between which times is it recorded?

10:01A

3 This graph shows the journey of a car from A to B, 200 km away.

a What is the average speed from A to B?

b Is the car driving faster at point P or point Q?

c Use the red tangent line drawn at R to determine the speed of the car at this point.

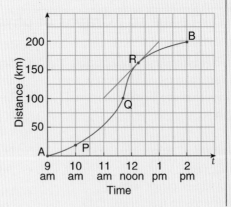

10:01B

4 A tennis ball was hit 75 m into the air and landed back on the ground after 4 seconds.

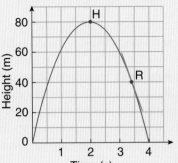

a Was the speed increasing or decreasing for the first 2 seconds? What tells you this?

b What was the average speed of the ball over the first 2 seconds?

c Use a tangent to find the speed at point *H*. What does this point represent?

d Determine the speed at point *R*, when the ball is at 40 m on the way down.

5 a How long does it take the water to reach a temperature of 80°C?

b What is the temperature of the water after 10 min?

c What is the temperature of the water after 20 min?

d From the graph it can be seen that the water doesn't cool at a constant rate. The dotted line represents a constant cooling rate. If the water had cooled at a constant rate, what would its temperature have been after 10 min?

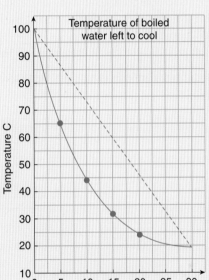

6 The graph shows the variation in solubility of three salts in water with change in temperature.

a How much of salt II will dissolve at 40°C?

b What temperature is needed to dissolve 40 g of salt III?

c Which salt would have the greatest solubility at 40°C?

d Will 50 g of salt II dissolve at 30°C?

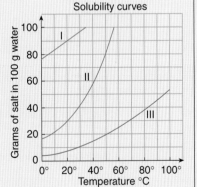

7 Draw a line graph to represent:

a how the water level in a tank varies against time as it is being constantly filled

b how the intensity of light changes as the sun rises and falls during the day

c the average temperature each month for a year in Sydney

Chapter 10 | Revision Assignment

1 The graph shows the trips of Ms Chew and Ms Travers and gives their distance from town A at different times.
   a At 10 am how far is Ms Chew from A?
   b At 10 am how far is Ms Travers from A?
   c At what time are they the same distance from A?
   d Who completes the trip by returning to A?
   e How far is Ms Chew from A when Ms Travers is 20 km from A? (*Note:* There are two possible answers.)

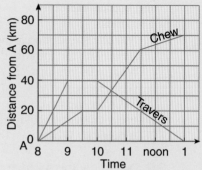

2 Draw a travel graph which shows the information given.
   Briony left home at 9 am, walking at 5 km/h until 11 am when she accepted a lift from a friend. The car travelled at an average speed of 40 km/h for 2 hours. Briony then stopped for lunch until 1:30 pm. She then caught a train and arrived home at 3 pm.
   The horizontal axis should show the time and the vertical axis the distance from home.

3 Choose the heading from the list to the right that would best fit each graph.

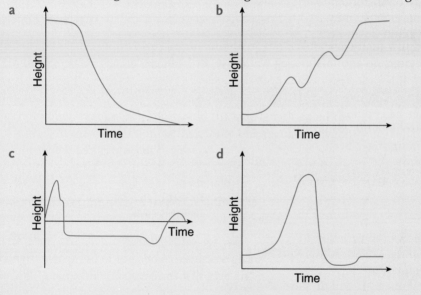

   A The hook of a fishing line while fishing.
   B An arrow fired into the air.
   C Flying a kite.
   D Position of my head while pole vaulting.
   E A parachute jump.
   F Position of my foot as I kick a ball.

4 Describe what is happening on each graph in question **3** as time passes, using the heading most appropriate for that graph.

5 Give a reasonable story or explanation for the information shown on this graph.

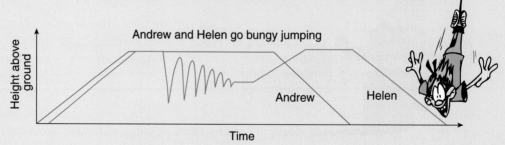

Chapter 10 | Working Mathematically

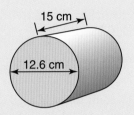

10B

1 Use ID Card 7 on page xix to identify:
   a 5   b 8   c 9   d 10   e 11
   f 12   g 18   h 22   i 23   j 24

2 Naomi bought a computer system for Luke. The marked price was $2300.
   She paid a deposit of $1200 and 12 monthly payments of $115.
   a How much did she pay?
   b How much more than the marked price did she pay?
   c What percentage was the extra money paid of the amount owing after the deposit was
      paid? (Give the percentage correct to 1 decimal place.)

3 For this cylinder find:
   a the area of the base
   b the curved surface area
   c the total surface area

15 cm

12.6 cm

4 A salesman's wages are $230 per week plus a commission of $4\frac{1}{2}$% on his sales. How much
   will he earn in a week when he sells $7000 worth of goods?

5 a What month has the highest rainfall?
   b What month has the lowest rainfall?
   c Which month recorded a rainfall of
      180 mm?
   d What rainfall was recorded in May?
   e How much rain fell in the year?
   f How much rain fell during winter
      (June, July, August)?
   g How much less rain fell in autumn
      than in spring?

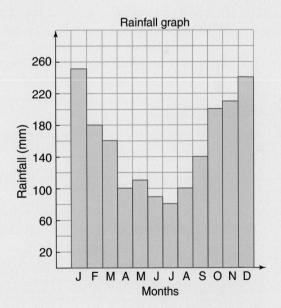

Rainfall graph

6

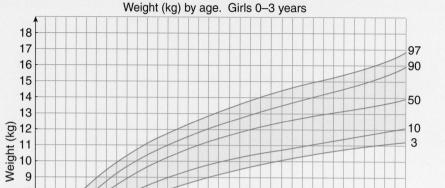

Weight (kg) by age. Girls 0–3 years

The graph above shows the 'normal' weight for girls aged 0 to 3 years. The numbers on the right side of the graph are percentages. (Only 3% of girls 3 years old have a weight less than 11·3 kg.)

a   Why are there two 3s on the horizontal axis?
b   What is the median weight for girls of age:
   i   3 months?   ii   1 year?   iii   19 months?
   iv   2 years 3 months?   v   1 year 2 months?
c   What percentage of 3-year-old girls have a weight between 13·9 kg and 16 kg?
d   What weights would be considered 'normal' for a girl of age 2 months?
e   What weights would be considered 'normal' at birth for a girl?

• I swim 400 m in 6 min 42 s. What is my average time per lap? (A lap is 50 m.)

Deductive Geometry

Chapter Contents

Learning Outcomes

Students will be able to:

- Solve problems related to the angles sum of interior and exterior angles of polygons.
- Solve numerical problems related to angles created when families of parallel lines are cut by a transversal.
- Use deductive geometry to solve problems involving congruent triangles and quadrilaterals.
- Solve problems using Pythagoras' theorem and its converse.
- Relate and interpret graphs of physical phenomena.

Areas of Interaction

Approaches to Learning (Knowledge Acquisition, Problem Solving, Communication, Logical Thinking, Reflection), Human Ingenuity, Environments

11:01 | Deductive Reasoning in Numerical Exercises

Use ID Card 6 on page xviii to identify:

1 15   **2** 14   **3** 13   **4** 16

5 18   **6** 19   **7** 20

Use ID Card 5 on page xvii to identify:

8 15   **9** 17   **10** 18

11:01A   Exercises using parallel lines

worked examples

1

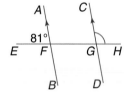

EF//GH. Find the size of ∠*GCD.* Give reasons.

2

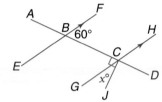

AB//CD. Find the size of ∠*CGH.* Give reasons.

3

EF//GH. Find the size of *x.* Give reasons.

Solutions

1 ∠*EBC* = 76°
(vert. opp. ∠s)
∠*GCD* = 76°
(corresp. ∠s, *EF//GH*)

2 ∠*FGC* = 81°
(corresp. ∠s, *AB//CD*)
∠*CGH* = 99°
(adj. supp. ∠s)

3 ∠*BCG* = 60°
(alt. ∠s, *EF//GH*
$x + 60 = 90$ (comp. ∠s)
$x = 30$

Exercise 11:01A

1 Find the size of ∠*ABC* in each diagram. Give reasons.

a

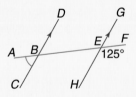

b

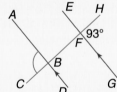

c

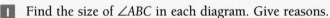

2 Find the value of x in each diagram. Give reasons.

a
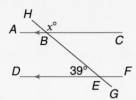

b

c
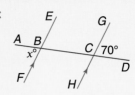

d
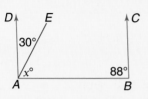

e

f
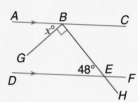

3 Find the value of x in each diagram. Give reasons.

a
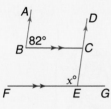

b

c
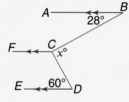

d
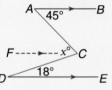

e
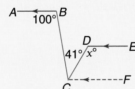

f
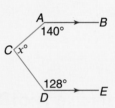

g
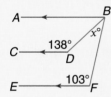

h
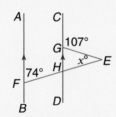

i
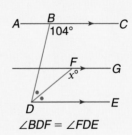

$\angle BDF = \angle FDE$

11:01B Exercises using triangles

1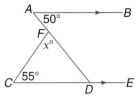

AB//CE. Find the size of *x*. Give reasons

Solution 1

$\angle FDC = 50°$ (alt. $\angle$s, *AB//CE*)
$x + 55 + 50 = 180$ ($\angle$sum of Δ)
$\therefore x = 75$

2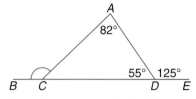

Find the size of $\angle BCA$. Give reasons.

Solution 2

$\angle ADC = 55°$ (adj. supp. $\angle$s)
$\angle BCA = 82° + 55°$ (ext. $\angle$ of Δ)
$\therefore \angle BCA = 137°$

3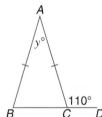

Find the value of *y*.
Give reasons.

Solution 3

$\angle ACB = 70°$ (adj. supp. $\angle$s)
$\therefore \angle ABC = 70°$ (base $\angle$s of isos. Δ)
$y + 70 + 70 = 180$ (angle sum of Δ)
$\therefore y = 40$

Base angles are equal.

Exercise 11:01B

1 Find the size of $\angle ABC$ in each diagram. Give reasons.

a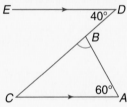

b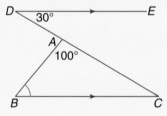

c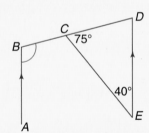

2 Find the value of *x* in each diagram. Give reasons.

a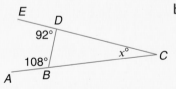

b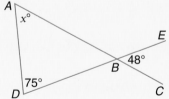

c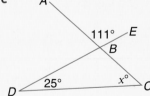

3 Find the size of ∠*ABC* in each diagram. Give reasons.

a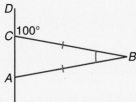

b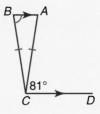

c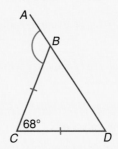

4 Find the value of *x* in each diagram. Give reasons.

a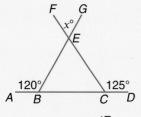

b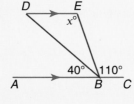

c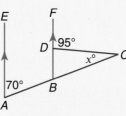

d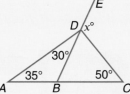

e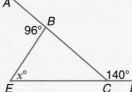

f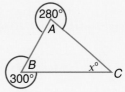

5 Find the value of *x* in each diagram. Give reasons.

a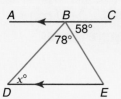

b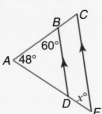

- Copy the diagram.
- Write down the sizes of as many angles as you can.
- Look for a connection.

c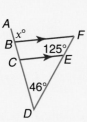

d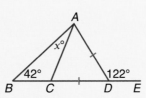

e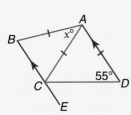

AB = *AC* = *AD*

f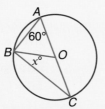

O is the centre.

11:01C   Exercises using quadrilaterals

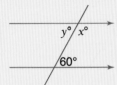

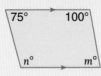

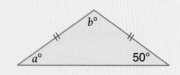

Find the value of:

1 x **2** y

Find the value of:

3 m **4** n

Find the value of:

5 a **6** b

For the parallelogram shown, find the value of:

7 a **8** b **9** c

10   Complete: The angle sum of a quadrilateral is _____

worked examples

1

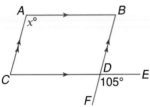

ABDC is a parallelogram. Find the size of x.
Give reasons.

Opposite angles of a parallelogram are equal.

Solution 1
$\angle BDC = x°$ (opp. $\angle$s of a par'm)
$\angle BDC = 105°$ (vert. opp. $\angle$s)
$\quad \therefore x = 105$

2

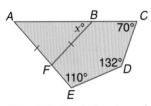

AF = BF. Find the size of x. Give reasons.

3

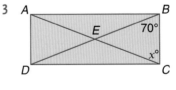

ABCD is a rectangle. Find the value of x.
Give reasons.

Solution 2
$\angle EAC = 360° - (70° + 132° + 110°)$
$\qquad$ ($\angle$ sum of quad.)
$\qquad = 48°$
$\quad \therefore x = 48$ (base $\angle$s of isos. Δ)

Solution 3
$\quad EB = EC$ (diagonals of a rectangle bisect
$\qquad\qquad$ each other and are equal)
$\therefore x = 70$ (base $\angle$s of isos. ΔBEC)

1 Find the value of *x* in each diagram. Give reasons.

a
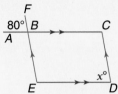

b
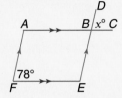

c
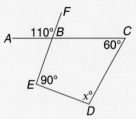

d
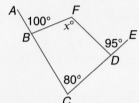

e
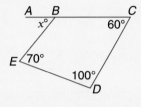

f
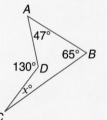

2 Find the value of ∠*ABC* in each diagram. Give reasons.

a
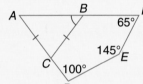

b
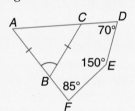

c
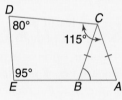

d
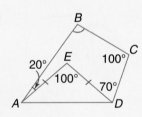

e
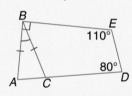

f
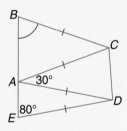

3 *ABCD* is a rectangle. Find the value of *x*. Give reasons.

a
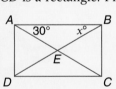

b
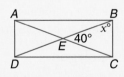

c
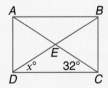

4 Find the value of *x*. Give reasons.

a
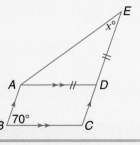

b
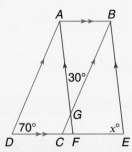

c
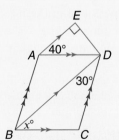

11:02 | Review of Polygons

- *The Pentagon* — the most famous polygonal building in the world.

In Book 3 you learnt that:

- A polygon is a plane figure with straight sides.
- A polygon is said to be regular if all of its sides and angles are equal.
  (If they are not, it is said to be irregular.)
- Some polygons are named according to the number of sides they have.

A regular hexagon   An irregular hexagon   A concave hexagon

I see! Two convex and one concave.

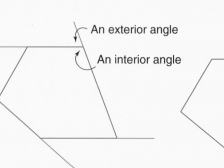

- A polygon can be concave or *convex*.
- In a *convex* polygon all the angles are acute or obtuse.
  If a polygon has any reflex angles it is said to be concave.

The exterior angle sum of a convex polygon

- An exterior angle of a polygon is an angle that forms a straight line with one of the interior angles.
- If the interior angle is a reflex angle then no exterior angle exists.

An exterior angle

An interior angle

No exterior angle at this vertex

> ▨ The angle sum of the interior angles of a polygon = $(n - 2) \times 180°$
> ▨ The sum of the exterior angles of a polygon is $360°$.

1 A regular polygon has 12 sides (a dodecahedron).
   a What is the size of each interior angle?
   b What is the size of each exterior angle?
2 A regular polygon has an interior angle of 140°. How many sides does it have?

Solutions

1 a Sum of interior angles = $(n - 2) \times 180°$
   for this polygon, $n = 12$.
   Sum of interior angles = $(12 - 2) \times 180°$
   $= 1800$
   If it is a regular polygon, all sides and angles are equal.
   ∴ size of an interior angle $= \dfrac{1800}{12}$
   $= 150°$

   b Sum of exterior angles = 360°
   the number exterior angles = the number of sides
   ∴ size of an interior angle $= \dfrac{360}{12}$
   $= 30°$

2 Interior angle = 140°
   ∴ exterior angle = 40°
   ∴ number of exterior angles $= \dfrac{360}{40} = 9$
   ∴ number of sides = 9

Exercise 11:02

1 Find the size of each (i) interior angle and (ii) exterior angle of the following
   a equilateral triangle
   b square
   c regular pentagon
   d regular hexagon
   e regular octagon
   f regular 10-sided polygon (decagon)

2 Find the number of sides in a regular polygon with an exterior angle of:
   a 30°   b 15°   c 24°   d 20°   e 10°

3 Find the number of sides in a regular polygon with an interior angle of:
   a 168°   b 160°   c 170°   d 175°   e 90°

4 A tessellation is made when polygons are put together to make a pattern as shown in the diagram. Here regular hexagons form a tessellation on their own.
   a What other regular polygons will tessellate on their own?
   b Try to list combinations of regular polygons that will tessellate.

Investigation 11:02A | Regular polygons and tessellations

Please use the Assessment Grid on the following page to help you understand what is required for this Investigation.

A tessellation is a tiling pattern. If a shape can form a tile pattern on its own, it is said to tessellate.

The diagram below is part of a tessellation based on a regular hexagon.

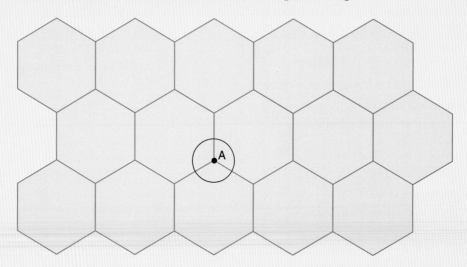

1 What is the size of an interior angle in a regular hexagon?

2 How many hexagons meet at the vertex, A?

3 If a shape tessellates, what must be the angle sum at each vertex?

4 Use the diagram on the right to explain why a regular pentagon will not tessellate?

5 What are the other two regular polygons that will tessellate?

6 Can you find and discuss any possible real life uses of tessellations?

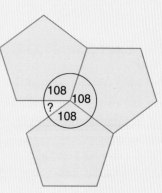

Assessment Grid for Investigation 11:02A | Regular polygons and tessellations

The following is a sample assessment grid for this investigation. You should carefully read the criteria *before* beginning the investigation so that you know what is required.

Assessment Criteria (B, C, D) for this investigation				Achieved ✓
Criterion B Investigating Patterns	a	None of the following descriptors has been achieved.	0	
	b	Some help was needed to apply mathematical techniques and answer questions 1–3.	1	
			2	
	c	Mathematical techniques have been selected and applied to use the properties of polygons and tessellations to effectively answer questions 1–3, and attempt questions 4 and 5.	3	
			4	
	d	Questions 1–3 are correctly answered with a reasonable explanation for questions 4 and 5.	5	
			6	
	e	The student has completely answered all questions, explained all patterns evident and justified their results.	7	
			8	
Criterion C Communication in Mathematics	a	None of the following descriptors has been achieved.	0	
	b	There is a basic use of mathematical language and representation. Working out and explanations are insufficient.	1	
			2	
	c	There is satisfactory use of mathematical language and representation. Working and explanations are clear and the student has been able to use the properties of polygons well to explain results.	3	
			4	
	d	There is good use of mathematical language and representation. Answers are correct and explanations are complete and concise.	5	
			6	
Criterion D Reflection in Mathematics	a	None of the following descriptors has been achieved.	0	
	b	An attempt has been made to explain whether the results make sense. An attempt has been made to make connection to the real-life applications.	1	
			2	
	c	There is a correct but brief explanation of whether results make sense and how they were found. A description of the important aspects of polygons and tessellations is given.	3	
			4	
	d	There is a critical explanation of the results obtained and their relation to real life. The answers to questions 4 and 5 are fully explained with consideration of the accuracy of the results obtained and possible further applications of tessellations.	5	
			6	

Investigation 11:02B | Spreadsheet

The spreadsheet below is used to calculate:
- the angle sum of a polygon
- the size of an interior angle in a regular polygon.

	File Edit View Insert Format Tools Data Window Help					
	C8	▼	=	=B8/A8		
	A	B	C	D	E	F
1	**Number of Sides**	**Interior Angle Sum**	**Size of Interior Angle**			
2	3	180	60			
3	4	360	90			
4	5	540	108			
5	6	720	120			
6	7	900	128.5714286			
7	8	1080	135			
8	9	1260	140			
9	10	1440	144			
10	11	1620	147.2727273			
11	12	1800	150			
12	13	1980	152.3076923			
13	14	2160	154.2857143			
14	15	2340	156			
15	16	2520	157.5			
16	17	2700	158.8235294			
17	18	2880	160			
18	19	3060	161.0526316			
19	20	3240	162			
20						

The following steps show how the spreadsheet was reproduced.

1 Entering text

Open the Microsoft Excel program, move the cursor to cell **A1** and type **Number of Sides** then press ENTER. Move the cursor to cells **B1** and **C1** and add the other headings.

2 Adjusting the column width

The width of the columns can be adjusted by selecting FORMAT from the top menu bar followed by COLUMN and then WIDTH. The number shown is the present width. Typing a larger or smaller number in the box followed by clicking the OK will increase or decrease the column width.

The column width can also be adjusted in other ways.

3 Using a formula

Move the cursor to cell **A2** and press 3 followed by ENTER. The cursor will move to **A3**. Enter a formula by typing =A2+1 followed by ENTER. The number 4 will now appear in cell **A3**. In cells **B2** and **C2** enter the formulae =(A2-2)*180 and =B2/A2 respectively. The numbers 180 and 60 should appear in cells **B2** and **C2** respectively.

4 Copying a formula

Move the cursor to cell **A3**. Now select EDIT on the top menu bar and then choose COPY. Highlight the cells **A3** to **A19** by holding down SHIFT and then pressing the down arrow ↓. Cells **A4 to A19** should be blackened. Choose EDIT from the menu followed by PASTE. The numbers in cells **A3 to A19** will now appear as shown. (To remove the flashing cursor from cell **A3** move the cursor to **A3** and press ENTER.)

Move the cursor to cell **B2** and then select EDIT followed by COPY. Highlight cells **B2 to B19** using the SHIFT and down arrow key as before. Select EDIT followed by PASTE and the numbers in cells **B2 to B19** will appear.

Move the cursor to cell **C2** and select EDIT followed by COPY. Then highlight cells **C2 to C19**. Select EDIT followed by PASTE and the numbers in cells **C2 to C19** will appear.

QUESTIONS

1. Move the cursor to cell A2 and type the number 10 followed by ENTER. What are the numbers in cells A16, B16 and C16 and what do they represent?

2. By changing the number in cell A2 find the angle sum and size of an interior angle in a regular polygon with 90 sides.

3. Move to cell A2 and type 3 followed by ENTER. Now extend the table to row 49 using the copying and highlighting skills used above.

    From the numbers you have produced read off:
    a How many sides has the first polygon with an angle sum greater than 5000°?
    b How many sides has the first polygon with an angle sum greater than 6000°?
    c How many sides must a regular polygon have for its interior angle to be larger than 172°?

11:02 Spreadsheet

Challenge worksheet 11:02 Regular polygons and tessellations

Fun Spot 11:02 | The game of Hex

Hex is played on a board of hexagons like the one shown. This board has 7 hexagons along each edge, but bigger boards may be used.

The game is played between two players, one having a supply of white counters, the other a supply of black counters. Each takes it in turn to place a counter anywhere on the board, with the object being to form a continuous chain of one's own counters from one side of the board to the other. The player with the white counters must form a chain connecting the two 'white' edges of the board before black can join the two 'black' edges.

(This game was invented by a Dane named Piet Hein. He introduced the game in 1942 under the name of 'Polygon'.)

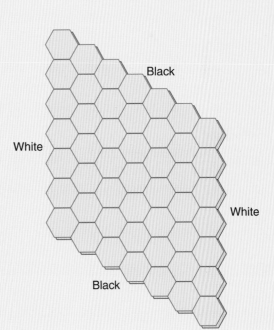

11:03 | Deductive Reasoning in Non-Numerical Exercises

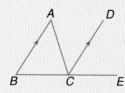

Copy the diagram.

1 Mark ∠ABC with 'x'.   **2** Mark ∠BAC with '•'.

In the diagram, which angle is equal to:

3 ∠ABC?   **4** ∠BAC?

5 Which angle is adjacent to ∠DCE?

6 Which two adjacent angles make ∠ACE?

7 If $a + b = 180$, then $180 - a = \ldots$?   **8** If $a + c = 180$, then $c = \ldots$?

9 If $b = 180 - a$ and $c = 180 - a$, then $b = \ldots$?   **10** If $a = b$ and $b = c$, what can we say about a and c?

Many problems in geometry are non-numerical. In these problems, the reasoning process becomes more involved. As there are no numbers involved, pronumerals are used to represent unknown quantities. With the use of pronumerals, the reasoning will involve algebraic skills learned in other parts of the course.

Because exercises do not involve specific numbers, the results we obtain will be true irrespective of the numbers used. The results obtained are called **generalisations** or, more commonly, **proofs**.

worked examples

1 In the diagram, prove that $x = y$.

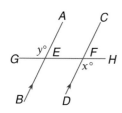

2 In the diagram, prove that $∠ABD = ∠CEF$.

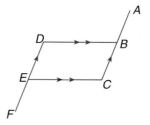

Solutions

1   ∠CFE = $x°$ (vert. opp. ∠s)
      ∠CFE = $y°$ (corresp. ∠s, AB//CD)
      ∴ $x = y$ (both equal to ∠CFE)

2   ∠ABD = ∠BDE (alt. ∠s, AC//DF)
        ∠CEF = ∠BDE (corresp. ∠s DB//EC)
      ∴ ∠ABD = ∠CEF (both equal to ∠BDE)

I'll have to be wide awake for this work!

I DON'T DO MORNINGS

3 In the diagram, prove that:
  a $\angle ABD = \angle DAC$
  b $\angle BAD = \angle ACD$

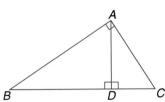

4 $\triangle ABC$ is isosceles with $AB = BC$. AB is produced to D and BE is drawn through B parallel to the base AC. Prove that BE bisects $\angle CBD$.

Solutions

3

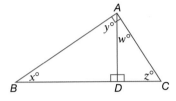

Let $\angle ABD = x°$, $\angle BAD = y°$,
$\angle DAC = w°$ and $\angle ACD = z°$.

a $x + y = 90$ (comp. $\angle$s in $\triangle ABD$)
       $w + y = 90$ (comp. $\angle$s)
       $\therefore x = w$
    $\therefore \angle ABD = \angle DAC$

b $x + y = 90$ (comp. $\angle$s in $\triangle ABD$)
       $x + z = 90$ (comp. $\angle$s in $\triangle ABC$)
       $\therefore y = z$
    $\therefore \angle BAD = \angle ACD$

4

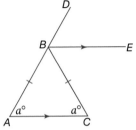

    Let $\angle BAC = a°$
      $\therefore \angle BCA = a°$ (base $\angle$s of isos. $\triangle$)
   Now $\angle EBC = a°$ (alt. $\angle$s, $BE//AC$)
        $\angle DBE = a°$ (corresp. $\angle$s, $BE//AC$)
     $\therefore \angle DBE = \angle EBC$
   $\therefore BE$ bisects $\angle CBD$

Exercise 11:03

Foundation Worksheet 11:03

Non-numerical proofs
1 Prove $\angle ABC = 2 \times \angle BDC$.

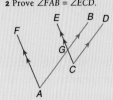

2 Prove $\angle FAB = \angle ECD$.

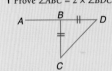

1 Prove that $x = y$ in each of the following.
  a

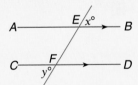

  b

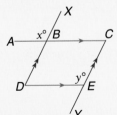

2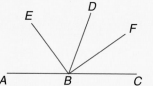

∠ABC is a straight angle. BE and BF bisect ∠ABD and ∠DBC respectively. Prove that EB is perpendicular to BF.

3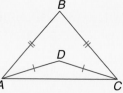

△ABC and △ADC are isosceles. AC is the base of both triangles. Prove that ∠BAD = ∠BCD.

The word 'respectively' means 'in the order given'.

4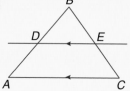

A line drawn parallel to the base AC of an isosceles △ABC cuts the equal sides at D and E. Prove that △DBE is isosceles.

5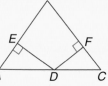

△ABC has AB and BC equal. D is any point on AC, and DE and DF are perpendicular to AB and BC respectively. Prove that ∠EDA = ∠FDC.

6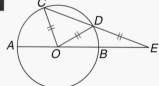

△ABC and △BDC are isosceles. AB = BC and BD = DC. BC is a common side, while A and D lie on opposite sides of BC. Prove that ∠BCD = 2 × ∠BCA.

7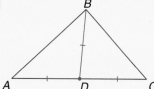

D is a point on the side AC of △ABC. D is equidistant from the three vertices of the triangle. Prove that ∠ABC is a right angle.

8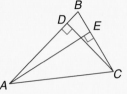

A, B and C are collinear. AD = AB, BC = EC and AD//EC. Prove that ∠DBE is a right angle.

9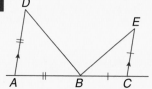

AB is a diameter and CD is a chord of a circle which has centre O. CD produced meets AB produced at E and DE = OD. Prove that ∠AOC = 3 × ∠DOB.

10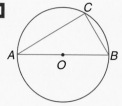

In △ABC, AE and CD are perpendicular to BC and AB respectively. Prove that ∠BAE = ∠BCD.

11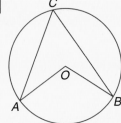

AB is the diameter of a circle centred at O. Prove that ∠ACB = 90°.

> **Hint!**
> Join CO.

12

O is the centre of the circle. Prove that ∠AOB = 2 × ∠ACB.

11:04 | Congruent Triangles

In Years 7 and 8, congruent figures would have been studied.
- Congruent figures are the same shape and size. When one is superimposed on the other, they coincide exactly.
- Congruent figures are produced by translations, reflections and rotations.
- When congruent figures are placed on top of each other so that they coincide exactly, the matching sides and angles are obviously equal. The word *corresponding* is often used instead of *matching*.

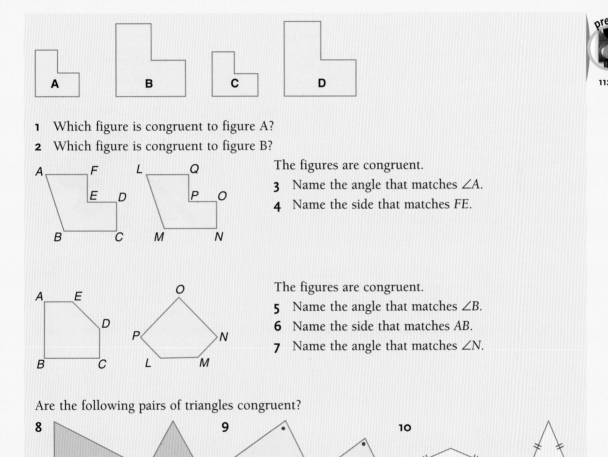

1 Which figure is congruent to figure A?
2 Which figure is congruent to figure B?

The figures are congruent.

3 Name the angle that matches ∠A.
4 Name the side that matches *FE*.

The figures are congruent.

5 Name the angle that matches ∠B.
6 Name the side that matches *AB*.
7 Name the angle that matches ∠N.

Are the following pairs of triangles congruent?

8

9

10

Congruent triangles
- In geometry, we are often asked to show that two sides or two angles are equal. A common way of doing this is by showing that they are the matching sides or angles of congruent triangles.
- To check that two triangles are congruent, we would normally need to compare six pieces of information (three sides and three angles).
- In the next exercise we will investigate the **minimum conditions** for congruent triangles. A minimum condition is the smallest amount of information that we need to know about two triangles before we can say they are congruent.

Exercise 11:04

1 Sketch two possible triangles with:
    a a side of 5 cm   **b** an angle of 60°
    c sides of 4 cm and 5 cm   **d** angles of 50° and 60°
    e a 5 cm side and a 60° angle.

2 Are two triangles congruent if they:
    a have only one side equal?   **b** have only one angle equal?
    c have only two sides equal?   **d** have two angles equal?
    e have one side and one angle equal?

3 Can two triangles be congruent if we can compare only two pieces of information on each one?

To compare three pieces of information we could compare:
- 3 sides
- 2 sides and 1 angle
- 1 side and 2 angles
- 3 angles.

Same angles— Different sizes...

4 **a** When a photograph is enlarged, are:
      i the angles in the photo and the enlargement the same?
      ii the photo and the enlargement congruent?
    b If two triangles have their three angles equal, does it mean they are congruent?

5 In Years 7 and 8 you would have been shown how to construct a triangle given its three sides (eg 3 cm, 4 cm and 5 cm). The diagrams show the four possible shapes, starting with a side *AB*.

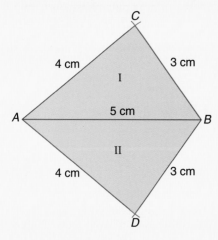

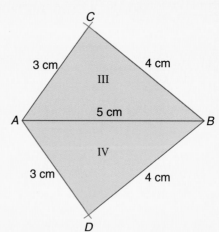

    a Is triangle I a reflection of triangle II?
    b Is triangle II a reflection of triangle IV?

c Are the four triangles congruent?

d When you construct a triangle given the lengths of its three sides, can you obtain solutions that are not congruent?

e If two triangles have all their sides equal, are they congruent?

6

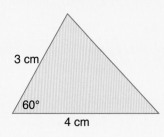 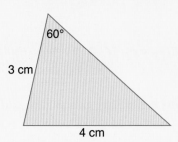

a Do the triangles above have two sides and one angle equal?

b Are the triangles congruent? (Check by measuring the third side.)

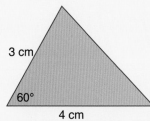 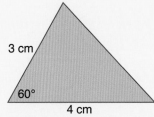

c Do the triangles above have two sides and one angle equal?

d Are the triangles congruent? (Check the length of the third side.)

e Where is the angle in relation to the sides?

f Explain why placing the angle between the two sides automatically fixes the length of the third side and the sizes of the other angles.

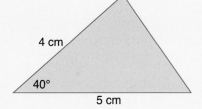

7 **a** If a triangle has angles of 60° and 70°, what is the size of the third angle?

b If you are given two angles of a triangle, do you also know the size of the third angle?

c In any triangle, is the largest side opposite the largest angle?

d In any triangle, where is the smallest side in relation to the angles?

e The two triangles drawn below have a 50° angle, 60° angle and a 4 cm side. Are they congruent?

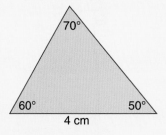 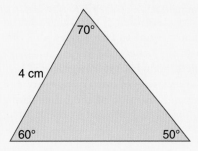

f The two triangles below also have a 50° angle, a 60° angle and a 4 cm side. Are they congruent?

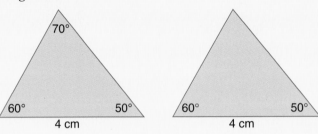

g You are told that two triangles have two angles (and, hence, the third angle) and one side equal. Where must the side be placed in relation to the angles if the triangles are to be congruent?

8 Right-angled triangles have a special set of minimum conditions.

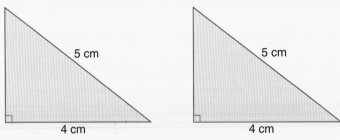

a If two triangles have all their sides equal, are they congruent?

b Which theorem allows us to calculate the third side of a right-angled triangle given the other two?

c If two right-angled triangles have their hypotenuses and one other pair of sides equal, are they congruent?

The results from questions **5** to **8** are summarised below.

Summary
- **Two triangles are congruent if three sides of one triangle are equal to three sides of the other. (SSS)**
- **Two triangles are congruent if two sides and the included angle of one triangle are equal to two sides and the included angle of the other. (SAS)**
- **Two triangles are congruent if two angles and a side of one triangle are equal to two angles and the matching side of the other. (AAS)**
- **Two right-angled triangles are congruent if the hypotenuse and one side of one triangle are equal to the hypotenuse and one side of the other triangle. (RHS)**

- *SSS means 'side, side, side'.*
- *SAS means 'side, angle, side'.*
- *AAS means 'angle, angle, side'.*
- *RHS means 'right angle, hypotenuse, side'.*

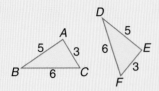

Name the side that corresponds to:

1 AC **2** AB **3** BC

Name the angle that corresponds to:

4 $\angle A$ **5** $\angle B$ **6** $\angle C$

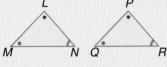

Name the side that corresponds to:

7 LM **8** MN

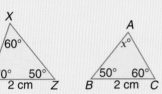

9 Find the value of x.

10 Are the 2 cm sides corresponding?

'Corresponding' can be used instead of 'matching' when describing position.

The minimum conditions deduced in the last section are used to prove that two triangles are congruent. Special care must be taken in exercises that involve overlapping triangles.

worked examples

Examples

1 Prove that $\triangle ABC \equiv \triangle DFE$ and list the pairs of matching sides and angles.

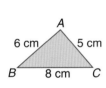

2 Show that $\triangle ABC \equiv \triangle DCB$.

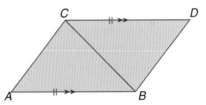

Solutions

1 $\triangle ABC$ and $\triangle DFE$ have all their sides equal.
$\therefore \triangle ABC \equiv \triangle DFE$ (SSS)
The pairs of matching angles are:
$\angle A$ and $\angle D$, $\angle B$ and $\angle F$, $\angle C$ and $\angle E$.
The pairs of matching sides are:
AB and DF, AC and ED, BC and EF.

2 In $\triangle ABC$ and $\triangle DCB$
  i $\angle ABC = \angle DCB$
    (alt. angles, $DC // BA$)
  ii $AB = CD$
  iii $BC = BC$
$\therefore \triangle ABC \equiv \triangle DCB$ (SAS)

'$\equiv$' means 'is congruent to'.

If $\triangle ABC$ is congruent to $\triangle DEF$, we write $\triangle ABC \equiv \triangle DEF$

When working with congruent figures, the term 'corresponding' is often used instead of the term 'matching' to refer to angles or sides in the same position.

continued ➔➔➔

Examples

3 Are these two triangles congruent?

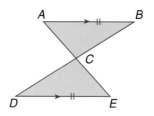

4 Prove that $\triangle ABC \equiv \triangle EDC$.

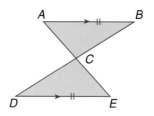

Solutions

3
- Because we are only given the length of one side we cannot use SSS, SAS or RHS conditions.
- Hence we can only look at the AAS condition.
- We can see that both triangles have the same angles, as the missing angle in $\triangle XYZ$ must be 50° because the angle sum of a triangle is 180°.
- Now, the 4 cm side is opposite the 50° angle in $\triangle ABC$ and opposite the 60° angle in $\triangle XYZ$.
- Hence the sides are not corresponding.
- Therefore the triangles are not congruent.

4 In $\triangle$s ABC and EDC:

1	$\angle ABC = \angle ECD$	(vert. opp. $\angle$s)
2	$\angle CAB = \angle CED$	(alt. $\angle$s $AB//DE$)
	$AB = DE$	(given)
3	$\therefore \triangle ABC \equiv \triangle EDC$	(AAS)

> ▨ When writing congruent triangle proofs, write the vertices in matching order as shown in the examples.

Exercise 11:05

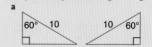
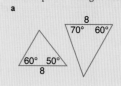
1 The following pairs of triangles are congruent. State the congruence condition used to establish the congruence. All side lengths are in the same units.

a

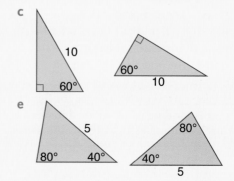

b

c

d

e

2 State whether the triangles in the following pairs are congruent. For those that are, state the congruence condition used.

a

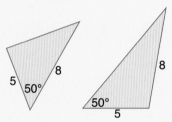

b

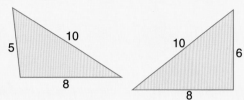

c

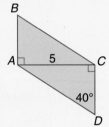

d

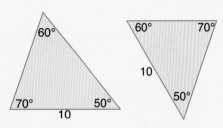

3 In each of the following, prove that the two triangles are congruent.

a

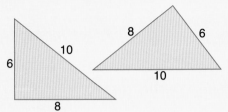

b

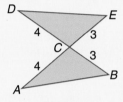

c

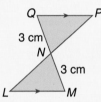

d

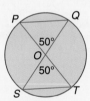

O is the centre of the circle.

e

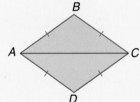

f

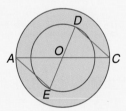

O is the centre of both circles.

4 a Prove that
$\triangle ABC \equiv \triangle DEC$.

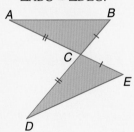

b Prove that
$\triangle ABD \equiv \triangle BAC$.

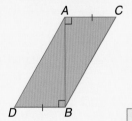

You will have to find 3 facts about each pair of triangles. Put reasons in parentheses.

Setting Out Proofs
In Δs ABC and DEF:
1 $AB = DE$ (Given)
2 ..... = ...   (............)
3 ..... = ...   (............)
∴ $\triangle ABC \equiv \triangle DEF$ (............)

c Prove that
$\triangle ABD \equiv \triangle ACD$.

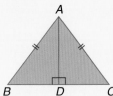

d Prove that
$\triangle ABC \equiv \triangle ADC$.

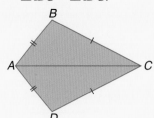

e Prove that
$\triangle ABD \equiv \triangle ACD$.

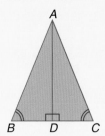

f

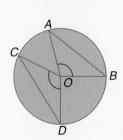

O is the centre of the circle. Prove that
$\triangle AOB \equiv \triangle COD$.

g

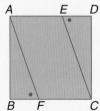

$ABCD$ is a square.
$\angle AFB = \angle CED$.
Prove that $\triangle ABF \equiv \triangle CDE$.

5 **a**

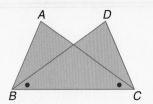

$\angle DBC = \angle ACB$, and
$BD = CA$. Prove that
$\triangle ABC \equiv \triangle DCB$.

b

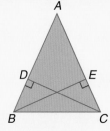

$\angle ABC = \angle ACB$.
Prove that
$\triangle DBC \equiv \triangle ECB$.

They're not tricky.
Just follow
these hints!

■ *Hints*
1 Write down the three
   sides of each triangle.
2 Match up the ones
   that are equal.
3 Repeat the above for
   the angles.

11:06 | Using Congruent Triangles to Find Unknown Sides and Angles

If two triangles can be shown to be congruent, then, of course, all matching sides and angles are equal.

Using congruent triangles to find the values of unknown angles and sides or to prove relationships is very important in geometry.

worked examples

1   Show that $\triangle ABC \equiv \triangle DFE$ and hence find the length of DE.

2   $AC = CD$, $\angle ACB = \angle BCD$. Prove that $\triangle ACB \equiv \triangle DCB$, and hence that $BD = 15$ cm.

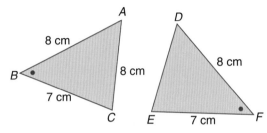

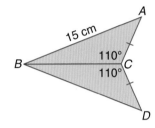

Solutions

1   $\triangle ABC \equiv \triangle DFE$ (SAS)
    $\therefore DE = AC$
    (matching sides of cong't $\triangle$s)
    $\therefore DE = 8$ cm

2   In $\triangle$s ABC and DBC:
    1   $AC = DC$ (given)
    2   $\angle ACB = \angle DCB$ (given)
    3   BC is common to both $\triangle$s.
    $\therefore \triangle ABC \equiv \triangle DBC$ (SAS)
    $\therefore AB = DB$ (corresp. sides of cong't $\triangle$s)
    $\therefore BD = 15$ cm

Exercise 11:06

Note that in questions involving circles, O is the centre of the circle.

I   In each of the following, state why $\triangle ABC \equiv \triangle DEF$ and hence find the value of DE.

a

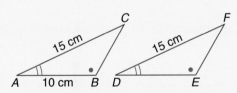

b

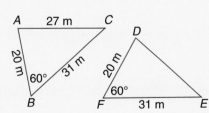

2 Find the value of the pronumeral in each of the following, giving reasons for your answers.

a

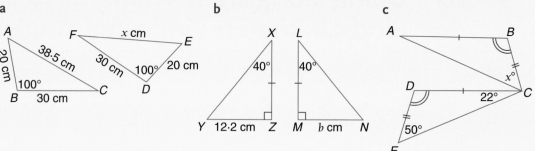

b

c

3 By proving two triangles are congruent, find the value of the pronumeral in each of the following.

a

b

c

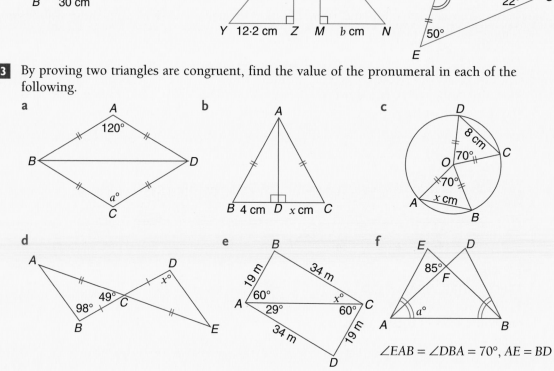

d

e

f

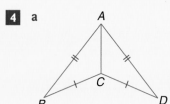

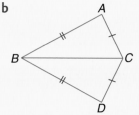

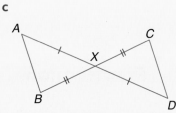

∠EAB = ∠DBA = 70°, AE = BD

4 **a**

A

b

A

c

A

C

B
C
D

Prove that ∠BAC = ∠DAC.

B
C
D

Prove that ∠ABC = ∠CBD.

B
X
D

Prove that ∠BAX = ∠CDX, and hence that AB//CD.

d

e

f

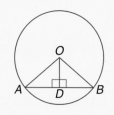

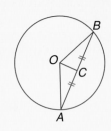

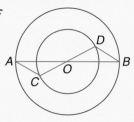

Prove that AD = DB.

Prove that ∠OCA = ∠OCB = 90°.

Prove that AC = DB and AC//DB.

11:07 | Deductive Geometry and Triangles

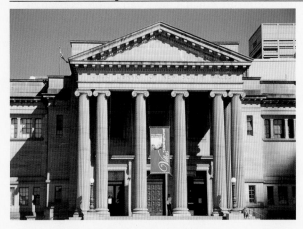

- Isosceles triangles are often found in architecture.

If you were asked to define an equilateral triangle, you could say:

'it is a triangle with all its sides equal'

or

'it is a triangle with all its angles equal'

or

'it is a triangle with all its sides equal and all its angles equal'.

Geometrical figures have many properties and it is not practicable to mention them all when defining the figure.

Hmm...don't say more than you have to!

A definition is the minimum amount of information needed to identify a particular figure.

In deductive geometry, the definitions serve as starting points. The properties of the figures can then be proved using basic geometrical facts.

The proved result is known as a theorem and this can then be used to produce other theorems.

Definitions
- **A scalene triangle is a triangle with no two sides equal in length.**
- **An isosceles triangle is a triangle with at least two sides equal in length.**
- **An equilateral triangle is a triangle with all sides equal in length.**

Observation
A triangle with 3 equal sides has at least 2 sides equal.
Conclusion
A triangle that is equilateral must also be isosceles.

The definitions imply that an equilateral triangle must also be an isosceles triangle. Hence, any property of an isosceles triangle must also be a property of an equilateral triangle.

1. Use congruent triangles to prove that the angles opposite equal sides in an isosceles triangle are equal.

Solution

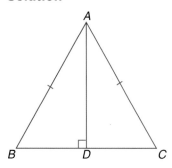

Data:	$\triangle ABC$ is isosceles with $AB = AC$.
Aim:	To prove that $\angle ABC = \angle ACB$.
Construction:	Draw AD perpendicular to BC, meeting BC in D.
Proof:	In $\triangle$s ABD and ACD:

    1 $AB = AC$ (data)

    2 AD is common.

    3 $\angle ABD = \angle ADC$ ($AD \perp BC$)

    $\therefore \triangle ABD \equiv \triangle ACD$ (RHS)

    $\therefore \angle ABD = \angle ACD$ (corresponding $\angle$s of congruent $\triangle$s)

    $\therefore \angle ABC = \angle ACB$

2. Prove that the sum of the interior angles of a triangle is 180°.

Solution

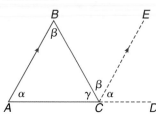

Data:	$\triangle ABC$ is any triangle with angles α, β and γ.
Aim:	To prove that $\alpha + \beta + \gamma = 180°$ (ie the angle sum is 180°).
Construction:	Extend AC to D. Draw CE parallel to AB.
Proof:	$\angle BCE = \beta$ (alternate to $\angle ABC$, $AB//CE$)

    $\angle ECD = \alpha$ (corresponding to $\angle BAC$, $AB//CE$)

    $\angle BCA = \gamma$ (given)

    $\therefore \gamma + \beta + \alpha = 180°$ ($\angle ACD$ is a straight angle)

    $\therefore$ the angle sum of a triangle is 180°.   Q.E.D.

3. Use isosceles triangles to prove that any triangle drawn in a semicircle is right-angled.

Solution

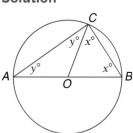

Data:	$\triangle ABC$ is any triangle drawn on the diameter AB. O is the centre of the circle.
Aim:	To prove that $\angle ACB = 90°$.
Construction:	Join CO.

Proof:

Now $AO = BO = CO$ (radii of a circle)

$\therefore$ Δs OBC and OAC are isosceles.

Let $\angle OBC = x°$ and $\angle OAC = y°$

$\therefore$ $\angle OCB = x°$ (base $\angle$s of isos. ΔOBC)

    $\angle OCA = y°$ (base $\angle$s of isos. ΔOAC)

$\therefore$ $x + x + y + y = 180$ (angle sum of ΔABC)

$\therefore$ $2x + 2y = 180$

$\therefore$ $x + y = 90$

But $\angle ACB = \angle OCB + \angle OCA$

           $= x° + y°$

           $= 90°$

$\therefore$ ΔABC is right-angled.

Exercise 11:07

1 It is a well-known result that 'the exterior angle of a triangle is equal to the sum of the interior opposite angles'.

Complete the proof started below.

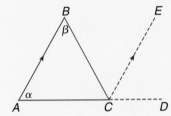

Aim: To prove that the exterior angle $\angle BCD$ is equal to the sum of the interior opposite angles (ie $\angle BCD = \alpha + \beta$).

Construction: Draw CE parallel to AB.

Proof: $\angle BCE = \beta$ (..........)

        $\angle ECD = \alpha$ (..........)

$\therefore$ $\angle BCD = $ ....

2 Use the result above to prove that the sum of the exterior angles of a triangle is 360°.

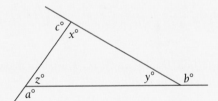

3 Use isosceles triangles and the exterior angle theorem to prove that the reflex angle $AOB = 2 \times \angle ACB$.

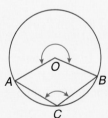

O is the centre of the circle.

4 Use the fact that an equilateral triangle is also an isosceles triangle to prove that each angle of an equilateral triangle is equal to 60°.

5 a Use congruent triangles to prove that if two angles of a triangle are equal then the sides opposite those angles are equal.

b Use the result in **a** to prove that a triangle that is equiangular must be equilateral.

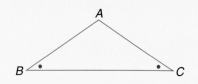

6 Use congruent triangles to prove the following properties of isosceles triangles.

a A line drawn at right angles to the base of an isosceles triangle through the third vertex bisects the base.

b A line drawn from the midpoint of the base of an isosceles triangle to the third vertex is perpendicular to the base.

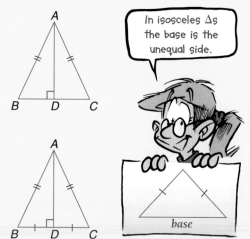

In isosceles △s the base is the unequal side.

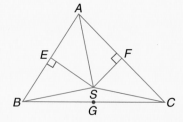

base

7 Regular polygons can be inscribed in circles, as shown on the right.

a Find the size of x.

b For which regular polygon would the side length equal the radius of the circle? Why is there only one regular polygon for which this can occur?

8 A well-known property of triangles is that *the perpendicular bisectors of the sides are concurrent.*

The 'Data', 'Aim' and 'Construction' for the congruence proof of the above result are given below. Answering the questions will give an outline of the proof.

Data: $\triangle ABC$ is any triangle. E, F, G are the midpoints of AB, AC and BC respectively. Perpendiculars drawn from E and F meet at S.

Aim: To show that $SG \perp BC$ (ie that the perpendicular drawn from G passes through S).

Construction: Join SA, SB, SC.

a Why is $\triangle AES \equiv \triangle BES$?   **b** Why does $AS = BS$?

c Why is $\triangle AFS \equiv \triangle CFS$?   **d** Why does $AS = CS$?

e Why does $BS = CS$?   **f** What type of triangle is $\triangle ASC$?

g What result proved in question **6** can be used to justify that $SG \perp BC$?

11:08 | Deductive Geometry and Quadrilaterals

As we have seen with triangles, the definitions of the quadrilaterals are minimum definitions.

> **Definitions**
> - **A trapezium is a quadrilateral with at least one pair of opposite sides parallel.**
> - **A parallelogram is a quadrilateral with both pairs of opposite sides parallel.**
> - **A rhombus is a parallelogram with two adjacent sides equal in length.**
> - **A rectangle is a parallelogram with one angle a right angle.**
> - **A square is a rectangle with two adjacent sides equal**
>   **OR**
>   **A square is a rhombus with one angle a right angle.**

Many people find the definitions above a little unusual at first.

- They start from the simplest shape and by adding more and more constraints end up at the most complex shape.
- The definitions are hierarchical. Each new shape is defined in terms of a simpler shape which has already been defined.

  eg *a rhombus is a parallelogram . . .*

  This saves repetition and states that a rhombus is in fact a special type of parallelogram.
  It has all the properties of a parallelogram and some extra properties as well.

- They are minimum definitions. Not every property of the shape is given. By using the definition and other geometrical techniques the other properties can be deduced.

  eg *a rectangle is a parallelogram with a right angle.*
  There is no need to say that it has four right angles as this can be derived using the fact that it is a parallelogram and our knowledge of co-interior angles and parallel lines.

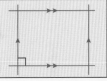

If one angle is a right angle, they all must be.

worked examples

1   Prove that the sum of the interior angles of a quadrilateral is 360°.

Solution

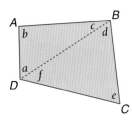

Data: *ABCD* is a quadrilateral.
Aim: To prove that the angle sum of a quadrilateral is 360°.
Construction: Draw in the diagonal *DB*.
Proof: Let a, b, c, d, e, f be the sizes of angles on the figure.

$$\text{Now} \qquad a + b + c = 180° \text{ (angle sum of } \triangle ABD)$$
$$\text{and} \qquad d + e + f = 180° \text{ (angle sum of } \triangle BCD)$$
$$\angle A + \angle B + \angle C + \angle D = b + (c + d) + e + (a + f)$$
$$= (a + b + c) + (d + e + f)$$
$$= 180° + 180°$$
$$= 360° \text{ Q.E.D.}$$

continued ➜➜➜

2 Prove that a quadrilateral is a parallelogram if its opposite angles are equal.

Solution

Data: *ABCD* is a quadrilateral with $\angle A = \angle C$ and $\angle B = \angle D$.

Aim: To prove that *AB//DC* and *AD//BC*.

Proof: Let $\angle A = \angle C = b°$ and $\angle B = \angle D = a°$.

$2(a + b) = 360$ ($\angle$ sum of quad.)

$\therefore a + b = 180$

$\therefore \angle ADC + \angle DAB = 180°$

$\therefore AB//DC$ (co-int. $\angle$s are supp.)

Also, $\angle ADC + \angle DCB = 180°$

$\therefore AD//BC$ (co-int. $\angle$s are supp.)

$\therefore ABCD$ has opposite sides parallel.

$\therefore ABCD$ is a parallelogram.

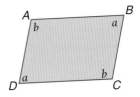

Exercise 11:08

1 Follow the flowchart below and choose the correct names from the list, to be inserted into the boxes ① to ⑥.

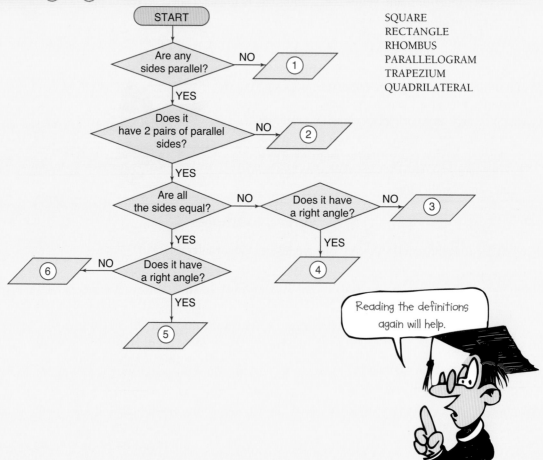

SQUARE
RECTANGLE
RHOMBUS
PARALLELOGRAM
TRAPEZIUM
QUADRILATERAL

Reading the definitions again will help.

2 *ABCD* is a parallelogram.

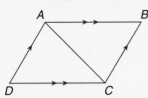

a Why does ∠*BAC* equal ∠*DCA*?
b Why does ∠*BCA* equal ∠*DAC*?
c Does ∠*BAD* equal ∠*BCD*?
d Prove that Δ*ABC* ≡ Δ*CDA*. Hence prove that:
  i ∠*ABC* = ∠*CDA*
  ii *AB* = *DC* and *BC* = *AD*

You have proved that the opposite sides and opposite angles of a parallelogram are equal.

3 Using the fact that the opposite sides of a parallelogram are equal, prove that Δ*ABE* ≡ Δ*CDE* and hence that *AE* = *EC* and *EB* = *ED*.

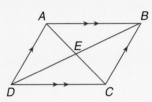

This question proves that the diagonals of a parallelogram bisect each other.

4 A rhombus is a parallelogram with a pair of adjacent sides equal. Using this definition and the properties of the parallelogram already proven, answer the following.

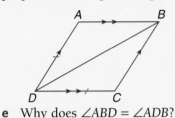

a Why does *AB* = *DC*?
b Why does *BC* = *AD*?
c Show that all the sides of the rhombus are equal.
d Using your answer to **c**, what type of triangle is:
  i Δ*ABD*?
  ii Δ*CBD*?
e Why does ∠*ABD* = ∠*ADB*?   **f** Why does ∠*CBD* = ∠*CDB*?
g Why does ∠*ABD* = ∠*CDB*?   **h** Which angles are equal to ∠*ABD*?
i Prove that the diagonal *AC* bisects the angles *DAB* and *DCB*.

5

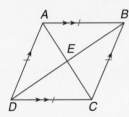

a Why does *AE* = *EC*?
b Prove that Δ*ABE* ≡ Δ*CBE* and hence that ∠*AEB* = ∠*CEB* = 90°.

The last two questions have proved that the diagonals of a rhombus bisect each other at right angles, and that they bisect the angles through which they pass.

6

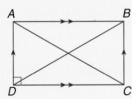

A rectangle is a parallelogram with a right angle.
a Prove that all the angles must be right angles.
b Assuming the answer to **a** and the properties of a parallelogram, prove that Δ*ABD* ≡ Δ*DCA* and hence *AC* = *DB*.

This question proves that all the angles of a rectangle are right angles and that its diagonals are equal in length.

To show that a quadrilateral is a parallelogram, we could of course show that both pairs of opposite sides are parallel (ie use the definition).

There are other tests which can be used to show that a given quadrilateral is a parallelogram. These are very useful and are given below.

Tests for parallelograms
A quadrilateral is a parallelogram if any one of the following is true.
1   Both pairs of opposite sides are equal.
2   Both pairs of opposite angles are equal.
3   One pair of sides is both equal and parallel.
4   The diagonals bisect each other.

7   *ABCD* is a quadrilateral that has opposite sides equal. Prove that it is a parallelogram (ie that its opposite sides are parallel).

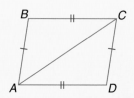

8   The 'Data' and 'Aim' for the congruence proof of Test 4 above are given below. Answering the questions will give an outline of the proof.

If alternate angles are equal, then the lines are parallel.

Data: *ABCD* is any quadrilateral where diagonals *AC* and *BD* bisect each other at *E*.

Aim: To show that *ABCD* is a parallelogram (ie *AD//BC* and *AB//CD*).

a   Why does ∠*AED* equal ∠*CEB*?
b   Why is △*AED* congruent to △*CEB*?
c   Which angle in △*CBE* is equal to ∠*ADE*? Why?
d   How does your answer to **c** prove that *AD//BC*?
e   Why is △*AEB* congruent to △*CED*?
f   Why is ∠*BAE* equal to ∠*DCE*?
g   Why is *AB* parallel to *CD*?

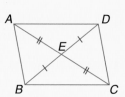

9   Use congruent triangles to prove that if one pair of sides in a quadrilateral is both equal and parallel, then the quadrilateral is a parallelogram.

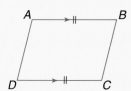

Use the tests for parallelograms and the properties of parallelograms to do questions 10 and 11.

10 In the diagram, *ABCD* and *ABEF* are parallelograms. Prove that *DCEF* is a parallelogram.

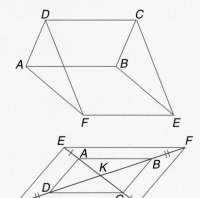

11 *ABCD* is a parallelogram with diagonals produced so that $EA = CG$ and $DH = BF$. Prove that *EFGH* is a parallelogram.

- Builders often use the properties of quadrilaterals in building.

There are also tests for a rhombus and a rectangle. These are given below.

Tests for a rhombus
1 **All sides are equal.   OR**
2 **Diagonals bisect each other at right angles.**

Tests for a rectangle
1 **All angles are equal.   OR**
2 **Diagonals are equal and bisect each other.**

12 Show how Test 1 for a rhombus could be proved using Test 1 for a parallelogram.

13 Prove Test 1 for rectangles.

14 a Does a square have all the properties of a rectangle?
   b Is a square a special rectangle?
   c Is a rectangle a square? Give a reason for your answer.
   d Does a square have all the properties of a rhombus?
   e Is a square a special rhombus?
   f Is a rhombus a square? Give a reason for your answer.

15 Carol and Sharon thought that a good test for a square would be 'equal diagonals that bisect each other at right angles'. Do you agree with their test?

Investigation 11:08 | Theorems and their converses

A theorem usually connects two pieces of information and can be written in the form 'If *A* then *B*'.

A is usually called the 'supposition' or 'assumption' while *B* is called the 'conclusion'.

If *A* and *B* are interchanged then we have the statement 'If *B* then *A*'. This is called the converse of the theorem.

Even if a theorem is true, its converse may not be, as shown by the following example.

Theorem: If (two angles are vertically opposite) then (the angles are equal). This is true.

Converse: If (two angles are equal) then (they are vertically opposite). This is false.

For the following theorems, state their converse and whether the converse is true.

1 If a triangle has all its sides equal then it has all its angles equal.
2 If a quadrilateral is a square then its diagonals are equal.
3 If a quadrilateral is a parallelogram then its opposite angles are equal.

If I have given good service then I get a tip or conversely... If I get a tip then I have given good service.

Fun Spot 11:08 | What do you call a man with a shovel?

Work out the answer to each part and put the letter for that part in the box above the correct answer.

Which congruence test can be used to state why the triangles in each pair are congruent?

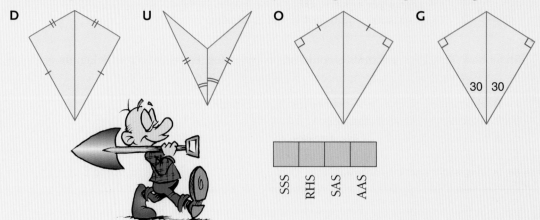

D   U   O   G

30 | 30

SSS	RHS	SAS	AAS

11:09 | Pythagoras' Theorem and its Converse

During your Stage 4 studies, you would have encountered the most famous of all geometric theorems — Pythagoras' theorem. Both the theorem and its converse are true.

The theorem states that:

If a triangle is right-angled then the square on the longest side is equal to the sum of the squares on the two smaller sides.

For the triangle shown, this means that $c^2 = a^2 + b^2$.

- Pythagoras' theorem is still used to check that buildings are square.

Furthermore, the converse states that:

If the square on the longest side is equal to the sum of the squares on the two smaller sides then the triangle is right-angled.

investigation

11:09

Investigation 11:09 | Proving Pythagoras' theorem

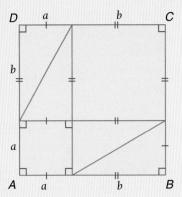

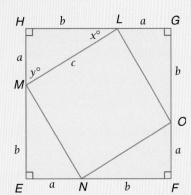

1 How could the two squares above be used to prove Pythagoras' theorem?
2 Investigate other proofs of Pythagoras' theorem.

worked examples

1. Calculate the perpendicular height of an equilateral triangle if its sides are 6 cm long.

2. A rhombus has diagonals 8 cm and 4 cm in length. What is the side length of the rhombus?

Solutions

1

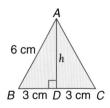

$BD = 3\,\text{cm}$ (D is midpoint of BC)
$6^2 = h^2 + 3^2$ (Pythag. Thm)
$36 = h^2 + 9$
$h^2 = 27$
$\quad h = \sqrt{27}$
$\quad\ = 3\sqrt{3}$

2

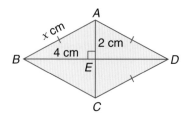

$AE = 2,\ BE = 4$
(Diagonals bisect at rt. $\angle$s)
$x^2 = 2^2 + 4^2$ (Pythag. Thm)
$\quad = 20$
$\quad x = \sqrt{20}$
$\quad\ = 2\sqrt{5}$

3

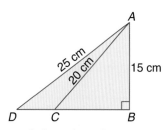

Find the value of DC.

Solutions

In $\triangle ABD$,
$\quad 25^2 = 15^2 + BD^2$
$\quad 625 = 225 + BD^2$
$\quad BD^2 = 400$
$\quad BD = 20$
In $\triangle ABC$,
$\quad 20^2 = 15^2 + BC^2$
$\quad 400 = 225 + BC^2$
$\quad BC^2 = 175$
$\quad BC = \sqrt{175}$
Now $DC = BD - BC$
$\quad\quad\quad = 20 - \sqrt{175}$
$\quad\quad\quad = (20 - 5\sqrt{7})\ \text{cm}$

4

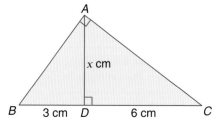

Find the value of x.

In $\triangle ABD$,
$\quad AB^2 = x^2 + 9$
In $\triangle ADC$,
$\quad AC^2 = x^2 + 36$
In $\triangle ABC$,
$\quad BC^2 = AB^2 + AC^2$
$\quad 9^2 = (x^2 + 9) + (x^2 + 36)$
$\quad 81 = 2x^2 + 45$
$\quad 2x^2 = 36$
$\quad x^2 = 18$
$\quad x = \sqrt{18}$
$\quad\ = 3\sqrt{2}$

Exercise 11:09

 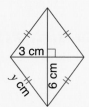
1 Find the value of the pronumerals in each of the following.

a   b

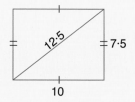 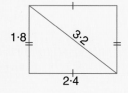

2 Use the converse of Pythagoras' theorem to find which of the following are rectangles.

a   b   c

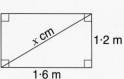 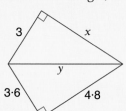

3 Find the values of x and y in each of the following. (All measurements are in cm.)

a   b   c

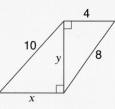 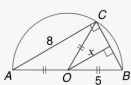 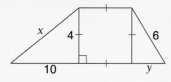

4 a   b   c

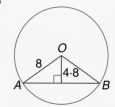 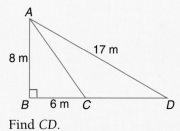

  Find the length of AB.   Find x.   Find CD.

5 a   b   c

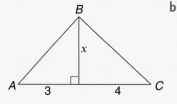 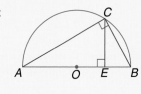

What must x be if $\angle ABC = 90°$?   Find AB. O is the centre of a semicircle of radius 6·5 cm. $EB = 3$ cm. Find AC.

Mathematical Terms 11

adjacent angles
- Share a common arm and vertex.
- Lie on opposite sides of the common arm.

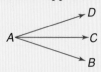

∠DAC and ∠BAC are adjacent angles.

alternate angles
- A pair of angles on opposite sides of the transversal between the other two lines.
- In the diagram, the alternate angles are 1 and 3, 2 and 4.
- Are equal when *AB//CD*.

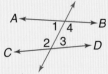

co-interior angles
- A pair of angles on the same side of the transversal and between the other two lines.
- In the diagram the co-interior angles are 1 and 2, 3 and 4.
- Are supplementary when *AB//CD*.

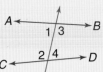

complementary angles
- Angles that add up to give 90°.

congruent triangles
- Triangles that are identical in shape and size.

converse (of a theorem)
- If a theorem is stated in the form 'If A then B', the converse is the statement 'If B then A'.

corresponding angles
- Angles that are in corresponding positions at each intersection.
- In the diagram, the corresponding angles are: 1 and 5, 2 and 6, 3 and 7, 4 and 8.
- Are equal when *AB//CD*.

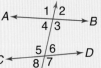

deductive
- A system in which results called theorems are produced from a set of basic facts that are accepted to be true.

definition
- A statement that describes the essential properties of something.

exterior angle
- An angle formed when the side of a convex polygon is produced.

matching angles (or sides)
- Sides (or angles) that are in the same (or corresponding) positions in congruent figures.

polygon
- A plane figure with straight sides.
- *Regular* polygons have all sides and angles equal.
- *Convex* polygon has all its angles either acute or obtuse.
- Some polygons have special names. (See Investigation 11:02A.)

proof
- A series of steps that establishes the truth of a result.

quadrilateral
- A polygon with 4 sides.
- There are six special quadrilaterals. (See 11:08 or ID Card 4.)

supplementary angles
- angles that add up to give 180°.

theorem
- The statement of a result that has been proved by reasoning.
- Usually stated in an 'If A then B' form.

triangle
- A polygon with 3 sides.
- *Equilateral, isosceles* and *scalene triangles* have 3 sides, 2 sides and no sides equal in length respectively.
- *Acute-angled triangle* has three acute angles.
- *Right-angled triangle* has one right angle.
- *Obtuse-angled triangle* has one obtuse angle.

vertically opposite angles
- Two pairs of equal angles formed when two straight lines cross.

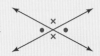

Mathematical terms 11

Diagnostic Test 11: | Deductive Geometry

- Each part of this test has similar items that test a certain type of question.
- Errors made will indicate areas of weakness.
- Each weakness should be treated by going back to the section listed.

Section

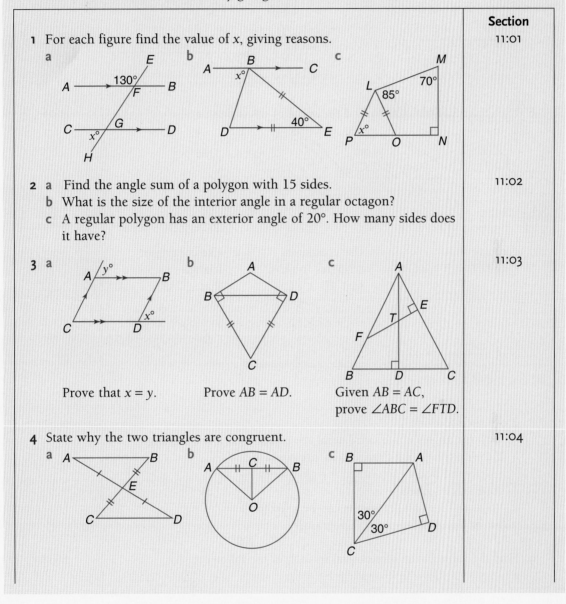

1 For each figure find the value of x, giving reasons.

11:01

a

b

c

2 a Find the angle sum of a polygon with 15 sides.

11:02

b What is the size of the interior angle in a regular octagon?

c A regular polygon has an exterior angle of 20°. How many sides does it have?

3 a

11:03

b

c

Prove that x = y.   Prove AB = AD.   Given AB = AC, prove ∠ABC = ∠FTD.

4 State why the two triangles are congruent.

11:04

a

b

c

5 a Prove that
∠ABD = ∠ACD.

b Prove that
∠AOB = ∠COD.

c Prove that
AX = AY.

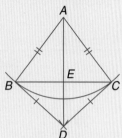

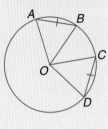

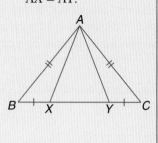

6 Use congruent triangles to find the value of the pronumerals.

a

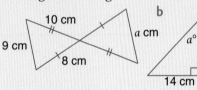

b

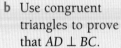
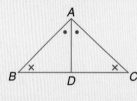

c

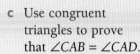
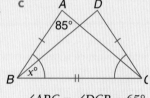

∠ABC = ∠DCB = 65°

7 a Prove that
∠ACD = 3 × ∠CAD.

b Use congruent
triangles to prove
that AD ⊥ BC.

c Use congruent
triangles to prove
that ∠CAB = ∠CAD.

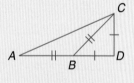

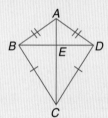

8 Prove the following.

a If all the angles of a quadrilateral are equal, then it is a rectangle.

b If the diagonals of a quadrilateral are equal in
length and bisect each other at right angles,
then it is a square.

c What test for parallelograms can be used to
prove that ABCD is a parallelogram?

9 Find the value of the pronumeral in each of the following.

a

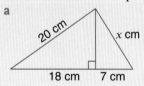

b

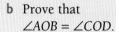
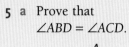

c

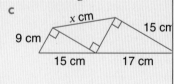

ABCD is a square.

1 In each of the following, find the value of x. Give reasons for your answer.

a

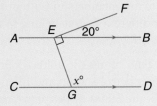

b

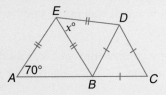

c

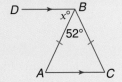

d

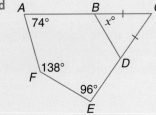

2 a A special hexagon is made with four of its angles equal and the remaining two angles are both half the size of the others. This is shown in the diagram. Find the size of the angles.

b Sharon makes a regular pentagon from three isosceles triangles as shown. Find the sizes of the angles in the triangles.

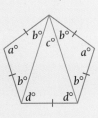

3

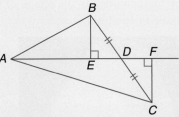

$\triangle ABC$ is any triangle. D is the midpoint of BC, and BE and CF are perpendiculars drawn to AD, produced if necessary. Prove that $BE = CF$.

4

From a point D on the base AC produced of the isosceles triangle ABC, a straight line is drawn perpendicular to the base cutting AB produced at E and BC produced at F. Prove that $\triangle BEF$ is isosceles.

5

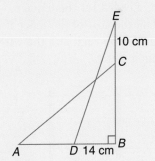

$AC = DE = 50\,\text{cm}$, $EC = 10\,\text{cm}$, $DB = 14\,\text{cm}$. Find AD.

6

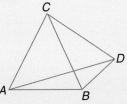

$\angle CAB = \angle CBA$ and $\angle CBD = \angle CDB$. Prove that $\angle CAD = \angle CDA$.

Chapter 11 | Working Mathematically

1 Describe mathematically the shape of the lamp-shade in the photograph.

2 The ISCF group has 20 members. The school choir has 16 members. Only Sue and Graham are members of both groups. How many different people belong to these two groups altogether?

3 The petrol tank of my car holds 45 litres. I drove into a petrol station and filled the tank. It cost me $9.90. If the petrol cost 82·5 cents per litre, how many litres did I buy? How much was in the tank before it was filled?

4 In the card game of cribbage, two points are scored when any combination of cards totals 15. An Ace counts as 1 and the Jack, Queen and King each counts as 10. For example, for the hand below, the score is 6.

$$2 + 3 + K = 15$$
$$5 + K = 15$$
$$3 + 5 + 7 = 15$$

What would the score be for these hands?
a J, K, Q, 5, 5   b 4, 5, 6, 5, 6

5 A block of land (as shown in the diagram) is to be enclosed with a fence of the type shown.
  a Calculate the amount of wire needed to complete the fence.
  b If posts are to be placed at 3 m intervals (as a maximum), calculate the number of posts needed for the fence.
  c Calculate the cost of the fence if the posts are $8.50 each and the wire is 95 cents a metre.

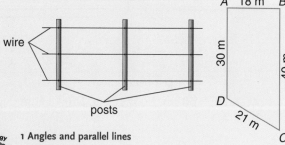

wire

posts

6 The graph shows the height of an object fired into the air.
  a How high is the object above ground level after 1 second?
  b At what times is the object 10 m above ground level?
  c What is the greatest height reached by the object?
  d How long does it take for the object to fall from its maximum height to ground level?
  e For how long is the object above a height of 17·5 m?

A 18 m B

30 m

40 m

D

21 m

C

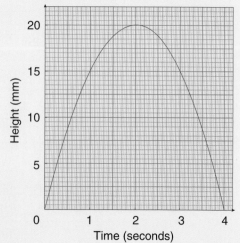

Height of object above ground level

1 Angles and parallel lines

2 Triangles

3 Quadrilaterals

4 Angle sum of polygons

5 Pythagoras' theorem

Measurement

Chapter Contents

Learning Outcomes

Students will be able to:

- Use formulae and Pythagoras' theorem to calculate the perimeter and area of figures composed of rectangles, triangles and parts of circles.
- Calculate the volume and surface area of right prisms including cylinders.
- Apply formulae to find the volume and surface areas of pyramids, cones and spheres.
- Calculate the capacity of a solid using fluid measure.

Areas of Interaction

Approaches to Learning (Knowledge Acquisition, Problem Solving, Communication, Logical Thinking, Reflection), Human Ingenuity, Environments

 The perimeter of a plane figure is the length of its boundary.

To calculate the perimeter:
- find the lengths of all the sides
- add the lengths together.

The geometrical properties of some figures allow the perimeter to be calculated using a simple formula.

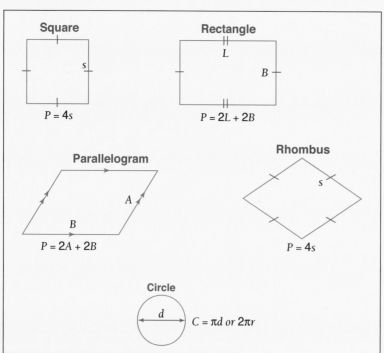

Square

$P = 4s$

Rectangle

L

B

$P = 2L + 2B$

Parallelogram

A

B

$P = 2A + 2B$

Rhombus

s

$P = 4s$

Circle

d

$C = \pi d \text{ or } 2\pi r$

Remember! The perimeter of a circle is called the 'circumference'.

- To find the arc length of a sector, l, first find what fraction the sector is of the circle by dividing the sector angle θ by 360°. Then find this fraction of the circumference.

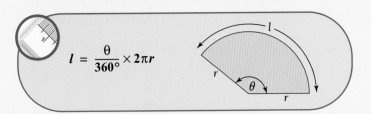

$$l = \frac{\theta}{360°} \times 2\pi r$$

- Composite figures are formed by putting simple figures together or by removing parts of a figure. The calculation of the perimeter of composite figures is shown in the examples below.

Challenge 12:01 | Staggered starts

12:01

When athletes run around a track with circular ends, they have a 'staggered start', since the perimeter of the outer lanes is greater.

If the width of a lane is 1 metre, how much start should a runner in lane 1 give to the runner in lane 2, if the runner in lane 1 is to complete exactly one lap of the field?

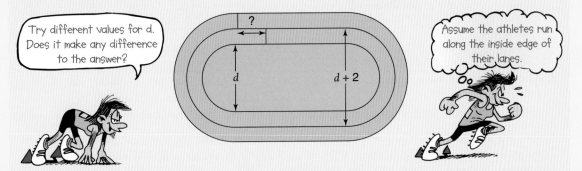

Try different values for d. Does it make any difference to the answer?

Assume the athletes run along the inside edge of their lanes.

Can you find out how much start the inside runner appears to give the outside runner on an official Olympic track for a 400 m event?

Investigation 12:01A | Skirting board and perimeter

Please use the Assessment Grid on the following page to help you understand what is required for this Investigation.

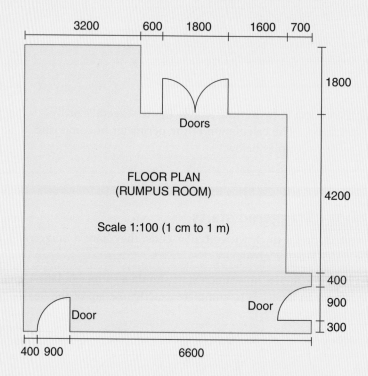

FLOOR PLAN
(RUMPUS ROOM)

Scale 1:100 (1 cm to 1 m)

- The diagram is a scale drawing of a rumpus room in a house. All measurements are in millimetres. Rob Young, a local builder, has been asked to fit skirting board to the room. (Skirting board is used to cover the gap between the wall and the floor of a building.)

- The skirting board is to be placed around the perimeter of the room except for the doorways. It can be ordered in lengths from 300 mm to 6·6 m at increments of 300 mm (ie 300 mm, 600 mm, 900 mm, 1·2 m and so on, up to 6·6 m).

Exercises

1 Rob has been asked to do the job without any joins (except at corners). Is this possible? Give reasons for your answer.

2 What is the total length of skirting board required?

3 Rob has nine 3·3 m lengths of skirting left from earlier jobs. Show how he could use these to do the job. What is the smallest number of joins he could have?

4 If Rob has no skirting board, what would he need to order to complete the job with the smallest number of joins and the smallest amount of waste?

Assessment Grid for Investigation 12:01A | Skirting board and perimeter

The following is a sample assessment grid for this investigation. You should carefully read the criteria *before* beginning the investigation so that you know what is required.

			Assessment Criteria (C, D) for this investigation		Achieved ✓
Criterion C Communication in Mathematics		a	None of the following descriptors has been achieved.	0	
		b	There is basic use of mathematical language and representation. Working out and explanations are insufficient.	1	
				2	
		c	There is satisfactory use of mathematical language and representation. Working and explanations are clear though not always complete.	3	
				4	
		d	There is good use of mathematical language and representation. Answers are correct and explanations are complete and concise.	5	
				6	
Criterion D Reflection in Mathematics		a	None of the following descriptors has been achieved.	0	
		b	An attempt has been made to explain whether the results make sense. An attempt has been made to make connection to the real-life applications.	1	
				2	
		c	There is a correct but brief explanation of whether results make sense and how they were found. A description of the relevance of perimeter in the context of the problem is given.	3	
				4	
		d	There is a critical explanation of the results obtained and their relation to real life. The answers to questions 3 and 4 are fully explained with consideration of the accuracy of the results.	5	
				6	

Measurement of area

- The area of a plane figure is the amount of space it occupies.

- Area is measured by calculating how many squares it would take to cover the figure. Small squares are used to measure small areas and large squares are used to measure large areas. It should not be surprising then that the units for measuring area are called square units.

- $1\,cm^2$ is the area within a square with 1 cm sides.
  $1\,m^2$ is the area within a square with 1 m sides.
  1 ha is the area within a square with 100 m sides.
  $1\,km^2$ is the area within a square with 1 km sides.

- Area is calculated using a formula.

My square is $1\,m^2$.

1 m

1 m

one square metre ($1\,m^2$)

Area formulae

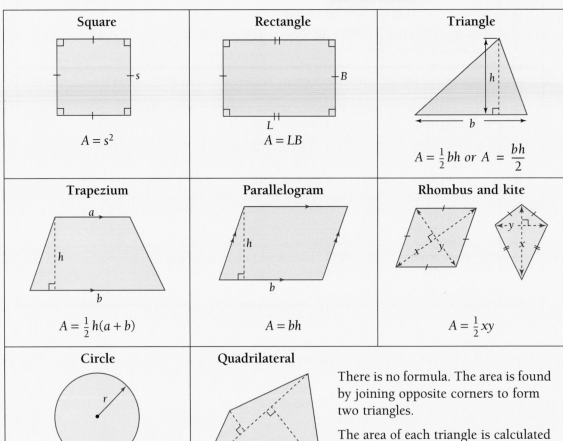

Square	Rectangle	Triangle
s $A = s^2$	B L $A = LB$	h b $A = \frac{1}{2}bh$ or $A = \frac{bh}{2}$
Trapezium	**Parallelogram**	**Rhombus and kite**
a h b $A = \frac{1}{2}h(a+b)$	h b $A = bh$	x y	$-y-$ x $A = \frac{1}{2}xy$
Circle	**Quadrilateral**	

Circle	Quadrilateral	
r $A = \pi r^2$		There is no formula. The area is found by joining opposite corners to form two triangles. The area of each triangle is calculated and the two areas added to give the area of the quadrilateral.

- To find the area of a sector, first find what fraction the sector is of the circle by dividing the sector angle θ by 360°. Then find this fraction of the area of the circle.

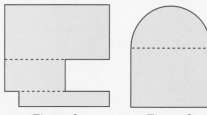

$$\text{Area} = \frac{\theta}{360} \times \pi r^2$$

- The area of composite figures can be calculated by either of the two methods.

Method I (by addition of parts)

We imagine that smaller figures have been joined to form the figure, as in Figures 1 and 2.

1 Copy the figure.
2 Divide the figure up into simpler parts. Each part is a shape whose area can be calculated directly, eg square or rectangle.
3 Calculate the area of the parts separately.
4 Add the area of the parts to give the area of the figure.

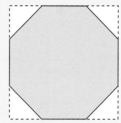

Figure 1   Figure 2

Method II (by subtraction)

We imagine the figure is formed by cutting away simple shapes from a larger complete figure, as shown.

1 Copy the figure and mark in the original larger figure from which it has been cut.
2 Calculate the area of the larger original figure.
3 Calculate the area of the parts that have been removed.
4 Area of figure = (area of original figure) − (area of parts that have been removed).

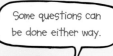

Some questions can be done either way.

Think carefully before deciding which method to use.

1 ADDITION   or   2 SUBTRACTION

1 $\frac{1}{2} \times 10.6 \times 4.8$

2 $\frac{3.4 \times 1.2}{2}$

3 $\frac{1}{2} \times 4.6 \times (10.7 + 3.5)$

4 Simplify $L \times B$

Evaluate:

5 LB if $L = 4$ and $B = 5$
6 $\frac{1}{2} bh$ if $b = 5$ and $h = 8$
7 $\frac{bh}{2}$ if $b = 5$ and $h = 8$
8 ab^2 if $a = 3$ and $b = 4$

Complete the following:

9 $1\,\text{m} = \ldots \text{cm}$
10 $1\,\text{cm} = \ldots \text{mm}$

12:01

worked examples

Find the (a) perimeter and (b) area of the following plane shapes (use the π button on your calculator where necessary). Answer correct to three significant figures.

1

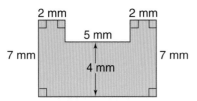

2

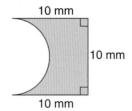

3

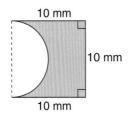

4

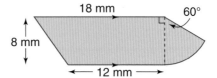

Solutions

1

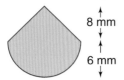

Perimeter — find the distance around the border. Work out the missing lengths (in blue) and add all the sides:
$P = 7 + 7 + 9 + 9 + 3 + 3$
$\quad = 38$ mm

Area — Make one whole rectangle and subtract the small rectangle:
$A = 7 \times 9 - 5 \times 3$
$\quad = 48$ mm^2

2

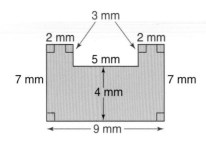

Perimeter — find the distance around the border. Work out the circumference of the semi-circle and add the straight edges:
$P = \dfrac{\pi \times 10}{2} + 10 + 10 + 10$
$\quad = 45 \cdot 7$ mm

Area — Make one whole rectangle and subtract the semi-circle:
$A = 10 \times 10 - \dfrac{\pi \times 5^2}{2}$
$\quad = 60 \cdot 7$ mm^2

> ▨ Remember that the radius is half the diameter.

3

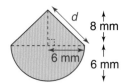

Perimeter — find the distance around the border. Work out the circumference of the semi-circle and add the straight edges (d). To find d use Pythagoras' theorem:

$$d = \sqrt{6^2 + 8^2}$$

$$= 10 \text{ mm}$$

> Remember that the radius is half the diameter.

$$P = \frac{\pi \times 12}{2} + 10 + 10$$

$$= 38 \cdot 8 \text{ mm}$$

Area — Find the area of the semi-circle and add the area of the triangle:

$$A = \frac{\pi \times 6^2}{2} + \frac{12 \times 8}{2}$$

$$= 105 \text{ mm}^2$$

4

Perimeter — find the distance around the border. Work out the length of the arc (l) and add the straight edges. To find d use Pythagoras' theorem:

$$l = \frac{60}{360} \times \pi \times 16$$

> Remember that the radius is half the diameter.

$$d = \sqrt{6^2 + 8^2}$$

$$= 10 \text{ mm}$$

$$P = \frac{60}{360} \times \pi \times 16 + 18 + 10 + 12$$

$$= 48 \cdot 4 \text{ mm}$$

Area — Find the area of the sector, rectangle and triangle and add them together:

$$A = \frac{60}{360} \times \pi \times 8^2 + 12 \times 8 + \frac{6 \times 8}{2}$$

$$= 154 \text{ mm}^2$$

Investigation 12:01B | Conversions

Please use the Assessment Grid on the following page to help you understand what is required for this Investigation.

Complete the table using the shapes given – the first one has been started for you.

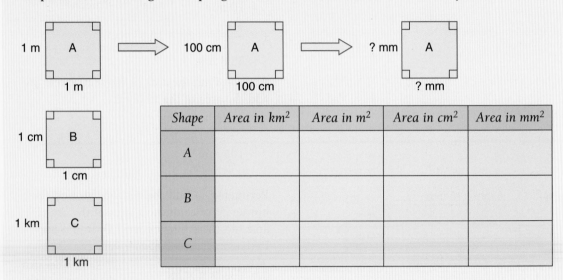

Shape	Area in km²	Area in m²	Area in cm²	Area in mm²
A				
B				
C				

- What is the pattern in the answers?
- Try the same thing with some more shapes and see if the pattern continues (eg: rectangles, triangles and circles).
- Write a rule that would help you convert between units² given the basic conversions below:

  1 km = 1000 m, 1 m = 100 cm, 1 cm = 10 mm

- What is the connection between the unit of area called a hectare (ha) and a square?

You will need the rules you found in Investigation 12:01B to answer some of the questions in Exercise 12:01.

Can you find common uses for each of these different measurements, including hectares?

Assessment Grid for Investigation 12:01B | Conversions

The following is a sample assessment grid for this investigation. You should carefully read the criteria *before* beginning the investigation so that you know what is required.

			Assessment Criteria (B, C, D) for this investigation		Achieved ✓
Criterion B Investigating Patterns	a		None of the following descriptors has been achieved.	0	
	b		Some help was needed to complete the table and identify the simple patterns.	1	
				2	
	c		Measurement techniques have been selected and applied to complete the table with some suggestion of patterns and conversion rules.	3	
				4	
	d		The student has used the patterns evident in the table to calculate similar areas of other shapes and find appropriate conversion rules.	5	
				6	
	e		The patterns evident between the different measurements have been explained, shown to be consistent for different shapes, summarised as mathematical rules and justified using all working.	7	
				8	
Criterion C Communication in Mathematics	a		None of the following descriptors has been achieved.	0	
	b		There is a basic use of mathematical language and representation. Lines of reasoning are insufficient.	1	
				2	
	c		There is satisfactory use of mathematical language and representation. Tables and explanations are clear but not always complete.	3	
				4	
	d		There is a good use of mathematical language and representation. Tables are complete. Explanations and rules are logical and concise.	5	
				6	
Criterion D Reflection in Mathematics	a		None of the following descriptors has been achieved.	0	
	b		An attempt has been made to explain whether the results make sense, with connection to possible real-life applications.	1	
				2	
	c		There is a correct but brief explanation of whether results make sense and how they were found. A description of the possible uses of the different measurements is given.	3	
				4	
	d		There is a complete explanation of the rules obtained and their related equations. All results are fully explained with appropriate accuracy considered and specific examples of real-life applications are given.	5	
				6	

Exercise 12:01

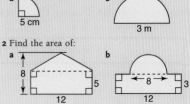

Foundation Worksheet 12:01
Area
1 Find the area of:
a 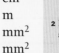 5 cm   b   3 m
2 Find the area of:
a 8 ... 12 ... 5   b 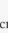 8 ... 12 ... 3

1 Complete the following conversions

  a 25 mm =   cm   **b** 40 m =   cm

  c 6 cm =   mm   **d** 6 cm =   m

  e 250 m =   km   **f** 25 cm^2 =   mm^2

  g 5 m^2 =   cm^2 **h** 5 m^2 =   mm^2

  i 200 mm^2 =   cm^2 **j** 250 mm^2 =   m^2

2 Find the perimeter of the following shapes
(correct to two decimal places where necessary).
Note: you might need to use Pythagoras' theorem in some questions to work out missing sides.

a

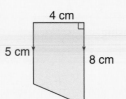

5 m   7 m   10 m

b

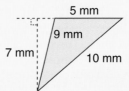

5 mm   9 mm   7 mm   10 mm

c

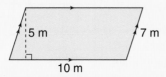

4 cm   5 cm   8 cm

d

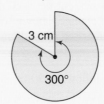

3 cm   300°

e

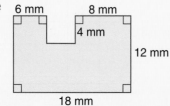

6 mm   8 mm   4 mm   12 mm   18 mm

f

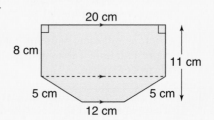

20 cm   8 cm   11 cm   5 cm   5 cm   12 cm

g Segment of circle centre O

6 m   O 6 m

h

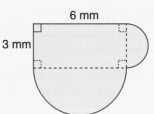

6 mm   3 mm

i

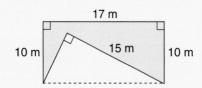

17 m   10 m   15 m   10 m

j 2 semi-circles make this shape

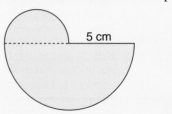

5 cm

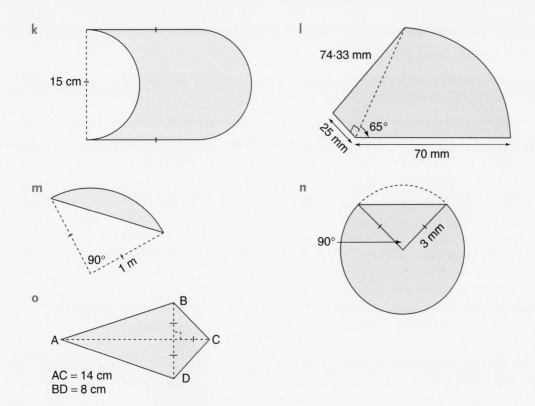

k 15 cm

l 74·33 mm, 65°, 25 mm, 70 mm

m 90°, 1 m

n 90°, 3 mm

o B, A, C, D, AC = 14 cm, BD = 8 cm

3 Find the area of the shapes in question 2 – find the shaded area where indicated.

Investigation 12:01C | Covering floors

When covering a floor with tiles or carpet it is not just a matter of calculating the area of the floor. Other practical considerations alter the problem.

The following examples illustrate some of the factors that need to be considered.

Laying tiles

When laying tiles, an exact number may not cover an area, or a whole number may not lie along each edge. Look at this diagram.

If the tiles are 10 cm by 10 cm, we can see that 15 tiles are needed, presuming that the pieces of tile cut off are not good enough to be used elsewhere. (This is true even though the area is 28 cm × 45 cm, ie 1260 cm². Divide this by 100 cm² (the tile area) and this would suggest that only 12·6 or 13 tiles might be needed.)

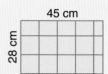

1 How many tiles 10 cm × 10 cm would be needed to cover an area 3·25 m by 2·17 m?

2 How many tiles 300 mm by 300 mm would be needed to cover an area 2·5 m by 3·8 m?

I think I've found an easy way to do these!

Laying carpet

Carpet comes in rolls, approximately 3·6 m wide. So when we buy a 'metre of carpet' we are getting a rectangular piece 3·6 m wide by 1 m long. The diagram represents a room 2·9 m wide and 4·25 m long.

When laying carpet, a carpetlayer can 'run' it *along* the room or *across* the room. The aim is to avoid joins in the carpet and reduce waste. The way the carpet is run will determine how many 'metres of carpet' must be bought.

1 How many metres of carpet must be bought if it is run lengthways? How much waste would there be? Would there be any joins?

2 Repeat question 1 for the carpet if it is run across the room.

12:02 | Review of Surface Area of Prisms

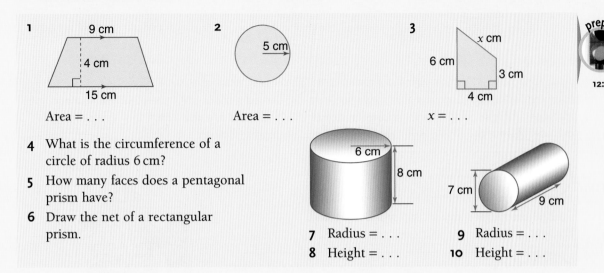

1   9 cm / 4 cm / 15 cm

Area = . . .

2   5 cm

Area = . . .

3   x cm / 6 cm / 3 cm / 4 cm

x = . . .

4 What is the circumference of a circle of radius 6 cm?

5 How many faces does a pentagonal prism have?

6 Draw the net of a rectangular prism.

6 cm / 8 cm

7 cm / 9 cm

7 Radius = . . .

8 Height = . . .

9 Radius = . . .

10 Height = . . .

If we look at solid shapes such as those pictured below, we can see that the faces of these solids are plane shapes.

  The surface area of a solid is the sum of the areas of its faces.

To calculate the surface area, you must know the number of faces and the shapes of the faces of the solid.

In all of the solids encountered so far, the faces have been plane figures, such as squares, rectangles, triangles and trapeziums.

With the cylinder, this is no longer the case. The cylinder's surface area is made up of a curved surface and two circles.

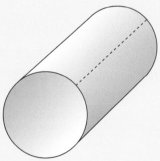

Cylinders are like 'circular prisms'.

To calculate the area of the curved surface, imagine that the cylinder is hollow. If we cut the curved surface along the dotted line and flattened it out, it would form a rectangle.

The area of this rectangle would be the same as the area of the curved surface.

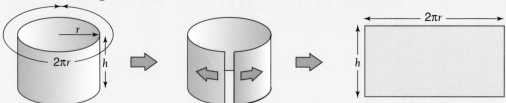

From the series of diagrams above, we see that the curved surface area is equivalent to a rectangle that has a length equal to the circumference of the circle and a width equal to the height of the cylinder. Using the formula for the area of a rectangle, we obtain:

   Curved surface area = $2\pi rh$

To find the surface area of the cylinder we add the area of the two circular ends.

   Surface area = curved surface area + area of circles
= $2\pi rh + 2\pi r^2$

worked examples

Find the surface area of each of the following solids.

1

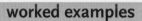

2

Solutions

1

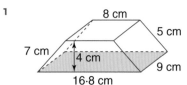

2

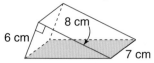

Area of trapezoidal faces
$$= 2 \times \frac{1}{2} h(a+b)$$
$$= 2 \times \frac{1}{2} \times 4 \times (16 \cdot 8 + 8)$$
$$= 99 \cdot 2 \text{ cm}^2$$

Area of rectangular faces
$$= (7 + 8 + 5 + 16 \cdot 8) \times 9$$
$$= 331 \cdot 2 \text{ cm}^2$$

$\therefore$ Surface area $= 331 \cdot 2 + 99 \cdot 2 \text{ cm}^2$
$$= 430 \cdot 4 \text{ cm}^2$$

First calculate x.
Now $x^2 = 6^2 + 8^2$ (Pythagoras' theorem)
$$= 100$$
$$\therefore x = 10$$

Surface area = area of triangular faces +
area of rectangular faces
$$= 2 \times \frac{1}{2} \times 6 \times 8 + (6 + 8 + 10) \times 7$$
$$= 216 \text{ cm}^2$$

1 Find the surface area of a cylinder that has a radius of 8 cm and a height of 9·5 cm.
  Give your answer correct to 2 decimal places.

2 For cylinder A, find:
  a the curved surface area
  b the area of the circular ends
  c the surface area
  Give the answers correct to 3 significant figures.

3 Find the curved surface area of cylinder B,
  correct to 1 decimal place.

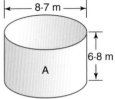

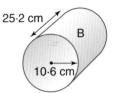

Solutions

1 Surface area = $2\pi r^2 + 2\pi rh$
  $= 2 \times \pi \times 8^2 + 2 \times \pi \times 8 \times 9.5$
  $= 879.65 \text{ cm}^2$ (correct to 2 decimal places)

2 a Curved surface area
  $= 2\pi rh$
  $= 2\pi \times 4.35 \times 6.8$
  $= 59.16\pi$
  $= 186 \text{ m}^2$ (correct to
     3 significant figures)

  b Area of circular ends
  $= 2\pi r^2$
  $= 2\pi \times (4.35)^2$
  $= 37.845\pi$
  $= 119 \text{ m}^2$ (correct to
     3 significant figures)

  c Surface area
  $= 59.16\pi + 37.845\pi$
  $= 305 \text{ m}^2$ (correct to
     3 significant figures)

3 Curved surface area
  $= 2\pi rh$
  $= 2 \times \pi \times 10.6 \times 25.2$
  $= 1678.4 \text{ cm}^2$ (correct to 1 decimal place)

Exercise 12:02

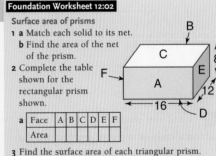

1 Find the surface area of each of the following,
  giving answers correct to one decimal place.

a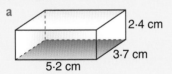
  2·4 cm
  3·7 cm
  5·2 cm

b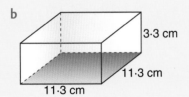
  3·3 cm
  11·3 cm
  11·3 cm

c
  1·6 m
  6·7 m
  1·6 m

2 Calculate the surface area of the following triangular prisms.

a
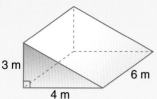
3 m
6 m
4 m

b
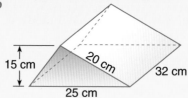
15 cm
20 cm
32 cm
25 cm

c
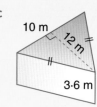
10 m
12 m
3·6 m

d
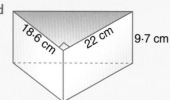
18·6 cm
22 cm
9·7 cm

e
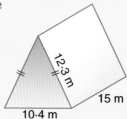
12·3 m
15 m
10·4 m

f
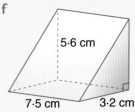
5·6 cm
7·5 cm
3·2 cm

3 For each of the following cylinders find:
  i the curved surface area
  ii the area of the circular ends
  iii the total surface area

Give answers correct to 2 decimal places.

a
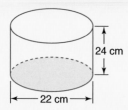
24 cm
22 cm

b
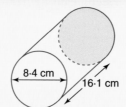
8·4 cm
16·1 cm

c
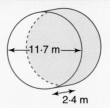
11·7 m
2·4 m

d
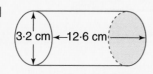
3·2 cm ← 12·6 cm →

e
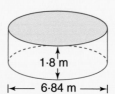
1·8 m
6·84 m

f
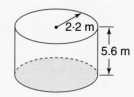
2·2 m
5·6 m

4 Find the surface area of the following cylinders, giving your answers correct to 1 decimal place.
  a radius = 6 cm, height = 9 cm
  b radius = 4·8 m, height = 1·8 m
  c radius = 2·1 m, height = 10·1 m
  d diameter = 10 m, height = 11·4 m
  e diameter = 14·6 cm, height = 21·5 cm
  f diameter = 1·6 m, height = 4·2 m
  g radius = 50 cm, height = 1·5 m
  h diameter = 2·4 m, height = 750 mm

Remember: All measurements must be in the same units.

5 Calculate the volume of the following closed cylinders. Give answers correct to one decimal place.

a

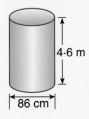

5·8 m

7·6 m

b

1·2 m

10·6 m

c

12·8 cm

25·6 cm

6 Calculate the volume of the following closed cylinders. Give answers correct to three significant figures.

a

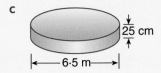

4·6 m

86 cm

b

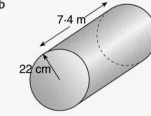

7·4 m

22 cm

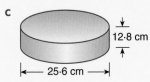

Remember!
Keep all units
the same.
Don't mix them.

c

25 cm

6·5 m

Keep all units the same.

7 Each of the following prisms can be formed from rectangular prisms. Calculate the volume of each prism.

a

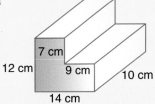

7 cm

12 cm

9 cm

10 cm

14 cm

b

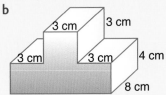

3 cm

3 cm

3 cm

3 cm

4 cm

8 cm

c

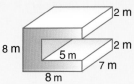

2 m

8 m

5 m

2 m

7 m

8 m

8 Each of the following prisms has been made by joining rectangular and triangular prisms. Find the volume of each prism.

a

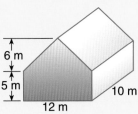

6 m

5 m

12 m

10 m

b

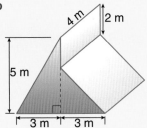

4 m

2 m

5 m

3 m

3 m

c

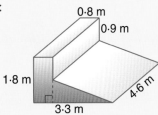

0·8 m

0·9 m

1·8 m

3·3 m

4·6 m

9 The following solids have been formed from a cylinder. Calculate the surface area of each, correct to 3 significant figures.

a

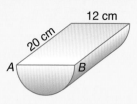

AB is a diameter.

b

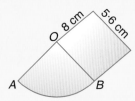

AOB is a quadrant.

c

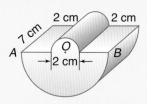

O is the centre of both semicircles.

10 Investigate prisms or other solids that have a uniform cross-sectional area. How is the surface area of the solid related to the cross-sectional area? Can you write a formula to express the relationship?

11 Calculate the surface area of each of these solids.

a

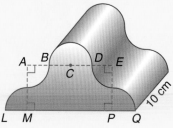

AB = BC = CD = DE = 5 cm
LM = PQ = 5 cm

b

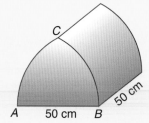

Arc AC is drawn from B.
Arc BC is drawn from A.

12 Calculate the surface area of the following solids. Give the answer correct to 1 decimal place. (Measurements are in metres.)

a

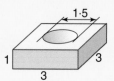

b

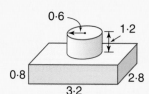

c

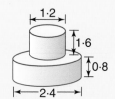

13 Calculate the surface area of the following solids. Give the answer correct to 1 decimal place. (Measurements are in metres.)

a

b

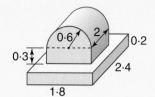

c

12:03 | Volume of Prisms and Cylinders

Previously, you would have calculated the volume of simple prisms and cylinders. You should remember that:
- volume is the amount of space occupied by a three-dimensional figure
- volume is measured using cubic units; that is, cubic centimetres (cm^3) or cubic metres (m^3).

A prism is a solid with a uniform cross-sectional area. This means it can be 'sliced' parallel to one of its faces so that you always get the same shape.

When you cut a loaf of bread, you are cutting parallel to the cross–section, but not when you cut a piece of cake.

The fact that a prism can be cut into identical layers makes the calculation of its volume simple.

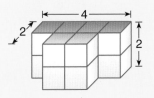
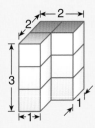

The cross-section is shaded blue.

Use the prisms above to check the following relationships.
1 The number of cubic units in each layer is the same as the cross-sectional area, *A*.
2 The number of layers is the same as the height of the prism, *h*.
3 The volume of the prism obtained by counting the cubic units is the same as the product *Ah*.

The above relationships give rise to the following formula.

 The volume of all prisms is given by the formula $V = Ah$, where V = volume, A = cross-sectional area and h = height of the prism.

If we think of a cylinder as a circular prism, the same formula can be applied as for prisms.

Since the cross-section is a circle, the cross-sectional area A is the area of a circle. Hence, for a cylinder, the formula $V = Ah$ becomes $V = \pi r^2 h$.

 The volume of a cylinder is given by the formula:
$V = \pi r^2 h$,   where r = radius of the cylinder
               h = height of the cylinder

worked examples

Find the volume of the following solids. Give answers correct to one decimal place.

1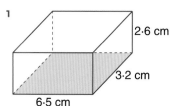

2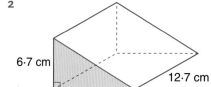

3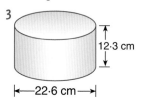

Solutions

1    $V = Ah$
     $A = 6.5 \times 3.2 \text{ cm}^2$
     $h = 2.6 \text{ cm}$
     $\therefore V = 6.5 \times 3.2 \times 2.6$
         $= 54.1 \text{ cm}^3$

2    $V = Ah$
     $A = \dfrac{6.7 \times 9.4}{2}$
        $= 31.49 \text{ cm}^2$
     $h = 12.7 \text{ cm}$
     $\therefore V = 31.49 \times 12.7$
        $= 399.9 \text{ cm}^3$

3    $V = \pi r^2 h$
     $r = 22.6 \div 2$
       $= 11.3 \text{ cm}$
     $h = 12.3 \text{ cm}$
     $\therefore V = \pi \times (11.3)^2 \times 12.3$
        $= 4934.1 \text{ cm}^3$

Investigation 12:03 | Tank sizes

1 Use the fact that a tank with a volume of 1 m³ has a capacity of 1 kL (or 1000 L) to calculate the capacity in litres of the three tanks shown.

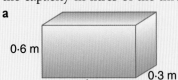

a

0·6 m
1 m
0·3 m

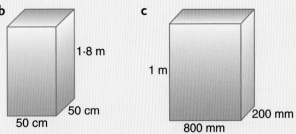

b

1·8 m
50 cm
50 cm

c

1 m
200 mm
800 mm

2 A tank is to hold 1000 L. Give the dimensions of three tanks with this capacity. Assume that all the tanks are rectangular prisms.

Convert all measurements to metres before calculating volumes.

12:04 | Volume of Prisms, Cylinders and Composite Solids

The prism shown has been made from layers of cubes. Each cube has a volume of 1 cm³.

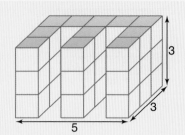

1. How many cubes are there in each layer?
2. How many layers are there?
3. Calculate the volume of the prism by counting cubes.
4. How could the answers to 1 and 2, be used to calculate the volume?
5. The cross-sectional area, A, has been shaded. What is the value of A?
6. What is the height, h, of the prism?
7. What is the value of Ah?
8. Are the answers to questions 1 and 5 the same?
9. Are the answers to questions 2 and 6 the same?
10. Are the answers to questions 3 and 7 the same?

> This loaf of bread is like a prism. It can be thought of as a series of identical layers of equal volume.

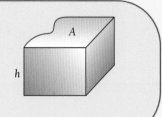

The Prep Quiz should have reminded you that for solids with a uniform cross-section, such as prisms and cylinders, the following relationships are true.

- The number of cubic units in each layer is the same as the cross-sectional area, A.
- The number of layers is the same as the height of the prism, h.
- The volume of the prism obtained by counting the cubic units is the same as the product Ah.
  The exercise above suggests two ways in which the volume could be calculated.

  Volume = (number of cubic units in each layer) × (number of layers)
  or
  Volume = (area of cross-section, A) × (height of prism, h)

It is the second of these methods that is the most widely applicable.

The volume of all prisms, cylinders and prism-like solids is given by the formula
$$V = Ah$$
where:
  V = volume
  A = cross-sectional area
  h = height of the prism.

For a cylinder, the cross-section is a circle and $A = \pi r^2$.
The formula is then rewritten as
$$V = \pi r^2 h$$

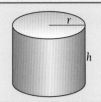

worked examples

Find the volumes of the following solids.

1
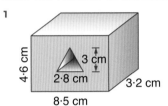

2
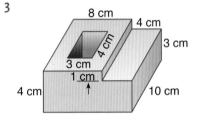

3

Solutions

1 $V = Ah$

$A = \dfrac{\text{area of}}{\text{rectangle}} - \dfrac{\text{area of}}{\text{triangle}}$

$= (8 \cdot 5 \times 4 \cdot 6) - \left(\dfrac{2 \cdot 8 \times 3}{2} \right)$

$= 39 \cdot 1 - 4 \cdot 2$

$= 34 \cdot 9 \text{ cm}^2$

$h = 3 \cdot 2 \text{ cm}$

$\therefore V = 34 \cdot 9 \times 3 \cdot 2$

$= 111 \cdot 68 \text{ cm}^3$

In questions that involve π, it's best to leave your answer in terms of π.

2 The solid consists of three cylinders, two of which are identical.

Volume of top cylinder, V_1
$= \pi r^2 h$
$= \pi \times 6^2 \times 2$
$= 72\pi$

Volume of middle cylinder, V_2
$= \pi r^2 h$
$= \pi \times 4^2 \times 6$
$= 96\pi$

$\therefore$ Volume of solid
$= 2V_1 + V_2$
$= 2 \times 72\pi + 96\pi$
$= 240\pi$
$= 754 \text{ cm}^3$
(to nearest cm^3)

3 The solid consists of a rect. prism which has had two rect. prisms removed. The removal of one of these prisms has formed a hole.

Volume of rect. hole, V_1
$= A \times h$
$= (3 \times 4) \times 4$
$= 48 \text{ cm}^3$

Volume of other removed rect. prism, V_2
$= A \times h$
$= (4 \times 10) \times 1$
$= 40 \text{ cm}^3$

Volume of original rect. prism, V
$= A \times h$
$= (12 \times 10) \times 4$
$= 480 \text{ cm}^3$

$\therefore$ Volume of solid
$= V - V_1 - V_2$
$= 480 - 48 - 40$
$= 392 \text{ cm}^3$

Exercise 12:04

1 Calculate the volume of the following prisms.
(All measurements are in centimetres.)

a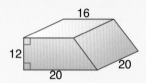

b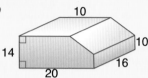

 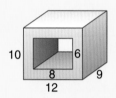 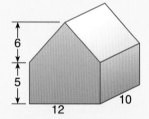

c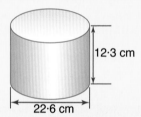

d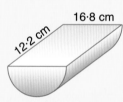

e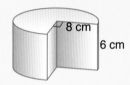

2 Calculate the volume of the following cylinders or parts of cylinders. (Give answers correct to the nearest cubic centimetre.)

a

12·3 cm

22·6 cm

b

16·8 cm

12·2 cm

c

8 cm

6 cm

3 Calculate the volume of the following prisms. (All measurements are in cm.)

a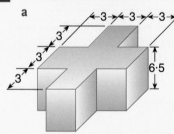

b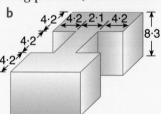

c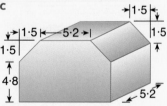

4 Calculate the volume of the following prisms. All measurements are in cm. Give answers correct to 1 decimal place.

a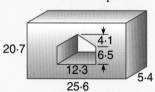

20·7   4·1   6·5   12·3   25·6   5·4

b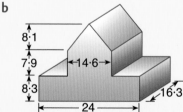

8·1   7·9   8·3   ←14·6→   24   16·3

c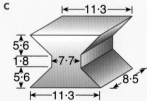

←11·3→   5·6   1·8   5·6   ←7·7→   ←11·3→   8·5

5 Calculate the volume of the following solids, correct to 3 significant figures.

a
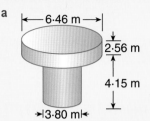

b
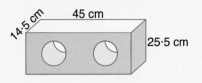

Both holes have a diameter of 8·6 cm.

c
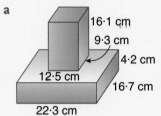

Make sure all measurements are in the same units.

6 Find the volume of the following composite solids.

a
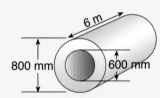

b
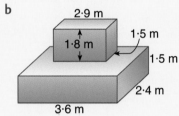

c
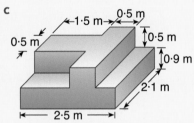

7 Calculate the volume of the following composite solids. All measurements are in centimetres. Give all answers correct to 1 decimal place.

a
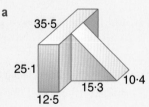

b
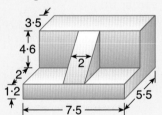

c
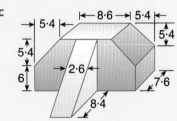

8 Calculate the volume of the following solids. All measurements are in centimetres and answers are to be given correct to 1 decimal place.

a
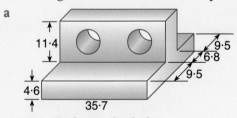

Note: Both circular holes have a diameter of 8·5 cm.

b
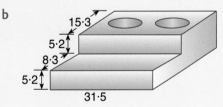

Note: Both circular holes have a diameter of 10·2 cm.

Investigation 12:04 | Perimeter, area and volume

Please use the Assessment Grid on the following page to help you understand what is required for this Investigation.

1 A piece of wire 60 cm long is bent to form a rectangle.
  a Give the dimensions of four rectangles that could be formed.
  b Use the dimensions for the rectangles in **a** to complete this table.

	Length (L)	Breadth (B)	Area (A)	L − B
Rectangle 1				
Rectangle 2				
Rectangle 3				
Rectangle 4				

  c What happens to A as L − B becomes smaller?
  d Predict the largest area that could be obtained.
  e What is the area of the largest rectangle that can be formed from a piece of wire 100 m long?

2 A rectangular piece of cardboard 60 cm long and 20 cm wide is bent to form a hollow rectangular prism with a height of 20 cm.

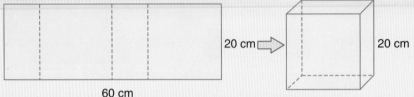

  a From the results of question **1**, predict the maximum volume of a rectangular prism formed from this piece of cardboard.
  b If the piece of cardboard were bent to form a cylinder, what would be the volume of the cylinder? Will the volume of the cylinder be greater than the maximum volume obtained in part **a**?

3 Suppose a farmer has 40 m of fencing to make a chicken pen. What dimensions would you recommend to give the chickens the maximum living area? Give support for your answer. What if the farmer built against an existing fence?

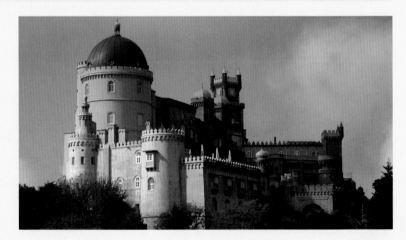

• Composite solids of many types are present in these buildings. How would you describe them?

Assessment Grid for Investigation 12:04 | Perimeter, area and volume

The following is a sample assessment grid for this investigation. You should carefully read the criteria *before* beginning the investigation so that you know what is required.

		Assessment Criteria (B, C, D) for this investigation		Achieved ✓
Criterion B Investigating Patterns	a	None of the following descriptors has been achieved.	0	
	b	Some help was needed to complete the table and identify the simple patterns.	1	
			2	
	c	Measurement techniques have been selected and applied to complete the table with some suggestion of emerging patterns.	3	
			4	
	d	The student has used the measurements in the table to describe the patterns and make predictions about area.	5	
			6	
	e	The patterns evident in the table have been explained and justified, and used to answer questions 2 and 3 appropriately.	7	
			8	
Criterion C Communication in Mathematics	a	None of the following descriptors has been achieved.	0	
	b	There is basic use of mathematical language and representation. Lines of reasoning are insufficient.	1	
			2	
	c	There is satisfactory use of mathematical language and representation. Tables and explanations are clear but not always complete.	3	
			4	
	d	There is a good use of mathematical language and representation. Tables are complete and well set out. Explanations and answers are logical and concise.	5	
			6	
Criterion D Reflection in Mathematics	a	None of the following descriptors has been achieved.	0	
	b	An attempt has been made to explain whether the results make sense, with mention of possible real-life applications.	1	
			2	
	c	There is a correct but brief explanation of whether results make sense and how they were found. A good attempt has been made to answer questions 3 and 4 with working shown.	3	
			4	
	d	There is a complete explanation of the results obtained and their application to other real-life situations. All answers are fully explained with appropriate accuracy considered.	5	
			6	

12:05 | Practical Applications of Measurement

A knowledge of perimeter, area and volume is extremely useful in dealing with many everyday activities.

Many tradesmen require a knowledge of area and volume to carry out their work, but it is also useful for everyday people who do their own painting, concreting or tiling. Measurement is clearly the basis of all building activities.

When calculating the capacity of a container the following relationship is used.

Every cubic metre is 1000 L.

$1m^3 = 1kL$
$= 1000 L$

The amount of liquid needed to occupy a volume of 1 cm³ is 1 mL. Hence:
$1 \text{ cm}^3 = 1 \text{ mL}$
This converts to:
$1 \text{ m}^3 = 1 \text{ kL}$

Exercise 12:05

1 Find the volume and capacity of the water tanks pictured below. Give the answers correct to three significant figures.

a
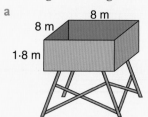
8 m
8 m
1·8 m

b
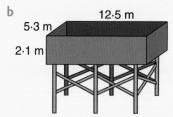
12·5 m
5·3 m
2·1 m

c
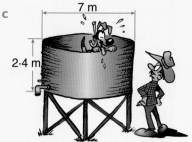
7 m
2·4 m

2 A concrete slab is to be 3000 mm by 4000 mm by 100 mm. How many cubic metres of concrete would be needed for this slab? What would be the cost of the concrete if it costs $130 a cubic metre?

3 Calculate the capacity of the swimming pools pictured below. Give your answer correct to three significant figures.

a
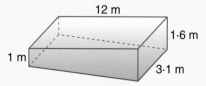
12 m
1·6 m
1 m
3·1 m

b
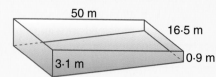
50 m
16·5 m
3·1 m
0·9 m

4 An above-ground pool has semi-circular ends joined by straight sides.
  a Calculate the volume of the pool if it is filled to a depth of 1·2 m. Give the answer correct to one decimal place.
  b Find the capacity of the pool to the nearest kilolitre.

5 A swimming pool is 25 m long, 10 m wide and 1·8 m high. Assuming that the pool is a rectangular prism, find:
  a the surface area of the pool and the cost of tiling it at $30 per m²
  b the capacity of the pool in litres if it is filled to a depth of 1·5 m (1 m³ = 1000 L)
  c the number of special edging tiles needed to go around the perimeter of the pool if the tiles are 25 cm long

6 A roller is cylindrical in shape. It has a diameter of 0·6 m and a width of 1·2 m.
  a Find the area covered by the roller when it makes one revolution. (Give your answer correct to 1 decimal place.)
  b Find the volume of the roller correct to 3 decimal places.
  c Find the mass of the roller to the nearest kilogram, if 1 m³ weighs 1200 kg. (The handle weighs 25 kg.)

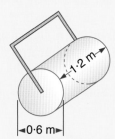

7 **a** Calculate the volume of metal in the pipe shown, correct to 1 decimal place.
  b Calculate the weight of the pipe if 1 cm³ of metal weighs 5·8 g. Answer correct to 1 decimal place.

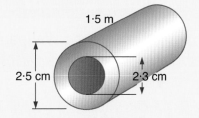

8 The solid pictured is formed by filling a mould with molten metal. Calculate the mass of this object if 1 cm³ of metal weighs 11·4 g. Give the answer correct to 2 significant figures.

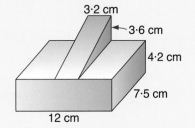

9 A swimming pool has the shape of a trapezoidal prism as shown in the diagram. Find:
  a the cost of tiling the pool at $45 per m²
  b the volume of the pool in cubic metres
  c how far the water level will be from the top of the pool if it is three-quarters full. (Answer to the nearest centimetre.)

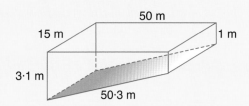

10 Calculate the area of shade cloth needed for the greenhouse.

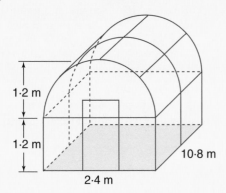

11 When rainwater falls on the roof of a garage it is drained by the gutter into a tank. Only one side of the roof is drained.

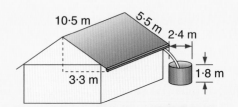

  a If 100 mm of rain falls, find how many litres of water are drained into the tank.

  b By how much would the water level in the tank rise when the water from **a** was added?

  c How many millimetres of rain would need to fall on the roof to fill the tank?

> ▪ A rainfall of 100 mm means the rain would cover the horizontal area on which it fell to a depth of 100 mm.

---

investigation

12:05

Investigation 12:05 | Wallpapering rooms

Please use the Assessment Grid on the page 370 to help you understand what is required for this Investigation.

Figure 1 shows a wall that is 3·6 m long and 2·4 m high. It is to be covered with wallpaper that comes in rolls 52 cm wide and 15 m long.

To calculate the number of rolls needed, follow the steps below.

Step 1 Work out the number of drops needed.

$$\text{Number of drops} = \frac{\text{Length of room}}{\text{Width of wallpaper}}$$

Note: Drops can be full or partial. Partial drops occur when a wall contains a door or window.

Figure 1

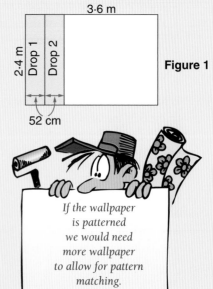

> *If the wallpaper is patterned we would need more wallpaper to allow for pattern matching.*

Step 2 Calculate the length of wallpaper needed.

$$\text{Length of wallpaper} = \begin{pmatrix} \text{Number of} \\ \text{full drops} \end{pmatrix} \times \begin{pmatrix} \text{Length of a} \\ \text{full drop} \end{pmatrix} + \text{length of partial drops}$$

Step 3 Determine the number of rolls by comparing the length of a roll to the length of wallpaper required.

$$\text{Number of rolls} = \frac{\text{Length of wallpaper}}{\text{Length of a roll}}$$

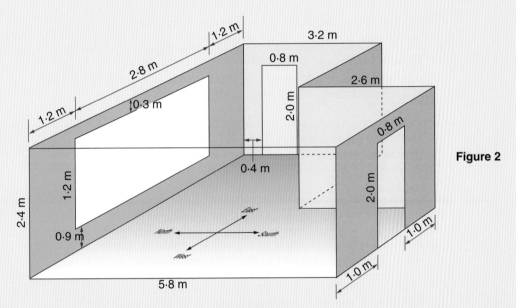

Figure 2

Use the room shown in Figure 2 to answer these questions.

1 How many rolls, correct to 1 decimal place, would be used to wallpaper:
  a the western wall?   **b** the southern wall?   **c** the northern wall?

2 How many rolls, correct to 1 decimal place, would be used to wallpaper the three walls on the eastern side?

3 Using your answers from above, how many rolls are needed to paper the whole room? How many rolls would you need to buy?

4 a Calculate the perimeter of the room.
  b Ignoring windows and doors, use the perimeter to calculate the number of drops of wallpaper needed for the whole room.
  c Use your answer to **b** to estimate the number of rolls needed. Compare this with your answer to question **3**.

The following is a sample assessment grid for this investigation. You should carefully read the criteria *before* beginning the investigation so that you know what is required.

			Assessment Criteria (C, D) for this investigation		Achieved ✓
Criterion C Communication in Mathematics	a		None of the following descriptors has been achieved.	0	
	b		There is basic use of mathematical language and representation. Working out and explanations are insufficient.	1	
				2	
	c		There is satisfactory use of mathematical language and representation. Working and explanations are well set out and easy to follow. The student is able to apply the given steps easily.	3	
				4	
	d		There is good use of mathematical language and representation. Answers are correct and explanations are thorough, complete and concise. All parts are linked together well.	5	
				6	
Criterion D Reflection in Mathematics	a		None of the following descriptors has been achieved.	0	
	b		An attempt has been made to explain whether the results make sense in the context of the information given.	1	
				2	
	c		There is a correct but brief explanation of whether results make sense and how they were found. A description of the relevance of the findings to real life is given.	3	
				4	
	d		There is a critical explanation of the results obtained and their relation to real life. The answers in questions 3 and 4 are fully explained with consideration of the accuracy of the results.	5	
				6	

Mathematical Terms 12

area
- The amount of space inside a two-dimensional shape.
- Units of area:
  square millimetre (mm²)
  square centimetre (cm²)
  square metre (m²)
  hectare (ha)
  square kilometre (km²)
- Formulae are used to calculate the area of the common plane figures.

circumference
- The length of a circle's boundary.
- The circumference is calculated using either the formula:
  $C = \pi D$ or $C = 2\pi r$

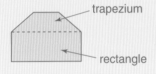

composite figure
- A figure that is formed by joining simple figures.

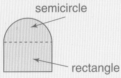

trapezium

rectangle

semicircle

rectangle

composite solid
- A solid that is formed by joining simple solids.

cross-section
- The shape on the face where a solid has been sliced.

cross-section

cylinder
- A prism-like solid with a circular cross-section.
- It has two circular ends and a curved surface.

hectare
- An area of 10 000 m².
- A square with a side of 100 m.

perimeter
- The length of a plane figure's boundary.

prism
- A solid with two identical ends joined by rectangular faces.

sector
- A part of a circle bounded by two radii and an arc.

surface area
- The sum of the areas of the faces (or surfaces) of a three-dimensional figure (or solid).

volume
- The amount of space (cubic units) inside a three-dimensional shape.

Mathematical terms 12

Diagnostic Test 12: | Measurement

- Each part of this test has similar items that test a certain question type.
- Errors made will indicate areas of weakness.
- Each weakness should be treated by going back to the section listed.

	Section
1 Find the circumference of each of the following circles. Give your answer correct to 3 significant figures. a diameter = 7·6 cm b radius = 1·45 m	12:01
2 Find the perimeter of each of the following figures. Lengths are in metres.	12:01
3 Find the perimeter of the following figures.	12:01
4 Find the perimeter of each of the following figures (correct to 2 decimal places).	12:01
5 Find the perimeter of each of the following composite figures. (Where it is necessary, answer correct to 2 decimal places.)	12:01
6 Calculate the area of all shapes in questions **3**, **4** and **5** (correct to 2 decimal places).	12:01

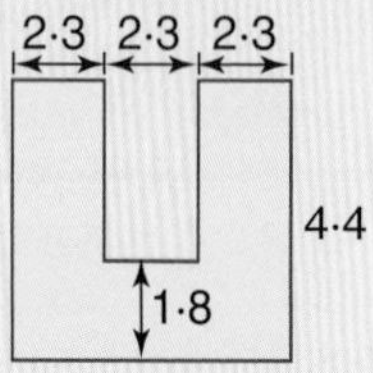

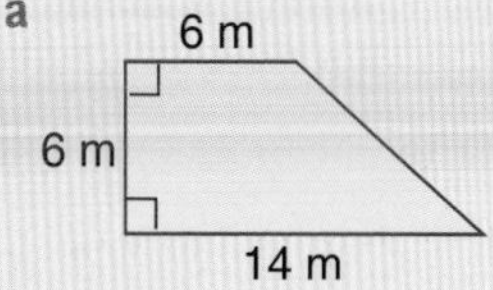

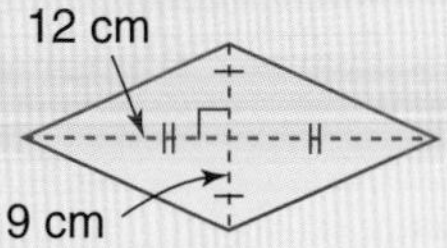

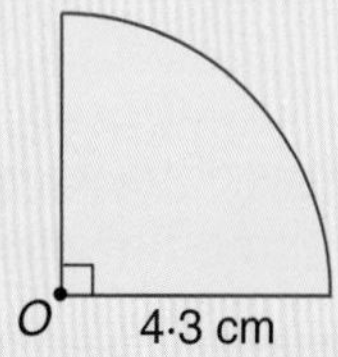

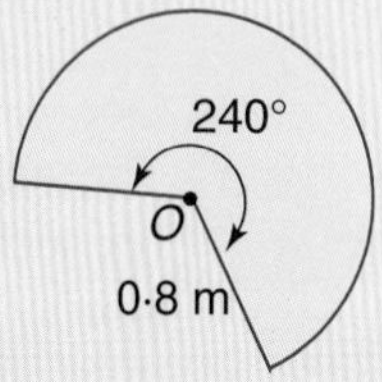

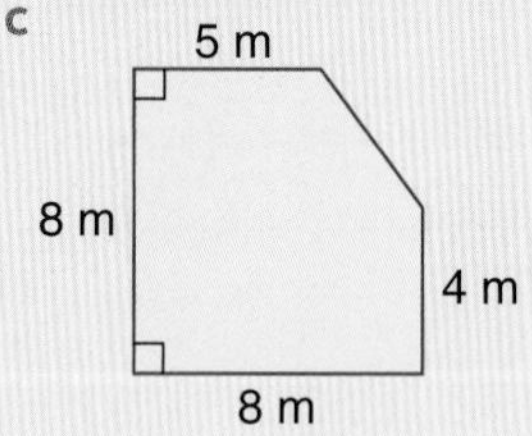

2
a 5·1
4·5
3·2
9·3

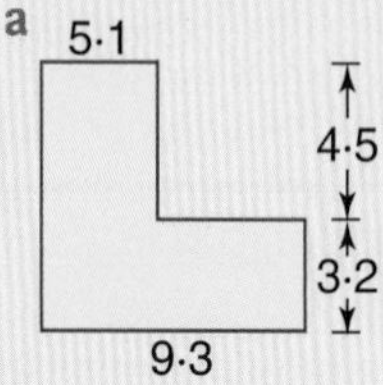

b 2·3 2·3 2·3
4·4
1·8

3
a 6 m
6 m
14 m

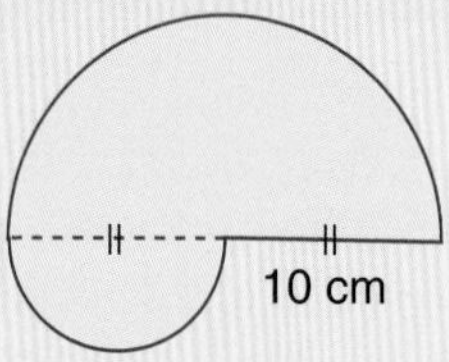

b 12 cm
9 cm

4
a O   4·3 cm

b 240°
O
0·8 m

5
a 2 m
2 m
2 m

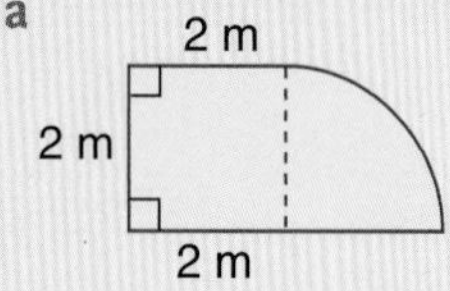

b 10 cm

c 5 m
8 m
4 m
8 m

6
a 10 cm
5 cm
14 cm

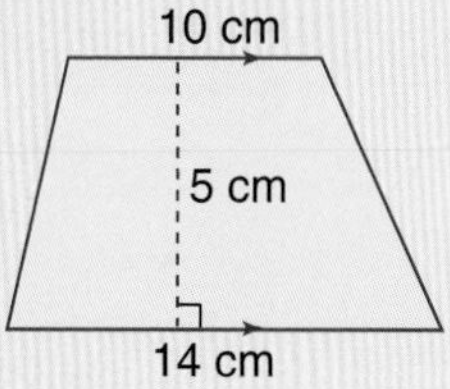

b 6·1 cm
12·6 cm

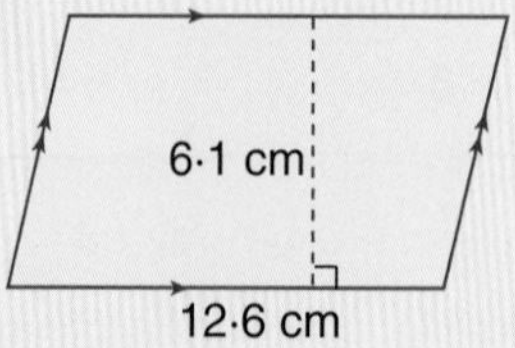

c 4·2 cm
12·3 cm

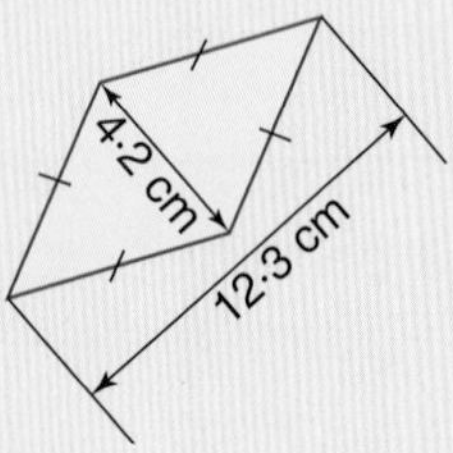

7 Calculate the surface area of the following prisms.

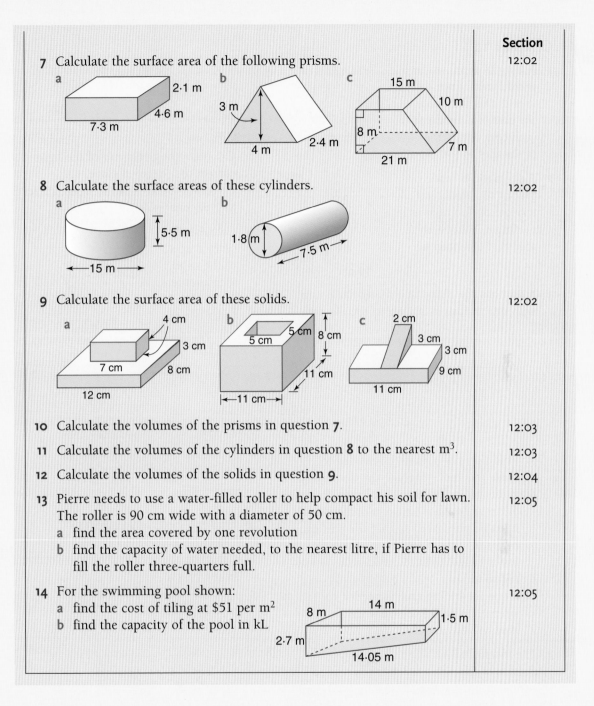

a 2·1 m 4·6 m 7·3 m

b 3 m 4 m 2·4 m

c 15 m 10 m 8 m 21 m 7 m

8 Calculate the surface areas of these cylinders.

a 5·5 m 15 m

b 1·8 m 7·5 m

12:02

9 Calculate the surface area of these solids.

a 4 cm 3 cm 7 cm 8 cm 12 cm

b 5 cm 5 cm 8 cm 11 cm 11 cm

c 2 cm 3 cm 3 cm 9 cm 11 cm

12:02

10 Calculate the volumes of the prisms in question **7**. 12:03

11 Calculate the volumes of the cylinders in question **8** to the nearest m³. 12:03

12 Calculate the volumes of the solids in question **9**. 12:04

13 Pierre needs to use a water-filled roller to help compact his soil for lawn. The roller is 90 cm wide with a diameter of 50 cm.
  a find the area covered by one revolution
  b find the capacity of water needed, to the nearest litre, if Pierre has to fill the roller three-quarters full. 12:05

14 For the swimming pool shown:
  a find the cost of tiling at $51 per m²
  b find the capacity of the pool in kL

8 m 14 m 1·5 m 2·7 m 14·05 m 12:05

Chapter 12 | Revision Assignment

1 A floor is as shown in the diagram. Find the area of this floor and the cost of covering it with cork tiles if the cost of the tiles is $40 per m².

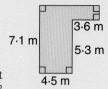

7·1 m, 3·6 m, 5·3 m, 4·5 m

2 A pentagon is made by placing an equilateral triangle on top of a rectangle. What is the area of the pentagon?

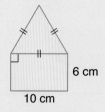

6 cm, 10 cm

3 A tent has the shape of a triangular prism with dimensions as shown in the diagram.

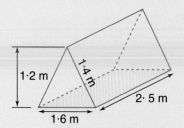

1·2 m, 1·4 m, 2·5 m, 1·6 m

a Find the area of material needed to make this tent. (Include the floor area.)

b If the material comes in rolls which are 3·7 m wide, what length of material must be purchased so that the tent can be made without any joins except those at the edges? (*Hint:* Consider the net of the solid.)

c If special joining tape is needed to strengthen each join, what length of tape will be needed?

4 The inside and outside of this container are painted. Calculate the area that has to be painted.

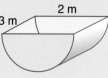

2 m, 3 m

5

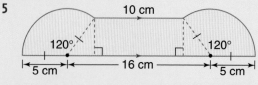

10 cm, 120°, 120°, 5 cm, 16 cm, 5 cm

a Calculate the perimeter of the figure correct to 1 decimal place.

b Calculate the area of the figure correct to 1 decimal place.

6 a Calculate the surface area of the solid. Measurements are in metres.

b Calculate the volume of the solid.

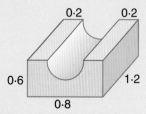

0·2, 0·2, 0·6, 1·2, 0·8

7

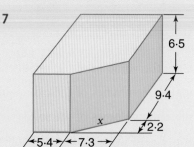

6·5, 9·4, x, 2·2, 5·4, 7·3

a Find the value of x correct to 1 decimal place.

b Calculate the area of the cross-section of the prism.

c Calculate the surface area of the pentagonal prism.

d Calculate the volume of the prism.

8

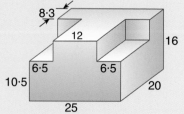

8·3, 12, 16, 6·5, 6·5, 10·5, 20, 25

a Calculate the volume of the solid.

b Calculate the surface area of the solid.

Technology Applications
Drag and Drops

1 Perimeter
2 Area of sectors and composite figures
3 Surface area
4 Volume

1 Use ID Card 6 on page xviii to give the correct mathematical term for:

  a 13   b 14   c 15   d 16   e 18
  f 19   g 20   h 9   i 10   j 11

2 Heather is 7 years younger than Rachel. Ester is six times as old as Heather. Kuan is 7 years older than Ester. If Kuan is 43, how old is Rachel?

12B

3 Four different playing cards are dealt into two piles: left first, then right, then left, and then right. The left pile is then placed on top of the right pile. How many times must this process be repeated before the cards return to their original positions? How many times would the process need to be repeated if there had been eight cards?

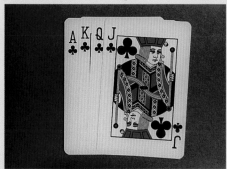

4 Every male bee has only one parent, a female. Every female bee has two parents, a male and a female. In the 8th generation back, how many ancestors has a male bee? (Assume that no ancestor occurs more than once.)

5 If $3! = 3 \times 2 \times 1$ (pronounced 3 factorial), $5! = 5 \times 4 \times 3 \times 2 \times 1$ and $10! = 10 \times 9 \times 8 \times 7 \times 6 \times 5 \times 4 \times 3 \times 2 \times 1$, how many zeros are there on the end of $20!$?

6 George Junkiewicz has prepared the timeline below to show when his employees will take their holidays. He has designed it so that no more than two employees are on holidays at the same time. The dots at the end of each line are explained below.

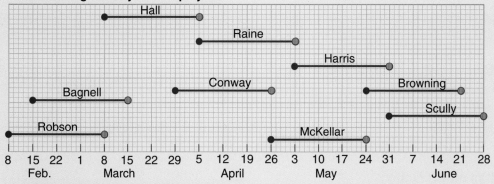

'Fine Flooring' holidays for employees

● Included in holiday   ● Not included in holiday

  a What is the first day of Conway's holiday?   b On what day does Conway return to work?
  c Which two employees are on holidays in the week starting on the 8th of March?
  d Which two employees are also on holidays during McKellar's holiday?
  e George has to take four weeks of holidays. He is prepared to fit in wherever he can. When must he take his holidays?

13

Trigonometry

Chapter Contents

Learning Outcomes

Students will be able to:

- Apply trigonometry to solve problems including those with angles of elevation and depression.
- Apply trigonometry to problems involving compass bearings.
- Apply the sine rule, cosine rule and area of a triangle rule to the solution of problems.

Areas of Interaction

Approaches to Learning (Knowledge Acquisition, Problem Solving, Communication, Logical Thinking, IT Skills, Collaboration, Reflection), Human Ingenuity, Environments

Trigonometry is a branch of geometry that is very important in fields such as navigation, surveying, engineering, astronomy and architecture. Basic trigonometry is used to find unknown sides and angles in right-angled triangles. The word trigonometry is actually derived from two Greek words: 'trigonon', which means triangle, and 'metron', which means measurement.

Measurement of unknown sides in right-angled triangles has been met before when using Pythagoras' theorem. However, this could only be used to find one side when the other two were known.

13:01 | Right-angled Triangles

Before introducing trigonometry, we need to be aware of some further information concerning right-angled triangles.

From Pythagoras' theorem we know that the longest side in a right-angled triangle is called the **hypotenuse**. The other two sides also have names that refer to one of the acute angles in the triangle. The side furthest from the angle is the **opposite** side, whereas the side next to the angle is the **adjacent** side.

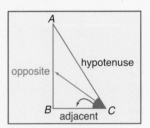

worked examples

1 Name the sides in these two right-angled triangles with reference to the angle marked.

a 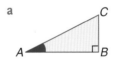 b

2 Find the value of these ratios in ΔPQR.

a $\dfrac{\text{side opposite angle } R}{\text{hypotenuse}}$

b $\dfrac{\text{side opposite angle } Q}{\text{side adjacent angle } Q}$

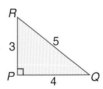

Solutions

1 a BC = opposite side
AB = adjacent side
AC = hypotenuse

b XY = opposite side
XZ = adjacent side
YZ = hypotenuse

2 a Side opposite angle $R = 4$
Hypotenuse $= 5$
$\therefore$ Ratio $= \frac{4}{5}$

b Side opposite angle $Q = 3$
Side adjacent angle $Q = 4$
$\therefore$ Ratio $= \frac{3}{4}$

1 Name the side opposite the marked angle in each triangle.

a

b

c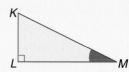

d

e

f

2 Name the adjacent side in each of the triangles in question **1**.

3 Name the hypotenuse in each triangle in question **1**.

4 In triangle *ABC* to the right:
   a which side is opposite angle *B*?
   b which side is adjacent to angle *C*?
   c which angle is opposite side *AB*?
   d which angle is adjacent to side *AC*?

5 Find the value of the ratio $\dfrac{\text{side opposite angle } P}{\text{side adjacent angle } P}$ in these triangles.

a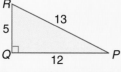

b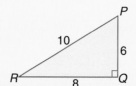

c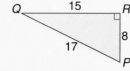

6 Find the value of the ratio $\dfrac{\text{side adjacent angle } P}{\text{hypotenuse}}$ for each triangle in question **5**.

- Trigonometry is used in the building industry to determine the length of sides and the size of angles.

13:02 | Right-angled Triangles: the ratio of sides

For each triangle, state whether *AB* is opposite the angle marked, adjacent to the angle marked, or is the hypotenuse.

1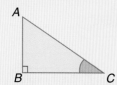

2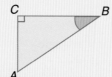

3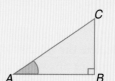

Triangle I was enlarged to produce triangle II.

For triangles I and II, find the value of the following ratios:

4 $\dfrac{\text{side opposite angle } P}{\text{side adjacent angle } P}$

5 $\dfrac{\text{side opposite angle } P}{\text{hypotenuse}}$

6 $\dfrac{\text{side adjacent angle } P}{\text{hypotenuse}}$

7 Is the pair of ratios in **4** equal?

8 Is the pair of ratios in **5** equal?

9 Is the pair of ratios in **6** equal?

10 The triangles are similar.

Does $\dfrac{x}{6} = \dfrac{9}{12}$?

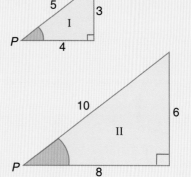

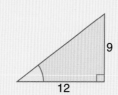

Exercise 13:02

1 Complete the table on the next page using these three triangles.

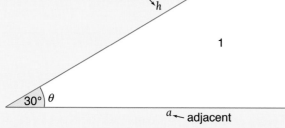

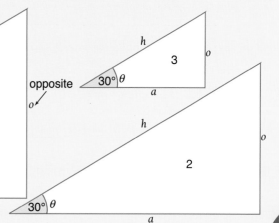

	θ	$\dfrac{o}{h}$	$\dfrac{a}{h}$	$\dfrac{o}{a}$
1				
2				
3				

2 Complete the table below using these three triangles.
(Give your answer correct to one decimal place.)

	θ	$\dfrac{o}{h}$	$\dfrac{a}{h}$	$\dfrac{o}{a}$
1				
2				
3				

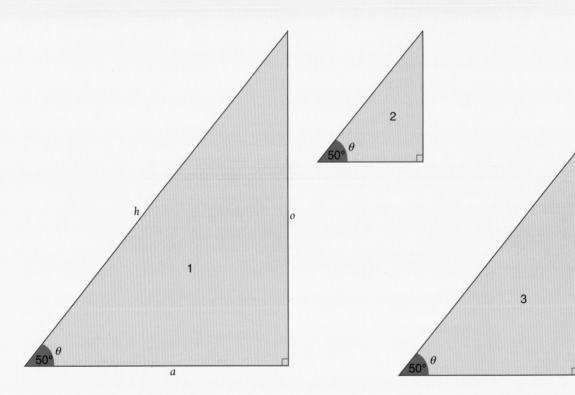

3 Complete the table below, giving answers correct to 1 decimal place.

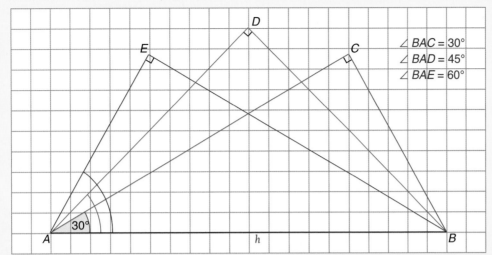

$\angle BAC = 30°$
$\angle BAD = 45°$
$\angle BAE = 60°$

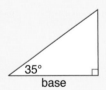	θ	opposite side (o)	adjacent side (a)	hypotenuse (h)	$\dfrac{o}{h}$	$\dfrac{a}{h}$	$\dfrac{o}{a}$
ΔBAC	30°						
ΔBAD	45°						
ΔBAE	60°						

4 **a** In question **1**, are the respective ratios $\dfrac{o}{h}$, $\dfrac{a}{h}$, $\dfrac{o}{a}$ the same for each triangle?

    b In question **2**, are the respective ratios $\dfrac{o}{h}$, $\dfrac{a}{h}$, $\dfrac{o}{a}$ the same for each triangle?

5 **a** Using a protractor and ruler, construct a right-angled triangle with an angle of 35° and a base of 5 cm. By measurement, calculate the value of each of the ratios given, correct to 1 decimal place.

    i $\dfrac{o}{h}$ **ii** $\dfrac{a}{h}$ **iii** $\dfrac{o}{a}$

    b Construct another right-angled triangle with an angle of 35° and a base of 10 cm and calculate again the value of the ratios:

    i $\dfrac{o}{h}$ **ii** $\dfrac{a}{h}$ **iii** $\dfrac{o}{a}$

    c What conclusion can you draw from the results in **a** and **b**?

13:03 | The Trigonometric Ratios

In questions **1** and **2** of Exercise 13:02, each of the three triangles had angles of the same size. When this happens the triangles are said to be *similar*.

Similar right-angled triangles can always be superimposed to produce a diagram like the one below.

Check the results in the table below.

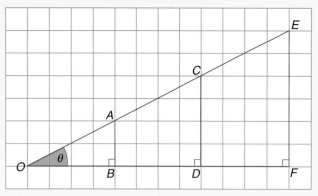

	θ	$\dfrac{o}{h}$	$\dfrac{a}{h}$	$\dfrac{o}{a}$
$\triangle AOB$	26·5°	0·4	0·9	0·5
$\triangle COD$	26·5°	0·4	0·9	0·5
$\triangle EOF$	26·5°	0·4	0·9	0·5

These similar triangles overlap!

1 dec. pl.

■ Answers are given correct to one decimal place.

• Each of the right-angled triangles in this diagram (ie AOB, COD, EOF) is similar to the others, since the corresponding angles in each are the same. The angle at O is obviously the same for each triangle.

• The ratios $\dfrac{o}{h}$, $\dfrac{a}{h}$, $\dfrac{o}{a}$ are equal in all of the triangles.

• These ratios are called the trigonometric ratios (abbreviated to *trig. ratios*) and are given special titles.

The ratio $\dfrac{o}{h}\left(\dfrac{\text{side opposite angle }\theta}{\text{hypotenuse}}\right)$ is called the *sine ratio*. It is abbreviated to sin θ.

The ratio $\dfrac{a}{h}\left(\dfrac{\text{side adjacent to angle }\theta}{\text{hypotenuse}}\right)$ is called the *cosine ratio*. It is abbreviated to cos θ.

The ratio $\dfrac{o}{a}\left(\dfrac{\text{side opposite angle }\theta}{\text{side adjacent to angle }\theta}\right)$ is called the *tangent ratio*. It is abbreviated to tan θ.

• The three ratios have constant values for any particular angle irrespective of how big the right-angled triangle may be.

• For any angle, the values of the ratios can be obtained from a calculator.

• As the lengths of right-angled triangles can often be surds, many trig. ratios are irrational numbers.

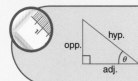

 $\sin \theta = \dfrac{\text{opposite}}{\text{hypotenuse}}$ $\cos \theta = \dfrac{\text{adjacent}}{\text{hypotenuse}}$ $\tan \theta = \dfrac{\text{opposite}}{\text{adjacent}}$

- Because $\dfrac{o}{h} \div \dfrac{a}{h} = \dfrac{o}{h}$, we also have that:

$\sin \theta \div \cos \theta = \tan \theta$ or $\tan \theta = \dfrac{\sin \theta}{\cos \theta}$

worked examples

1   Find $\sin \theta$, $\cos \theta$ and $\tan \theta$ for each triangle, and express each as a decimal correct to three decimal places.

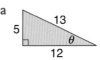

2   Find $\sin \alpha$, $\cos \beta$ and $\tan \alpha$.

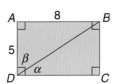

Solutions

1   a $\sin \theta = \dfrac{\text{opp.}}{\text{hyp.}}$ $\qquad$ $\cos \theta = \dfrac{\text{adj.}}{\text{hyp.}}$ $\qquad$ $\tan \theta = \dfrac{\text{opp.}}{\text{adj.}}$

$\qquad = \dfrac{5}{13}$ $\qquad\qquad = \dfrac{12}{13}$ $\qquad\qquad = \dfrac{5}{12}$

$\qquad \doteqdot 0{\cdot}385$ $\qquad\qquad \doteqdot 0{\cdot}923$ $\qquad\qquad \doteqdot 0{\cdot}417$

b   First the hypotenuse must be calculated using Pythagoras' theorem. So, then:

$\sin \theta = \dfrac{7}{\sqrt{74}}$ $\qquad$ $\tan \theta = \dfrac{7}{5}$

$\qquad \doteqdot 0{\cdot}814$ $\qquad\qquad \doteqdot 1{\cdot}400$

$\cos \theta = \dfrac{5}{\sqrt{74}}$

$\qquad \doteqdot 0{\cdot}581$

$h^2 = 5^2 + 7^2$
$\quad = 25 + 49$
$\quad = 74$
ie $h = \sqrt{74}$

2   $ABCD$ is a rectangle.

Hence $DC = 8$, $BC = 5$

Also $BD = \sqrt{89}$ (Pythagoras' theorem)

$\therefore \sin \alpha = \dfrac{BC}{BD}$ $\qquad$ $\cos \beta = \dfrac{AD}{BD}$ $\qquad$ $\tan \alpha = \dfrac{BC}{DC}$

$\qquad = \dfrac{5}{\sqrt{89}}$ $\qquad\qquad = \dfrac{5}{\sqrt{89}}$ $\qquad\qquad = \dfrac{5}{8}$

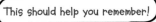

This should help you remember!

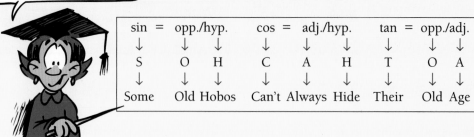

sin	=	opp./hyp.	cos	=	adj./hyp.	tan	=	opp./adj.
↓	↓	↓	↓	↓	↓	↓	↓	↓
S	O	H	C	A	H	T	O	A
↓	↓	↓	↓	↓	↓	↓	↓	↓
Some	Old	Hobos	Can't	Always	Hide	Their	Old	Age

Exercise 13:03

1 Find sin θ, cos θ and tan θ in these triangles (as a simple fraction).

a
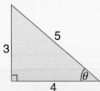

b
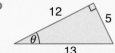

c
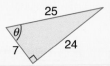

2 Evaluate sin A, cos A and tan A for each triangle. Give your answers in decimal form correct to 3 decimal places.

a
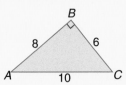

b
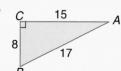

c
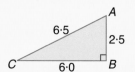

3 Find the unknown side using Pythagoras' theorem and then find sin θ and cos θ in decimal form.

a
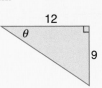

b
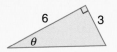

c
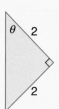

4 Use Pythagoras' theorem to find side YZ, then state the value of tan X.

a
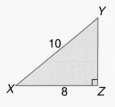

b
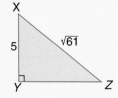

c
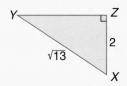

5 Complete the statements below.

a

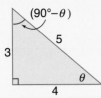

$$\sin \theta = \dots$$
$$\cos (90° - \theta) = \dots$$

b

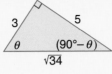

$$\cos \theta = \dots$$
$$\sin (90° - \theta) = \dots$$

c

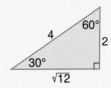

$$\sin 60° = \dots$$
$$\cos 30° = \dots$$

6 For the triangle on the right, complete the following:

a $\sin \theta = \dots$ **b** $\cos \theta = \dots$

$\cos (90° - \theta) = \dots$ $\sin (90° - \theta) = \dots$

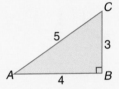

7 Find the value of x, given that:

a $\cos 25° = \sin x°$ **b** $\sin 60° = \cos x°$ **c** $\cos 10° = \sin x°$

8 a For the triangle shown, write down the value of:

   i $\sin A$ **ii** $\cos A$

   iii $\tan A$ **iv** $\sin A \div \cos A$

b Does $\tan A = \dfrac{\sin A}{\cos A}$?

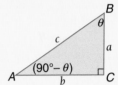

9 a Use Pythagoras' theorem to find the value of the missing side as a surd. Hence find the value of $\sin 30°$, $\cos 30°$ and $\tan 30°$. (Leave your answer as a surd.)

b By rationalising the denominator, arrange the values for $\sin 30°$, $\cos 30°$ and $\tan 30°$ in ascending order.

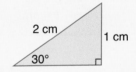

10 a If $\sin A = \dfrac{1}{4}$, find the values of $\cos A$ and $\tan A$.

b It is known that $\cos \theta = \dfrac{3}{4}$. What is the value of $\sin \theta$?

11 a Find   **i** $\sin A$ **ii** $\sin C$ **b** Find   **i** $\sin \theta$ **ii** $\cos \alpha$

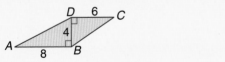

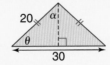

12 a By finding tan θ in two different triangles, find the value of m.

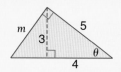

b Find x and y.
  (*Note:* $DE = x$ and
      $CE = y$.)

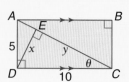

c Find:
   i $\sin \theta$ **ii** $\cos \theta$
   iii m **iv** n
   v $\sin 2\theta$
   vi Show that $\sin 2\theta = 2 \times \sin \theta \times \cos \theta$

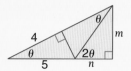

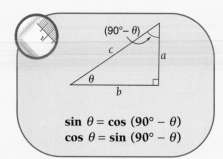

$$\sin \theta = \cos (90° - \theta)$$
$$\cos \theta = \sin (90° - \theta)$$

- Trigonometry is used in surveying to calculate lengths and areas.

Challenge worksheet 13:03 **The range of values of the trig. ratios**

13:04 | Trig. Ratios and the Calculator

As we have already found, the values of the trig. ratios are constant for any particular angle and these values can be found from a calculator. You can also use the calculator to find an angle when you are given the ratio.

Finding a ratio given the angle

To find tan 31°, ensure your calculator is operating in 'degrees' and then press:

 tan   31   =

The calculator should give tan 31° = 0·600 860 6, correct to 7 decimal places.

Degrees and minutes

So far the angles have all been in whole degrees. One degree, however, can be divided into 60 minutes.

For example, $31\frac{1}{2}°$ would equal 31 degrees and 30 minutes. This would be written as:

    31°30′.

We can now find the trigonometric ratios of angles given to the nearest minute by using the calculator as shown in the examples below.

1 degree = 60 minutes
$1° = 60′, \left[\ 1′ = \frac{1}{60}°\right]$

worked examples

Find:

1   sin 25°41′   2   tan 79°05′

Give your answers correct to 4 decimal places.

Solutions

Two methods are shown, one for each solution. Choose the one that best suits your calculator.

Method 1:

1   For calculators with a *Degrees/Minutes/Seconds* button. This is usually marked in either of two ways.

    DMS or o′″

    Press: sin 25 DMS 41 =

    The calculator gives 0·433 396 953.

> ■ *Warning:*
> Your calculator may work differently to the one used here.

Method 2:

2   We convert 79°05′ into decimal degrees by realising that 05′ is $\frac{5}{60}$ of one degree.

    Press tan 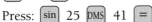 (79 + 5 ÷ 60) =

    The calculator gives 5·184 803 521.

Finding an angle, given the ratio

If the value of the trigonometric ratio is known and you want to find the size of the angle to the nearest minute, follow the steps in the examples below.

worked examples

1 If $\sin \theta = 0.632$, find θ to the nearest minute.
2 If $\cos \theta = 0.2954$, find θ to the nearest minute.

Solutions

Note: One minute may be divided further, into 60 seconds, and this fact will be used to round off answers to the nearest minute.

Again two methods are shown that correspond to the two methods on the previous page.

1 If $\sin \theta = 0.632$ press: 2nd F sin 0.632 =

The calculator now displays 39·197 833 53°. To convert this to degrees/minutes/seconds mode, press DMS. The calculator gives 39°11′52·2″.

∴ $\theta = 39°12′$ (to the nearest minute)

2 If $\cos \theta = 0.2954$, press 2nd F cos 0.2954 =

The answer on the screen is 72·818 475 degrees. The alternative method of converting this to degrees and minutes is to find what 0·818 475 of one degree is, in minutes; ie 0·818 475 × 60′, which gives an answer of 49·1085 minutes, ie 49′ (to the nearest minute).

∴ $\theta = 72°49′$.

Exercise 13:04

1 Using the *degrees/minutes/seconds* button on your calculator, write each of the following in degrees and minutes, giving answers correct to the nearest minute.
   a 16·5°   b 38·25°   c 73·9°   d 305·75°
   e 40·23°   f 100·66°   g 12·016°   h 238·845°

2 Write in degrees, correct to 3 decimal places where necessary.
   a 17°45′   b 48°16′   c 125°43′   d 88°37′
   e 320°15′   f 70°54′   g 241°29′   h 36°53′

3 Use your calculator to find the value of the following, correct to 4 decimal places.
   a sin 30°   b cos 30°   c tan 30°   d sin 71°
   e cos 58°   f tan 63°   g sin 7°   h cos 85°

4 Find the size of θ (to the nearest degree) where θ is acute.
   a $\sin \theta = 0.259$ b $\sin \theta = 0.934$ c $\sin \theta = 0.619$
   d $\cos \theta = 0.222$ e $\cos \theta = 0.317$ f $\cos \theta = 0.9$
   g $\tan \theta = 1.2$ h $\tan \theta = 0.816$ i $\tan \theta = 3$

5 Find, correct to 3 decimal places, the following ratios.

a sin 30°10′　　b sin 62°45′　　c cos 52°30′　　d cos 83°03′

e tan 61·25°　　f tan 79·36°　　g sin 17·8°　　h tan 72·57°

6 Find θ, to the nearest minute, given that θ is acute.

a sin θ = 0·6　　　　b sin θ = 0·43　　　c sin θ = 0·645

d cos θ = 0·2　　　　e cos θ = 0·031　　f cos θ = 0·5216

g tan θ = 1·3　　　　h tan θ = 0·625　　i tan θ = 2·67

7 Redo question **6**, this time giving answers in degrees correct to 2 decimal places.

8 What is the value of $\dfrac{o}{a}, \dfrac{o}{h}, \dfrac{a}{h}$ for each of the following triangles, correct to 3 dec. pl.?

a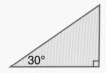

30°

b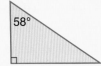

58°

c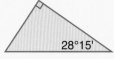

28°15′

9 Find the value of $\dfrac{x}{10}$ for each of the following, correct to 3 decimal places.

a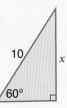

10　　x

60°

b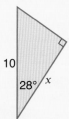

10

28°　x

c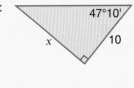

47°10′

x　　10

10 a If $\dfrac{x}{10}$ = cos 60° , find the value of x.

b If $a = 3 \sin 40° + 4 \cos 30°$, find the value of a correct to 3 decimal places.

c By substituting values for A and B, find if sin A + sin B = sin $(A + B)$.

d If $\sin A = \frac{1}{2}$ and $\sin B = \frac{1}{3}$ find $A + B$.

e Jim thinks that if you double the size of an angle you double its sine, that is sin $2A = 2 \times$ sin A. Is Jim correct?

- Trigonometry is used in many branches of science.

ΔABC is an equilateral triangle of side 2 units.
AD is perpendicular to BC.

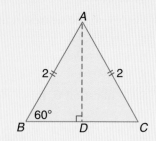

1   Copy the diagram and write in the size of BD and $\angle BAD$.

2   Using Pythagoras' theorem, calculate the length of AD as a surd.

3   Now, from ΔABD, write down the values of sin, cos and tan for 30° and 60°.

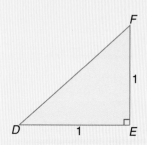

ΔDEF is a right-angled isosceles triangle. The two equal sides are 1 unit in length.

4   Why is $\angle EDF$ equal to 45°?

5   What is the length of DF as a surd?

6   Write down the values of sin 45°, cos 45° and tan 45°.

> ■ Leave surds in your answers.

Leave your answers in surd form. Do not approximate.

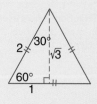

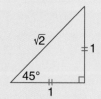

$$\sin 60° = \frac{\sqrt{3}}{2}, \quad \sin 30° = \frac{1}{2}$$

$$\cos 60° = \frac{1}{2}, \quad \cos 30° = \frac{\sqrt{3}}{2}$$

$$\tan 60° = \sqrt{3}, \quad \tan 30° = \frac{1}{\sqrt{3}}$$

$$\sin 45° = \frac{1}{\sqrt{2}}$$

$$\cos 45° = \frac{1}{\sqrt{2}}$$

$$\tan 45° = 1$$

For the triangle given, state:

1 the hypotenuse
2 the side opposite the marked angle
3 the side adjacent to the marked angle

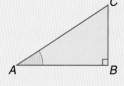

Write *true* or *false* for these triangles:

4 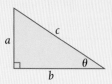 5 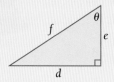 6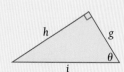

$$\sin \theta = \frac{c}{a}$$ $$\cos \theta = \frac{e}{f}$$ $$\cos \theta = \frac{g}{i}$$

Find correct to 3 decimal places:

7 $\sin 75°$ 8 $\tan 25°30'$ 9 If $\tan 25° = \dfrac{x}{4}$ then $x = \ldots$ 10 If $\tan 25° = \dfrac{4}{x}$ then $x = \ldots$

Pythagoras' theorem is used to find an unknown side in a right-angled triangle when the other two sides are known. Trigonometry is used when only one side and one of the acute angles are known.

worked examples

1 Find a in these triangles, correct to 1 decimal place.

a 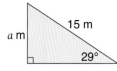 b 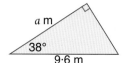 c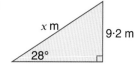

2 A ladder that is 8 metres long leans against a wall, and makes an angle of 21° with the wall. How far does the ladder reach up the wall, to the nearest centimetre?

3 Find the length of a guy rope that must be used to secure a pole 12·5 m high, if the angle the guy rope makes with the ground is 56°.

Solutions

Use the trig. button on your calculator.

1 a $\dfrac{a}{15} = \sin 29°$

∴ $a = (\sin 29°) \times 15 \leftrightarrow$ [sin] 29 [×] 15 [=]

$= 7·272\ 144\ 3$

So $a = 7·3$ (to 1 decimal place)

Make sure your calculator is operating in 'degrees' mode.

continued ➜➜➜

b $\dfrac{a}{9\cdot6} = \cos 38°$

$\therefore a = (\cos 38°) \times 9\cdot6 \leftrightarrow \boxed{\cos}\ 38\ \boxed{\times}\ 9\cdot6\ \boxed{=}$

$= 7\cdot564\ 903\ 2$

$= 7\cdot6$ (to 1 decimal place)

c $\dfrac{9\cdot2}{x} = \sin 28°$

$\dfrac{x}{9\cdot2} = \dfrac{1}{\sin 28°}$

(Note that x is the denominator of the fraction, not the numerator.)

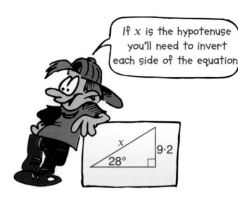

$\therefore x = \dfrac{9\cdot2}{\sin 28°} \leftrightarrow 9\cdot2\ \boxed{\div}\ 38\ \boxed{\sin}\ 28\ \boxed{=}$

$= 19\cdot6$ (to 1 decimal place)

2 From the information in the question, a diagram like the one to the right can be drawn. Let the height up the wall be h m.

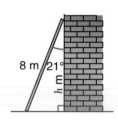

So: $\dfrac{h}{8} = \cos 21°$

$h = 8 \times \cos 21° \leftrightarrow 8\ \boxed{\times}\ \boxed{\cos}\ 21\ \boxed{=}$

$= 7\cdot468\ 643\ 4$

$= 7\cdot47$ (to the nearest centimetre)

$\therefore$ The ladder reaches $7\cdot47$ m up the wall.

3 Let the length of the rope be x metres.

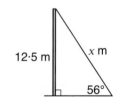

Then: $\dfrac{12\cdot5}{x} = \sin 56°$

so: $\dfrac{x}{12\cdot5} = \dfrac{1}{\sin 56°}$

$x = \dfrac{12\cdot5}{\sin 56°}$

$\doteqdot 15\cdot08$

$\therefore$ The rope is $15\cdot08$ metres long (to the nearest centimetre).

Exercise 13:05

1 Find the value of the pronumeral in each triangle, correct to 1 decimal place.

Foundation Worksheet 13:05

Using trigonometry to find side lengths

1 Find x correct to 1 decimal place:
  a $\dfrac{x}{8} = \sin 15°$ **b** $\dfrac{y}{6·8} = \tan 38°$ ...

2 Find x correct to 1 decimal place:
  a $\dfrac{15}{x} = \cos 40°$ ...

3 In each of the following state which trig. ratio needs to be used to find x and then find it correct to 1 decimal place.

  a   **b**

4 In each of the following state which trig. ratio needs to be used to find the length of the hypotenuse and then find it correct to 1 decimal place.

  a   **b**

a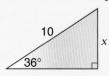

b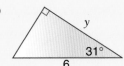

c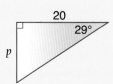

d

e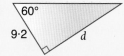

f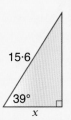

g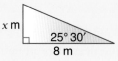

h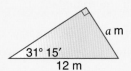

i

j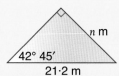

k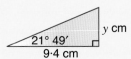

l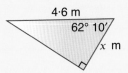

2 Determine the value of each pronumeral, correct to 1 decimal place.

a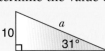

b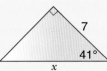

c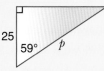

d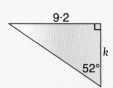

e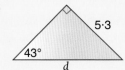

f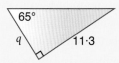

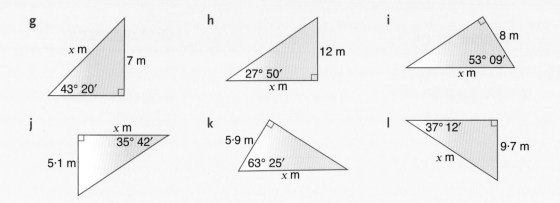

For questions **3** to **11** the diagrams relate to the questions below them.

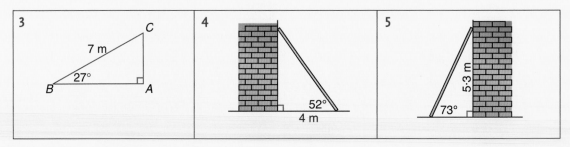

3 Find out everything you can about the triangle.

4 A ladder leans against a wall so that the angle it makes with the ground is 52° and its base is 4 m from the wall. How far does the ladder reach up the wall (to the nearest centimetre)?

5 A ladder leaning against a wall reaches 5·3 m up the wall when the angle between the ground and the ladder is 73°. How long, to the nearest centimetre, is the ladder?

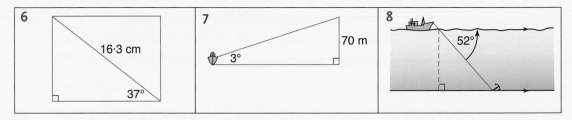

6 The diagonal of a rectangle is 16·3 cm long and makes an angle with the longest side of 37°. Find the length of the rectangle, to the nearest centimetre.

7 A ship out at sea observes a lighthouse on the top of a 70 m cliff at an angle of 3°. How far out to sea is the ship (to the nearest metre)?

8 A boat is anchored in a river that is 3·2 m deep. If the anchor rope makes an angle of 52° with the surface of the water, how long is the rope from the surface of the water? (Answer to the nearest centimetre.)

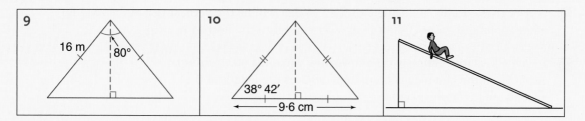

9 The equal sides of an isosceles triangle are 16 metres long and the apex angle is 80°. Find, to the nearest centimetre, the length of the base.

10 The base of an isosceles triangle is 9·6 cm long and each of the base angles is 38°42′. Find the length of each of the equal sides. (Answer correct to 3 significant figures.)

11 If the length of a child's slippery-dip is 3·4 m and one end makes an angle of 38°42′ with the ground, how high above the ground is the other end? (Answer to the nearest centimetre.)

For questions **12** to **20**, draw a diagram first!

12 **a** In $\triangle ABC$, $\angle A = 90°$, $\angle B = 63°25′$ and $BC = 6$ m. Find AC, correct to the nearest centimetre.
　　b In $\triangle XYZ$, $\angle Z = 90°$, $\angle X = 42°34′$ and $XZ = 9·2$ m. Find YZ, correct to the nearest centimetre.
　　c In $\triangle ABC$, $\angle B = 90°$, $\angle A = 52°$ and $AB = 2·7$ cm. Find AC, to 1 decimal place.
　　d In $\triangle XYZ$, $\angle X = 90°$, $\angle Y = 31°20′$ and $XZ = 10·3$ cm. Find XY, to 1 decimal place.

13 The diagonal of a square is 21·2 cm. Find the length of each side (to the nearest millimetre).

14 Find the length of the diagonal of a rectangle if the length of the rectangle is 7·5 cm and the diagonal makes an angle of 25° with each of the longer sides. (Answer correct to the nearest millimetre.)

15 Find the length of a rectangle if its diagonal is 34 cm long and the angle the diagonal makes with the length is 27°50′. (Answer correct to the nearest centimetre.)

16 Find the base of an isosceles triangle if the height is 8·2 cm and the base angles are each 39°. (Answer correct to the nearest millimetre.)

17 When the altitude of the sun is 51°47′, a vertical stick casts a shadow 45 cm long. How high, to the nearest millimetre, is the stick?

18 A painting is hung symmetrically by means of a string passing over a nail with its ends attached to the upper corners of the painting. If the distance between the corners is 55 cm and the angle between the two halves of the string is 105°, find the length of the string, correct to the nearest millimetre.

19 The vertical rise from the bottom to the top of a track that slopes uniformly at 6°54′ with the horizontal is 36 m. Find, to 1 decimal place, the length of the track.

20 A road rises steadily at an angle of 6°45′. What will be the vertical rise of the road for a horizontal distance of 300 m? (Answer correct to the nearest metre.)

21 At noon a factory chimney casts a shadow when the sun's altitude is 85°24′. If the chimney is 65 m high, what is the length of the shadow, to the nearest centimetre?

22

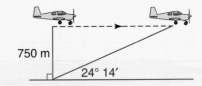

Calculate the sloping area of this roof that needs to be tiled, given that the width of the roof is 5·4 m and its length is 9·2 m. Each roof section is pitched at an angle of 23°. (Answer correct to the nearest square metre.)

23 A plane is flying at an altitude (height) of 750 metres. A boy on the ground first observes the plane when it is directly overhead. Thirty seconds later, the angle of elevation of the plane from the boy is 24°14′.

  a Through what distance did the plane fly in 30 seconds, to the nearest metre?

  b Calculate the speed of the plane in km/h, correct to 3 significant figures.

24 Calculate the area of a right-angled triangle that has a hypotenuse 8 cm long and an angle of 50°.

25 A regular hexagon of side a units is made by joining six equilateral triangles together, as shown in the diagram.

We want to find a formula for the area of the hexagon in terms of its side length, a.

Consider the area of *one* of the equilateral triangles.

  a Using the exact trig. ratios on page 469, find the exact length of DC.

  b What is the area of $\triangle ABC$?

  c What is the area of a hexagon of side a units?

  d Find the area of a hexagon with a side length of:
  i 2 cm ii 5 cm iii 10 cm

Complete the ratios below for each triangle.

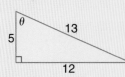

1 $\sin \theta =$
2 $\cos \theta =$

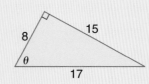

3 $\tan \theta =$
4 $\sin \theta =$

Given that θ is acute, find θ to the nearest degree, if:

5 $\tan \theta = 0.635$ 6 $\sin \theta = 0.2135$ 7 $\cos \theta = 0.0926$

If $0° \leqslant A \leqslant 90°$, find A to the nearest minute if:

8 $\sin A = 0.52$ 9 $\tan A = 2.673$ 10 $\cos A = 0.7231$

We have already seen in 13:04 that a calculator can be used to find the size of an angle if the value of the trigonometric ratio is known.

worked examples

1 Find the size of angle θ.
   Answer to the nearest degree.

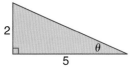

2 What angle, to the nearest minute, does the diagonal of a rectangle make with its length, if the dimensions of the rectangle are 12·6 cm by 8·9 cm?

Solutions

1 In the triangle,

$$\tan \theta = \frac{2}{5}$$

$$= 0.4 \leftrightarrow \boxed{\text{2nd F}} \boxed{\text{tan}} \; 0.4 \; \boxed{=}$$

$$\therefore \theta = 21.801\ 409°$$

so $\theta = 22°$ (to the nearest degree).

> Remember '2nd F' may be called 'SHIFT' on some calculators.

2

Let the required angle be θ. Then:

$$\tan \theta = \frac{8.9}{12.6} \quad \boxed{\text{2nd F}} \boxed{\text{tan}} \boxed{(} \; 8.9 \; \boxed{\div} \; 12.6 \; \boxed{)} \boxed{=} \boxed{\text{2nd F}} \boxed{\text{DMS}}$$

$$\therefore \theta = 35°14'7.59''$$

$$\therefore \theta = 35°14' \text{ (to the nearest minute).}$$

Exercise 13:06

1 Find the size of the angle marked θ in each triangle. Give your answers correct to the nearest degree.

a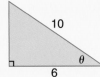

b

c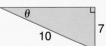

d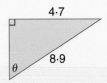

e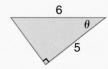

f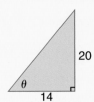

g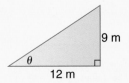

h

i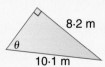

2 For each, find the size of θ correct to the nearest minute.

a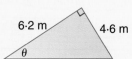

b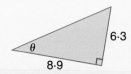

c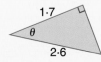

d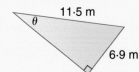

e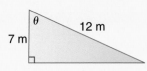

f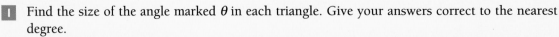

3 Use trigonometry to find *x* in three different ways.

4 **a** In △LMN, ∠M = 90°, LN = 9·2 m and LM = 8·2 m.
Find ∠L, to the nearest degree.

b In △PQR, ∠R = 90°, PR = 6·9 m and QR = 5·1 m.
Find ∠P, to the nearest minute.

5 **a** A ladder reaches 9 m up a wall and the foot of the ladder is 2 m from the base of the wall. What angle does the ladder make with the ground? (Answer correct to the nearest degree.)

b What angle will a 5 m ladder make with the ground if it is to reach 4·4 m up a wall? (Answer correct to the nearest degree.)

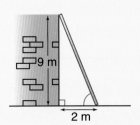

6 The beam of a see-saw is 4·2 m long. If one end is 1·2 m above the ground when the other end is resting on the ground, find the angle the beam makes with the ground, correct to the nearest degree.

7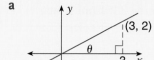

A road is inclined so that it rises 1 m for each horizontal distance of 8 m. What angle does the road make with the horizontal? (Answer correct to the nearest minute.)

8 At a certain time of the day, a tree 25 m high casts a shadow 32 m long. At this time of day, what angle do the rays of the sun make with the ground? (Answer correct to the nearest minute.)

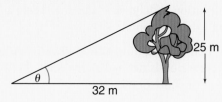

9 What angle does a diagonal of a rectangle make with each of the sides if the dimensions of the rectangle are 4·7 m by 3·2 m? (Answer correct to the nearest minute.)

10 Find the angle θ in each of the following. (Answer correct to the nearest minute.)

a
b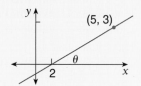
c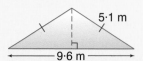

11 The cross-section of a roof is an isosceles triangle. Find the pitch of the roof (the angle it makes with the horizontal) if the width of the roof is 9·6 m and the length of one of the pitched sections is 5·1 m. Give your answer correct to the nearest minute.

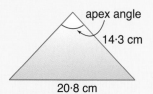

12 Find the size of the base angles of an isosceles triangle if the length of the base is 10 cm and the height is 8·4 cm. (Answer to the nearest minute.)

13 Find the apex angle of an isosceles triangle, if the length of each of the equal sides is 14·3 cm and the length of the base is 20·8 cm. Give your answer to the nearest minute.

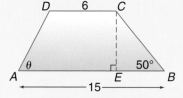

14 The diagram shows a trapezium.
 a If $BC = 8$, find θ.
 b If $CE = 8$, find θ.

13:07 | Miscellaneous Exercises

Before continuing with further trigonometric examples there is some general information that should be mentioned.

Angles of elevation and depression

When looking upwards towards an object, the **angle of elevation** is defined as the angle between the line of sight and the horizontal.

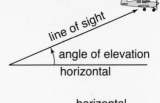

When looking downwards towards an object, the **angle of depression** is defined as the angle between the line of sight and the horizontal.

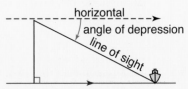

worked examples

1   The angle of elevation of the top of a vertical cliff is observed to be 23° from a boat 180 m from the base to the cliff. What is the height of the cliff? (Answer correct to 1 decimal place.)

2   An observer stands on the top of a 40-metre cliff to observe a boat that is 650 metres out from the base of the cliff. What is the angle of depression from the observer to the boat? (Answer to the nearest minute.)

Solutions

1   For this example, the diagram would look like the one on the right.

Let the height of the cliff be h metres.

Then: $\dfrac{h}{180} = \tan 23°$

ie $h = (\tan 23°) \times 180$

               $= 76.405\,467$ (from calculator)

∴ Height of cliff = 76.4 m (to 1 decimal place).

2

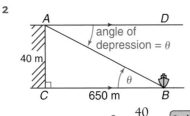

Note: The angle of depression $\angle DAB = \angle ABC$ (alternate angles and parallel lines).

$\tan \theta = \dfrac{40}{650}$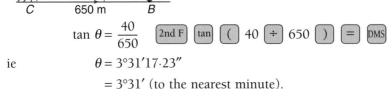

ie $\theta = 3°31'17.23''$

               $= 3°31'$ (to the nearest minute).

Compass bearings

The direction of a point *Y* from an original point *X* is known as the **bearing** of *Y* from *X*. This is mainly expressed in one of two ways. Examine the diagram below.

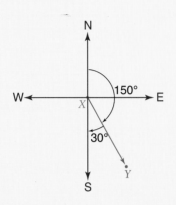

The bearing of *Y* from *X* can be given as:

1   150° (the angle between the interval *XY* and the north line measured in a clockwise direction),

   or,

2   south 30° east (S30°E).

Sometimes, only letters are used. So SE (or south-east) is halfway between south (180°) and east (90°); that is, 135° or S45°F.

This has great bearing on trigonometry!

Other examples would look like these.

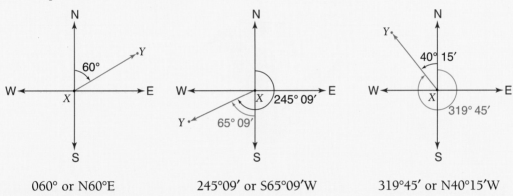

060° or N60°E   245°09′ or S65°09′W   319°45′ or N40°15′W

worked examples

1   If the town of Bartley is 5 km north and 3 km west of Kelly Valley, find the bearing of Bartley from Kelly Valley.

2   Two people start walking from the same point. The first walks due east for 3·5 km and the second walks in the direction 123° until the second person is due south of the first person. How far did the second person walk (to the nearest metre)?

continued ➜➜➜

Solutions

1 The diagram for this question would look like the one on the right.

Let the angle indicated in the diagram be θ.

Thus: $\tan \theta = \dfrac{3}{5}$

$\qquad = 0{\cdot}6$

So: $\qquad \theta = 31°$ (to the nearest degree)

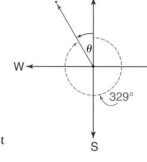

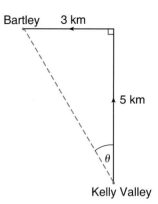

So the bearing of Bartley from Kelly Valley would be N31°W or simply 329°.

2 This diagram shows the information in the question above.

Since $\angle SAB = \angle CBA$
(alternate angles, $AS \,/\!/\, CB$)

then $\angle CBA = 57°$

So: $\dfrac{3{\cdot}5}{x} = \sin 57°$

ie $\dfrac{x}{3{\cdot}5} = \dfrac{1}{\sin 57°}$

$\qquad x = \dfrac{3{\cdot}5}{\sin 57°}$

$\qquad = 4{\cdot}173$ km

Press: 3·5 ÷ sin 57 =

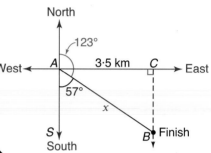

Check out this step!

Exercise 13:07

Foundation Worksheet 13:07

Angles of elevation and depression, and bearings

1 Find the bearing of B from A if B is 6 km north and 3 km east of A.

2 From a lighthouse 105 m above the sea the angle of depression of a boat is 2°. How far is the boat from the shore?

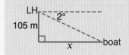

1 The angle of elevation of the top of a tower from a point 35 m from the base of the tower was measured with a clinometer and found to be 63°. Find the height of the tower, correct to 1 decimal place.

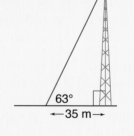

2

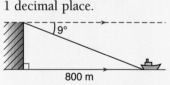

The angle of depression of a boat 800 m out to sea from the top of a vertical cliff is 9°. Find the height of the cliff, to the nearest metre.

3 From the top of a cliff 72 m high, the angle of depression of a boat is 12°47′. How far is the boat from the base of the cliff? (Answer to the nearest metre.)

4 A vertical shadow stick has a height of 1·8 m. If the angle of elevation of the sun is 42°, what is the length of the shadow at that time, correct to 1 decimal place?

5 Find the angle of elevation of the top of a vertical tower from a point 25 m from its base, if the height of the tower is 40 m. (Answer to the nearest degree.)

6 From a lighthouse 70 m above sea level a ship, 1·2 km out to sea, is observed. What is the angle of depression from the lighthouse to the ship? (Answer to the nearest minute.)

7 A kite is on the end of a string 80 metres long. If the vertical height of the kite, above the ground, is 69 metres, find the angle of elevation of the kite from the person holding the string. (Assume the string is a straight line, and answer to the nearest minute.)

8 A cyclist travels 15 km in the direction N15°27′E. How far has he travelled in a northerly direction (to the nearest metre)?

9 A ship sails from *P* to *Q* a distance of 150 km on a course of 120°30′. How far is *P* north of *Q*? Also, how far is *Q* east of *P*? (Answer to the nearest kilometre.)

10 Two towns, *A* and *B*, are 9 km apart and the bearing of *B* from *A* is 320°. Find how far *B* is west of *A* (to the nearest kilometre).

11 Two cars leave from the same starting point, one in a direction due west, the second in a direction with a bearing of 195°. After travelling 15 km, the first car is due north of the second. How far has the second car travelled (to the nearest kilometre)?

12 An aircraft flew 10 km south and then 6 km west. What is its bearing from its starting point? (Answer to the nearest degree.)

13 *A*, *B* and *C* are three towns. *A* lies 7 km north-east of *B*, and *B* lies 12·5 km north-west of *C*. Find the bearing of *A* from *C*. Also, how far is *A* from *C*? (Answer to the nearest metre.)

14 A ship is 5 nautical miles from a wharf on a bearing of 321°, and a lighthouse is 11·5 nautical miles from the wharf on a bearing of 231°. Find the bearing of the ship from the lighthouse. (Answer correct to the nearest minute.)

15 The bearings from a point *P* of two landmarks *X* and *Y* are 35° and 125° and their distances from *P* are 420 m and 950 m respectively. Find the bearing of *Y* from *X* (to the nearest minute).

16 *X* is due north of *Y* and 2 km distant. *Z* is due east of *Y* and has a bearing of S35°12′E from *X*. How far, to the nearest metre, is *Z* from *X*?

17 A wire is stretched from point *A* on the top of a building 21·3 m high, to point *B* on the top of a shorter building, 15·6 m high. The angle of depression from *A* to *B* is 20°15′.

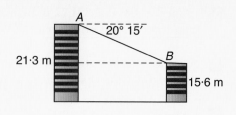

a What is the horizontal distance between the buildings (to the nearest centimetre)?

b How long is the wire (to the nearest centimetre)?

18 *PQ* is a diameter of the circle, centre *O*, as shown with ∠*PRQ* = 90°. If the radius of the circle is 6 cm, find, to the nearest millimetre, the length of the chord *PR*, given that ∠*PQR* = 40°.

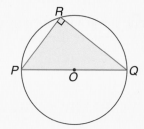

19 A tangent of length 16 cm is drawn to a circle of radius 7·5 cm from an external point *T*. What is the angle, marked *θ* in the diagram, that this tangent subtends at the centre of the circle?

20 The diagonals of a rhombus are 11 cm and 7·6 cm. Find the angles, to the nearest degree, of the rhombus.

21 Find the acute angle, to the nearest minute, between the diagonals of a rectangle that has sides of 8 cm and 14 cm.

22 The eaves of a roof sloping at 23° overhang the walls, the edge of the roof being 75 cm from the top of the wall. The top of the wall is 5·4 metres above the ground. What is the height above the ground of the edge of the roof, to the nearest centimetre?

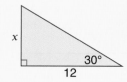

23 The arms of a pair of compasses are each 12 cm long. To what angle (to the nearest minute) must they be opened to draw a circle of 4 cm radius? How far from the paper will the joint be, if the compasses are held upright? (Answer to the nearest millimetre.)

24 Find the *exact* value of *x* in each of the following.

a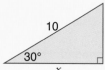

b

c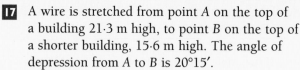

25 **a** A rectangle is 10 cm long. The angle between the diagonal and the length is 30°. What is the exact area of the rectangle?

b A pole is to be supported by three guy wires. The wires are to be fixed 10 m from the base of the pole and must form an angle of 60° with the ground (which is horizontal). What will be the exact length of each guy wire?

c Find the exact value of x in the diagram.

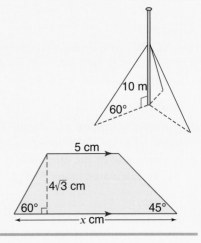

13:08 | Problems Involving Two Right Triangles

Some problems can be solved by the consideration of two right-angled triangles within the problem.

Examine the following two problems carefully and then attempt Exercise 13:08.

> No, you're wrong! I'm right!

> I'm more right than you!

worked examples

Example 1

1

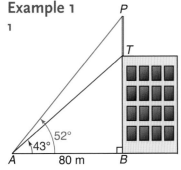

A pole *PT* stands on the top of a building *BT*. From a point *A*, located 80 m from *B*, the angles of elevation of the top of the building and the top of the pole are 43° and 52° respectively. Find the height of the pole, *PT*, correct to the nearest metre.

Solution 1

1 To find the length of the pole *PT*, the lengths *PB* and *TB* are calculated and of course $PT = PB - TB$.

In $\triangle PBA$, $\dfrac{PB}{80} = \tan 52°$ 　　　　In $\triangle TBA$, $\dfrac{TP}{80} = \tan 43°$

　　　　$PB = 80 \tan 52°$ 　　　　　　　　　$TB = 80 \tan 43°$

Now 　　$PT = PB - TB$

　　　　　$= 80 \tan 52° - 80 \tan 43°$

　　　　　$= 80 (\tan 52° - \tan 43°)$

　　　　　$= 28$ m (to the nearest metre)

continued ➔➔➔

Example 2

P, *Q* and *R* are three villages. *Q* is 5 km and N25°E from *P*. *R* is east of *Q* and is 6·7 km from *P*. What is the bearing of *R* from *P*, to the nearest degree?

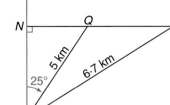

Solution 2

To find the bearing of *R* from *P*, we need to find the size of angle *NPR*. In △*NPR* we know the length of *PR*, but we need to know one of the other sides, either *NR* or *NP*. Side *NP* can be calculated using △*NPQ*.

In △*NPQ*: $\dfrac{NP}{5} = \cos 25°$

ie $\qquad NP = 5 \cos 25°$

In △*NPR*: $\cos \angle NPR = \dfrac{NP}{6·7}$

$$= \dfrac{5 \cos 25°}{6·7}$$

$$= 0·676\,349$$

$$\therefore \angle NPR = 47° \text{ (to the nearest degree)}$$

∴ The bearing of *R* from *P* is N47°E.

Exercise 13:08

Foundation Worksheet 13:08

Problems with more than one triangle

1

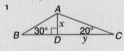

a Use △*ABD* to find *x*.
b Use △*ADC* to find *y*.

2

Use the fact that *a* = *y* − *x* to find the value of *a*.

1 The top of a 20-metre tower is observed from two positions, *A* and *B*, each in line with, but on opposite sides of, the tower. If the angle of elevation from *A* is 27° and from *B* is 35°, how far is point *A* from point *B* (to the nearest metre)?

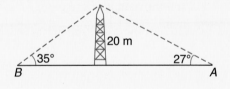

2 In triangle *ABC*, *BD* is perpendicular to *AC*. Given that *AB* = 13 m, *BD* = 11 m and *DC* = 10 m, find, to the nearest degree, the size of angle *ABC*.

3 Two points, *P* and *Q*, are in line with the foot of a tower 25 m high. The angle of depression from the top of the tower to *P* is 43° and to *Q* is 57°. How far apart are the points? (Answer to the nearest metre.)

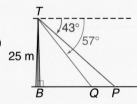

4

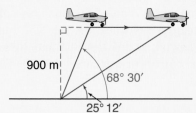

A plane is flying at an altitude of 900 m. From a point P on the ground, the angle of elevation to the plane was $68°30'$ and 20 seconds later the angle of elevation from P had changed to $25°12'$. How far had the plane flown in that time, and what was its speed, to the nearest kilometre per hour? (Find the distance to the nearest metre.)

5 Find x in each diagram. Give answers correct to 2 decimal places.

a
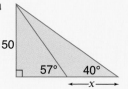

b
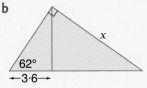

Find a different side first.

c
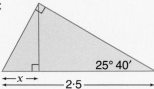

d
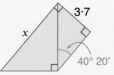

6 a A
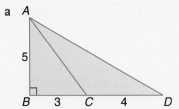

b

Find $\angle CAD$ to the nearest minute.   Find θ to the nearest minute.

7 a From ΔXWY, show that $XW = z \cos X$.
b From ΔZWY, show that $ZW = x \cos Z$.
c Hence show that $y = z \cos X + x \cos Z$.

8 a Show that $AM = c \sin B$.
b Hence show that the area of $\Delta ABC = \frac{1}{2} ac \sin B$.

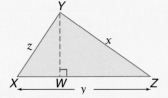

9 Two ladders are the same distance from the base of a wall. The longer ladder is 15 m long and makes an angle of 58° with the ground. If the shorter ladder is 12·6 m long, what angle does it make with the ground? (Answer to the nearest degree.)

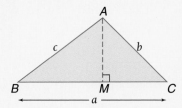

10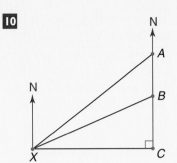

A, B and C are three towns where A and B are due north of C. From a position X on a map, A has a bearing of N27°E and B has a bearing of N67°E. Town C is due east of X and 7·5 km from it. Find the distance, correct to 1 decimal place, between A and B.

11 Find the exact value of CE given that AE = 16.

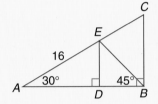

12 In △ABC, AB = 12, ∠CAB = 60° and ∠CBA = 75°. Find as exact values:

a AC
b BC
c area of △ABC

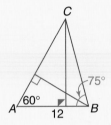

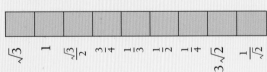

Challenge worksheet 13:08 Three-dimensional problems

Mathematical Terms 13

adjacent side (to a given angle)
- The side of a triangle which together with the hypotenuse forms the arms of a given angle.

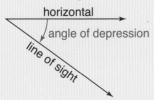

angle of depression
- When looking down, the angle between the line of sight and the horizontal.

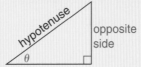

angle of elevation
- When looking up, the angle between the line of sight and the horizontal.

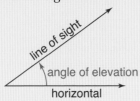

bearing
- An angle used to measure the direction of a line from north.
- Bearings can be recorded in two ways.
eg 120° or S60°E

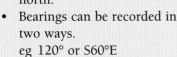

cosine ratio (of an angle θ)
- The ratio $\dfrac{\text{side adjacent to angle } \theta}{\text{hypotenuse}}$
- Abbreviated to cos θ.

hypotenuse
- The longest side in a right-angled triangle.
- The side which is not one of the arms of the right-angle in a right-angled triangle.

opposite side (to a given angle)
- The side of a triangle which is not one of the arms of the given angle.

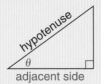

similar triangles
- Two triangles that have the same shape but a different size.
- Triangles that can be changed into each other by either an enlargement or reduction.
- Triangles that have matching angles equal.
- Triangles where the ratio of matching sides is constant.

sine ratio (of an angle θ)
- The ratio $\dfrac{\text{side opposite angle } \theta}{\text{hypotenuse}}$
- Abbreviated to sin θ.

tangent ratio (of an angle θ)
- The ratio $\dfrac{\text{side opposite angle } \theta}{\text{side adjacent to angle } \theta}$
- Abbreviated to tan θ.

trigonometric (trig.) ratios
- A collective name for different ratios of the side lengths of right-angled triangles.
- The ratios have constant values for any particular angle.

trigonometry
- A branch of mathematics, part of which deals with the calculation of the sides and angles of triangles.

Technology Applications

1 The trigonometric ratios 4 Bearings 1
2 Finding sides   5 Bearings 2
3 Finding angles

Technology Applications

Mathematical terms 13

Diagnostic Test 13: | Trigonometry

- Each section of the diagnostic test has similar items that test a certain question type.
- Errors made will indicate areas of weakness.
- Each weakness should be treated by going back to the section listed.

	Section

1 Evaluate, correct to 4 decimal places: 13:04
  a tan 75°   **b** sin 23°   **c** cos 68·3°   **d** tan 48·25°

2 Evaluate, correct to 3 decimal places: 13:04
  a sin 25°30′   **b** tan 59°09′   **c** cos 173°21′   **d** sin 342°12′

3 If $0° \leqslant \theta \leqslant 90°$, find θ, to the nearest minute, given that: 13:04
  a $\cos \theta = 0.639$ **b** $\sin \theta = 0.741$ **c** $\tan \theta = 0.071$
  d $\tan \theta = 3.46$

4 Name the side asked for in each triangle with respect to θ.   13:01

 a   **b**   **c**

  adjacent side   hypotenuse   opposite side

5 State, as a fraction, the value of the ratio asked for.   13:03

 a   **b**   **c**

  $\sin \theta = \ldots$ $\tan \theta = \ldots$ $\cos \theta = \ldots$

6 Find x, correct to 1 decimal place.   13:05

 a   **b**

 c   **d**

7 Find a, correct to 1 decimal place.   13:05

 a   **b**

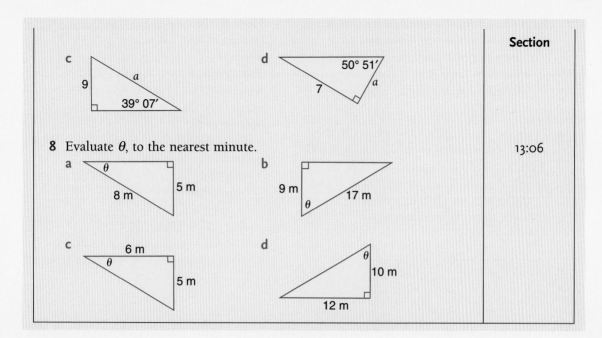

c

9

a

39° 07′

d

50° 51′

7   a

8 Evaluate θ, to the nearest minute.

a

θ

8 m   5 m

b

9 m   17 m

θ

c

6 m

θ

5 m

d

θ

10 m

12 m

Chapter 13 | Revision Assignment

1 Find the value of the pronumeral correct to 2 sig. figs.

a

x

23°57′

14·7

b

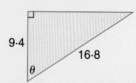

9·4   16·8

θ

c

θ

5·1

4·8

b

5·6

17°37′

x

c

x

43°05′

21·7

2 Find θ to the nearest minute.

a

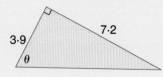

7·2

3·9

θ

3 a A ship's captain measures the angle of elevation of a lighthouse as 4°. If he knows that the lighthouse is 105 m above the sea, how far is he from the coast (to the nearest 100 m)?

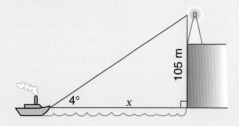

105 m

4° x

b A plane flies at a speed of 650 km/h. It starts from town A and flies on a bearing of 120° for 3 hours. At that time, how far is it
  i south of A?
  ii east of A?

4 From the top, T, of a 135-metre cliff, the angles of depression of two cabins at A and B are 23° and 42° respectively. How far apart are A and B, assuming that A, B and X, the foot of the cliff, are collinear? (Answer to the nearest metre.)

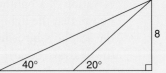

5 From A, the bearing of a tower, T, is 330°. From B, which is 10 km north of A, the bearing of the tower is 290°.

a In the diagram show that
  i $x = h \tan 70°$
  ii $x = (h + 10)\tan 30°$
b Use the equations above to find x.
c Find the distance of the tower from B.

Technology Applications
Animations

Trigonometry ratios

Chapter Review

Questions

assignment

13B

Chapter 13 | Working Mathematically

1 Use ID Card 6 on page xviii to identify:
  a 2 **b** 3 **c** 4 **d** 10 **e** 11
  f 12 **g** 14 **h** 15 **i** 16 **j** 17

2 Use ID Card 7 on page xix to identify:
  a 5 **b** 8 **c** 9 **d** 10 **e** 11
  f 12 **g** 18 **h** 22 **i** 23 **j** 24

3 Why is the diagram shown impossible?

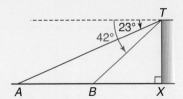

4 a If 6 men can do a piece of work in 8 days, in what time will 18 men do it, working at the same rate?
  b If 14 men can do a piece of work in 12 days, how many men will be needed to do the work in 21 days, working at the same rate?

5 A solid is formed from a cube by cutting off the corners in such a way that the vertices of the new solid will be at the midpoints of the edges of the original cube. If each of the new edges is a units long, what is the surface area of the solid?

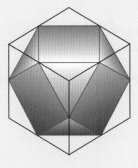

6 Two shops sell the same drink for the same price per bottle. Shop A offers a 10% discount, while shop B offers 13 bottles for the price of 12. Which shop offers the better discount if 12 bottles are bought?

14

Vectors

What's our vector Victor?

How should I know and who are all these other birds following me?

Chapter Contents

Learning Outcomes

Students will be able to:
- Understand the definition of a vector.
- Identify relationships between vectors.
- Perform operations with vectors.
- Calculate the magnitude of a vector.
- Solve problems using vectors.

Areas of Interaction

Approaches to Learning (Knowledge Acquisition, Reflection), Human Ingenuity, Environments

14:01 | What is a Vector?

In Chapter 8 you studied different aspects of intervals on the Cartesian plane.

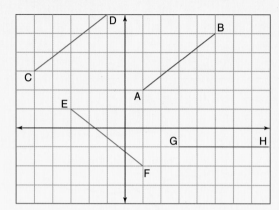

All the intervals shown on this Cartesian plane have one thing in common:

They all have the same length:

$$AB = \sqrt{(5-1)^2 + (5-2)^2}$$
$$= 5$$
$$CD = \sqrt{(6-3)^2 + (-5--1)^2}$$
$$= 5$$
$$EF = \sqrt{(1--2)^2 + (-3-1)^2}$$
$$= 5$$
$$GH = 5$$

Although the lengths of these intervals are the same, they are all distinct from one another.

> ■ A vector is different from an interval because it not only has length, which is called its magnitude, but also direction.

In order to represent this, an arrow is used to show the direction of a vector.

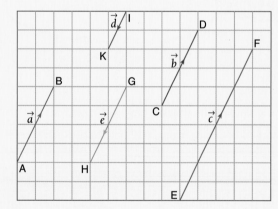

On the grid, five vectors are shown.
All have magnitude represented by their length.
All have direction, represented by the arrow.

Vectors can either be named by their endpoints
For example, $\overrightarrow{AB}$, $\overrightarrow{CD}$, $\overrightarrow{EF}$, $\overrightarrow{GH}$, $\overrightarrow{IK}$
(Note how the arrow above the letters gives the direction of the vector.)

Or by a single lower case letter either written with an arrow above it, or in bold type.
For example, $\vec{a}$, $\vec{b}$, $\vec{c}$, $\vec{d}$, $\vec{e}$ or **a, b, c, d, e**

Some points to note on the vectors shown in the grid above:

- vector $\vec{a}$ = vector $\vec{b}$ since they both have the same magnitude and direction.
- vector $\vec{c}$ = 2 × vector $\vec{a}$ since $\vec{c}$ has the same direction as vector $\vec{a}$ but twice the magnitude.
- vector $\vec{e}$ = −vector $\vec{a}$ since it has the same magnitude as vector $\vec{a}$ but goes the opposite direction.
- vector $\vec{d}$ = $-\frac{1}{2}$ × vector $\vec{a}$ since it has half the magnitude of vector $\vec{a}$ and goes the opposite direction.

So: $\vec{a} = \vec{b}$, $\vec{c} = 2\vec{a}$, $\vec{e} = -\vec{a}$ and $\vec{d} = -\frac{1}{2}\vec{a}$

Of course, you can use the other forms of notation instead if you wish.

Exercise 14:01

1 Express each of the following in terms of $\vec{w}$, $\vec{x}$ and $\vec{y}$.

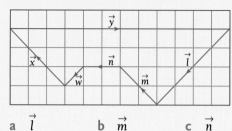

These vectors have magnitude and direction.

a $\vec{l}$ b $\vec{m}$ c $\vec{n}$

2 Write the relationship between the following pairs of vectors.

a $\vec{a}$ and $\vec{h}$ b $\vec{a}$ and $\vec{f}$

c $\vec{b}$ and $\vec{l}$ d $\vec{b}$ and $\vec{k}$

e $\vec{e}$ and $\vec{c}$ f $\vec{d}$ and $\vec{g}$

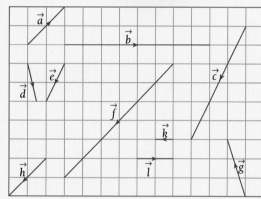

3 On a grid, draw the following vectors from those given in the diagram in question 2.

a $\dfrac{\vec{a}}{2}$ b $-2\vec{e}$ c $-\dfrac{3}{2}\vec{h}$ d $\dfrac{2\vec{f}}{3}$

14:02 | Column Vectors and Vector Operations

When we want to refer to a vector without drawing it, we can write it as a **column vector**.

To do this we must count how many units the vector goes horizontally and how many it goes vertically.

For example, consider the vectors shown in the diagram.

For the vector $\overrightarrow{AB}$ to travel from the start of the vector to the finish it goes 1 horizontally and 3 vertically.

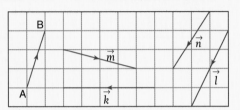

So $\overrightarrow{AB} = \begin{pmatrix} 1 \\ 3 \end{pmatrix}$ horizontal units on top
vertical units on the bottom

The numbers in the brackets are called the components.

Vector $\overrightarrow{m}$ goes 4 units horizontally and -1 unit vertically

So $\overrightarrow{m} = \begin{pmatrix} 4 \\ -1 \end{pmatrix}$

Vector $\overrightarrow{n}$ goes -2 units horizontally and -3 unit vertically

So $\overrightarrow{n} = \begin{pmatrix} -2 \\ -3 \end{pmatrix}$ which can be written $-\begin{pmatrix} 2 \\ 3 \end{pmatrix}$

Vector $\overrightarrow{k}$ goes -5 units horizontally and 0 unit vertically

So $\overrightarrow{k} = \begin{pmatrix} -5 \\ 0 \end{pmatrix}$

Vector $\overrightarrow{l}$ goes -2 units horizontally and -4 unit vertically

So $\overrightarrow{l} = \begin{pmatrix} -2 \\ -4 \end{pmatrix}$ which can be written $-\begin{pmatrix} 2 \\ 4 \end{pmatrix}$ or $-2\begin{pmatrix} 1 \\ 2 \end{pmatrix}$

Investigation 14:02 | Operating on vectors

Please use the Assessment Grid on the page 418 to help you understand what is required for this Investigation.

Each grid shows pairs of vectors, $\overrightarrow{AB}$ and $\overrightarrow{BC}$ joined end to end. This can represent a journey from A to C. Complete the table showing the column vectors for both $\overrightarrow{AB}$ and $\overrightarrow{BC}$ and the vector $\overrightarrow{AC}$ (not drawn) which represents a shortcut from A to C bypassing B.

1

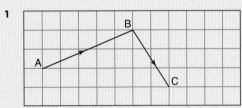

2

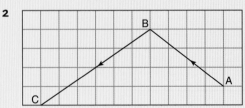

3

4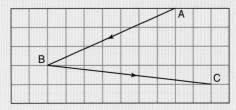

5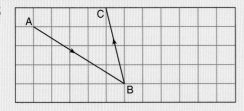

6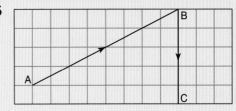

	$\overrightarrow{AB}$	$\overrightarrow{BC}$	$\overrightarrow{AC}$
1			
2			
3			
4			
5			
6			

Is there a pattern forming between the values in the column vectors for $\overrightarrow{AB}$ and $\overrightarrow{BC}$ and the values in the column vector for $\overrightarrow{AC}$?

Write this pattern down as a general rule if $\overrightarrow{AB} = \begin{pmatrix} a \\ b \end{pmatrix}$ and $\overrightarrow{BC} = \begin{pmatrix} c \\ d \end{pmatrix}$

Test out your general rule with **three** pairs of vectors of your own.

Now consider the two vectors $\vec{a}$ and $\vec{b}$ in this grid. Suppose $\vec{a}$ represents the direction and distance an aeroplane travelled on one part of a trip and $\vec{b}$ the direction and distance it travelled on the next part of its trip.

Unfortunately the navigator has been sloppy and has not started the second part from where the first finished.

How would you go about representing the direction and distance they would have travelled if it went from the start to the finish in a straight line (ie taking a shortcut)?

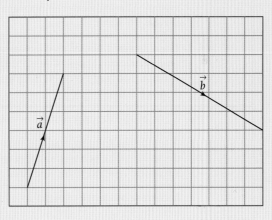

Once you have a vector that represents what the journey would have been in a straight line, it is possible to calculate how far from the starting point the plane finishes. It is also possible to calculate in what direction it could have flown to get there in a straight line.

Assuming that 1 unit on the grid represents 100 km, calculate these two values.

In what other real-life situations could vectors be used?

Assessment Grid for Investigation 14:02 | **Operating on vectors**

The following is a sample assessment grid for this investigation. You should carefully read the criteria *before* beginning the investigation so that you know what is required.

		Assessment Criteria (B, C, D) for this investigation		Achieved ✓
Criterion B **Investigating Patterns**	a	None of the descriptors below has been achieved.	0	
	b	With some help, mathematical techniques have been applied and the patterns in the table have been recognised.	1	
			2	
	c	Mathematical techniques have been selected and applied and the patterns in the table have been recognised and a general rule suggested.	3	
			4	
	d	Mathematical techniques have been selected and applied and the patterns in the table have been recognised and described as a general rule. Further examples are given in an effort to provide justification.	5	
			6	
	e	Further to (d), the rule that is identified is explained fully and its application in the final problem is used as part of the justification.	7	
			8	
Criterion C **Communication in Mathematics**	a	None of the descriptors below has been achieved.	0	
	b	There is a basic use of mathematical language and representation. Lines of reasoning are hard to follow.	1	
			2	
	c	There is sufficient use of mathematical language and representation. Lines of reasoning are clear but not always logical. Moving between diagrams and column vectors is done with some success.	3	
			4	
	d	There is good use of mathematical language and representation. Lines of reasoning are clear, logical and concise. Moving between diagrams and column vectors is done effectively.	5	
			6	
Criterion D **Reflection in Mathematics**	a	None of the descriptors below has been achieved.	0	
	b	Attempts have been made to explain whether the results in the table make sense and the importance of the findings in a real-life context using the final problem.	1	
			2	
	c	A correct but brief explanation whether the results in the table make sense is given. A description of the importance of the findings in a real-life context using the final problem is given.	3	
			4	
	d	A critical explanation whether the results in the table make sense is given. A detailed description of the importance of the findings in a real-life context using the final problem is given. The significance of the findings has been demonstrated in the solution to the final problem.	5	
			6	

Vector Operations and Vector Geometry

In Investigation 14:02, you should have seen that to combine two vectors you place them end to end, so that it is possible to travel from the beginning of the first vector to the end of the last vector.

Combining them in this way and drawing the shortcut from the start to the finish in a straight line is the same as adding the components of the column vectors.

For example, if the original vectors $\vec{a}$ and $\vec{b}$ are to be combined, we move $\vec{b}$ so that it starts where $\vec{a}$ ends; shown in blue.

When the start of the two vectors is joined to the end of the two vectors, the resultant vector is the sum of the two original vectors $\vec{a}$ and $\vec{b}$, shown in red.

When adding vectors on a diagram, they are placed head to tail. The resultant vector, which represents the sum, goes from the tail of the first vector to the head of the last.

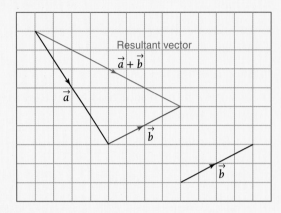

Alternatively the column vectors can be used:

For example, $\vec{a} = \begin{pmatrix} 4 \\ -6 \end{pmatrix}$ and $\vec{b} = \begin{pmatrix} 4 \\ 2 \end{pmatrix}$, so $\vec{a} + \vec{b} = \begin{pmatrix} 4+4 \\ -6+2 \end{pmatrix} = \begin{pmatrix} 8 \\ -4 \end{pmatrix}$

Check this result from the diagram.

worked examples

1   Vectors $\vec{a}$, $\vec{b}$ and $\vec{c}$ are shown in the diagram.

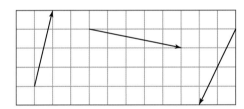

Add vectors head to tail.

By using the diagram, draw the resultant vector for $\vec{a} + \vec{b} + \vec{c}$.

Solution

Move $\vec{b}$ and $\vec{c}$ so that all three vectors are arranged head to tail.

The resultant vector starts at the tail of $\vec{a}$ and goes straight to the end of $\vec{c}$.

So $\vec{a} + \vec{b} + \vec{c} = \begin{pmatrix} 3 \\ -1 \end{pmatrix}$

To check, use the column vectors:

$\vec{a} + \vec{b} + \vec{c} = \begin{pmatrix} 1 \\ 4 \end{pmatrix} + \begin{pmatrix} 5 \\ -1 \end{pmatrix} + \begin{pmatrix} -3 \\ -4 \end{pmatrix} = \begin{pmatrix} 3 \\ -1 \end{pmatrix}$

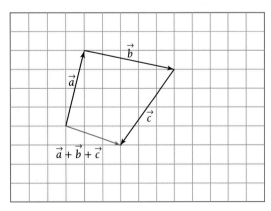

continued ➜➜➜

2 The vectors $\vec{a}$ and $\vec{b}$ are shown in the diagram. Use another vector diagram to show the resultant vector of $\vec{a} - \vec{b}$.

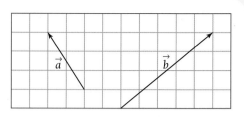

Solution

We can only add vectors so to do this problem, instead of subtracting $\vec{b}$ we add $-\vec{b}$.

Since $\vec{a} - \vec{b} = \vec{a} + (-\vec{b})$.

So $\vec{a}$ and $-\vec{b}$ are placed head to tail to get the resultant vector.

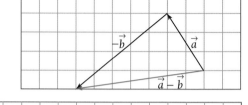

3 Use the diagram to express the following in terms of $\vec{a}$, $\vec{b}$ and $\vec{c}$.

   a $\overrightarrow{DA}$ **b** $\overrightarrow{AD}$ **c** $\overrightarrow{AC}$

   d $\overrightarrow{CA}$ **e** $\overrightarrow{DB}$ **f** $\overrightarrow{BD}$

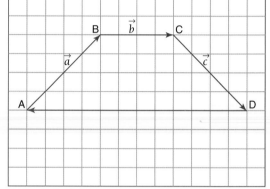

Solution

a $\overrightarrow{DA} = -12\vec{b}$

Alternatively, to get from D to A we could travel $-\vec{c}$ then $-\vec{b}$ then $-\vec{a}$ so that

$\overrightarrow{DA} = -\vec{c} - \vec{b} - \vec{a}$

b $\overrightarrow{AD} = -\overrightarrow{DA}$

so $\overrightarrow{AD} = -(-12\vec{b}) = 12\vec{b}$

or $\overrightarrow{AD} = -(-\vec{c} - \vec{b} - \vec{a}) = \vec{a} + \vec{b} + \vec{c}$

c $\overrightarrow{AC} = \vec{a} + \vec{b}$, in other words, to get from A to C you must travel along $\vec{a}$ then $\vec{b}$

d $\overrightarrow{CA} = -\overrightarrow{AC} = -(\vec{a} + \vec{b}) = -\vec{a} - \vec{b}$

e $\overrightarrow{DB} = -\vec{c} - \vec{b}$

f $\overrightarrow{BD} = -\overrightarrow{DB} = -(-\vec{c} - \vec{b}) = \vec{b} + \vec{c}$

1 Represent the following vectors on a grid.

   a $\vec{a} = \begin{pmatrix} 5 \\ 3 \end{pmatrix}$ b $\overrightarrow{AB} = \begin{pmatrix} -2 \\ 1 \end{pmatrix}$ c $d = \begin{pmatrix} -3 \\ -4 \end{pmatrix}$

   d $\vec{m} = \begin{pmatrix} 6 \\ -4 \end{pmatrix}$ e $\overrightarrow{YX} = \begin{pmatrix} 0 \\ 5 \end{pmatrix}$ f $f = \begin{pmatrix} 3 \\ 0 \end{pmatrix}$

2 From the vectors in question 1, calculate the resultant column vector for the following:

   a $\vec{a} + \vec{m}$ b $\vec{a} + d$ c $\overrightarrow{AB} + \overrightarrow{YX}$ d $\overrightarrow{AB} - \overrightarrow{YX}$

   e $\overrightarrow{AB} + \overrightarrow{XY}$ f $\overrightarrow{YX} - f$ g $\overrightarrow{AB} - \vec{m}$ h $\overrightarrow{BA} - \vec{m}$

   i $\vec{a} + \vec{m} + f$ j $3(\overrightarrow{AB} + \vec{m})$

3 By using the vectors shown in the grid and writing the vectors in column form, find the resultant vector of the following.

   a $\vec{a} + m$ b $\overrightarrow{PQ} - \vec{c}$

   c $\overrightarrow{WX} + d$ d $\overrightarrow{QP} + \vec{c}$

   e $m - d$ f $\vec{d} - \vec{a}$

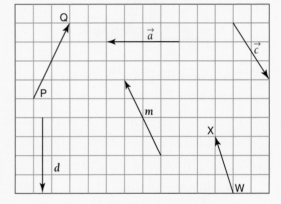

4 Express the vector $\vec{v}$ in terms of other vectors shown on the grid.

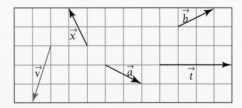

5 Given that X and Y are the midpoints of AC and AB respectively, express the following in terms of the vectors $\overrightarrow{CX}$ and $\overrightarrow{AB}$.

   a $\overrightarrow{CA}$ b $\overrightarrow{XA}$ c $\overrightarrow{AY}$ d $\overrightarrow{XY}$ e $\overrightarrow{BC}$

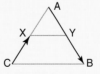

6 Looking at the results for (d) and (e) from question 1, what conclusions can you draw about the lines XY and CB?

7 Using the diagram, express the following in terms of $\overrightarrow{AB}$ and $\overrightarrow{CA}$.

a $\overrightarrow{CB}$ b $\overrightarrow{AD}$ c $\overrightarrow{DB}$

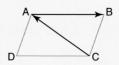

8 Using the diagram, express the following in terms of $\vec{a}$ and $\vec{b}$.

a $\overrightarrow{AB}$ b $\overrightarrow{CD}$ c $\overrightarrow{BD}$ d $\overrightarrow{BE}$

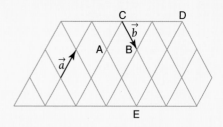

Same direction and same size gives equal vectors.

9 The quadrilateral ABCD is made up of three equilateral triangles. Express the following in terms of the vectors *x* and *y*.

a $\overrightarrow{AE}$ b $\overrightarrow{EB}$ c $\overrightarrow{CD}$ d $\overrightarrow{BD}$

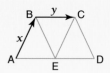

10 Show, with the aid of a diagram, how the vector $\vec{r} = \begin{pmatrix} -3 \\ 5 \end{pmatrix}$ can be formed by combining the following vectors:

$$\vec{p} = \begin{pmatrix} 3 \\ 1 \end{pmatrix} \qquad \vec{s} = \begin{pmatrix} -1 \\ 2 \end{pmatrix} \qquad \vec{q} = \begin{pmatrix} 0 \\ -2 \end{pmatrix}$$

$$\vec{u} = \begin{pmatrix} 6 \\ -1 \end{pmatrix} \qquad \vec{t} = \begin{pmatrix} 4 \\ 2 \end{pmatrix}$$

14:03 | Magnitude of a Vector

Practical Activity 14:03 | **Magnitude of a vector**

1 For each of the vectors shown on the grid, complete a right triangle as in the example vector $\vec{a}$.

2 Complete the table below as for the example vector $\vec{a}$.

Vector	Column vector	Magnitude
$\vec{a}$	$\begin{pmatrix} 2 \\ 3 \end{pmatrix}$	$\sqrt{2^2 + 3^2} = \sqrt{13}$ units
$\vec{b}$		
c		
$\overrightarrow{DE}$		
$\vec{f}$		
g		

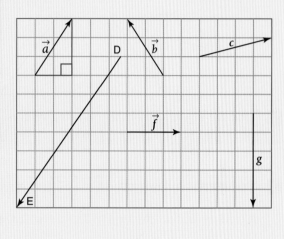

You should have discovered that for any vector $\vec{v} = \begin{pmatrix} a \\ b \end{pmatrix}$ the magnitude of the vector is given by $\sqrt{a^2 + b^2}$.

When writing the magnitude of the vector $\vec{v}$ we write $|\vec{v}|$ sometimes called the modulus of the vector.

> ■ So the magnitude or modulus $|\vec{v}|$ of the vector $\vec{v} = \begin{pmatrix} a \\ b \end{pmatrix}$ is given by $|\vec{v}| = \sqrt{a^2 + b^2}$

Pythagoras strikes again.

1 Find the magnitude of the vectors shown in the grid.

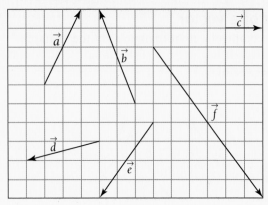

2 Find the magnitude of the following vectors.

a $\vec{a} = \begin{pmatrix} 15 \\ 8 \end{pmatrix}$ b $\vec{b} = \begin{pmatrix} -6 \\ 8 \end{pmatrix}$ c $\vec{c} = \begin{pmatrix} -20 \\ -21 \end{pmatrix}$ d $\vec{d} = \begin{pmatrix} 12 \\ -5 \end{pmatrix}$ e $\vec{e} = \begin{pmatrix} -2 \\ 10 \end{pmatrix}$

3 Evaluate the following if $\overrightarrow{AB} = \begin{pmatrix} 5 \\ -3 \end{pmatrix}$, $\vec{t} = \begin{pmatrix} -1 \\ 6 \end{pmatrix}$, $\vec{u} = \begin{pmatrix} 1 \\ 11 \end{pmatrix}$.

a $|\overrightarrow{AB} + \vec{t}|$ b $|\vec{u} + \overrightarrow{AB}|$ c $|\vec{t} + \vec{u}|$ d $|2\vec{u} - \vec{t}|$ e $|\vec{t} - \overrightarrow{AB}|$

14:04 | Solving Problems Using Vectors

Vectors are often used to represent objects that are in motion. The length of the vector represents the magnitude of the motion (distance or speed), and the direction of the vector, the direction of the object.

You will need to use trigonometry to solve these problems.

worked examples

1 A hiker walks on a bearing of 10° for a distance of 5 km and then on a bearing of 60° for another 5 km. How far, and in what direction is he, from his starting point?

Solution

Let the vectors $\vec{a}$ and $\vec{b}$ represent the first and second legs of the hike respectively.

To add the vectors to get the resultant vector $\vec{r}$ we need to calculate the vertical and horizontal components of $\vec{a}$ and $\vec{b}$.

If $\vec{a} = \begin{pmatrix} A_x \\ A_y \end{pmatrix}$, then using trigonometry

$$\cos 80 = \frac{A_x}{5} \quad \text{and} \quad \sin 80 = \frac{A_y}{5} \quad \text{since } |\vec{a}| = |\vec{b}| = 5$$

$$\therefore A_x = 5 \cos 80 \quad \text{and} \quad A_y = 5 \sin 80$$

$$\therefore \vec{a} = \begin{pmatrix} 5 \cos 80 \\ 5 \sin 80 \end{pmatrix}$$

Similarly, if $\vec{b} = \begin{pmatrix} B_x \\ B_y \end{pmatrix}$ then $B_x = 5 \cos 30$ and $B_y = 5 \sin 30$

$$\therefore \vec{b} = \begin{pmatrix} 5 \cos 30 \\ 5 \sin 30 \end{pmatrix}$$

The resultant vector $\vec{r} = \vec{a} + \vec{b}$

$$= \begin{pmatrix} 5 \cos 80 + 5 \cos 30 \\ 5 \sin 80 + 5 \sin 30 \end{pmatrix}$$

$$= \begin{pmatrix} 5 \cdot 20 \\ 7 \cdot 42 \end{pmatrix}$$

The distance from the starting position is given by $|\vec{r}| = \sqrt{(5 \cdot 20)^2 + (7 \cdot 42)^2}$

$$= 9 \cdot 06 \text{ km}$$

The direction from the starting point can be found by considering the components of the resultant vector as a triangle.

$$\tan \theta = \frac{7 \cdot 42}{5 \cdot 20}$$

$$\theta = \tan^{-1}\left(\frac{7 \cdot 42}{5 \cdot 20}\right)$$

$$\theta = 55°$$

As a result, after his hike, the hiker is 9·06 km from his starting point on a bearing of 45°.

continued ➜➜➜

2 An aeroplane is flying at a ground speed of 200 km/h on a bearing of 300°. A crosswind is blowing at 50 km/h on a bearing of 50°. Use vectors to calculate the resultant velocity and direction of the aeroplane.

Solution

Here the magnitude of the vector represents the speed.

The vectors $\vec{p}$ and $\vec{w}$ must be resolved into their vertical and horizontal parts.

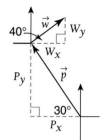

$$\vec{p} = \begin{pmatrix} P_x \\ P_y \end{pmatrix} \qquad \text{and} \qquad \vec{w} = \begin{pmatrix} W_x \\ W_y \end{pmatrix}$$

$$\vec{p} = \begin{pmatrix} -|\vec{p}|\cos 30° \\ |\vec{p}|\sin 30° \end{pmatrix} \qquad \text{and} \qquad \vec{w} = \begin{pmatrix} |\vec{w}|\cos 40° \\ |\vec{w}|\sin 40° \end{pmatrix}$$

where $|\vec{p}| = 200$ km/h $\qquad$ and $\qquad |\vec{w}| = 50$ km/h

$$\therefore \ \vec{p} = \begin{pmatrix} -200\cos 30° \\ 200\sin 30° \end{pmatrix} \qquad \text{and} \qquad \vec{w} = \begin{pmatrix} 50\cos 40° \\ 50\sin 40° \end{pmatrix}$$

So the resultant vector $\vec{r}$ which is $\vec{p} + \vec{w} = \begin{pmatrix} -200\cos 30° + 50\cos 40° \\ 200\sin 30° + 50\sin 40° \end{pmatrix}$

$$= \begin{pmatrix} -134\cdot 91 \\ 132\cdot 14 \end{pmatrix}$$

Note: It is important that these signs are correct so that the final direction can be worked out.

Therefore the resulting velocity is given by $|\vec{r}| = \sqrt{(-134\cdot 91)^2 + (132\cdot 14)^2}$
$$= 188\cdot 8 \text{ km/h}$$

The direction of the plane is given by $270° - \theta$, where $\tan\theta = \dfrac{132\cdot 14}{134\cdot 91}$

So that $\theta = \tan^{-1}\left(\dfrac{132\cdot 14}{134\cdot 91}\right)$
$$= 44\cdot 4°$$

In conclusion, the aeroplane is flying at 188·8 km/h on a bearing of 314·4°.

Exercise 14:04

1 A yacht sails on a bearing of 100° for a distance of 54 nautical miles and then on a bearing of 40° for a distance of 80 nautical miles. How far (to the nearest nautical mile) and in what direction (to the nearest degree), is the yacht from its starting point? (Remember: from the diagram, the first y component is negative.)

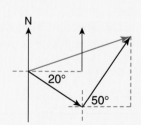

2 Crazy Ivan has set off to cross the Gobi desert. He first walked for 35 km on a bearing of 200° and realised he was heading the wrong way so he then walked for 20 km on a bearing of 310°. How far, and in what direction (to the nearest whole degree) is he now from his starting point?
(Remember: from the diagram, the first x and y components are negative and the second x component is negative.)

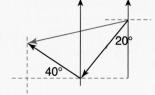

3 A plane flew first on a bearing of 320° for 150 km and then due east for 150 km. How far, and in what direction, is the plane from its starting point?
(Remember: due east only has an x component.)

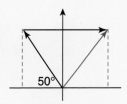

4 A balloonist is at the mercy of the wind. When he first takes off, the wind blows him on a bearing of 100° for 80 km and then on a bearing of 200° for 100 km.
What is the balloonist's distance and direction from the starting position?

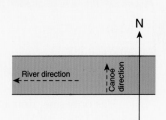

5 A canoeist is paddling due north across a river which runs from east to west.
If the canoeist is paddling at 3 km/h and the river is flowing at 5 km/h, find the resultant speed and direction of the canoe.

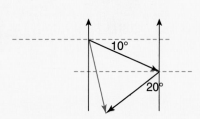

6 A plane is flying on a bearing of 050° at a ground speed of 180 km/h. The wind is blowing on a bearing of 200° at a speed of 50 km/h. Find the resulting speed and direction of the plane.
(Answer to the nearest whole km/h and degree.)

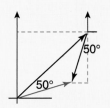

7 A flock of seagulls is flying on a bearing of 135° at a ground speed of 8 km/h. The wind is blowing on a bearing of 70° at a speed of 5 km/h. Find the resulting speed and direction of the seagulls.
(Answer with speed correct to 3 significant figures and the bearing to the nearest degree.)

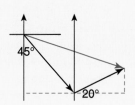

8 A woman is rowing across a 600 m wide river, starting at point A, at a speed of 3 km/h. The current is moving at 5 km/h. If the woman starts rowing straight across the river:

a how far downstream from point B will she finish?

b what will be her resulting speed (3 significant figures) and direction (nearest whole degree) if B is due north of A?

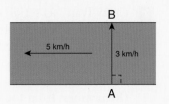

Mathematical Terms 14

interval

- Represented by a straight line joining two points.
  Has only one dimension: length.

vector

- Represented by an arrow joining two points.
  Has two dimensions: length and direction.

column vector

- Represents a vector by its horizontal and vertical component parts.
  Is written in the form $\begin{pmatrix} x \\ y \end{pmatrix}$

resultant vector

- The result of putting a number of vectors head to tail in order to add them.
  Goes from the tail of the first vector to the head of the last vector.

magnitude of a vector

- The length of a vector.
  Denoted by $|\ |$
  For example the magnitude of vector $\vec{v} = \begin{pmatrix} x \\ y \end{pmatrix}$ is given by $|\vec{v}| = \sqrt{x^2 + b^2}$

modulus of a vector

- The same as the magnitude of a vector.

bearing

- The direction in which an object is from some starting position.
  Always measured clockwise from north and given as a three digit number.

Diagnostic Test 14: | Vectors

- Each section of the diagnostic test has similar items that test a certain question type.
- Errors made will indicate areas of weakness.
- Each weakness should be treated by going back to the section listed.

Section

1 Express each of the following vectors in terms of $\vec{v}$ and $\vec{w}$.

14:01

a $\vec{a}$ b $\vec{b}$ c $\vec{c}$

d $\vec{d}$ e $\vec{e}$ f $\vec{f}$

g $\vec{g}$ h $\vec{h}$ i $\vec{i}$

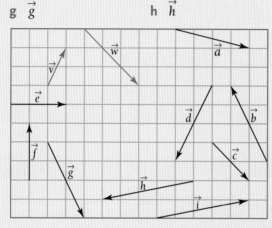

2 Using the vectors $\vec{v}$ and $\vec{w}$ shown, draw the following on grid paper.

14:01

a $\vec{a} = \vec{v} + \vec{w}$ b $\vec{b} = \vec{v} - \vec{w}$ c $\vec{c} = -2\vec{v}$

d $\vec{d} = -2\vec{v} + \vec{w}$ e $\vec{e} = \vec{w} - \vec{v}$ f $\vec{f} = \frac{1}{2}\vec{v} - \vec{w}$

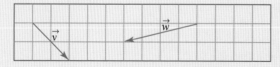

3 Represent the vectors in the grid as column vectors.

14:02

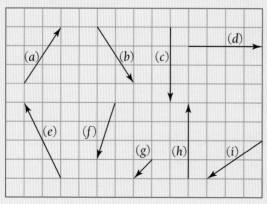

4 If $\vec{a} = \begin{pmatrix} 3 \\ -1 \end{pmatrix}$, $\vec{b} = \begin{pmatrix} 0 \\ 5 \end{pmatrix}$ and $\vec{c} = \begin{pmatrix} -4 \\ -4 \end{pmatrix}$ write the resultant vector for each of the following:

Section 14:02

    a $\vec{a} + \vec{b} + \vec{c}$ **b** $\vec{a} - \vec{b}$ **c** $2\vec{a} - \vec{c}$

    d $\vec{c} - 2\vec{b}$ **e** $2(\vec{b} - \vec{a})$ **f** $\vec{c} - \vec{b} - \vec{a}$

5 If $\vec{a} = \begin{pmatrix} 15 \\ -8 \end{pmatrix}$, $\vec{b} = \begin{pmatrix} 6 \\ 10 \end{pmatrix}$ and $\vec{c} = \begin{pmatrix} 20 \\ 21 \end{pmatrix}$ evaluate the following correct to 3 significant figures.

14:03

    a $|\vec{a}|$ **b** $|\vec{b}|$ **c** $|\vec{c}|$

    d $|2\vec{a}|$ **e** $|\vec{a} + \vec{b}|$ **f** $|\vec{c} - \vec{a}|$

6 Find the value of x in the following. Answer correct to 3 significant figures where necessary.

14:03

    a $\left| \begin{pmatrix} 3 \\ x \end{pmatrix} \right| = 5$ **b** $\left| \begin{pmatrix} 12 \\ x \end{pmatrix} \right| = 13$ **c** $\left| \begin{pmatrix} x \\ 9 \end{pmatrix} \right| = 12$

    d $\left| \begin{pmatrix} 5 \\ 8 \end{pmatrix} \right| = x$ **e** $\left| \begin{pmatrix} 17 \\ x \end{pmatrix} \right| = 28$

7 Solve the following problems by first drawing vector diagrams.

14:04

    a A plane, flying in still air flies on a bearing of 120° for 150 km and then on a bearing of 250° for 200 km. What distance and bearing is the plane from its starting position? (Answer to the nearest metre and whole degree.)

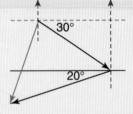

    b A yacht is sailing at a still water speed of 10 knots on a bearing of 330°. The ocean current is running at a speed of 3 knots on a bearing of 040°. What is the resulting speed and bearing of the yacht? (Answer both to the nearest whole number.)

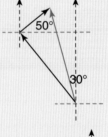

    c A plane is flying on a bearing of 210° at a ground speed of 200 km/h. The wind is blowing at 25 km/h on a bearing of 280°. Find the resulting speed (correct to 1 decimal place) and bearing (to the nearest whole degree) of the plane.

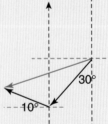

Chapter 14 | Revision Assignment

1 Use vectors $\vec{v}$ and $\vec{w}$ to draw the following.

a $\vec{v} + \vec{w}$ b $\vec{v} - \vec{w}$

c $2\vec{v} + 3\vec{w}$ d $\vec{w} - \frac{1}{2}\vec{v}$

e Write vectors $\vec{v}$ and $\vec{w}$ as column vectors.

f Find $|\vec{v}|$ and $|\vec{w}|$.

g Calculate the magnitude of the vectors you found in **a** to **d**.

2 The first two legs of a hike can be represented by the vectors
$$\vec{a} = \begin{pmatrix} 3 \\ -4 \end{pmatrix} \text{ and } \vec{b} = \begin{pmatrix} 5 \\ -12 \end{pmatrix} \text{ (units in km)}.$$

a Calculate the total distance covered.

b Calculate how far the hiker is from his starting point.

c Represent this graphically.

3 A plane flies on a bearing of 60° for 800 km for its first stop then flies another 1200 km on a bearing of 135°.

a How far, and in what direction is the plane from its starting point?

b For the plane's third trip it travels at a speed of 400 km/h on a bearing of 330°. If a crosswind of 60 km/h has bearing of 45°, find the resultant velocity and direction.

Statistics

Chapter Contents

Learning Outcomes

Students will be able to:

• Collect and analyse data using measures of central tendency and range.
• Group, tabulate and graph data to aid analysis.
• Use measures of spread to analyse data.

Areas of Interaction

Approaches to Learning (Knowledge Acquisition, Problem Solving, Communication, Logical Thinking, IT Skills, Collaboration, Reflection), Human Ingenuity, Environments

15:01 | Review of Statistics

In Books 2 and 3, the work in statistics concentrated on the collection, organisation and analysis of data.

The topics covered included:
- frequency tables and graphs
- analysing data: range, mode, mean, median
- cumulative frequency tables and graphs
- grouped data
- sampling a population
- stem-and-leaf displays and dot plots

Here is a list of the statistical measures that were used.

The *range* = highest score − lowest score.
The *mode* is the outcome that occurs the *most*.
The *median* is the middle score for an odd number of scores.
The *median* is the average of the middle two scores for an even number of scores.
The *mean* is the arithmetic average.

$$\text{mean} = \frac{\text{sum of the scores}}{\text{total number of scores}} = \left[\frac{\text{sum of } fx \text{ column}}{\text{sum of } f \text{ column}}\right] = \frac{\sum fx}{\sum f}$$

I know that ...I think ...

worked example

The following marks out of ten were obtained in a class quiz.

5   3   8   6   7   5   7   3   4   5
7   8   5   5   4   6   6   6   3   6
6   3   6   4   5   3   7   5   6

1 Organise these scores into a frequency distribution table.
2 Add a cumulative frequency and *fx* column to the table.
3 Use the table to calculate the mode, median and mean mark for the quiz.

Solution

Mark (x)	Tally	Frequency (f)	Cumulative frequency (c.f.)	fx
3	⅃Ж	5	5	15
4					3	8	12
5	⅃Ж ||	7	15	35
6	⅃Ж |||	8	23	48
7						4	27	28
8				2	29	16
Totals		29		154

■ *fx* means frequency times score.

■ c.f. is the cumulative frequency.

continued ➜➜➜

- As the mode is the outcome that occurs the most, the mode is 6.

- The median is the middle score when the scores are arranged in order. As there are 29 scores, the 15th score will be the middle score. Using the cumulative frequency column, which counts the scores in order, it can be seen that the 15th score is a 5. Hence, the median is 5.

- $$\text{The mean} = \frac{\text{sum of } fx \text{ column}}{\text{sum of } f \text{ column}} = \frac{\sum fx}{\sum f}$$

$$= \frac{154}{29}$$

$$= 5 \cdot 3 \text{ (correct to 1 dec. pl.)}$$

Finding the mean using the calculator

Once the calculator is put into the statistics mode, it can be used to calculate the mean from a frequency table.

Mark	Frequency
3	5
4	3
5	7
6	8
7	4
8	2
Total:	29

Press 3 $\boxed{\times}$ 5 $\boxed{x}$

4 $\boxed{\times}$ 3 $\boxed{x}$

5 $\boxed{\times}$ 7 $\boxed{x}$

6 $\boxed{\times}$ 8 $\boxed{x}$

7 $\boxed{\times}$ 4 $\boxed{x}$

8 $\boxed{\times}$ 2 $\boxed{x}$

Then press $\boxed{\bar{x}}$ to obtain the mean, 5·3 (to 1 dec. pl.).

■ *Remember*
Keys may be marked differently on some calculators

Pressing $\boxed{n}$ shows the number of scores to be 29.

Exercise 15:01

1 Determine the **i** range, **ii** mode, **iii** median and **iv** mean for each set of scores.
- **a** 5, 9, 2, 7, 5, 8, 4
- **b** 5, 8, 5, 7, 8, 5, 9, 7
- **c** 21, 24, 19, 25, 24
- **d** 1·3, 1·5, 1·1, 1·5, 1·6, 1·4, 1·7, 1·9

2 Use your calculator to evaluate $\bar{x}$ for each set of scores.
- **a** 6, 9, 7, 8, 5
  4, 9, 6, 5, 4
  3, 8, 8, 5, 7
  6, 5, 7, 5, 4
- **b** 61, 47, 56, 87, 91
  44, 59, 65, 77, 73
  49, 39, 82, 60, 51
  84, 73, 67, 65, 55
- **c** 8, 8, 8, 8, 8, 8
  6, 6, 6, 6, 6, 6
  7, 7, 7, 7, 7, 7
  9, 9, 9, 9, 3, 3

d Outcome	Freq.
1	6
2	9
3	11
4	7
5	2

e Outcome	Freq.
48	6
49	11
50	27
51	15
52	8
53	3

f Outcome	Freq.
12	2
13	15
14	43
15	67
16	27
17	8

3

Outcome	Freq.	fx	c.f.
5	1		
6	4		
7	6		
8	7		
9	5		
10	2		
Totals			

a Copy and complete this table and then determine the mode, mean and median for this set of data.

b How many scores were greater than the mean? How many scores were less than the mean?

c What is the range of the scores?

d Add a relative frequency column to the table. Express the relative frequencies as decimals.

4 Use the cumulative frequency histogram shown to complete the table below.

Outcome	Frequency (f)	fx	c.f.
5			
6			
7			
8			
9			
10			
	$\Sigma f =$	$\Sigma fx =$	

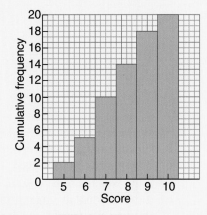

From the table, determine, for this set of scores, the:

a mode
b mean
c median
d range

To find the:
mode use the f column
median use the c.f. column
mean use the fx and f columns.

5 Use the cumulative frequency graphs below to determine the range and median. (*Note*: These graphs have the same range but different medians.)

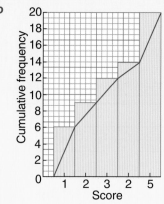

a

Cumulative frequency vs *Score*

b

Cumulative frequency vs *Score*

6 This frequency polygon represents a survey conducted of all families in Allyson Street.

a Using this data, complete the table.

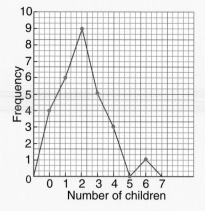

Frequency vs *Number of children*

Children	Frequency	fx	c.f.
0			
1			
2			
3			
4			
5			
6			

b How many families were surveyed in Allyson Street?
c How many children lived in Allyson Street?
d What was the most common number of children per family (mode)?
e If the national average number of children per family is 2·0, is the average number of children per family in Allyson Street above or below this national average?

7 Grade 9's maths results have been organised into an ordered stem-and-leaf plot using a class size of 5 as shown.

a Complete the frequency column and use it to determine the modal class.
b Complete the cumulative frequency column and use it to find the median class.

Stem	Leaf	Frequency	Cumulative frequency
6(5)	88999		
7(0)	000012234		
7(5)	555566777788		
8(0)	00011112344		
8(5)	58		
9(0)	00012334		
9(5)	789		

8 Each golfer listed on the right completed three rounds of golf in the tournament, ie Steve Allan scored 66, 64 and 68.

a Copy and complete the table below to record the score for each round played in this tournament.

Class	Class centre (c.c.)	Frequency (f)	f × c.c.	Cumulative frequency (c.f.)
64–66	65	25		
67–69		74		
70–72		73		
73–75		24		
76–78		2		

b What is the range of the scores?

c What is the modal class?

d Use the class centres to find an approximation for the mean.

e What is the median class?

f How many rounds were completed with a score less than 73?

Steve Allan (Vic) 66 64 68..............................
Aaron Baddeley (Vic) 70 64 65 ....
Rich Beem (USA) 66 64 69..............................
Craig Parry (WA) 66 65 68..............................
Gavin Coles (NSW) 68 64 68..............................

Adam Crawford (Qld) 67 68 66 ....
Charles Howell III (USA) 65 66 70 ....
Robert Allenby (Vic) 71 65 65 ....
Adam Scott (Qld) 69 64 69..............................
Geoff Ogilvy (Vic) 66 70 67 ....

Chris Downes (Qld) 66 71 67 ....
Richard Green (Vic) 71 69 64..........................
Phil Tataurangi (NZ) 73 67 65 ....
Scott Laycock (Vic) 69 72 64..........................
Craig Carmichael (ACT) 70 69 67 ....

Craig Jones (Qld) 70 67 69 ....
Peter Lonard (NSW) 69 68 69..........................
James McLean (Vic) 69 69 68..........................
Richard Moir (Am) (Qld) 72 68 66 ....
Paul Sheehan (NSW) 74 66 67 ....

Greg Chalmers (WA) 73 69 65..........................
Mathew Goggin (Tas) 72 67 68 ....
Jason King (NSW) 70 65 72..............................
Peter O'Malley (NSW) 71 65 71 ....
Gareth Paddison (NZ) 70 68 69 ....

Peter Fowler (NSW) 71 70 67 ....
Jarrod Moseley (WA) 74 67 67..........................
Jens Nilsson (Swe) 67 70 71 ....
Alan Patterson (Vic) 70 70 68 ....
John Senden (Qld) 68 70 71 ....

Stuart Appleby (Vic) 67 68 74 ....
Andrew Tschudin (Vic) 68 68 73 ....
Scott Hend (Qld) 70 70 69..............................
Rod Pampling (Qld) 70 67 72 ....
Peter Senior (Qld) 69 72 69 ....

Andrew Buckle (Qld) 70 72 68 ....
Steven Conran (NSW) 69 69 72......................
Wayne Grady (Qld) 67 68 75 ....
Steven Alker (NZ) 69 69 72 ....
Leigh McKechnie (NSW) 71 71 68

Nick O'Hern (WA) 69 71 70..............................
Wayne Riley (NSW) 72 71 67 ....
Stephen Leaney (WA) 73 68 70 ....
Michael Long (NZ) 69 72 70............................
David McKenzie (Vic) 69 69 73

Mal Baker (WA) 69 69 74..................................
Tony Carolan (Qld) 74 67 71............................
Nick Dougherty (Eng) 70 71 71 ....
Nathan Gatehouse (Tas) 72 71 69 ....
Anthony Painter (NSW) 70 73 69 ....

Mahal Pearce (NZ) 71 70 71 ....
Westley Rudel (NSW) 68 75 69 ....
Andre Stolz (NSW) 72 71 70 ....
Andrew Webster (Vic) 70 73 70 ....
Marcus Wheelhouse (NZ) 74 69 70 ....

Tommy De Wit (NSW) 69 73 71....................
Jason Norris (Vic) 71 72 70............................
Bob Shearer (Vic) 70 70 74..............................
Michael Wright (Qld) 73 69 72......................
Alastair Sidford (NZ) 74 69 72......................

Greg Turner (NZ) 69 74 72..............................
Mark Allen (Vic) 70 68 77..............................
Ernie Rose (HK) 72 71 72 ....
Jarrod Lyle (Am) (Vic) 73 68 75 ....
James Nitties (Am) (NSW) 68 70 78 ....

Neil Kerry (NSW) 73 70 75..............................

Source: *Sydney Morning Herald*, 25 November 2002

9 A test of twenty spelling words was given to one hundred students. These marks are the results.

a Tabulate this data in a frequency distribution table.

b Draw a cumulative frequency histogram and polygon.

c From your graph, determine the median number of spelling words answered correctly.

d If Kylie spelt seventeen words correctly, was she above or below the mean?

Number correct

17	19	15	13	20	19	15	16	14	20
18	19	15	17	19	12	9	20	19	16
12	14	14	18	16	19	20	19	18	14
10	9	18	16	15	11	15	16	19	20
20	13	14	17	17	19	18	14	15	17
18	20	20	17	19	12	11	17	16	19
17	20	19	16	13	17	15	15	20	20
12	14	20	19	17	18	14	18	18	12
9	16	17	19	20	17	19	17	20	19
17	15	14	20	18	13	14	15	19	18

e If this information is to be displayed as a grouped frequency distribution, would it be best to use a class interval of 2, 5 or 10?

f Display the information above as a grouped frequency distribution using class intervals of:

  i 2 (ie 9–10, 11–12, …, 19–20)

  ii 5 (ie 6–10, 11–15, 16–20)

  iii 10 (ie 1–10, 11–20)

  Explain how changing the grouping of the data has changed the shape of the display.

10 Grade 9 students decided to sell chocolates to earn sufficient money to buy a gift for each patient in the local nursing home. The list below shows the number of chocolates sold by each student.

a Prepare a grouped frequency table using a class interval of:

  i 2 ii 5 iii 10

b Draw a frequency histogram using the table with class interval:

  i 2 ii 5 iii 10

c From your results so far, choose the most appropriate class interval to display these scores. Give reasons for your choice.

Number sold				
7	0	35	14	22
17	30	11	5	29
26	20	12	24	15
10	16	32	39	28
19	28	11	24	30
21	32	18	21	4
30	19	6	20	35
38	26	23	8	37

• Transport providers, such as railways, airlines and bus companies, are large users of statistics.

15:02 | Measures of Spread: Inter-quartile Range

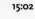

15:02

Find the range of the scores in:

1 Set A　　**2** Set B　　**3** Set C

4 Which set contains an outlier?

5 Is the range affected by an outlier?

Set A:	8, 8, 8, 8, 8
Set B:	7, 8, 8, 8, 8
Set C:	1, 8, 8, 8, 8
Set D:	8, 8, 8, 8, 8
Set E:	7, 8, 8, 8, 9
Set F:	6, 7, 8, 9, 10

What is the mean for:

6 Set D?　　**7** Set E?　　**8** Set F?

9 Which set of scores is the least spread out?

10 Which set of scores is the most spread out?

Scores that are unusually high or low are called outliers.

- To this point in statistics, we have concentrated on finding what are called the measures of central tendency. These are the mode, mean and median. They attempt to tell us how the scores tend to cluster.
- Another important characteristic of sets of data is how they are spread. So far we have used the range to measure this. But, as we can see from the Prep Quiz above, the range is easily affected by an outlier and so it is not a reliable measure of the spread.
- A much better measure of spread than the range is the **inter-quartile range**. This is the range of the middle 50% of scores.

worked examples

Example 1

Find the inter-quartile range of the scores:

　1, 2, 2, 5, 7, 9, 10, 10, 11, 11, 11, 11

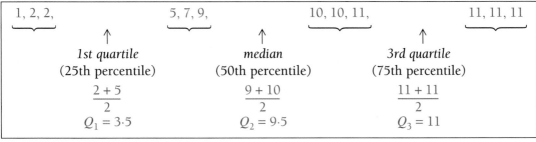

Score

Method 1

- Make sure that the scores are in ascending order.
- Divide the scores into 4 equal groups. (This is not always possible. See Example 2.)

1, 2, 2,		5, 7, 9,		10, 10, 11,		11, 11, 11
↑		↑		↑		
1st quartile		*median*		*3rd quartile*		
(25th percentile)		(50th percentile)		(75th percentile)		
$\dfrac{2+5}{2}$		$\dfrac{9+10}{2}$		$\dfrac{11+11}{2}$		
$Q_1 = 3\cdot5$		$Q_2 = 9\cdot5$		$Q_3 = 11$		

The 1st quartile (Q_1) lies between 2 and 5 (ie 3·5).

The 2nd quartile (median) lies between 9 and 10 (ie 9·5).

The 3rd quartile (Q_3) lies between 11 and 11 (ie 11).

- The inter-quartile range is the difference between the 3rd and 1st quartiles.

　Inter-quartile range $= Q_3 - Q_1$

　　　　　　　　　　　$= 11 - 3\cdot5$

　　　　　　　　　　　$= 7\cdot5$

continued ➔➔➔

Method 2

- Construct a cumulative frequency polygon.
- Come across from the vertical axis to the polygon from positions representing 25%, 50% and 75% of the scores. Take the readings on the horizontal axis to obtain 1st quartile, median and 3rd quartile.

x	f	c.f.
1	1	1
2	2	3
3	0	3
4	0	3
5	1	4
6	0	4
7	1	5
8	0	5
9	1	6
10	2	8
11	4	12

$$\Sigma f = 12$$

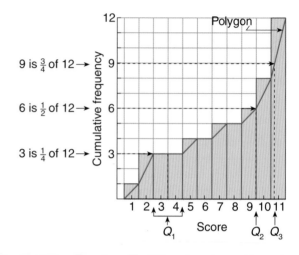

9 is $\frac{3}{4}$ of 12 →

6 is $\frac{1}{2}$ of 12 →

3 is $\frac{1}{4}$ of 12 →

The first quartile (Q_1) is somewhere in the range 2·5 to 4·5, as the polygon has the height 3 for those values. We resolve this problem by taking the average of 2·5 and 4·5.

$$\therefore Q_1 = \frac{2\cdot5 + 4\cdot5}{2}$$
$$= 3\cdot5$$

The cumulative frequency polygon is sometimes called an ogive.

The median (Q_2) is seen to be 9·5.
The 3rd quartile (Q_3) is seen to be 11 (or 10·75 if we consider the horizontal scale to be continuous rather than discrete).

- The inter-quartile range = $Q_3 - Q_1$
$$= 11 - 3\cdot5$$
$$= 7\cdot5$$

> The inter-quartile range is more useful when the number of scores is large. When the number of scores is small (eg 7), it is hard to define 'the middle half of the scores'.

 The *inter-quartile range* is:
- **the range of the middle 50% of the scores**
- **the difference between the points below which 75% and 25% of scores fall (the difference between the third and first quartiles)**
- **the median of the upper half of the scores minus the median of the lower half.**

Example 2

Find the inter-quartile range for the following sets of scores.

Set A: 1, 2, 2, 5, 7, 9, 10, 10, 11, 11, 11

Set B: 1, 2, 2, 5, 7, 9, 10, 10, 11, 11

Solution 2

When the number of scores in a set is not a multiple of 4, they cannot be divided into 4 equal groups.

The method is then as follows.

Set A has 11 scores. Hence the middle score, 9, is the median, (Q_2).

The middle score of the bottom 5 scores is Q_1.

The middle score of the top 5 scores is Q_3.

$$1, 2, ②, 5, 7, ⑨, 10, 10, ⑪, 11, 11$$

1st quartile	Median	3rd quartile
$Q_1 = 2$	$Q_2 = 9$	$Q_3 = 11$

$$\therefore \text{Inter-quartile range} = Q_3 - Q_1$$
$$= 11 - 2$$
$$= 9$$

Set B has 10 scores. Hence the median is between the 5th and 6th scores.

This divides the scores into two groups of 5 scores.

The middle scores of the bottom and top groups are Q_1 and Q_3 respectively.

$$\overset{8}{}$$
$$1, 2, ②, 5, 7, 9, 10, ⑩, 11, 11$$

1st quartile	Median	3rd quartile
2	$\dfrac{7+9}{2}$	10
$Q_1 = 2$	$Q_2 = 8$	$Q_3 = 10$

$$\therefore \text{Inter-quartile range} = Q_3 - Q_1$$
$$= 10 - 2$$
$$= 8$$

Exercise 15:02

Foundation Worksheet 15:02

Inter-quartile range

1 The following sets of scores have been arranged in order and divided into quartiles. For each set of scores find:
i the median, Q_2
ii the first and third quartiles, Q_1 and Q_3, and the inter-quartile range.
a 1, 2, | 2, 4, | 5, 6, | 6, 8
b 1, 2, | 3, 4, | 5, 6, | 9, 12
c 1, 2, 3, | 5, 5, 6, | 7, 8, 10, | 11, 12, 18
2 Find the inter-quartile range of each set of scores.
a 17, 20, 12, 15, 8, 10, 16, 12
b 4, 5, 15, 4, 6, 4, 5, 9, 8, 8, 9, 8

1 Use method 1 to find the inter-quartile range of each set of scores. (Rewrite the scores in order as the first step in each case.)

a   6, 4, 3, 8, 5, 4, 2, 7

b   1, 5, 2, 6, 3, 8, 7, 5, 4, 5, 7, 9

c   60, 84, 79, 83, 94, 88, 92, 99, 80, 90, 95, 78

d   15, 43, 30, 22, 41, 30, 27, 25, 28, 20,
    19, 22, 25, 24, 33, 31, 41, 40, 49, 37

e   Half-yearly examination:
    56, 83, 60, 72, 61, 52, 73, 24, 88, 70
    57, 63, 60, 48, 36, 53, 65, 49, 62, 65

2 The scores of 32 students have been used to graph this cumulative frequency histogram and polygon. Use the graph to find:
 a the median, Q_2
 b the 1st quartile, Q_1
 c the 3rd quartile, Q_3
 d the inter-quartile range, $Q_3 - Q_1$
 (*Note*: Here the answers are whole numbers.)

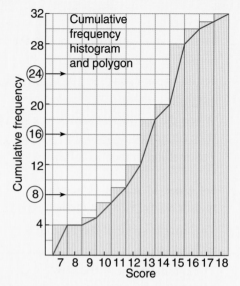

3

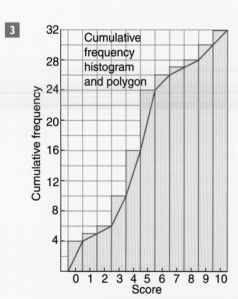

The same 32 students sat for a second test. The results have been used to draw this graph. Use the graph to find:
 a the median, Q_2
 b the 1st quartile, Q_1
 c the 3rd quartile, Q_3
 d the inter-quartile range, $Q_3 - Q_1$
 (*Note*: Here some answers will involve decimals.)

4 Make up a frequency distribution table for these scores.

7, 8, 6, 9, 4, 6, 5, 5, 4, 2
3, 7, 6, 6, 5, 8, 4, 5, 6, 4
7, 6, 8, 5, 3, 4, 8, 9, 6, 5
4, 5, 7, 3, 6, 6, 5, 5, 5, 6

Use your frequency distribution table to find:
 a the inter-quartile range using method 1
 b the inter-quartile range using method 2

5 Use a cumulative frequency polygon to find the inter-quartile range for each of the following.

 a

Marks	Frequency
16	3
17	4
18	5
19	5
20	3

 b

Times	Frequency
35	3
36	4
37	7
38	10
39	18
40	18

6 Find the inter-quartile ranges of the following sets of scores.

   a 25, 45, 46, 50, 58, 58, 65, 66, 70, 90

   b 25, 25, 26, 26, 26, 28, 29, 30, 30, 32, 32

   c 45, 45, 56, 56, 58, 59, 59, 59, 80

For question 6 see Example 2.

7 Use the cumulative frequency polygons to find the inter-quartile range of each set of scores.

   a

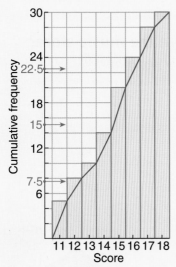

   b

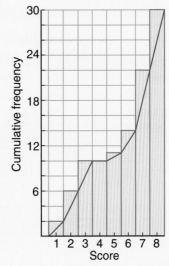

8 A cumulative frequency polygon (ogive) can also be used to obtain the inter-quartile range for grouped data.

The weights of 128 boys were measured to the nearest kilogram and grouped in classes of 50–54 kg, 55–59 kg, up to 85–89 kg.

Use the ogive to estimate the following.

   a first quartile

   b third quartile

   c inter-quartile range

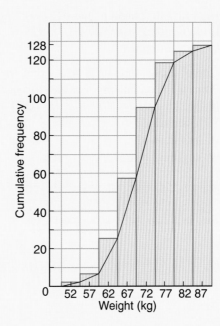

9 Find the quartiles for each of the following sets of data and then find the inter-quartile range. (Note that in both the dot plot and the stem-and-leaf plot, the scores have already been arranged in order.)

a

Score

b

Stem	Leaf
3	8
4	2 6 9
5	3 3 6 7
6	0 1 3 3 4 7 8
7	4 6 6 8 9
8	3 4 8 9

Fun Spot 15:02 | Why did the robber flee from the music store?

Work out the answer to each part, and put the letter for that part in any box that is above the correct answer.

- 12 students were rated 1 (*poor*) to 6 (*outstanding*) on a *coordination* test. The results are shown in the frequency table.

x	f	c.f.
1	4	
2	2	
3	1	
4	2	
5	1	
6	2	

What is:
A the mode? **E** the median?
E the range? **E** the highest score?
F the mean? **R** the relative frequency of 6?
F the cumulative frequency of 5?
H the cumulative frequency of 6?

How many people:
H were rated as *outstanding*?
H were rated higher than 6?
I were rated less than 4?
L were rated *poor*?

One of these students is selected at random.
What is the probability that the student's rank is:
N 3? **O** 1?
T less than 3?
U less than 5?
W anything but 3?

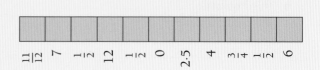

15:03 | Box-and-Whisker Plots

Sometimes the dot plot and stem-and-leaf display were used to illustrate certain aspects of a set of scores or distribution.

Another type of display is the box-and-whisker plot. This is drawn using a five-point summary of the data as shown below.

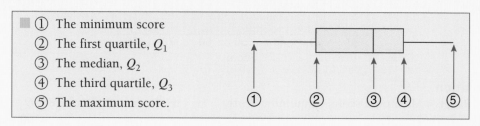

① The minimum score
② The first quartile, Q_1
③ The median, Q_2
④ The third quartile, Q_3
⑤ The maximum score.

In a box-and-whisker plot:
• the box shows the middle 50% (the inter-quartile range), while the whiskers extend from the box to the highest and lowest scores
• the whiskers show the range of the scores.

worked examples

1   The scores in an assessment task for a class were as follows.

40   71   74   20   43   63   83   57
63   26   43   87   74   89   66   63

Find the five-point summary of these marks and use it to construct a box-and-whisker plot.

Solution

Rearrange the scores in order, and find Q_2, then Q_1 and Q_3.

20   26   40   43   43   57   63   63   63   66   71   74   74   83   87   89

Q_1 Q_2 Q_3

The five-point summary is (20, 43, 63, 74, 89).

Use the five-point summary and a suitable scale (1 mark = 1 mm) to construct the box-and-whisker diagram.

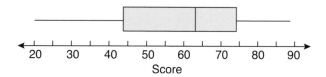

continued ➜➜➜

2   Use the box-and-whisker plot to find the following.
    a   range   b   inter-quartile range   c   median
    d   percentage of scores above 60
    e   percentage of scores below 36

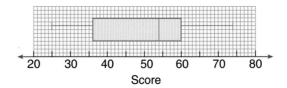

Score

Solution
    a   Range = Maximum score − minimum score   b   Inter-quartile range = $Q_3 - Q_1$
                = 74 − 25   = 60 − 36
                = 49   = 24
    c   As 60 = Q_3, then 25% of the scores are above 60.
    d   As 36 = Q_1, then 25% of the scores are below 36.

Exercise 15:03

1   Use each box-and-whisker plot to find the following.
    i median   ii range   iii inter-quartile range

a
b
c

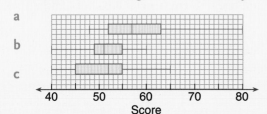

40   50   60   70   80
Score

2   Find the five-point summary for each of the following sets of data and use it to construct
    a box-and-whisker plot.
    a   7, 7, 8, 8, 8, 9, 9, 9, 10, 12, 12, 12
    b   16, 24, 25, 25, 26, 28, 28, 28, 28, 30, 32, 33, 34, 34, 37, 38
    c   14, 19, 29, 36, 40, 43, 43, 44, 46, 46, 47, 49

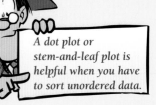

*A dot plot or
stem-and-leaf plot is
helpful when you have
to sort unordered data.*

3 Find the five-point summary for each of the following sets of data and use it to construct a box-and-whisker plot.

 a 43, 37, 42, 48, 39, 39, 40, 40, 44, 47, 45, 44
 b 75, 78, 63, 59, 68,
    72, 74, 83, 87, 86,
    59, 75, 82, 82, 84,
    85, 77, 76, 70, 83

4 These box-and-whisker plots represent the distance travelled to school by members of Grade 8 and Grade 9.

 a What percentage of Grade 8 students travel:
    i further than 7 km?
    ii further than 5 km?

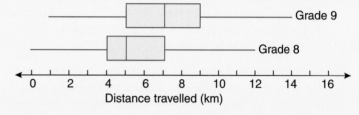

 b What percentage of Grade 9 students travel:
    i further than 7 km?
    ii further than 5 km?

 c Find the inter-quartile range for:
    i Grade 8   **ii** Grade 9
 d Which group does more travelling?

5 **a** Use the dot plot to find the five-point summary for the scores.
 b Construct the box-and-whisker plot for the scores.

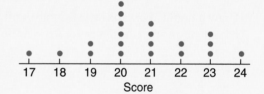

6 The marks of 24 students in a half-yearly test are recorded in the stem-and-leaf display.
 a Find the five-point summary for these marks.
 b Construct a box-and-whisker plot for the marks.

Test scores

Stem	Leaf
2	6 7 8
3	5 8 8 9
4	0 1 3 8 9
5	2 5 6 7 7
6	7 9 9
7	5 5
8	2 2

7 Ray and Kim play 40 games of golf over a one-year period. Their scores are shown on the double box-and-whisker plot below.

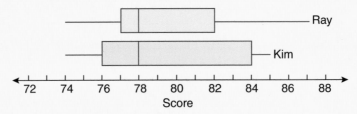

a What is the five-point summary for Kim's scores?
b Which golfer's scores have the smaller range?
c Which golfer's scores have the smaller inter-quartile range?
d Given your answers to **b** and **c**, which golfer do you think is the most consistent? Give a reason for your answer.

8 Ricardo recorded how long it took him to drive to work over 28 consecutive days. The times taken to the nearest minute are shown in the frequency table.

Time (minutes)	38	39	40	41	42	43	44	52
Frequency	1	2	6	7	5	4	2	1

One year later, after the addition of traffic lights and other traffic management measures, Ricardo repeated the process and obtained the following results.

Time (minutes)	38	39	40	41	42	43	45
Frequency	1	4	8	9	4	1	1

Draw a double box-and-whisker plot to illustrate the before and after results and use it to comment on the effectiveness of the traffic changes.

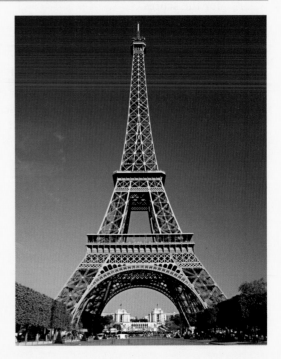

• How many tourists visit France each year? How do the numbers vary throughout the year and where do they go? What other sorts of statistical information would be of interest to the French tourist industry?

15:04 | Measures of Spread: Standard Deviation

Another measure of spread is the **standard deviation**.

> The *standard deviation* is a measure of how far the scores are spread about the mean.
> - It can be thought of as the *average distance of the scores from the mean.*
> - The smaller the standard deviation, the less the spread of the scores.

The graphs below show the distribution of four sets of nine scores. Each set of scores has a mean of 7, but clearly the spread of each set of scores is different.

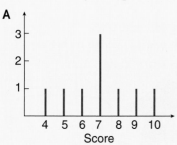

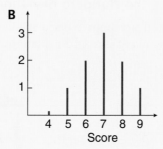

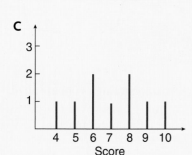

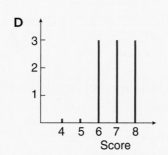

The range is also a simple measure of spread.

How do the standard deviations for the sets vary?

- Set D clearly has the smallest spread of scores about the mean. Three of the scores are on the mean and the other six scores are only one from the mean. It will have the smallest standard deviation.

- Sets A and C are identical except for the distribution of the scores from six to eight. In this range, it can be seen that set A has three scores on the mean and two scores that are one unit from the mean, while set B has only one score on the mean and four scores that are one unit from the mean. So the scores in set C are spread further from the mean than those of set A. Hence, the standard deviation of set C is greater than the standard deviation of set A.

- The scores in set B are not as spread as the scores of sets A and C, but are further spread than those of set D.

The standard deviation for set B will be higher than that of set D, but lower than that of set A.

Calculating the standard deviation (σ_n), by calculator

Step 1 Make sure that the calculator is in the statistics (or SD) mode.

Step 2 Enter the scores.

Step 3 Press the $\boxed{\sigma_n}$ key.

Note: There are two standard deviations: the population standard deviation (σ_n) and the sample standard deviation (σ_{n-1} or S_x). In this course, we will only use the population standard deviation. For instance, if each of the scores 9, 6, 8, 5, 2, 7, 4, 7 is entered into the calculator and $\boxed{\sigma_n}$ is pressed, the answer 2·12 (correct to 2 dec. pl.) is obtained.

> ■ The $\boxed{\sigma_x}$ or $\boxed{\sigma_n}$ key is used to give the population standard deviation.

Comparing performances using the standard deviation

- The standard deviation may be used to compare performances on different tests.
- We compare marks by seeing how many standard deviations each mark is above or below the mean.
- Consider the results below.

	Score	$\bar{x}$	σ_n
Mathematics	72	60	12
English	72	60	4

> Of course, you'll want to know how standard deviation is used.

The scores seem the same until we notice that the English marks have a much smaller standard deviation.

- A small standard deviation means that the scores are clustered together, so an English mark of 72 is possibly the highest English mark.
- A large standard deviation means that the scores are well spread. The Mathematics mark of 72 is above average but nowhere near the top of the class.

For Mathematics, 72 is 1 standard deviation above the mean.
For English, 72 is 3 standard deviations above the mean.
The English mark is far more impressive.

---

worked example

The marks from two tests are shown below. In which test would a result of 15 be more impressive?

Test A: 9, 11, 12, 12, 13, 13, 14, 15, 15, 16
Test B: 5, 7, 9, 10, 12, 13, 13, 15, 17, 19

Solution

Using the calculator, we can find the mean and standard deviation for each test.

Test A: $\bar{x} = 13$ $\sigma_n = 2 \cdot 0$
Test B: $\bar{x} = 12$ $\sigma_n = 4 \cdot 1$ (correct to 1 dec. pl.)

For test A, 15 is 1 standard deviation above the mean.
For test B, 15 is 0·73 standard deviations above the mean.

This means that a result of 15 on test A is more impressive.

Exercise 15:04

Foundation Worksheet 15:04

Standard deviation

1 The following sets of scores all have a mean of 8. By looking at the spread of the scores, find which set of scores has:
   i the smallest standard deviation   **ii** the largest standard deviation

a

2 Use your calculator to find the standard deviation of the following sets of scores.
   a 1, 2, 3, 4, 5   **b** 2, 2, 3, 4, 4

1 Each of the following sets of scores has a mean of 7. Which set of scores has:
   i the smallest standard deviation?
   ii the largest standard deviation?

a
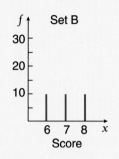
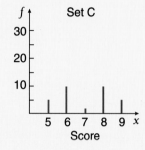

b
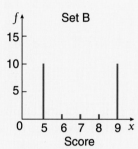
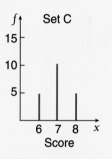

c
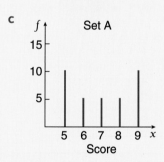
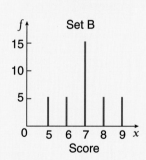
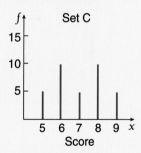

2 Each of the sets of scores A to D has a mean of 60. Without calculating the standard deviations, arrange the sets in order of increasing standard deviation.

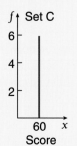
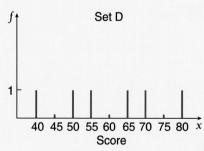

3 Which of the set of scores A to D has a standard deviation of:
  a 0?
  b 1?
  c 4?
  d 0·8 (correct to 1 dec. pl.)?
  The mean for each set is coloured red.

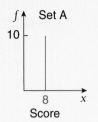

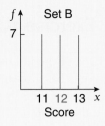

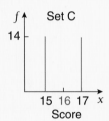

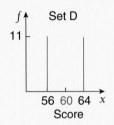

4 Use your calculator to find the mean ($\bar{x}$) and standard deviation (σ_n) for each set of scores (correct to one decimal place).
  a 5, 3, 7, 9, 8, 8, 6, 3
  2, 1, 9, 7, 6, 6, 5, 2

  b 11, 9, 15, 16, 8, 14, 14, 10
  12, 13, 17, 17, 10, 8, 19, 11

  c 9, 7, 2, 5, 6, 3, 9, 7
  3, 9, 4, 8, 8, 4, 5, 2
  4, 6, 3, 2

  d 61, 92, 47, 32, 56, 72, 39, 51
  27, 32, 84, 90, 67, 59, 77, 66
  53, 67, 75, 81, 49, 72, 36, 29

5 Use your calculator to determine the mean and standard deviation of each set of scores represented in the tables below. Give answers correct to two decimal places.

a

Score	Freq.
1	2
2	5
3	7
4	4
5	2

b

Score	Freq.
8	1
9	5
10	9
11	11
12	3
13	2

c

Score	Freq.
10	5
20	9
30	14
40	11
50	8
60	3

d

Score	47	48	49	50	51	52
Freq.	8	11	16	21	14	10

e

Score	5	10	20	25	30	35	40	45	50
Freq.	3	9	11	16	22	17	12	8	2

6 Set A: 20, 60, 65, 68, 73
  Set B: 58, 60, 65, 68, 73
  a Calculate the standard deviation for both sets of scores.
  b What is the only difference between the sets of scores?
  c Do you think that the standard deviation is influenced by an outlier?

7 Sets A and B are identical except for the minimum score.
Set A: 15, 48, 50, 58, 60, 60, 70, 70, 75, 80, 82, 84, 85, 86
Set B: 48, 48, 50, 58, 60, 60, 70, 70, 75, 80, 82, 84, 85, 86
  a Calculate the mean and standard deviation for both sets of scores.
  b Do you think the effect of an outlier is as great when there are a larger number of scores?

8 A building supervisor measured the time it took in days for two builders to build the same houses under similar conditions. Both builders had the same mean of 190 days, but the standard deviation for builder A was 21 days, while for builder B it was 12 days.

On the basis of this data, which builder is most likely to finish a house:
  a in the shortest time?
  b in the longest time?
  c closest to 190 days?

9 Ricardo and Georgio have played 20 rounds of golf on their local golf course.
The mean and standard deviation for each was:

	Mean	Standard deviation
Ricardo	80	5·6
Georgio	80	9·2

> In golf, low scores are better than high scores.

  a On the basis of these results, in their next game, who is most likely to have:
    i the lower score?
    ii the higher score?
    iii a score closest to 80?
  b Who do you think is the better golfer? Give a reason for your answer.

10 Brigitte was considering working for a year in two different cities. After researching the internet, she found the following information about their temperatures.

Temperatures

	Summer		Winter	
	$\bar{x}$	σ_n	$\bar{x}$	σ_n
City A	32°	1°	24°	2°
City B	32°	4°	24°	6°

  a Which city is most likely to experience the hottest summer temperatures?
  b Which city is most likely to experience the coldest winter temperatures?
  c Brigitte prefers a climate where the temperature does not fluctuate greatly. Which city should she choose to work in?

11 For a class of 20 students, the percentage Mathematics and English marks were:

Mathematics: 72, 63, 87, 94, 55, 46, 66, 81, 62, 84
97, 59, 75, 77, 49, 57, 68, 77, 51, 70
English: 61, 39, 52, 45, 79, 59, 51, 63, 71, 75
66, 60, 53, 48, 59, 68, 61, 72, 46, 59

Calculate, for each set of marks, the mean and standard deviation correct to one decimal place. If Tom scored 75 in Mathematics and 70 in English, which is the better mark, relative to the class results?

12 For each of the following, indicate which you think is the better score.

		Score	Mean	σ_n
a	Andrew	70	60	5
	Tom	75	60	10
b	Klare	62	55	7
	Jane	74	70	8
c	James	63	57	12
	Cate	63	59	4
d	Allyson	18	20	4
	John	16	22	6
e	Kylie	41	50	6
	Adam	40	49	9
f	Michelle	50	62	8
	Alan	48	55	7

'σn' refers to standard deviation.

13 The mean of a set of 20 scores is 10 and the standard deviation of the scores is 2·5. What effect will an additional score have upon the mean and the standard deviation, if the score is:

a 6? b 11? c 13?

14 a Find the range, mean and standard deviation for:

i

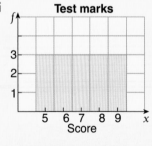

Test marks

ii

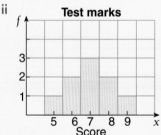

Test marks

iii

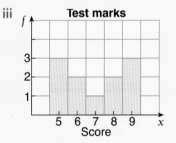

Test marks

b Compare the range, mean and standard deviation for the histograms above. Give σ_n correct to one decimal place.

c Investigate what happens to the range, mean and standard deviation of each set of scores in part **a**, when 10 is added to each score.

d Investigate what happens to the range, mean and standard deviation of each set of scores in part **a**, when each score is multiplied by 10.

15:05 | Comparing Sets of Data

Statistics are often used to look at the similarities and differences between sets of data. Here are some examples.

- Teachers are often interested in comparing the marks of a class on different topics or comparing the marks of different classes on the same topic.
- Medical researchers could compare the heart rates of different groups of people after exercise.
- Coaches might compare the performances of different players over a season or the same player over different seasons.
- Managing directors of companies could compare sales and profits over different periods.

As well as calculating the measures of cluster (the mean, median and mode) and the measures of spread (the range, inter-quartile range and standard deviation) a comparison would usually involve using graphical methods. Back-to-back stem-and-leaf plots, double-column graphs, double box-and-whisker plots and histograms are useful ways of comparing sets of data.

Shape of a distribution

A significant feature of a set of data is its shape. This is most easily seen using a histogram or stem-and-leaf plot.

For some data sets with many scores and a large range, the graph is often shown as a curve.

The graphs below show the results of 120 students on four different problem-solving tests.

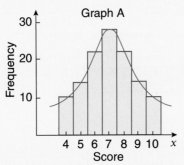
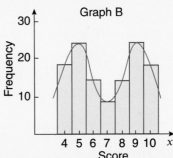

- Graphs A and B are examples of **symmetric distributions**. Graph A has one mode; it is said to be unimodal. Graph B has two modes; it is bimodal.
- A unimodal symmetric distribution is quite common in statistics and is called a **normal distribution**.
- Symmetric distributions are evenly distributed about the mean.

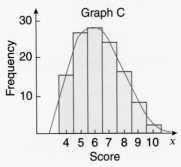
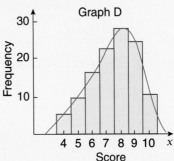

- Graphs C and D are examples of **skewed distributions**.
- If most of the scores are at the low end, the skew is said to be positive.
- If most of the scores are at the high end, the skew is said to be negative.

worked example

Our class was given a topic test in which we performed poorly. Our teacher decided to give a similar test one week later, after a thorough revision of the topic. The results are shown on this back-to-back stem-and-leaf display. (This is an **ordered display**.)

Test scores (4/1 represents 41)

First topic test		Second topic test
Leaf	Stem	Leaf
9 8 6 6 0	3	
9 7 7 3 1 1 1	4	3 6 6 8 8
8 8 5 3 3 0	5	1 7 9 9
9 8 7 5 3	6	3 8 9
	7	0 5 5 5 8 9
	8	2 6 7 7
0	9	0 0 1 3

Compare the results of the class on the two tests.

Solution

- The improvement in the second test is clear to see. The medians, which are easily found, verify this, as do the means.

	Test 1	Test 2
Median	49·5	72·5
Mean	51·5	69·8

- The spread of the scores in Test 1 is smaller than in Test 2. Both the inter-quartile range and the standard deviations confirm this.

	Test 1	Test 2
Inter-quartile range	19·5	29
Standard deviation	13·6	16·0
Range	60	50

The presence of the outlier in Test 1 had made the range an unreliable measure of spread.

Exercise 15:05

1 The age distributions of students in four international schools are shown below.

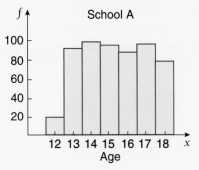

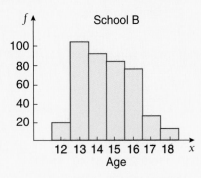

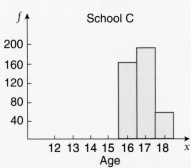

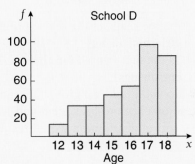

a Which school's age distributions are skewed? What causes the skew?
b Which school's age distribution is closest to being distributed evenly?
c In which school would the mean age of a student be:
  i closest to 15?   **ii** below 15?
  iii over 15?   **iv** the largest?

2 The marks for two classes on the same test are shown in the dot plot below.

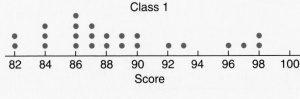

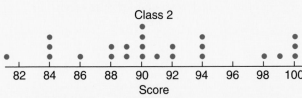

a Which set of results is more skewed?
b By just looking at the dot plots, estimate which class has:
  i the higher mean   **ii** the greater spread of scores
c Check your answer to part **b** by calculating the mean and standard deviation for each set of scores.

3 A school librarian was interested in comparing the number of books borrowed by boys and girls. At the end of the year, she looked at the number of books borrowed by each child and prepared the following graphs.

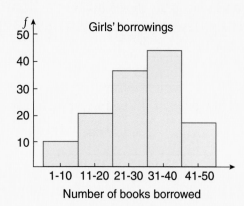

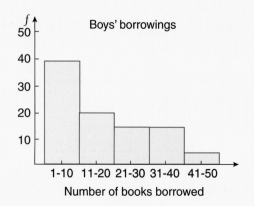

   a Describe the shape of the distribution for:
     i the girls' borrowings   **ii** the boys' borrowings
   b What is the first impression that the shapes of the distributions give about the boys' and girls' borrowings?
   c Why do you think two grouped frequency histograms were used to display the results instead of a back-to-back stem-and-leaf plot?
   d What sort of distribution would result if the librarian combined the boys' and girls' results?

4 The stem-and-leaf plot shows the marks of a class on two different topic tests.
   a Which set of marks is nearly symmetric?
   b Which set of marks has the smaller spread? What measures of spread can you use to support your answer?
   c Calculate the median and mean for each set of marks. What do they suggest about the class' performance on the two tests?

Topic 1		Topic 2
Leaf	*Stem*	*Leaf*
6 5	3	
9 3 0	4	4 6 7 9
9 8 4 3 0	5	4
9 8 8 6 0	6	2 3 7
9 8 4 4	7	0 8 8 9
6 5	8	3 5 8 8 8 9 9
	9	5

■ To check the shape of the distribution turn the stem-and-leaf plot side on.

5 Thirty students entered a swimming program hoping to improve their swimming. Before and after the program, students were rated as
non-swimmer (N),
weak swimmer (W),
competent swimmer (C),
good swimmer (G) or
excellent swimmer (E).

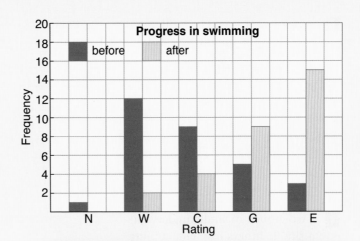

a What was the mode rating before the program?

b What was the mode rating after the program?

c Before the program, what percentage of students were rated either *non-swimmers* or *weak swimmers*?

d After the program, what percentage of students were rated *good* or *excellent swimmers*?

e How would you describe the success of the program?

6

Problem test 1				
5	1	3	4	3
4	1	1	2	2
5	3	3	1	1
2	4	3	2	4
4	3	2		

Problem test 2				
0	2	4	4	2
2	3	0	0	2
4	4	1	3	3
2	2	3	2	2
0	2	2		

In two problem-solving tests, 5 questions were given to a class. The scores are shown above.

a Arrange the scores into a frequency distribution table and use frequency histograms to display the data.

b Calculate the mean and median for each test. What do they suggest about the difficulty of the tests?

c Both sets of scores have a range of 4. Which set of scores has the greater spread? Give a reason for your answer.

7 This box-and-whisker plot represents the height of 30 Year 10 students. The histogram also represents the heights of 30 students.

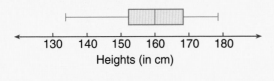

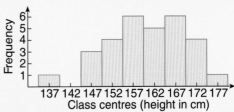

a What information is shown on the box-and-whisker plot?

b Could the information in the histogram represent the same 30 Year 10 students as are represented in the box-and-whisker plot? Explain.

8 A researcher tested two different brands of batteries to see how long they lasted. Her results are shown in the double box-and-whisker plot below.

Use the box-and-whisker plots to compare the performance of Brand X and Brand Y.

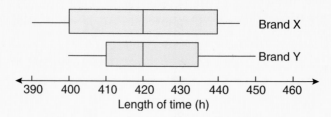

9 Two groups of adults underwent a simple fitness test. One minute after undergoing a period of strenuous exercise, their heart rates were measured.

The results are shown in the back-to-back stem-and-leaf plot.

Heart rates		
Group 1	*Stem*	*Group 2*
7 5 5	11	
9 9 9 9 8 8 7 7 6	12	5 5 6
6 6 4 4 0	13	4 6 8 8
4 2 0	14	2 3 6 6 7 8 8
	15	3 5 5 7
	16	2 4

a What does the shape of the stem-and-leaf plot suggest about the data?

b Calculate the median and inter-quartile range for each group and use them to compare the results for each group.

10 A local council was interested in speeding up the time it took to approve applications to build a house. It looked at the time taken in days to process 40 applications. After reviewing its procedures and monitoring processes, it then looked at another 40 applications. The results are shown below.

			Before								*After*				
44	53	38	39	52	41	40	41	40	39	43	42	54	48	46	44
43	43	42	57	47	45	50	50	51	52	44	38	40	40	51	52
68	50	45	42	58	48	40	39	39	46	46	49	52	51	42	43
44	46	52	45	46	53	54	40	40	45	44	39	50	43	48	40
48	47	43	38	43	42	54	55	52	53	38	40	47	44	47	42

a Discuss an appropriate way to organise and display the data.

b What measures of cluster and spread would you use to describe the data?

c How effective have the council's review procedures been in reducing the approval time?

Mathematical Terms 15

box-and-whisker plot
- A diagram obtained from the five-point summary.
- The box shows the middle 50% of scores (the inter-quartile range).
- The whiskers show us the extent of the bottom and top quartiles as well as the range.

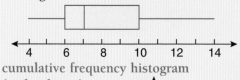

cumulative frequency histogram (and polygon)
- These show the outcomes and their cumulative frequencies.

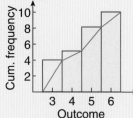

dot plot
- A graph that uses one axis and a number of dots above the axis (see page 234).

five-point summary
- A set of numbers consisting of the minimum score, the three quartiles and the maximum score.

frequency histogram (and polygon)
- These show the outcomes and their frequencies.

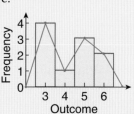

inter-quartile range
- The range of the middle 50% of scores.
- The median of the upper half of scores minus the median of the lower half of scores: inter-quartile range = $Q_3 - Q_1$.

mean
- The number obtained by 'evening out' all the scores until they are equal.
  eg If the scores 3, 6, 5, 3, 5, 5, 4, 3, 3, 6 were 'evened out', the number obtained would be 4·3
- To obtain the mean, use the formula:
  $$\text{Mean} = \frac{\text{sum of scores}}{\text{total number of scores}}$$

median
- The middle score for an odd number of scores or the mean of the middle two scores for an even number of scores.

median class
- In grouped data, the class that contains the median.

mode (modal class)
- The outcome or class that contains the most scores.

outlier
- A score that is separated from the main body of scores.

quartiles
- The points that divide the scores up into quarters.
- The second quartile, Q_2, divides the scores into halves (Q_2 = median).
- The first quartile, Q_1, is the median of the lower half of scores.
- The third quartile, Q_3, is the median of the upper half of scores.
  $$4\ 5\ 6\ |\ 6\ 7\ 7\ |\ 7\ 9\ 9\ |\ 11\ 12\ 15$$
  $$Q_1 = 6 \quad Q_2 = 7 \quad Q_3 = 10$$

range
- The difference between the highest and lowest scores.

shape (of a distribution)
- A set of scores can be symmetric or skewed.

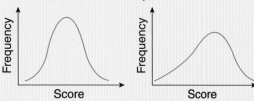

standard deviation
- A measure of spread that can be thought of as the average distance of scores from the mean.
- The larger the standard deviation the larger the spread.

stem-and-leaf plot
- A graph that shows the spread of scores without losing the identity of the data.

Technology Applications

Mathematical terms 15

Diagnostic Test 15 | Statistics

- These questions reflect the important skills introduced in this chapter.
- Errors made will indicate areas of weakness.
- Each weakness should be treated by going back to the section listed.

		Section

Section

1 The results for a Grade 9 mathematics test are given in the frequency table below.

15:01

x	5	6	7	8	9	10	11	12	13	14	15	16	17	18	19	20
f	1	0	2	4	5	9	11	14	18	23	10	8	5	1	4	2

For the set of scores shown above, find:
a the mode   b the median   c the range   d the mean
e the cumulative frequency of the score 9

2 Copy and complete the table on the right.
Use the table to draw:
a a frequency histogram and polygon
b a cumulative frequency histogram and polygon

15:01

x	f	c.f.
0	3	
1	1	
2	5	
3	4	
4	2	
5	1	

3 These are the scores gained by each team competing in a car rally this year.

15:01

27   18   0   45   63   49   50   31   9   26
4   41   38   20   69   38   17   43   16   37
28   14   58   52   37   43   38   51   44   33
25   38   11   43   40   56   62   48   53   22

a Draw a grouped frequency table using classes 0–9, 10–19, etc. Use the columns: *class, class centre, tally, frequency* and *cumulative frequency*.
b Prepare a stem-and-leaf display for the scores above.

4 a Find the inter-quartile range of the scores:
    1,   2,   2,   5,   7,   9,   10,   10,   11,   11,   11,   11
b Draw a cumulative frequency polygon using the frequency distribution table below and use it to find the inter-quartile range of the scores.

15:02

x	10	11	12	13	14	15	16	17	18	19
f	2	0	5	4	5	6	5	6	3	4

c The lengths of 16 fish caught were measured. The results are shown on this dot plot.

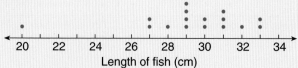

Length of fish (cm)

What is the inter-quartile range?

d What is the inter-quartile range of the times shown in the stem-and-leaf plot?

Time	
Stem	Leaf
3	8 8
4	0 3 4 5 8
5	1 3 4 4
6	0

5 Find the five-point summary for each set of data in question 4.

15:03

6 Draw a box-and-whisker plot for the data in question 4a, b and c.

15:03

7 These box-and-whisker plots were drawn to compare the results of Year 10 on two tests.

15:03

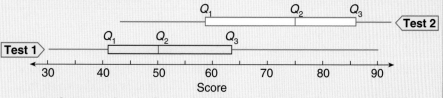

Score

a By how much was the median for test 2 higher than the median of test 1?

b What was the range and inter-quartile range of test 1?

8 Use a calculator to find the standard deviation for each of these tests (correct to two decimal places).

15:04

Test A: 9, 11, 12, 12, 13, 13, 14, 15, 15, 16
Test B: 5, 7, 9, 10, 12, 13, 13, 15, 17, 19
Test C: 10, 15, 16, 8, 13, 3, 6, 16, 8, 5

For which test would the result 15 be more impressive?

9

15:05

Test 1 scores					
12	17	19	12	15	10
9	22	24	11	18	8
25	15	18	20	18	18

Test 2 scores					
21	15	18	7	11	16
20	12	23	12	10	13
12	19	12	14	20	9

a Draw a dot plot for the scores of test 1.

b Draw a back-to-back stem-and-leaf display to compare the scores on test 1 and test 2.

c Draw a double box-and-whisker plot to compare the scores on tests 1 and 2.

Chapter 15 | Revision Assignment

1 The length of the index fingers of 24 teachers was measured. The results are shown on this dot plot.

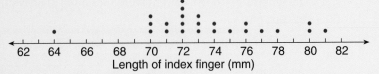

Length of index finger (mm)

a Are any outliers present in this data?

b Find the five-point summary for the data if the outlier is:
  i included   ii omitted

c What is the inter-quartile range if the outlier is:
  i included?   ii omitted?

d Comment on the shape of the distribution (ignore the outlier in this case).

2 A class performed well in a test, all scoring over 60%, except for Jin, who had been away sick before the test. She scored 31%. The teacher decided not to include Jin's result when recording the class statistics for this test. What effect would this have on the mean and standard deviation?

3 Nik and Dylan are golfers. Each has played ten rounds of golf on the same course and their scores have been recorded below. Calculate the mean and standard deviation for each set of scores.
Nik's scores:
73, 81, 77, 85, 76, 76, 84, 73, 80, 75
Dylan's scores:
70, 84, 82, 78, 83, 73, 73, 74, 85, 78
Considering your results, who is the more *consistent* golfer?

4 Identify the distinctive features of the following sets of data. You could comment on *clusters of scores*, *outliers* and the *shape of the distribution*.

a

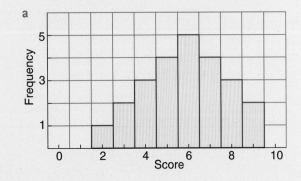

b

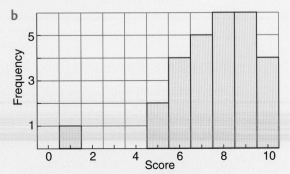

5 Grade 3 and Grade 4 students were tested on their knowledge of multiplication tables. The results are shown in this back-to-back stem-and-leaf display.

Test scores (5/1 represents 51)

Grade 3 results   *Grade 4 results*

Leaf	Stem	Leaf
9 8 3 0	3	5
8 8 7 4 2 2 2	4	
8 7 7 4 0	5	1 4 6 6 9
7 6 3	6	0 2 2 5 8
1	7	3 6 8 8 9 9 9
	8	0 0

Compare the results of Grade 3 and Grade 4 on this test. (You will need to refer to at least one measure of cluster and one measure of spread.)

Chapter 15 | Working Mathematically

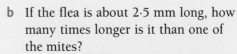
1   You have forgotten the last three digits of your personal identification number (PIN). You do remember, however, that the digits are different and they add up to 6. How many possible endings are there to your PIN?

2   Find the number of routes through the network (S to F), assuming that travel must always be from left to right.

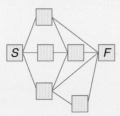

3   The photo below shows mites living in the exoskeleton of a flea. The magnification factor is about 210 times.
   a   In cm, what is the length of a mite?

b   If the flea is about 2·5 mm long, how many times longer is it than one of the mites?

4   A tapered shaft has a length of 60 cm. The diameter at the smaller end is 20 cm. If the taper is 3° (as shown), find the diameter, d cm, of the larger end of the shaft.

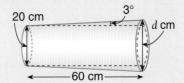

5   Max's best time for 50 m freestyle is 40 seconds, while Joshua's is 25 seconds. If they both swam in the same 50 m freestyle race, how far behind Joshua would Max be when Joshua finished? (Assume that they both swim at constant rates.)

- Chinks in the armour. Spaces between the cuticle plates of a flea's exoskeleton provide a toehold for mites which hitch a ride on their host. Thus the flea saga, an interplay between host and parasite, recapitulates itself on an even smaller scale.

6 Fatalities by time of day and day of week of crash for major road user categories, Australia, 2000–2002.

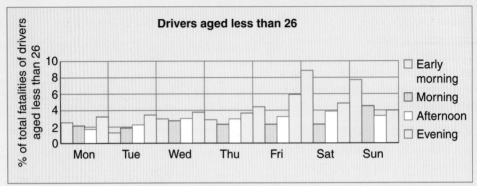

Drivers aged less than 26

% of total fatalities of drivers aged less than 26

Legend: Early morning, Morning, Afternoon, Evening

Mon Tue Wed Thu Fri Sat Sun

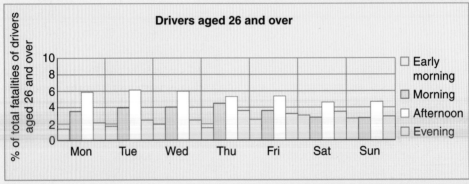

Drivers aged 26 and over

% of total fatalities of drivers aged 26 and over

Legend: Early morning, Morning, Afternoon, Evening

Mon Tue Wed Thu Fri Sat Sun

Source: Federal Bureau of Road Safety 2002

a What do the graphs above suggest is the most dangerous time of day for:
  i drivers aged less than 26?   **ii** drivers aged 26 and over?
b Suggest a reason why the times in **a** are the most dangerous.

Chapter Review
Questions

Technology
Applications
Activities

Mean and standard deviation

Technology
Applications
Drag and Drops

1 Box-and-whisker plots
2 Inter-quartile range

- What sort of statistical data would be needed in calculating the water needs of a large city like Sydney?

Probability

Chapter Contents

Learning Outcomes

Students will be able to:
- Calculate the experimental probability of an event given a table of results.
- Calculate the theoretical probability of an event.
- Organise outcomes of compound events.
- Identify dependent and independent events.
- Use tree diagrams, dot diagrams, tables and Venn diagrams.
- Simulate experiments.

Areas of Interaction

Approaches to Learning (Knowledge Acquisition, Problem Solving, Communication, Logical Thinking, IT Skills, Collaboration, Reflection), Human Ingenuity, Environments, Community

16:01 | Probability Review

- The probability of an event is its chance of happening.
  This will be a number from 0 to 1.
  $0 \leqslant$ probability of an event $\leqslant 1$, $0 \leqslant P(E) \leqslant 1$.

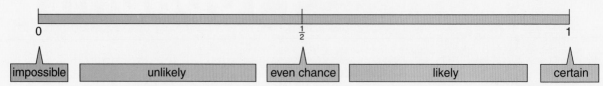

| 0 | | $\frac{1}{2}$ | | 1 |

| impossible | unlikely | even chance | likely | certain |

- The probability may be expressed as a fraction, a decimal or a percentage.

> The *theoretical probability* of an event, E, is the number of times the event can occur, divided by the total number of possible outcomes (as long as each outcome is equally likely to occur).
>
> $$P(E) = \frac{n(E)}{n(S)}$$
>
> **S is used to represent the sample space, which is the set of possible outcomes.**

worked example

A card is chosen at random from a group of ten cards numbered 0 to 9.
What is the probability of choosing the 9?

I want to choose the 9.

Solution
The cards are: 0, 1, 2, 3, 4, 5, 6, 7, 8 and 9.
The probability of choosing the 9 is:

$P(E) = \dfrac{n(E)}{n(S)}$

$P(E) = \dfrac{1}{10}$ or   0·1   or   10%

- The sum of the probabilities of all possible outcomes is always 1.
- Two events are **complementary** if the sum of their probabilities is 1.

> **If P(E) is the probability that an event E will occur and P(E′) is the probability that event E will not occur, then:**
> $$P(E') = 1 - P(E)$$

worked example

If the probability of an event occurring is $\frac{1}{5}$, then the probability that the event will not occur is $1 - \frac{1}{5}$, or $\frac{4}{5}$.

Exercise 16:01

Foundation Worksheet 16:01

Probability review
1 Ten cards are labelled 1 to 10.
 Find the probability of choosing:
 a the number 7
 b a number less than 7

1 **a** Describe the chance of each of these events happening, using
   the terms *certain*, *likely*, *unlikely*, *impossible* and *even chance*.
   A It will snow here some time during the next week.
   B We will have rain tomorrow.
   C There will be a holiday on 25 December.
   D I can walk from home to school without resting.
   E I will travel overseas next month.
   F I will live to the age of 94.
   G I will sit for a mathematics test during the next three months.
   H My favourite football team will win at least one of its next three matches.
 b Put the events **A** to **H** in order from least likely to most likely.

2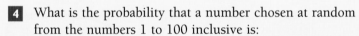

| certain | probable | even chance | improbable | impossible |

Which of the words above best describes an event that has a probability of:

a 0·5? **b** 2%? **c** $\frac{17}{20}$? **d** 0? **e** 1? **f** 50%?

> ■ Write the answers to probability questions as
> fractions unless you are told to do otherwise.

3 In stock, Julio had 13 clear and 7 pearl light globes.
He selected one of these at random. What would be
the probability that the globe was:

a clear? **b** pearl?
c clear or pearl? **d** red?
e not red? **f** not clear?

4 What is the probability that a number chosen at random
from the numbers 1 to 100 inclusive is:

a divisible by 5? **b** not divisible by 5?
c divisible by 6? **d** not divisible by 6?

5 From a standard pack of cards, a card is chosen at random.
What is the probability that the card is:

a black? **b** not black? **c** yellow?
d a 5? **e** not a 5? **f** a court card?
g a club? **h** not a club? **i** an Ace or a King?

6 There are two groups of students. Group A is made up entirely of boys, group B is made up
entirely of girls. A student is chosen at random from each group.
 a What is the probability of choosing a boy from group A?
 b What is the probability of choosing a girl from group B?
 c If the two groups were combined, would the probability of choosing a boy from the
   combined group by 0·5? Give reasons for your answer.

7 Into a barrel are placed 100 blue tickets numbered 1 to 100, 50 red tickets numbered 1 to 50, and 50 green tickets numbered 1 to 50. If one ticket is drawn at random from the barrel, what is the probability that the ticket:

a is green?
b is green or red?
c is a 36?
d is a 72?
e is less than 51?
f is less than 60?
g is not a 50?
h is not less than 60?
i is either a 36 or a 72?

8 Comment critically on these statements.

a Since there are ten digits in Australia's telephone number system, the probability that a person living in Sydney has a phone number that starts with 6 is one tenth.

b I am told that twenty different varieties of tree grow on Bear Mountain. If I choose one tree at random, the chance that it is a pine tree is one in twenty.

9 On a quiz show, a contestant spins this wheel until the wheel shows either *car* or *out*.

a Which of these two outcomes is more likely to occur first?

b If the wheel is spun 60 times, how many times would you expect:
    i *car* to come up?
    ii *out* to come up?

c What is the chance of getting *out* on the first spin?

d If the contestant continues to spin until the wheel shows either *car* or *out*, what is the probability of winning the car?

10 The order in which three students, A, B and C, are placed in a line is chosen at random. Make a list of all possible orders (ABC, ACB, BAC, etc). Use your list to find the probability that:

> Probabilities can be given as fractions, decimals or percentages.

a A is placed before B
b A is placed before both B and C
c A is placed between B and C
d A is placed before either B or C
e A is not placed before either B or C

11 A traffic light shows red for 3 minutes 30 seconds, and orange for 30 seconds, for every minute that the green light shows. Heather saw the light on her way home from work. What is the probability that it was:

a red?
b green?
c orange?
d orange or red?
e not red?
f blue?
g not blue?
h red or blue?

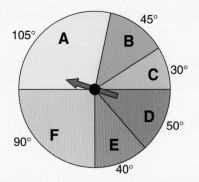

To determine the probability that the spinner will point to A, find the ratio of the angle in A (105°) to the angle of the whole (360°).

ie $P(A) = \frac{105}{306} = \frac{7}{24}$

If the spinner fixed to the circular board shown is spun, what is the probability that it will point to:

a F?

b B?

c C?

d D?

e E?

f E or F?

g A or B?

h A or D?

i B, C or D?

j anything but F?

k anything but A?

13 International school students were asked to vote on the predominant colour to be used on their country's Olympic Games uniform for the opening ceremony. The results are shown in the table on the right. If one of these people is chosen at random, what is the probability (as a percentage) that the person:

a is female? **b** chooses gold?

c is a male who chooses orange?

d is a female who chooses green?

e is not a female who chooses green?

f chooses either green or gold?

g chooses neither green nor gold?

	Male	Female
Green	38	40
Gold	44	32
Blue	7	8
Orange	2	14
Fawn	7	3
Other	2	3
Totals	100	100

Number of students = 200

14 In our city, we carried out a census of the 500 000 people of working age. The information below was collected.

Highest qualification	Number
Degree/diploma	75 000
Skilled/basic vocational	90 000
No qualification	335 000

Ability to speak English	Number
Uses English only	470 000
Speaks English fairly well	25 000
Speaks English poorly/not at all	5 000

If a person of working age were selected at random, what would be the probability that the person:

a had a degree/diploma?

b had no degree/diploma?

c had no qualification?

d had some qualification?

e uses English only?

f does not use English only?

g speaks English poorly/not at all?

15 Of 500 000 people of working age in our city, only 400 000 are working. Their statistics are given below:

Occupation	Number
Manager/administrative	48 000
Professional	60 000
Trades/clerks/sales	180 000
Plant/machine/labourers	72 000
Other	40 000

Income (€)	Number
Less than €40 000	220 000
From €40 000 to €50 000	120 000
Above €50 000	60 000

A worker is to be chosen at random. What is the probability that the worker's occupation will be:

a professional?   **b** not professional?

c manager/administrative?   **d** plant/machine/labourers?

What is the probability that the worker's income will be:

e less than €40 000?   **f** €40 000 or above?

g from €40 000 to €50 000?   **h** above €50 000?

i €50 000 or less?

16 a The probability of drawing two hearts from a standard pack of cards is $\frac{3}{51}$.
What is the probability that the two cards drawn are *not* both hearts?

b The probability of throwing a sum of either 5 or 6 using two dice is 0·25.
What is the probability that the sum is *neither 5 nor 6*?

c There is a 37% chance that I will be sent overseas next year.
What is the chance that I will not be sent?

d If 3 coins are tossed, the probability of getting 3 heads is 0·125. What is the probability of getting fewer than 3 heads?

e The probability of my dying this year is 0·5%. What is the probability that I will not die this year? To insure my life for $10 000 during this year would cost me $135. Does this represent good value? Explain your answer.

- From the results of an experiment or sample, we can calculate the *experimental probability*. This is used as an estimate of the *theoretical probability*.
- When carrying out an experiment to find the *experimental probability* of an event occurring, we are actually finding the *relative frequency* of that event.

$$\text{Relative frequency of a score} = \frac{\text{frequency of score}}{\text{total frequency}}$$

17 A factory tested a sample of 500 CDs and found 4 to be faulty. Use these results to estimate the probability that a CD produced by this factory would be:

a faulty   **b** not faulty

18 Two dice were thrown 100 times and each time the sum of the upper faces was recorded. The results are shown on this graph. Use these results to find the experimental probability of throwing a total:

a of 7   b of 6
c greater than 7   d other than 6
e of 6 or 7   f that is even

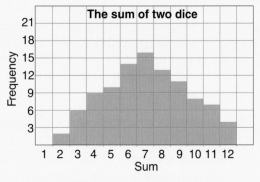

19 Two dice were thrown 80 times. In each case, the total was recorded in the table below. Complete the table, giving the experimental probability as a fraction, a decimal and a percentage.

The experimental probability is the same as the relative frequency.

Result	Tally	Freq.	Experimental probability
2	II	2	2/80 or 0·025 or 2·5%
3	ЖΗ	5	5/80 or 0·0625 or 6·25%
4	ЖΗ I	6	6/80 or 0·075 or 7·5%
5	ЖΗ III	8	8/80 or 0·1 or 10%
6	ЖΗ ЖΗ I	11	11/80 or 0·1375 or 13·75%
7	ЖΗ ЖΗ IIII	14	
8	ЖΗ ЖΗ II	12	
9	ЖΗ IIII	9	
10	ЖΗ I	6	
11	IIII	4	
12	III	3	
Totals:		80	

20 Three coins were tossed 50 times and the number of heads recorded each time. The results are written below. Use these to complete the table on the right.

Write experimental probability as a fraction and as a percentage.

> Experimental probability is the same as relative frequency.

```
1  1  2  1  2  2  3  1  1  1
2  1  2  2  0  1  2  2  2  0
3  3  1  1  2  0  3  2  3  2
0  2  2  1  3  1  2  1  1  0
2  1  1  1  2  0  3  2  2  1
```

Number of heads	Tally	Freq.	Experimental probability
0			
1			
2			
3			

a Draw a frequency histogram to show the experimental probability of getting 0, 1, 2 and 3 heads.

b According to these results, what would be the most likely outcome if I were to toss three coins?

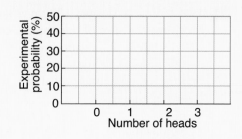

21 Jan three 100 darts at this target and recorded the score for each dart in the table below.

Score	1	2	3	4	5	6	7	8	9	10	11	12
Frequency	7	9	11	11	12	12	10	8	5	4	5	6

a What is the experimental probability (expressed as a decimal) of Jan hitting a:
  i 6?
  ii 1?
  iii 10?

b What is the experimental probability of Jan hitting the target:
  i on the right side?
  ii on the left side?

c What is the experimental probability of Jan hitting the target:
  i on the upper half?
  ii on the lower half?

d Use the results above to describe how Jan tends to throw her darts.

Write the answers as decimals.

16:01

Investigation 16:01 | Chance experiments

- Design a spinner that has two colours, red and blue, where the probability of spinning blue is 3 out of 5. Test your spinner over 50 trials. What did you find?
- Design a four-coloured spinner that would give one colour a chance of occurring that is twice that of any one of the other colours.
- From a bag containing 10 counters that are either red or green (the number of each being unknown), estimate, by repeatedly drawing out and returning one counter, the number of red counters in the bag.
- How many times would you expect to have to throw a dice before you get a 6? Investigate this question by recording the number of throws needed. Repeat the process at least 20 times and average the results.
- In roulette, consider the different placements of chips on squares of the roulette board and the chances of winning or losing each time. Is the game fair? Who is expected to win in the long run?

Fun Spot 16:01 | What is the difference between a songwriter and a corpse?

Work out the answer to each part, and put the letter for that part above the correct answer, below.

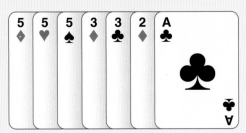

- A counter is taken at random from the container. What is the probability that the counter is:

  A yellow? **H** not yellow?

  C green? **D** not green?

  O white? **E** either white or yellow?

  S red? **T** either red or yellow?

- A card is drawn at random from those above. What is the probability that the card is:

  E a 5? **D** a 2?

  E a club? **O** not an Ace?

  C a 5 or a diamond?

  H a diamond or a spade?

- From a standard pack of playing cards, one card is drawn at random. What is the probability that the card is:

  E the 4♦? **O** a spade? **M** not a spade?

  S a court card? **N** a 4? **E** black?

  S not an Ace? **O** not a court card? **P** an 8 or 9?

  T a number between 2 and 8?

- A letter is chosen at random from the alphabet. What is the probability that it is:

  E an X? **O** a vowel? **M** a consonant? **N** an A, B or C?

  O a letter in the word 'mathematics'? **R** a letter *not* in the word 'mathematics'?

  P a letter in the word 'geometry'? **S** a letter *not* in the word 'geometry'?

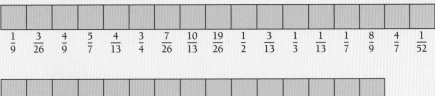

| $\frac{1}{9}$ | $\frac{3}{26}$ | $\frac{4}{9}$ | $\frac{5}{7}$ | $\frac{4}{13}$ | $\frac{3}{4}$ | $\frac{7}{26}$ | $\frac{10}{13}$ | $\frac{19}{26}$ | $\frac{1}{2}$ | $\frac{3}{13}$ | $\frac{1}{3}$ | $\frac{1}{13}$ | $\frac{1}{7}$ | $\frac{8}{9}$ | $\frac{4}{7}$ | $\frac{1}{52}$ |

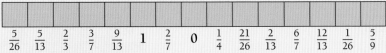

| $\frac{5}{26}$ | $\frac{5}{13}$ | $\frac{2}{3}$ | $\frac{3}{7}$ | $\frac{9}{13}$ | 1 | $\frac{2}{7}$ | 0 | $\frac{1}{4}$ | $\frac{21}{26}$ | $\frac{2}{13}$ | $\frac{6}{7}$ | $\frac{12}{13}$ | $\frac{1}{26}$ | $\frac{5}{9}$ |

16:02 | Organising Outcomes of Compound Events

16:03

prep quiz

List all possible outcomes of each event.

1 A dice is thrown.   **2** A coin is tossed.

3 A card is chosen at random from the picture cards of a standard pack.

4 Lyon's top football team plays Toulouse's top football team.

5 A digit is chosen at random from the counting numbers less than 10.

List all ordered pairs of counting numbers, like (1, 6) or (6, 1), that have a sum of:

6 7   **7** 2   **8** 3   **9** 4   **10** 5

In the Prep Quiz above, you have listed all possible outcomes of some simple events. The set of all possible outcomes of an event is called the **sample space** of that event. The sample space for throwing one dice, for example, is {1, 2, 3, 4, 5, 6}.

We need to use efficient ways of organising the complete sample space of compound events, where more than one activity is involved. We could use a list, a table or a tree diagram. Sometimes other types of diagrams are used.

worked example

A dice is thrown and a coin is tossed. Show all possible outcomes. (What is the sample space?)

Solution

To show the outcomes, we could use a list, a table or a tree diagram.

1 A list

(1, head)   (1, tail)
(2, head)   (2, tail)
(3, head)   (3, tail)
(4, head)   (4, tail)
(5, head)   (5, tail)
(6, head)   (6, tail)

There are 12 outcomes.

2 A table

	Head	Tail
1	✓	✓
2	✓	✓
3	✓	✓
4	✓	✓
5	✓	✓
6	✓	✓

From this table it is obvious that there are 12 different outcomes.

3 A tree diagram

```
           head   1H
      1 <
           tail   1T
           head   2H
      2 <
           tail   2T
           head   3H
      3 <
           tail   3T
Start <
           head   4H
      4 <
           tail   4T
           head   5H
      5 <
           tail   5T
           head   6H
      6 <
           tail   6T
```

There are 12 different outcomes.

A list is easy to make once the tree diagram is drawn.

I reckon it does look like a tree.

Exercise 16:02

Foundation Worksheet 16:02

Organising outcomes of compound events

1 Show the possible outcomes as a list for:
  a three children in a family
  b selecting two cards from five cards, labelled A, B, C, D, E
2 Show the possible outcomes for question 1 as a tree diagram.

The following questions refer to the diagrams above.

1 The spinner (showing a moon, spoon, star and crown) is spun and a coloured counter is drawn at random. Show all possible outcomes to this compound event as:
  a   a list   b   a table   c   a tree diagram

2 The coin is tossed and a coloured counter is selected at random. Show all possible outcomes to this compound event as:
  a   a list   b   a table   c   a tree diagram

3 The coin is tossed and a playing card from the five cards above is selected at random. Show the sample space of this compound event as:
  a   a list   b   a table   c   a tree diagram

> ▮ Treat the 5♦ and the 5♠ as different possibilities.

4 The dice is thrown and a coloured counter is chosen at random. Show the sample space of this compound event as:
  a   a list   b   a table   c   a tree diagram

5 How many outcomes would be in the sample space if:
  a   the spinner is spun and the coin is tossed?
  b   the spinner is spun and the dice is thrown?
  c   the spinner is spun and a playing card is chosen at random?
  d   the dice is thrown and a playing card is chosen at random?
  e   the dice is thrown and the coin is tossed?
  f   a counter and a playing card are chosen at random?

6 The coin is tossed, the spinner is spun and a counter is chosen at random. How many outcomes would be in the sample space of this compound event?

7 This tree diagram shows the same space produced if a counter is chosen at random, then returned to the container, and then another counter is chosen at random.

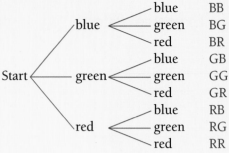

blue — blue — BB
blue — green — BG
blue — red — BR
Start — green — blue — GB
green — green — GG
green — red — GR
red — blue — RB
red — green — RG
red — red — RR

a How many outcomes are there?
b How many of the outcomes have both colours the same?
c How many outcomes contain at least one red counter?
d How many outcomes do not contain a red counter?

8 Draw a tree diagram to show the sample space produced when the coin is thrown twice.
a How many outcomes are there?
b How many outcomes contain at least one head?
c How many outcomes contain no heads?

9 Draw a tree diagram to show the sample space produced when the spinner is spun twice.
a How many outcomes are there?
b How many outcomes contain at least one spoon?
c How many outcomes contain no spoons?

10 A card is chosen at random, *not replaced*, and then a second card is chosen at random. The tree diagram below shows the sample space of this experiment.

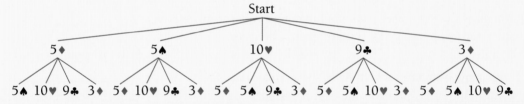

Start

5♦   5♠   10♥   9♣   3♦

5♠ 10♥ 9♣ 3♦ 5♦ 10♥ 9♣ 3♦ 5♦ 5♠ 9♣ 3♦ 5♦ 5♠ 10♥ 3♦ 5♦ 5♠ 10♥ 9♣

a Is it possible to draw the same card twice?
b How many outcomes are in the sample space?
c How many outcomes contain at least one diamond?
d How many outcomes contain no diamonds?
e How many outcomes have a sum of 15?
f How many outcomes have a sum less than 14?
g How many outcomes have a sum of 14 or more?
h Would it be true to say that there is an even chance that the sum will be less than 14?

11 Find the probability of choosing two Aces from a standard pack of cards in two draws:
a with replacement   **b** without replacement

challenge

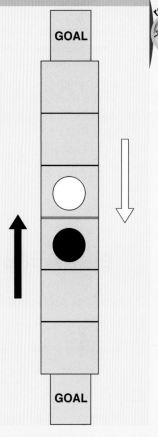

Rules of the game

To determine who goes first, each player throws two dice. The highest total goes first.

- The aim of the game is to reach your opponent's goal before your opponent reaches your goal.

- If black throws a double, a 7, or an 11, the black counter is moved one space closer to white's goal or the white counter is moved one space back towards its own goal.

- If white throws an odd total, then the white counter can be moved one space towards black's goal or the black counter moved one space back towards its own goal.

- The players take turns to throw the dice.

Exercise

1 Trial the game.
2 Why is it unfair?
3 Modify the rules to make it a fair game.
4 Make up a game of your own that is unfair.

16:03 | Dependent and Independent Events

Independent events are events where the outcome of one event does not affect the possible outcomes of the other.

Dependent events are events where the outcome of one event will affect the possible outcomes of the other.

The wording of a question will help you decide whether you are dealing with dependent or independent events.

worked example

Four cards marked 6, 7, 8 and 9 are in a hat. One card is drawn out and placed on a table. This is to be the tens digit of a two-digit number. Another card is then drawn out of the hat and placed beside the first card to complete the number.

a Draw a tree diagram to show the sample space of this experiment.
b How many outcomes are in the sample space?
c If the cards are drawn at random, what is the chance of getting the number 78?

continued ➜➜➜

Solution

a There are four ways of selecting the first digit. Once that is selected, there are only three ways of selecting the second digit. If 6 is selected first, for example, only 7, 8 and 9 are left to be selected as the second digit. The two events are **dependent**.

b Altogether 12 different two-digit numbers can be formed.

c 78 can be formed in only one way.

∴ P(78) = $\frac{1}{12}$

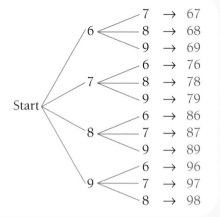

Exercise 16:03

In Questions 1 to 7, is each pair of events dependent or independent?

1 Whether the person wear glasses and that person's shoe size.

2 How hard a person works and that person's performance at school.

3 The age of a child and the child's shoe size.

4 Whether a person wears glasses and the age of that person.

5 A person's first choice in an election and a person's second choice in that election.

6 The number rolled on a dice and the card drawn from a pack.

7 The suburb in which I am driving and the next suburb through which I will drive.

Do Questions 8, 9, 10 and 11 show dependent or independent events?

8 I have an apple, an orange, a banana and two pears in a bowl.
Event 1: *I choose a piece of fruit and eat it.*
Event 2: *I choose a piece of fruit once again.*

9 I have an apple, an orange, a banana and two pears in a bowl.
Event 1: *I choose a piece of fruit and then return it to the bowl.*
Event 2: *I choose a piece of fruit once again.*

10 I have a pack of 52 playing cards.
Event 1: *I take a card and put it in my pocket.*
Event 2: *I take a card once again.*

> ☐ If the A♠ is taken in the first draw, can it also be taken in the second?

11 I have a pack of 52 playing cards.
Event 1: *I take a card and then return it to the pack.*
Event 2: *I take a card once again.*

12 A contestant on a quiz show must choose one box out of a possible three. In one of the boxes there is a diamond ring. The other two are empty. She chooses box A.

  a At this point of time, what is the probability that the ring is in box A?

  b The host does not know where the ring is. What is now the probability that the ring is in box A?

  c Box B is now opened. It does not contain the ring. What is now the probability that the ring is in box A?

  d After opening box C, the contestant is asked if she wants to change her mind. Would it improve her chances to win if she did so? Explain why or why not.

  e If the host knows where the ring is and, on purpose, opens the box not containing the ring (either B or C), would there be more chance that the ring is in box A or in the remaining box?

13 To find the winner of our team raffle, the names were written on the 10 tickets, and the tickets were placed in a hat. The tickets were taken out one at a time. The last ticket drawn out won the prize. I had bought 3 tickets.

  a What was my chance of winning before the draw commenced?

  b After four draws had been made I still had 2 tickets left in the hat. Had my chance of winning improved? What was the probability of my winning then?

  c After nine draws had been made, two of my tickets had been drawn out.

   i What was my probability of winning at this point of time?

   ii Were the draws dependent or independent events?

14 Three cards marked 5, 6 and 7 are placed in a hat. One card is drawn out and placed on a table. This is to be the tens digit of a two-digit number. Another card is then drawn out and placed beside the first card to complete the number.

  a Draw a tree diagram to show the sample space of the experiment.

  b How many outcomes are in the sample space?

  c If the cards are drawn out at random, what is the chance of making the number 75?

15 Two different names are to be chosen for a baby girl. The names being considered are Nina, Pearl, Ruby and Mimi.

 a In how many ways can the baby be named?
 b If the two names are chosen at random, what is the probability that the baby will be called Mimi Ruby?
 c What is the chance that the baby will be called Mimi Joy?

16 The name tags Julio, Alberto and Luca had been separated from the photographs of these three people.

The possible ways of matching the name tags to the photos are shown by this tree diagram.

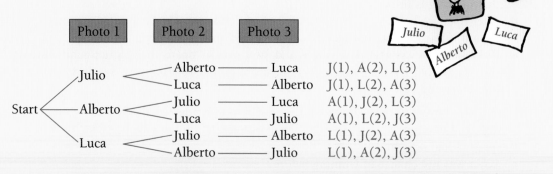

Photo 1	Photo 2	Photo 3	
Julio	Alberto — Luca		J(1), A(2), L(3)
	Luca — Alberto		J(1), L(2), A(3)
Alberto	Julio — Luca		A(1), J(2), L(3)
	Luca — Julio		A(1), L(2), J(3)
Luca	Julio — Alberto		L(1), J(2), A(3)
	Alberto — Julio		L(1), A(2), J(3)

Start

 a How many possible ways are there of matching the name tags with the photos?
 b How many correct ways are there of matching the name tags with the photos?
 c If we took a wild guess and randomly placed a name tag under each photo, what would be our chance of getting the names right?

17 From a committee of six people, A, B, C, D, E and F, a chairperson and a secretary are to be chosen. One person cannot fill both positions.

 a How many ways are there of choosing a chairperson?
 b If A is chosen as chairperson, who could be chosen as secretary?
 c If F is chosen as chairperson, how many ways are there of choosing the secretary?
 d In how many different ways can a chairperson and secretary be chosen?
 e If the chairperson and secretary are chosen at random, what is the probability that A is chosen to be chairperson and B is chosen to be secretary?

Investigation 16:03 | Will it be a boy or a girl?

- It is usually assumed that the chance of having a boy or girl is 1 in 2. However, my grandfather had six daughters and no sons and after having three daughters in a row, I wondered whether there might be a tendency in some families to have more children of one sex than the other.

  When my fourth child was a boy, I did not know what to believe.

- This tree diagram shows the possibilities for the first three children born to a couple.

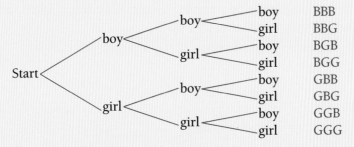

	boy	boy	BBB
		girl	BBG
boy	girl	boy	BGB
		girl	BGG
girl	boy	boy	GBB
		girl	GBG
	girl	boy	GGB
		girl	GGG

Start

- If the eight outcomes listed are equally likely, you would expect this pattern to occur in real life.

- Carry out a mathematical investigation to determine whether or not the outcomes listed are equally likely.

- Write a report on the investigation, including the following features, if appropriate:
  - a description of the problem
  - a description of any constraints and assumptions
  - an explanation of how technology was used
  - any relevant printouts
  - a description of any problems encountered
  - a description of any conclusions that were reached
  - a description of any possible extensions for further investigation.

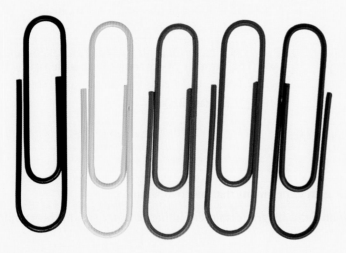

- These five paper clips were placed in a bag and selected one at a time. What is the probability of drawing them out in the same colour order shown here?

16:04 | Probability Using Tree and Dot Diagrams

A diagram or table helps to give clarity to a problem. 'A picture (or diagram) is worth a thousand words.'

Tree diagrams

The tree diagram method spreads out all the possible outcomes for a certain combination of simple events. For example, the tree diagram below shows the possible outcomes when three coins are tossed (or one coin is tossed three times).

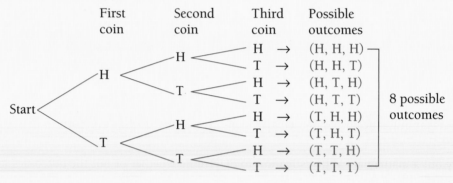

The tree diagram lays out, in a clear way, the eight possible combinations of heads and tails for three coins.

worked example

If three coins are tossed, what is the probability of getting:

a   3 heads?

b   2 heads and a tail?

c   only 1 head?

d   at least 2 heads?

Solution

The total number of possible outcomes for three coins is 8.

a   There is only one way of getting 3 heads, so:

$$P(3H) = \frac{1}{8}$$

b   The number of outcomes with 2 heads and 1 tail is 3, so:

$$P(2H, 1T) = \frac{3}{8}$$

c   The number of outcomes with only 1 head is 3, so:

$$P(1H) = \frac{3}{8}$$

d   The number of outcomes with **at least** 2 heads, ie 2 heads or 3 heads, is 4, so:

$$P(\text{at least } 2H) = \frac{4}{8}$$
$$= \frac{1}{2}$$

Dot diagrams

Dot diagrams are useful when examining an experiment that has two simple stages.

We can mark a set of outcomes clearly on a dot diagram, so the number of outcomes in the sample space is easy to see.

The dot diagram over the page shows the possible outcomes when two dice are tossed.

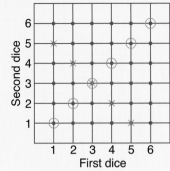

Second dice / First dice

Dot diagram showing
all possible outcomes.

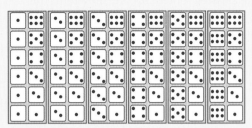

All possible outcomes are shown here.

On the diagram, the 5 outcomes that add up to 6 have been marked with crosses, ie (1, 5), (2, 4), (3, 3), (4, 2), (5, 1)

The 'double' outcomes (1, 1), (2, 2), (3, 3), (4, 4), (5, 5), (6, 6) have been marked with circles.

worked example

Find the probability of throwing with two dice:

a   a total of 6

b   a double

c   a total greater than 9

d   a 1 on at least one dice

Solution

The total number of possible outcomes, as can be seen from the above diagrams, is 36.

a   The number of outcomes that
   give a total of six is 5.
   ∴ P(total of 6) = $\frac{5}{36}$

b   The number of doubles is 6.
   ∴ P(double) = $\frac{6}{36}$
   = $\frac{1}{6}$

c   The outcomes that give a total
   greater than 9 are:
   (4, 6), (5, 5), (6, 4), (5, 6), (6, 5)
   and (6, 6)
   ∴ P(greater than 9) = $\frac{6}{36}$
   = $\frac{1}{6}$

d   The number of outcomes that
   include at least one 1 is 11.
   ∴ P(a 1 on at least one dice) = $\frac{11}{36}$

Exercise 16:04

1   This tree diagram shows all possible outcomes when two coins are tossed.
   a   How many possible outcomes are there?
   b   What is the probability of getting:
      i   2 heads?
      ii   a head and a tail (in any order)?
      iii   at least 1 tail?

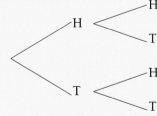

2 A red dice and a blue dice are thrown together. All possible outcomes are shown on this dot diagram. What is the probability of getting:

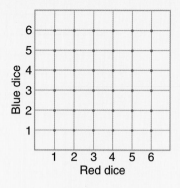

a a double 6?   **b** a double?
c a sum of 2?   **d** a sum of 3?
e a sum of 4?   **f** a sum of 5?
g a sum of 6?   **h** a sum of 7?
i a sum of 8?   **j** a sum of 9?
k a sum of 10?   **l** a sum of 11?
m a sum of 12?   **n** a sum of 1?
o at least one dice even?
p two even numbers?
q two odd numbers?
r one odd and one even number?
s What is the sum of the probabilities in **p**, **q** and **r**? Explain why this answer is obtained.
t What events give a probability of $\frac{1}{9}$?

3 This diagram represents the possible outcomes of a family having 2 children. Copy this diagram and extend it for 3 children.

a In how many different ways can a family have 3 children?
b How many of these outcomes have 2 girls and a boy (in any order)?
c If a family has 3 children, what is the probability that it has:
   i 3 girls?
   ii 2 boys and a girl?
   iii 3 of the same sex?
   iv at least 2 girls?

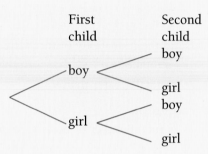

> Assume that having a boy or a girl is equally likely.

4 This dot diagram shows the possibilities that could occur if a coin is tossed and a dice is thrown. Find the probability of getting:

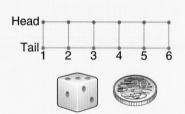

a a head and a three
b a tail and a six
c a tail on the coin
d an even number on the dice
e a tail on an even number
f a tail on a number less than 4.

5 Three cards labelled 1, 2 and 3 are placed in a hat. A card is chosen and then put back before a second card is chosen. Find the probability of:
  a the cards having the same number
  b getting at least one 3
  c the sum of the two numbers being 4
  d the cards being different.

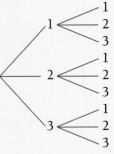

6 Three coins are tossed. The tree diagram on page 65 shows the sample space. Use the tree diagram to find the probability of tossing:
  a exactly one head
  b exactly two tails
  c more tails than heads
  d three heads
  e at least one head
  f either two heads or two tails
  g either one tail or more than one head.

7 A spinner with the numbers 1 to 4 on it was spun twice. Draw a dot diagram that shows the possible outcomes.
  a How many possible outcomes are there?
  b What is the probability of spinning:
    i a 3 on the first spin?
    ii a 3 on either spin?
    iii a total of 5?
    iv an odd total?
    v the same number twice?

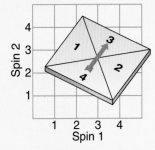

8 Three cards labelled 1, 2 and 3 are placed in a hat (as in question **5**) and a card is drawn. This is repeated 3 times, but each time the card is *not* put back in the hat. The tree diagram for this is drawn here.
  a How many 3-digit numbers can be formed?
  b What is the probability of the 3-digit number being:
    i 123?
    ii greater than 200?
    iii odd?
    iv divisible by 3?

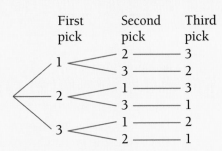

9 The letters A, B, C and D are written on cards and placed in a hat. A card is drawn and placed on a table. A second card is then drawn and placed to the right of the first card. A third card is then drawn and placed on the right of the other two.

a Construct a tree diagram to show the possible outcomes of the experiment.

b What is the probability that the order of letters chosen spells:
   i BAD?
   ii DAD?

c What is the probability of:
   i not drawing an A?
   ii drawing the letters in alphabetical order?

10 A letter A, B or C is drawn from a hat and a random number that is either odd or even is obtained from a calculator.

a Show the sample space of this compound event on a dot diagram.

b How many outcomes are there?

c What is the probability of getting:
   i B and an odd number?
   ii not getting both B and an odd number?
   iii not getting C?

A random number is obtained by pressing: 2nd F RAN

11 From the four Kings out of a pack of playing cards, two are chosen at random (ie one is chosen and then the second is chosen without the first card being replaced).

a Draw a tree diagram showing the possible pairs chosen.

b Determine the probability of getting:
   i two Kings the same colour
   ii at least one red King
   iii the King of spades.

K♥ K♦ K♣ K♠

12 From five people, a driver and a passenger for the front seat are chosen at random. In how many ways can this be done? What is the probability that:

a a particular person will be the driver?

b a particular person will be either the driver or the front seat passenger?

c two particular people will fill these two positions?

Reading mathematics 16:04 | Probabilities given as odds

The use of odds in gambling

*   Odds such as 5/1, 11/4, even money, 2/1 and 2/1 on (or 1/2) are used to give the ratio of what could be gained to what could be lost.

*   The fact that for odds of 5/1, $5 might be won while only $1 might be lost suggests that the probability of success would be 1 chance in 6. This is rarely the case, however, as odds are usually set so that the gambler is at a disadvantage. Odds of 5/1 may be offered when the probability is really 1 chance in 10. This is how the bookmaker, government (TAB) or insurance company makes a profit. This means that the ordinary gambler is sure to lose over time.

*   Odds offered on a horse race or a football match are subjective, as each of these events occurs only once. This is an application of subjective probability.

The use of odds in common language

*   The expression *He's a 100/1 chance of getting the job* means that he has very little chance, while the expression, *He's an even money proposition*, suggests that his probability of success is 1 in 2.

Discussion

1   What do odds of 10/1 mean?

2   Explain why the ordinary gambler must lose over time.

3   Is it healthy for the government of a nation to encourage its people to gamble? Why, or why not?

16:05 | Probability Using Tables and Venn Diagrams

Contingency tables

Contingency tables show information concerning two variables, with the categories of one variable listed along the top of the table and the categories of the other down the side.

We can use the information in contingency tables to calculate probabilities.

People indicated the colour they would prefer for the cover of this textbook. The contingency table summarises their preferences.

If one of their preferences was chosen at random, what is the probability that:

a the preference would be red?
b the preference would not be red?
c it would be from a boy?
d it would be from a male?
e it would be from a girl whose preference was blue?

	Boys	Girls	Men	Women	Totals
Red	11	10	8	2	31
Blue	9	11	6	6	32
Green	6	3	2	1	12
Orange	4	8	10	3	25
Totals	30	32	26	12	100

Contingency table

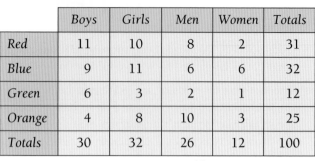

Solution

a A total of 31 people preferred red.
There were 100 preferences altogether.
$$\therefore \text{P(red)} = \frac{31}{100}$$

b As 31 of the 100 preferred red, the rest (69) did not prefer red.
$$\therefore \text{P(not red)} = \frac{69}{100}$$

c There were 30 boys in the sample.
$$\therefore \text{P(boy)} = \frac{30}{100}$$
$$= \frac{3}{10}$$

d There were 30 boys and 26 men.
$$\therefore \text{P(male)} = \frac{56}{100}$$
$$= \frac{14}{25}$$

e The number of girls whose preference was blue was 11.
$$\therefore \text{P(girl preferring blue)} = \frac{11}{100}$$

Frequency tables

The frequency of occurrence of certain events is often recorded in table form. This makes it easier to work out probabilities.

The absentee records of my Grade 9 students are displayed in this frequency table.

If a student is selected at random, find the probability that the student has missed:

a four days of school
b less than three days
c seven days of school
d from three to five days.

Days missed x	Number of students f
0	31
1	47
2	25
3	18
4	11
5	8
6	2
Total:	142

Solution

a 11 students out of 142 have missed
four days of school.

$\therefore$ P(4 days missed) $= \frac{11}{142}$

b P(less than 3 days) $= \frac{31 + 47 + 25}{142} = \frac{103}{142}$

c No one has been absent for seven days.

$\therefore$ P(7 days missed) $= 0$

d P(3 to 5 days missed) $= \frac{18 + 11 + 8}{142}$

$= \frac{37}{142}$

Venn diagrams

Venn diagrams are a convenient way of displaying information when working out probabilities.

worked example

Of 120 employees in our factory, 35 have a
beard and of these 5 are among the
47 employees working with heavy
machinery.

If one is chosen at random, what is the
probability that the employee:

a has a beard but does not work with
heavy machinery?

b neither has a beard nor works with
heavy machinery?

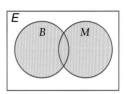

- B is the set of employees with
  beards.
- M is he set of employees
  working with heavy machinery.
- E is the set of all employees.

Solution

$n(E) = 120$ (ie number in E is 120)

$n(B) = 35$, $n(M) = 47$,

$n(B$ and $M) = 5$

We use the information given to place
numbers in each part of the Venn diagram.

a 30 bearded employees do not work
with heavy machines.

$\therefore$ P(B and **not** M) $= \frac{30}{120}$

$= \frac{1}{4}$

b 43 employees are not in either of the
two categories.

$\therefore$ P(**not** B and **not** M) $= \frac{43}{120}$

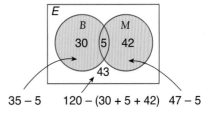

$35 - 5$ $120 - (30 + 5 + 42)$ $47 - 5$

There are 5 that belong in the part
where the circles overlap.

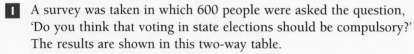

1 A survey was taken in which 600 people were asked the question, 'Do you think that voting in state elections should be compulsory?' The results are shown in this two-way table.

	Male	Female
Yes	103	196
No	239	62

a How many males were surveyed?

b How many people answered no?

c A person was chosen at random. What is the probability that the person:

　i said no?　　　　ii said yes?

　iii was male?　　　iv was female?

　v was a male who said yes?

　vi was a female who said no?

d What is the probability that a person who said no was a male?

e What is the probability that a male would say no?

2 A survey of 1000 people in the school grounds revealed the following information:

Eye colour

		Blue	Brown	Other
	Black	194	215	156
Hair colour	Blond	169	63	83
	Other	30	61	29

One of these people is chosen at random. What is the probability that the person has:

a blond hair?

b blue eyes?

c both blond hair and blue eyes?

d neither blond hair nor blue eyes?

e blond hair, given that the eyes are brown?

f blond hair, given that the eyes are neither blue nor brown?

3 Students were asked to choose one course of lectures out of the three that were being offered. The record of their choices is shown in this table. One student is chosen at random. What is the probability that the student:

	Boys	Girls	Totals
Art	26	16	40
Music	16	21	37
Woodwork	13	10	23
Totals	53	47	100

a was a girl?

b chose art?

c did not choose woodwork?

d was a boy who chose music?

e was a girl who did not choose art?

Give your answers as decimals.

4 The number of people employed in our town is 2461. The age distribution of these people is shown in the table. If one of these employed people is chosen at random, what is the probability that the age of the person is:

a from 55 to 64?
b 65 or over?
c less than 45?
d at least 55?
e less than 15?
f less than 91?
g under 25 or over 64?

Age (years) x	Number of people f
15–24	506
25–34	711
35–44	517
45–54	369
55–64	236
65–90	122
	2461

5 A tennis club and a golf club joined to make one club. There were 86 people in the tennis club and 137 people in the golf club but only 181 people in the combined club. A member of the combined club was chosen at random. What is the probability that the person chosen had belonged to:

a the tennis club?
b both clubs?
c the golf club but not the tennis club?

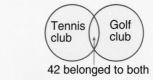

42 belonged to both

6 90 males and 60 females were asked to indicate their major study area. 20% of the total indicated library. Half of the females indicated psychology and 50 males and 10 females indicated mathematics.

a Use this information to complete the table.
b If one of these people is chosen at random, what is the probability that the person:
  i is female?
  ii is majoring in library?
  iii is a male majoring in library?
  iv is a female majoring in psychology?

	Male	Female	Totals
Library			30
Psychology		30	
Mathematics	50	10	
Totals	90	60	150

Library is my strength.

7 The 39 goals scored by our water polo team were recorded on a videotape. The table shows the number of goals scored by each player in the team. If a goal is played from the videotape at random, what is the probability that the goal scorer was:

a Craig?
b Evan?
c either Luke or Julian?
d neither Akos nor Nandor?
e someone who had scored 1 goal only?

Player	Number of goals
Craig	1
Rajiv	7
Sai	1
Evan	0
Mark	0
Akos	6
Nandor	5
Luke	10
Julian	9
	39

8 An engineering firm employs 87 people. Of these, 31 have special skills in engineering (E) and 23 have special skills in computing (C). Of those, 17 have special skills in both engineering and computing. An employee is chosen at random. What is the probability that the employee has special skills in:

a engineering?
b both engineering and computing?
c engineering but not computing?
d neither engineering nor computing?

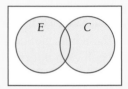

9 This table represents data collected on 300 athletes and compares height with weight.

a One of these athletes is chosen at random. What is the theoretical probability that the athlete is:
  i short?
  ii both short and light?
  iii either short or light?
  iv neither short nor light?
b If I chose an athlete who is not part of this group, what would be the experimental probability that the athlete would be:
  i tall and heavy?
  ii tall and light?
c Is the table relevant to people who are not athletes? Why, or why not?

Height \ Weight	Heavy	Light	Totals
Tall	70	20	90
Short	50	160	210
Totals	120	180	300

10 To investigate the cause of road accidents in which a fatality occurred, John studied a number of accidents chosen at random from those that occurred during the years 2001 and 2002. The details of fatal accidents occurring in Australia during that time are shown below.

Fatalities by state/territory and road user, 2001 and 2002								
	NSW	Vic	Qld	SA	WA	Tas	NT	ACT	Australia
2002	561	397	322	154	179	37	55	10	1715
2001	524	444	324	153	165	61	50	16	1737
% change 2001–02	7·1	−10·6	−0·6	0·7	8·5	−39·3	10·0	−37·5	−1·3
Average change 1997–02	−0·5	1·0	−2·2	0·8	−1·9	2·9	−1·7	−10·1	−0·6

a If John chose a fatal crash at random from 2002, give the probability (as a percentage) that the crash was:
  i from NSW
  ii from the ACT
  iii from Queensland
  iv not from Tasmania
  v from neither NSW nor the ACT

Give answers correct to the nearest tenth of 1%.

b If John had chosen a fatal crash at random from the year 2001, what is the probability (as a percentage) that the crash would have been:
  i from NSW?
  ii from the ACT?
  iii from Queensland?
  iv not from Tasmania?
  v from neither NSW nor the ACT?
Even though the percentage change in fatal crashes in the ACT is 37·5%, the probability of choosing a crash from the ACT had changed only 0·3%. Explain why the change in probability is so small.

Practical Activity 16:05 | Games of chance

In the game below, I always throw the dice first. A player must land on the home square to win.

Start	1	2	3	Miss a turn	5	Go to home	7	8	Home

Discuss the fairness of this game, considering the chances of winning or losing over many games. How could the game be made fair?

16:06 | Simulation Experiments

A simulation is a model of a real-life activity. Simple equipment such as coins, dice, spinners, cards or random numbers are used to represent real outcomes.

- When it is impossible or impractical to study actual data, simulation is a very useful tool. Simulation is useful:
    - **a** to speed up or slow down a situation (such as crop harvests)
    - **b** for economic reasons (such as rocket launches, pilot training)
    - **c** for safety reasons (such as study of reactions to disease)
    - **d** in order to change the variables more easily (such as aircraft design)
    - **e** in entertainment (such as car racing on video games).

- Simulations are usually designed to answer specific questions.

- A simulation is like a trial run. It allows you to consider likely outcomes in advance and to plan modifications before carrying out the real thing.

worked examples

Example 1

Julia wanted to know the probability of winning three chess games in a row against her brother knowing she usually wins 50% of the games they play.

Solution 1

Step 1   Design an experiment

Julia could have used a coin because there were only two equally likely possibilities: winning or not winning. She chose instead to use the random number key on her calculator.

- She decides that if the number is less than 0·500, this will represent *not* winning. If the number is greater than or equal to 0·500, this will represent a win.

Step 2   Reword the problem

- When three games are played in a row, how many times will Julia win all three?

Step 3   Make assumptions

- We must assume that the numbers generated by the calculator are completely random.

- We must also assume that the probability of Julia winning any particular game will not change.

That's a 'win'.

■ Consult your calculator handbook if you need help using the random number key.

Step 4 Make predictions

- We would expect that winning two games in a row would be less than 50% and winning three games in a row would be less again.

Step 5 Conduct the simulation

- Three random numbers were generated 12 times, giving the following results.

Trial	Numbers	Win or loss
1	0·411, 0·470, 0·827	L, L, W
2	0·021, 0·474, 0·134	L, L, L
3	0·886, 0·987, 0·704	W, W, W
4	0·205, 0·722, 0·615	L, W, W
5	0·167, 0·855, 0·672	L, W, W
6	0·472, 0·863, 0·858	L, W, W

Trial	Numbers	Win or loss
7	0·752, 0·318, 0·336	W, L, L
8	0·746, 0·166, 0·836	W, L, W
9	0·230, 0·304, 0·014	L, L, L
10	0·333, 0·668, 0·368	L, W, L
11	0·468, 0·785, 0·060	L, W, L
12	0·393, 0·054, 0·262	L, L, L

Step 6 Tabulate the results

Number of wins	Frequency
3	1
2	4
1	4
0	3

> ▪ A computer spreadsheet can also be used to generate random numbers.
> See Challenge 4:03.

Step 7 Describe observations and results and draw conclusions

- In twelve simulations, Julia only won all three games once. This would lead to a conclusion that the probability of Julia winning three games in a row is $\frac{1}{12}$.

- For these same simulations, however, Julia lost all three games three times. Since Julia would expect this to occur as often as winning three games, she would probably conclude that she needs to perform more trials to see if this outcome is consistent.

Example 2

In 50 births at a local hospital, how many times is it likely that 3 boys would be born in succession?

Solution 2

Step 1 Design an experiment

We could use a coin, random numbers, a dice or a set of playing cards to simulate the births. Let's use playing cards.

It's a boy!

- If we choose a heart or diamond as we cut the cards, it will stand for the birth of a girl. If we choose a club or spade, it will stand for the birth of a boy.

- We must be careful not to allow any bias to enter our experiment, so, after cutting the cards, we will shuffle them before cutting again.

continued ➜➜➜

Step 2 Reword the problem

- In 50 consecutive births, how many times would a run of 3 boys occur?

Step 3 Make assumptions

- We will assume that exactly 3 boys in a row is the condition being studied. If 4 boys occur in a row, the first 3 of these would not satisfy the condition.

- It would, of course, be possible to assume that any run of three boys is meant in the question. In that case, different conclusions would be made.

Step 4 Make predictions

- We wouldn't expect the condition to occur very often. If it did, we would have to check the design of our experiment.

Step 5 Conduct the simulation

- Take a standard pack of playing cards and shuffle and cut them 50 times.

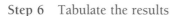

B G G B B G B G B G
B G G G G B G B B G
G G B B B G G G B B
G G B G B G B G B G
G G G B B G G B G G

Step 6 Tabulate the results

Number of boys in a row	Tally	f
1	JHT JHT	10
2	IIII	4
3	I	1
4		0
5		0

Number of girls in a row	Tally	f
1	JHT II	7
2	IIII	4
3	II	2
4	II	2
5		0

Step 7 Describe observations and results, and draw conclusions

- In the simulation of 50 births, *exactly 3 boys occurred once*. It is, however, clear that it may be different for other simulations, as exactly 3 girls has occurred here twice and the likelihood of this happening is the same as for 3 boys.

- It could be recommended that the simulation be carried out several times to get a clearer picture of what is likely to happen in a hospital.

- The most probable outcome would seem to be *1 or 2 runs of 3 boys* in each simulation.

 This last statement we have made is called an *inference*. An inference is a judgement made using the information at hand.

1 Tim was one of three brothers. He wondered what the chances were of three children in the same family all being boys. He used three coins with heads and tails representing boys and girls to simulate the birth of three children.

   a Carry out the simulation forty times and tabulate your results.

   b From your data, what is the probability of having three boys?

2 Franco has six good shirts that he wears to dances. Every Saturday night he chooses one of these shirts at random to wear to the dance.

   a Design a simulation that would allow you to investigate the number of times in one year that Franco would wear the same shirt he wore the week before. (Hint: Use each face of a dice to represent one of the shirts.)

   b Use the seven steps in the worked examples on pages 77 to 79 to record the results of your simulation.

   c Is it possible to use these results to predict the number of times he would choose the same shirt over a two-year period? Explain your answer.

3 When playing cards together, Alana, Rachel, Emily and Karim are all just as likely to win. They intend to play a series of forty games.

Design a simulation, showing the seven steps used in the worked examples, to estimate:

   a how many times Alana would win

   b how many times Alana would win immediately after Rachel had won

   c the longest run of losses any one of the four is likely to have

   d the longest run of wins any one of them is likely to have

   e how many times a group of four winners have names that are in alphabetical order

4 Maximo wanted to simulate the months in which he would be invited to weddings in the future. He decided to use the sum of two dice to indicate the month in which each wedding would occur. (He used 1 for January, 2 for February, and so on up to 12 for December.)

Using inappropriate models can give absurd results ...

   a Give at least two reasons why Maximo's simulation has a poor design.

   b What other problems can you see in designing a simulation of these weddings?

   c Could playing cards be used to simulate these events?

5 Grace has been selected to represent England in women's cricket. She has been made second reserve, however, and will only play if 2 of the 12 other players are unfit for a game. She is told that the likelihood of any single player being unfit is 5%.

a Use 20 playing cards, one of which is marked unfit, to simulate the likelihood of a particular player being unfit. Select one of these cards at random to determine if player number 1 is unfit. By repeating this 11 times, find the fitness level of the 12 other players for one game. Did Grace get to play in that game?
(To ensure randomness, shuffle between selections.)

b There are 10 games to be played on the tour. Repeat the simulation 9 times to estimate the number of games Grace is likely to play.

c Would it be reasonable to simply multiply the result of the first simulation by 10 instead of repeating it 9 times? Explain.

d Use your results to give the experimental probability that Grace will play in the last game.

6 The owner of Bellbird Caravan Park found that there was 1 chance in 10 that a person who booked a site for the school holidays would fail to arrive. This meant that the site would be left vacant for the holidays. As there was always a surplus of people wishing to book the 20 sites, the manager wanted to take bookings for 22 sites. However, the owner of the park did not want the embarrassment of turning people away.

• Assume that 22 bookings were taken for the 20 sites.

• Use random numbers generated by your calculator to simulate the arrival (digits 1 to 9), or non-arrival (digit 0), of each person who booked a site.

• In the table below, put an A under the booking number to show an arrival and an N to show a non-arrival.

Arrival/non-arrival for each booking

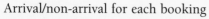

1	2	3	4	5	6	7	8	9	10	11

12	13	14	15	16	17	18	19	20	21	22

Sites occupied = ☐   Sites vacant = ☐   Number of people turned away = ☐

a In your simulation, was it necessary to turn anybody away?

b If no one was turned away in this simulation, does this mean that there is little chance of having to turn people away? Explain your answer.

c Repeat the simulation 9 times. In how many of the trials were people turned away?

d Suggest ways, other than overbooking, that would avoid loss of income through non-arrival.

e Use your results to give the experimental probability that people would have to be turned away.

7 Brekky Bits place 2 Australian wildlife cards in each of their breakfast cereal packets. There are 20 wildlife cards in the set and they are placed inside the packets in a random fashion.

a Run a simulation to investigate the number of packets Kayla would need to purchase to obtain the complete set. Use playing cards marked 1 to 20. Draw cards at random and complete the table below.

Card	Tally
1 bandicoot	
2 bat	
3 bilby	
4 boodie	
5 cuscus	
6 dunnart	
7 echidna	
8 kangaroo	
9 koala	
10 marsupial mouse	

Card	Tally
11 marsupial mole	
12 numbat	
13 platypus	
14 possum	
15 quokka	
16 quoll	
17 Tasmanian devil	
18 thylacine	
19 wallaby	
20 wombat	

b Compare your results with those of the class. Find the range and mean of the class results.

c Kayla's friend Cassie also collected these cards, so they decided to combine their resources. Continue your simulation until you have two complete sets of cards.

   i If each of the two households uses one packet of Brekky Bits each week, how long do you think it would take to complete the two sets?

   ii What is the minimum time possible for the two sets to be completed?

Generating random integers

A random number generator on a calculator or computer can be used to generate a set of integers by following these steps.

- **To generate integers from 1 to 6 (which might represent the faces on a dice), simply multiply the random number by 6 and then add 1. This will give a decimal number between 1·000 and 6·999.**
- **Then take the integer before the decimal point as the result.**

8 Use your calculator to generate integers from 1 to 6, thirty times. If these numbers represented the faces on a dice, how often did a 6 occur?

9 Kathrin was in a class of 15 students. She wanted to know the probability of 3 or more students having their birthdays in the same month.

   a Generate random integers from 1 to 12, using the instructions above, but this time multiplying each random number by 12. A set of 15 numbers would represent the class with the generated numbers representing the twelve months. Do this at least 20 times.

   b How often in each set of 15 numbers does the same integer (month) occur three times?

   c From your data, what do you think would be the probability of 3 students in Kathrin's class having the same birth month?

   d How many simulations would you have to do to draw a reasonable conclusion?

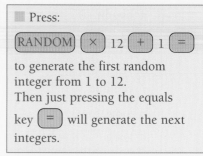

Press:

RANDOM × 12 + 1 =

to generate the first random integer from 1 to 12.
Then just pressing the equals key = will generate the next integers.

Some calculators may work differently.

Fun Spot 16:06 | Random numbers and calculator cricket

Generating random numbers

When using a calculator, a random number of the form 0·609 appears on the screen. If you want to record a one-digit random number, you write only the tenths digit.

For 0·014, you write 0. For 0·905, you write 9.

Calculator cricket

- Decide how many people will play.

- Player 1 continues to obtain one-digit random numbers from the screen of a calculator until a zero occurs. When a zero occurs, the player has lost a wicket. The player is out!

- After each player has had two turns, compare totals. The player with the highest total is the winner.

- Make a list of 40 one-digit random numbers.

- What is the chance of getting out with each ball faced?

- Examine your random numbers. What is the average number of balls faced before the person batting is out?

- In how many different orders could these four hurdlers finish the race?

Investigation 16:06 | Two-stage probability experiments

Please use the Assessment Grid on the following page to help you understand what is required for this Investigation.

Experiment 1

Place 3 black and 3 white counters in a container.

a Draw out two counters 100 times and record how often they are the same colour. (Use a tally.)

b Calculate the experimental probability of drawing two counters of the same colour.

Design a similar experiment of your own to find the probability of an event of your choosing.

Different colours
could be used.

Experiment 2

If two one-digit numbers are selected at random, what is the probability that they will be in order, smallest to largest?

- We could use a tree diagram to solve this problem but there would be 100 branches at the last stage.

- An approximation can be obtained by finding the experimental probability.

5, 9

Yes!

Steps

1 Generate sets of two random numbers using a calculator.

⎣2nd F⎦ ⎣RAN⎦ will probably generate

three random digits on your calculator. Just consider the last two digits given. (If your calculator gives only one random digit, you will need to repeat the process more often.)

5, 5

No ...

2 Repeat the experiment 100 times, entering your results in the tally column of this frequency table.
- Would you expect as many sets to decrease as to increase?
- Could counting decreasing sets be used as a check on your results?

Result	Tally	f
Increasing		
Decreasing		
Doubles		

Total:

3 Use your table of results to calculate the probability that two random digits will be in order, smallest to largest.

- You could investigate the probability that three one-digit numbers, selected at random, will be in order, smallest to largest.

Assessment Grid for Investigation 16:06 | **Two-stage probability experiments**

The following is a sample assessment grid for this investigation. You should carefully read the criteria *before* beginning the investigation so that you know what is required.

		Assessment Criteria (B, C) for this investigation		Achieved ✓
Criterion B — Investigating Patterns	a	None of the following descriptors has been achieved.	0	
	b	Some help was needed to complete the table and identify the simple patterns to calculate experimental probability.	1	
			2	
	c	Probability techniques have been selected and applied to complete the table and make some suggestions for answers to both experiments.	3	
			4	
	d	The student has used the patterns evident in the table to calculate the required probabilities and describe the relationships to the experiments.	5	
			6	
	e	The patterns evident have been explained and the results justified using the steps given. The student is able to use the same patterns found in question 3 to answer the final part for three one-digit numbers.	7	
			8	
Criterion C — Communication in Mathematics	a	None of the following descriptors has been achieved.	0	
	b	There is basic use of mathematical language and representation. Lines of reasoning are insufficient.	1	
			2	
	c	There is satisfactory use of mathematical language and representation. Tables and explanations are clear but not always complete.	3	
			4	
	d	There is good use of mathematical language and representation. Tables are complete and well set out. Explanations and answers are related to results.	5	
			6	

Challenge 16:06 | Computer dice

You can use a spreadsheet program such as Excel to simulate the throwing of two dice and then adding the two numbers.

- Open the spreadsheet program and type **DICE A** in cell A1, **DICE B** in cell B1 and **A + B** in cell C1. These are headings for columns A, B and C.

	A	B	C
1	DICE A	DICE B	A+B
2	=INT(RAND()*6+1)		
3			

- Type in the formula =INT(RAND()*6+1) into cell A2. This will also appear in the formula bar at the top.

	A	B	C
1	DICE A	DICE B	A+B
2	2		
3			

- Press ENTER and a number from 1 to 6 will appear in the cell.

	A	B	C
1	DICE A	DICE B	A+B
2	3	4	7
3			

- Repeat the above two steps in cell B2.

- Type the formula =A2+B2 into cell C2.

- Press ENTER and the total of the integers in cells A2 and B2 should appear.

- Using the mouse, click on the bottom right-hand corner of cell A2 and drag the cursor down to, say, cell A13. Release the button on the mouse and random numbers from 1 to 6 will appear.

	A	B	C
1	DICE A	DICE B	A+B
2	4	2	6
3	3		
4	1		
5	2		
6	1		
7	2		
8	4		
9	1		
10	1		
11	2		
12	2		
13	5		

- Repeat the above step for cell B2 and then cell C2.

- The cells in C2 should contain integers from 2 to 12, representing the sum of the faces of two dice.

	A	B	C
1	DICE A	DICE B	A+B
2	3	4	7
3	4	6	10
4	5	3	8
5	1	1	2
6	4	3	7
7	4	1	5
8	1	2	3
9	1	1	2
10	1	6	7
11	5	5	10
12	6	1	7
13	5	3	8

Examine these results to see how closely they represent the expected probabilities when two dice are thrown.

Mathematical Terms 16

complementary event
- The *opposite* event that covers all possibilities.
  eg If the event is throwing a 6, the complementary event would be not throwing a 6. Similarly, the complementary event to selecting a girl would be selecting a boy.

dependent events
- Events where the outcome of one event will affect the possible outcomes of the other.

experimental probability
- Determining the chance of an event occurring by observing what happens in a sample experiment.

$$\text{experimental probability} = \frac{\text{no. of times event occurred}}{\text{total number in sample}}$$

independent events
- Events where the outcome of one event does *not* affect the possible outcomes of the other.

inference
- An inference is a judgement made using the information at hand.

mutually exclusive events
- Events that cannot occur at the same time.
  eg throwing an even number and throwing a three with a dice.

outcomes
- The possible results when calculating a probability.
  eg the outcomes when tossing a coin are heads or tails.

probability
- the calculated chance of an event happening.

random
- Without predetermination.
- To choose 'at random' means that each outcome is equally likely to occur.

relative frequency
- $\text{relative frequency} = \dfrac{\text{frequency of a score}}{\text{total frequency}}$
- The relative frequency of an event is actually the same as its experimental probability.

sample
- The list of possible outcomes.
  eg when throwing a dice, the sample would be 1, 2, 3, 4, 5 or 6.

simulation
- An experiment that uses simple equipment, such as cards or coins, to represent a real event.
  eg using heads or tails to represent the birth of boys or girls.

survey
- To gather data or information from which conclusions might be drawn.
  eg to count the number of trucks in a line of traffic or to question a group of students about their favourite music.

theoretical probability
- The probability of an event that is determined by considering the possible outcomes.
  eg the probability of throwing a 6 with a dice is $\frac{1}{6}$, because there are 6 equally likely outcomes.

Mathematical terms 16

Diagnostic Test 16 | Probability

- These questions reflect the important skills introduced in this chapter.
- Errors made will indicate areas of weakness.
- Each weakness should be treated by going back to the section listed.

	Section
1 a What is the probability of choosing a 9 from a list of random digits, (0 to 9)?	16:01
b Fifty cards numbered 1 to 50 were shuffled. One of these cards is to be selected at random. What is the probability that the card will be: **i** 3? **ii** less than 11? **iii** not 3? **iv** prime?	

2 My last 44 scores on our golf course have been entered in this table.

Section 16:01

My score	90–93	94–97	98–101	102–105	106–109
Frequency	3	5	7	20	9

I am about to play another game. What is the experimental probability that my score will be:

a lower than 94?   **b** higher than 93?   **c** higher than 109?

Explain why the experimental probability that my score is higher than 109 is not the real probability.

3 A dice is thrown and a coin is tossed. Show all possible outcomes:

Section 16:02

  a as a list   **b** as a table   **c** as a tree diagram

4 Four cards marked 6, 7, 8 and 9 are in a hat. One card is drawn out and placed on a table. This is to be the tens digit of a two-digit number. Another card is then drawn out of the hat and placed beside the first card to complete the number.

Section 16:03

  a Draw a tree diagram to show the sample space of this experiment.

  b How many outcomes are in the sample space?

  c If the cards are drawn at random, what is the chance of getting the number 78?

5 This diagram shows the outcomes possible if a spinner showing 1, 2 and 3 is spun and a dice is thrown.

Section 16:03 16:04

Start

(1)   (2)   (3)

1 2 3 4 5 6 1 2 3 4 5 6 1 2 3 4 5 6

  a How many outcomes are in this compound event?

  b If the spinner is spun and the dice is thrown, what is the probability that we would get:

    i a 2 on the spinner and a 5 on the dice?

    ii a total of 7?   **iii** a total of 10 or more?

6 Rachel is choosing the background colour for three consecutive pages of her art assignment. For the first page she must choose either red, blue or green; for the second page, blue or orange; and for the third page, red or blue.
a Draw a tree diagram to show all possible choices.
b If Rachel selects each colour at random, find the probability that at least two of the pages will be blue.

7 This dot diagram shows the types of screwdriver that we manufacture. The dots show the ones we have in stock. Assume that each size is just as likely to be ordered.

a What is the probability that the next screwdriver ordered is in stock?
b What is the probability that the next one ordered is not in stock?

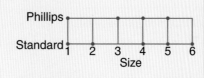

8 People chose the colour they would prefer in our new range of tennis racquets. The contingency table summarises their preferences. If one of their preferences were chosen at random, what is the probability that:

	Boys	Girls	Men	Women	Totals
Gold	15	10	3	6	34
Red	5	7	4	6	22
Blue	4	12	9	10	35
Green	8	2	7	2	19
Totals	32	31	23	24	110

a it would be red?
b it would be from a boy?
c it would be from a female?
d it would be from a girl whose preference was blue?

9 The absentee records of the factory workers have been displayed in this frequency table. If one is selected at random, what is the probability that the worker has been absent for:
a 4 days?
b less than 3 days?
c from 3 to 5 days?
d less than 7 days?

Days absent x	Number of workers f
0	7
1	3
2	11
3	6
4	2
5	1

10 Of 85 employees in our factory, 35 are
    married and of these 7 are among the
    15 office staff. If one is chosen at random,
    what is the probability that the employee:
    a is married?
    b is a married office worker?
    c is married but does not work in
       the office?
    d is neither married nor works in
       the office?

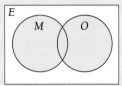

- *M* is the set of married
  employees.
- *O* is the set of office
  staff.
- *E* is the set of all
  employees.

Chapter 16 | Revision Assignment

16A

1

Hair type	Number
Brown	55
Blond	35
Red	10

Presuming that the figures shown in the
table are typical of the people in a certain
town, what is the probability of a person
chosen at random from this town being:
a   a blond?   b   a red-head?
c   *not* a blond?

2 If two dice are rolled, what is the
   probability that the total will be:
   a   8?   b   2 or 3?
   c   a prime number?   d   6 or a double?

3 A box contains 10 apples, 8 oranges and
   2 lemons. If a piece of fruit is picked at
   random, what is the chance of getting:
   a   an orange?
   b   a lemon?
   c   an orange or a lemon?
   d   a banana?

4

Card	Result
Ace	Win $1
K, Q or J	Win 50c
6, 7, 8, 9, 10	No result
2, 3, 4, 5	Lose 50c

A game is played by picking a card at
random from a pack of 52 playing cards.
The table shows the results for picking
various cards. If Erica picks a card, what
is the probability that she will:
a   lose money?
b   neither win nor lose?
c   win money?
d   not lose money?

5 Draw a tree diagram to show the possible
   outcomes when four coins are tossed.
   Use this to determine the probability
   of the following outcomes.
   a   4 heads   b   2 heads, 2 tails
   c   3 tails, 1 head   d   at least 2 tails

6 Five books are on a shelf and two are
   selected. What is the probability that:
   a   a particular book is included?
   b   a particular book is not included?
   Hint: Draw a tree diagram; let the books
   be A, B, C, D and E.

Chapter 16 | Working Mathematically

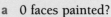

1 Of 30 people in our class, 9 can catch left-handed, 24 can catch right-handed and 6 can catch with both their left hands and their right hands.
   a How many can catch only with the left hand?
   b How many can catch only with the right hand?
   c How many cannot catch with one hand?

2 Tina's investment account had these conditions: '4% pa on minimum monthly balance. Interest credited twice yearly. Open account with $500 or more and maintain a minimum balance of $500. Deposits of any amount $1 and upwards are then accepted. Funds must be lodged for 30 days and then are available at call (without notice). Minimum withdrawal is $100 and a cash limit of $500 per day is placed on withdrawals.'
   a How often is interest credited to this account?
   b How often is interest calculated?
   c What is the least amount needed to receive the 4% rate?
   d How long must funds be left in the account before they are available?
   e What is the minimum amount that can be withdrawn?

3 A cubic block is made up of centimetre cubes, as shown in the diagram. If the entire outside is painted, how many centimetre cubes will have:

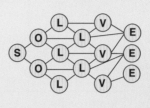

   a 0 faces painted?
   b 1 face painted?
   c 2 faces painted?
   d 3 faces painted?
   e 4 faces painted?

4 How many different pathways, leading from left to right, spell out the word SOLVE?

5 a Complete the table below for $n = 2a + 1$.

a	0	1	2	3	4	5	6
n							

■ {0, 1, 2, 3, . . .} are cardinal numbers.

   b If a and b are positive integers, are these expressions odd or even?
      i $2a$ ii $4ab$
      iii $2a + 1$ iv $2a + 2$
      v $2b + 1$
   c Prove that the product of two odd numbers is always odd. (*Hint:* Let the odd numbers be $2a + 1$ and $2b + 1$.)

Probability investigation

1 Theoretical probability
2 Probability and cards

CHAPTER 16 PROBABILITY **511**

Fatalities by road user category, gender and age, Australia, 2002							
	0–4 years	5–16 years	17–25 years	26–39 years	40–59 years	60–69 years	70+ years	All fatalities[a]
Drivers								
Males	0	4	166	175	138	45	64	592
Females	0	1	46	46	54	13	33	193
Persons[d]	0	5	212	221	192	58	97	785
Passengers								
Males	12	41	89	52	28	8	13	243
Females	7	19	50	27	29	12	34	178
Persons[d]	20	60	139	79	57	20	47	422
Pedestrians								
Males	3	15	28	29	45	21	26	167
Females	2	10	11	9	19	4	27	82
Persons[d]	5	25	39	38	64	25	53	249
Motorcyclists[b]								
Males	0	5	48	96	52	3	5	209
Females	0	2	3	4	5	1	0	15
Persons[d]	0	7	51	100	57	4	5	224
Bicyclists								
Males	0	7	4	6	6	3	4	31
Females	0	0	0	0	2	1	0	3
Persons[d]	0	7	4	6	8	4	4	34
All road users[c]								
Males	15	72	335	358	269	81	112	1243
Females	9	32	110	86	109	31	94	471
Persons[d]	25	104	445	444	378	112	206	1715

[a] Includes fatalities of unstated age
[b] Includes pillion passengers
[c] Includes fatalities of unstated road user group
[d] Includes fatalities of unstated gender

Source: Australian Federal Office of Road Safety

a   What percentage of all fatalities were female?
b   What percentage of 'driver' fatalities were male?
c   What percentage of all fatalities were motorcyclists?
d   What percentage of motorcyclist fatalities were male?
e   Is it fair to say that females are much safer motorcyclists than males?
    Give a reason for your answer.
f   The gender of one fatality was 'unstated'. In which category and age group did this
    person belong?
g   In which age group is the percentage of all female fatalities the lowest?

17

Logic — An Introduction

Chapter Contents

Learning Outcomes

Students will be able to:
- Understand and use the ideas behind propositions.
- Combine sub-propositions to make a compound proposition.
- Translate between words and logic notation.
- Use truth tables to evaluate when compound statements are true.
- Use truth tables to establish the logical equivalence of statements.
- Work with, and build, conditional statements.

Areas of Interaction

Approaches to Learning (Knowledge Acquisition, Logical Thinking, Communicating, Reflection), Human Ingenuity, Environments

17:01 | Propositions

Logic refers to the validity of given statements called **propositions**. In mathematics we use many of these in proofs so it is necessary to be able to decide when propositions are true or false.

A *proposition* is a *statement* that makes some declaration and is either true (T) or false (F). A proposition cannot be both true and false at the same time.

worked examples

Decide which of the following are propositions and which are true (T) and which are false (F).

	Statement	Validity	Reason
1	$5 \leqslant 10$	T	
2	Tennis is a game played with racquets and balls.	T	
3	Moscow is in the southern hemisphere.	F	Moscow is in the northern hemisphere
4	A triangle with only two sides equal is called isosceles.	T	
5	Sri Lanka is located in the Atlantic Ocean.	F	Sri Lanka is in the Indian Ocean.
6	The equation $x^2 = 9$ has only one solution.	F	It has two solutions: $+3$ and -3.
7	A square has two diagonals.	T	
8	What is your name?		This is not a proposition.
9	Put your bicycle away after using it.		This is not a proposition.
10	$(2 + 3) \times 5 \geqslant 25$	T	$25 = 25$

Exercise 17:01

1 Decide which of the following are propositions and which are true and which are false.

a Berlin is the capital of Germany.

b Is your name George?

c A circle has only one diameter.

d $x = 6$ is the solution of the equation $2x - 5 = 7$

e Please put your rubbish in the bin.

f Egypt is located in Europe.

g A rectangle is a parallelogram.

h A vector has both magnitude and direction.

i π is the result of dividing the circumference of a circle by its diameter.

j If the two short sides of a right triangle are 6 cm and 8 cm then the third side is 10 m.

17:02 | Compound Propositions

A **compound proposition** is one that makes more than one declaration. These declarations are called **sub-propositions**.

Sometimes a compound proposition combines sub-propositions with the word AND. In these cases, both sub-propositions must be true for the compound proposition to be true.

Sometimes a compound proposition combines sub-propositions with the word OR. In these cases, either one or both of the sub-propositions must be true for the compound proposition to be true.

worked examples

Decide which of the following are propositions and which are true (T) and which are false (F).

	Statement	Validity	Reason
1	Summer is warm and winter is cold.	T	
2	La Pas is the capital of Bolivia and Bolivia is in South America.	T	
3	Thailand is in Asia or Thailand is in Africa.	T	Since the first sub-proposition is true and OR is used
4	A rectangle is a square and a square is a rhombus.	T	

When is a rectangle not a parallelogram?

	Statement	Validity	Reason
5	A triangle is a three-sided figure and you will get me as glass of water.		The second half is not a proposition.
6	California is a state of the USA and France is in Africa.	F	Since the second sub-proposition is false and AND is used.
7	There are 26 letters in the English alphabet or there are 10 digits in the decimal system.	T	Both sub-propositions are true.
8	12 is a factor of 24 and a multiple of 5.	F	Although the first sub-proposition is true, the second sub-proposition is false.
9	18 is a factor of 54 or a multiple of 8.	T	Although the second sub-proposition is false, the first sub-proposition is true.
10	$(2 + 3) \times 5 \geqslant 30$ or $3^2 < 10$	T	Although the first sub-proposition is false, the second sub-proposition is true.

1 Decide which of the following compound propositions and are true and which are false.

a   A whale is a mammal and an eagle is a bird.

b   A rhombus is a parallelogram and a square is a rhombus.

c   A pentagon has five sides or $3^2 = 10$

d   A triangular prism has 6 surfaces or $3^2 = 9$

e   There are 10 millimetres in a centimeter and 100 millimetres in a metre.

f   A right angle is 90° or a scalene triangle has all angles equal.

g   The moon is a balloon or the expression $(x + 5)$ is a binomial.

h   Soccer uses a ball and hockey uses a puk.

i   Ireland is an island and Beijing is a country.

j $(2x - 1)^2 = 4x^2 - 4x - 1$ or there are 4·5 metres in 450 millimetres.

17:03 | Notation and Truth Tables

Usually letters are used to represent individual propositions and additional information is given to help decide the truthfulness of the proposition.

For example: Let p be the proposition that I have no homework and let q be the proposition that I will play basketball.

That is: p: I have no homework
q: I will play basketball

So that p and q: I have no homework *and* I will play basketball
And p or q: *Either* I have no homework *or* I will play basketball

Symbols are used for *and* and *or*.

> ■ The symbol ∧ represents *and*, while the symbol ∨ represents *or*

The whole truth table and nothing but the truth.

So using our original propositions:

$p \land q$:   I have no homework *and* I will play basketball
$p \lor q$:   *Either* I have no homework *or* I will play basketball

It is difficult to know whether propositions like p and q are true without extra information.

Suppose we are told that p is true and q is false. Then $p \land q$ is false and $p \lor q$ is true.

We can put this information into a table. This is called a **truth table**.

p	q	$p \land q$	$p \lor q$
T	F	F	T

Suppose, however, we don't know whether p and q are true and want to explore all the possible combinations of p and q being true or false. We then have to use a bigger truth table:

p	q	$p \wedge q$	$p \vee q$
T	T	T	T
T	F	F	T
F	T	F	T
F	F	F	F

Exercise 17:03

In the following questions, sometimes you are told a proposition is true and sometimes you have to decide whether it is true or not.

1 p: All even numbers are divisible by 2.
   q: All odd numbers are divisible by 3.
   a Translate into words:
   　i $p \wedge q$
   　ii $p \vee q$
   b Complete the following truth table.

p	q	$p \wedge q$	$p \vee q$

2 m: A quadrilateral with only two parallel sides is a trapezium.
   n: A hexagon has 5 sides.
   a Translate into words:
   　i $m \wedge n$
   　ii $m \vee n$
   b Complete the following truth table.

m	n	$m \wedge n$	$m \vee n$

3 a: Today I have no homework.
   b: This book has 20 chapters.
   a Translate into words:
   　i $a \wedge b$
   　ii $a \vee b$
   b Complete the following truth table.

a	b	$a \wedge b$	$a \vee b$

4 s: A revolution has 360°.

t: The angle sum of a quadrilateral is the same as a revolution.

a Translate into words:
  i $s \wedge t$
  ii $s \vee t$

b Complete the following truth table.

s	t	$s \wedge t$	$s \vee t$

5 p: $\sqrt{(-64)} = -8$

q: $\sqrt[3]{(-64)} = -4$

a Translate into words:
  i $p \wedge q$
  ii $p \vee q$

b Complete the following truth table.

p	q	$p \wedge q$	$p \vee q$

6 Interpret the following if x: All the diameters of a circle have the same length.
  y: Rajiv will play golf this weekend.
  $x \wedge y$: False
  $x \vee y$: True

17:04 | The Negative of a Statement ¬

If you turn a statement into its negative you are **negating** the statement.

For example: If a proposition says   The capital of India is New Delhi.
  Then the negative says   The capital of India is *not* New Delhi.

  So if p: The capital of India is New Delhi.
  Then the negative $\neg p$: The capital of India is *not* New Delhi.

> ■ Note the use of the symbol ¬ to represent the negative (we would usually say *not p*).
> Also note that if p is true then $\neg p$ is false and if p is false the $\neg p$ is true.

Using a truth table:

p	$\neg p$
T	F
F	T

1 If   *m*: The capital of India is New Delhi.
and *n*: All quadrilaterals have five sides.

Quadrilaterals have five sides – NOT!

a Translate into words
  i $m \lor n$
  ii $m \land \neg n$
  iii $\neg m \land \neg n$

b Complete the following truth table.

m	n	$\neg m$	$\neg n$	$m \land n$	$m \lor n$	$\neg m \land \neg n$	$m \lor \neg n$

Solution

a i $m \lor n$: Either the capital of India is New Delhi or all quadrilaterals have five sides.
  ii $m \land \neg n$: The capital of India is New Delhi and all quadrilaterals do not have five sides.
  iii $\neg m \land \neg n$: The capital of India is not New Delhi and all quadrilaterals do not have five sides.

b

m	n	$\neg m$	$\neg n$	$m \land n$	$m \lor n$	$\neg m \land \neg n$	$m \lor \neg n$
T	F	F	T	T	F	F	T

Exercise 17:04

1 If   *s*: All squares are rhombuses.
and *t*: All trapeziums are parallelograms.
a Translate into words:
  i $\neg t$ ii $s \lor t$ iii $s \land t$ iv $s \land \neg t$ v $\neg s \land t$
b Complete the following truth table to decide which of the propositions in (a) are true.

s	t	$\neg s$	$\neg t$	$s \lor t$	$s \land t$	$s \land \neg t$	$\neg s \land t$

2 If   *c*: It never rains in southern California.
and *d*: The rain in Spain falls mainly on the plain.
a Write the following using logic terminology.
  i It rains in Southern California.
  ii It rains in Southern California and the rain in Spain falls mainly on the plain.
  iii Either it never rains in southern California or the rain in Spain does not fall mainly on the plain.
  iv It rains in Southern California and the rain in Spain does not fall mainly on the plain.
  v Either it never rains in Southern California or the rain in Spain falls mainly on the plain.

b Complete the following truth table to decide which of the propositions in (a) are true.

c	d	¬c	¬d				
F	T						

I do not have a cat or a dog.

So you don't have a cat AND you don't have dog.

3 A compound proposition is given:

Michael is a good swimmer and the diagonals of a rectangle are equal.

Given the following truth table, write two sub-propositions p and q that are both true.

$p \wedge q$	$\neg p \wedge q$	$p \wedge \neg q$	$p \vee q$
F	T	F	T

4 **a** Complete the following truth table.

m	n	¬m	¬n	$m \wedge n$	$\neg m \wedge n$	$\neg m \wedge \neg n$	$\neg(m \wedge n)$
T	T						

b If m: All mammals breathe air.

     n: All pentagons have five sides.

Translate the remaining statements in the table into propositions.

5 x: today rain is not predicted

y: today I will play tennis

Use the truth table below to make a true statement using the word AND to join both of the above propositions.

$x \vee y$	$\neg(x \wedge y)$	$\neg x \vee y$
T	T	F

6 Use the truth table to determine the truthfulness of the following statements.

p: Stephen is not a very good mathematics student.

q: Music is Bob's favourite subject.

$p \wedge q$	$p \vee q$	$\neg p \vee q$
F	T	T

7 Complete this truth table using all the possible combinations of *p* and *q* being true or false as shown.

p	*q*	¬*p*	¬*q*	*p* ∧ *q*	*p* ∨ *q*	¬*p* ∧ ¬*q*	¬*p* ∨ ¬*q*
T	T						
T	F						
F	T						
F	F						

Investigation 17:04 | **The whole truth and nothing but the truth!**

Please use the Assessment Grid on the page 523 to help you understand what is required for this Investigation.

Complete the truth tables below showing outcomes for all possible combinations of true and false.

Table 1

p	*q*	*r*	*q* ∨ *r*	*p* ∨ *q*	*p* ∨ *r*	(*p* ∨ *q*) ∨ *r*	*p* ∨ (*q* ∨ *r*)
T	T	T					
T	T	F					
T	F	T					
F	T	T					
T	F	F					
F	T	F					
F	F	T					
F	F	F					

Table 2

p	*q*	*r*	*q* ∨ *r*	*p* ∧ *q*	*p* ∧ *r*	*p* ∧ (*q* ∨ *r*)	(*p* ∧ *q*) ∨ (*p* ∧ *r*)
T	T	T					
T	T	F					
T	F	T					
F	T	T					
T	F	F					
F	T	F					
F	F	T					
F	F	F					

Table 3

p	q	r	$q \wedge r$	$p \vee q$	$p \vee r$	$p \vee (q \wedge r)$	$(p \vee q) \wedge (p \vee r)$
T	T	T					
T	T	F					
T	F	T					
F	T	T					
T	F	F					
F	T	F					
F	F	T					
F	F	F					

- Are there any patterns formed in the tables in the highlighted columns?
  If so, what are they?
  Make a conclusion of what these patterns mean for the statements below:
  $(p \vee q) \vee r$ and $p \vee (q \vee r)$
  $p \wedge (q \vee r)$ and $(p \wedge q) \vee (p \wedge r)$
  $p \vee (q \wedge r)$ and $(p \vee q) \wedge (p \vee r)$
- Are there any similarities between these results and those in other branches of mathematics?
  Consider, for example, the following statements:
  $(5 \times 3) \times 4$
  $5 \times (x + y)$
- Suggest other similar relationships between statements of this type and justify your examples.

The following is a sample assessment grid for this investigation. You should carefully read the criteria *before* beginning the investigation so that you know what is required.

		Assessment Criteria (B, C, D) for this investigation		Achieved ✓
Criterion B Investigating Patterns	a	None of the following descriptors has been achieved.	0	
	b	Some help was needed to complete the tables and identify the simple patterns of the truth tables.	1	
			2	
	c	Mathematical techniques have been selected and applied to complete the tables and make some suggestions for the patterns evident within the highlighted columns.	3	
			4	
	d	The student has been able to describe the patterns in the tables, make appropriate conclusions and accurately interpret their meaning.	5	
			6	
	e	The patterns evident have been explained and all results justified with reference to the highlighted columns. The student is able to use the same patterns found in the tables to answer the final two parts of the investigation.	7	
			8	
Criterion C Communication in Mathematics	a	None of the following descriptors has been achieved.	0	
	b	There is basic use of mathematical language and representation. Lines of reasoning are insufficient.	1	
			2	
	c	There is satisfactory use of mathematical language and representation. Tables and explanations are clear but not always complete.	3	
			4	
	d	There is good use of mathematical language and representation. Tables are complete and well set out. Explanations and answers are related to results and patterns in tables.	5	
			6	
Criterion D Reflection in Mathematics	a	None of the following descriptors has been achieved.	0	
	b	An attempt has been made to explain whether the results make sense and to relate them to the statements given.	1	
			2	
	c	There is a correct but brief explanation of whether results make sense and of their implications for the statements given. A description of the relevance of the findings to other branches of mathematics is given.	3	
			4	
	d	There are clear, detailed explanations of the results obtained and of other possible applications in mathematics.	5	
			6	

17:05 | Logical Equivalence

> Two statements are logically equivalent if they have identical columns in their truth tables.

For example: Consider the statements $\neg(p \wedge q)$ and $\neg p \vee q\neg$

We complete truth tables for both statements for all possible combinations of p and q.

p	q	$\neg p$	$\neg q$	$p \wedge q$	$\neg(p \wedge q)$	$\neg p \vee \neg q$
T	T	F	F	T	F	F
T	F	F	T	F	T	T
F	T	T	F	F	T	T
F	F	T	T	F	T	T

All possible combinations of p and q

Identical columns

This means that $\neg(p \wedge q)$ and $\neg p \vee \neg q$ are equivalent statements. Or $\boxed{\neg(p \wedge q) \equiv \neg p \vee \neg q}$

Exercise 17:05

1 **a** Complete the following truth table to show that $\neg(p \vee q) \equiv \neg p \wedge \neg q$

p	q	$\neg p$	$\neg q$	$p \vee q$	$\neg(p \vee q)$	$\neg p \wedge \neg q$
T	T					
T	F					
F	T					
F	F					

  b If p: I have a pet cat.
   q: I live in a brick house.
   Translate each of the highlighted statements to show equivalence.

2 **a** Complete the following truth table to show that $\neg(m \wedge n) \equiv \neg m \vee \neg n$

m	n	$\neg m$	$\neg n$	$m \wedge n$	$\neg(m \wedge n)$	$\neg m \vee \neg n$
T	T					
T	F					
F	T					
F	F					

  b If m: Minh plays tennis well.
   n: George is a good algebra student.
   Translate each of the highlighted statements to show equivalence.

3 If *t*: I play a team sport.

   r: I play rugby.

   s: I play soccer.

a Translate the following into written statements:

   i $t \wedge (r \vee s)$

   ii $(t \wedge r) \vee (t \wedge s)$

b The truth table below shows all combinations of *t*, *r* and *s*.

   Decide what compound propositions need to go in the green columns to complete the table.

   Complete the table to show that $t \wedge (r \vee s) \equiv (t \wedge r) \vee (t \wedge s)$.

t	*r*	*s*				$t \wedge (r \vee s)$	$(t \wedge r) \vee (t \wedge s)$
T	T	T					
T	T	F					
T	F	T					
F	T	T					
T	F	F					
F	T	F					
F	F	T					
F	F	F					

4 If *s*: Jon is from South America.

   p: Jon speaks Spanish.

   u: Jon is studying at university.

a Translate the following into written statements:

   i $s \vee (p \wedge u)$

   ii $(s \vee p) \wedge (s \vee u)$

b Complete a truth table to show that $s \vee (p \wedge u) \equiv (s \vee p) \wedge (s \vee u)$

5 If *a*: Anne lives in Austria.

   b: Anne plays basketball.

   c: Anne spends her holidays in Croatia.

a Write the following compound propositions in logic notation.

   i Either Anne lives in Austria and plays basketball or she spends her holidays in Croatia.

   ii Anne either lives in Austria or spends holidays in Croatia and she either plays basketball or spends her holidays in Croatia.

b Complete a truth table to show that the above statements are logically equivalent.

17:06 | Conditional Statements

Conditional statements are those which take the form:

If *proposition 1* **then** *proposition 2*.

An example of a conditional statement would be:

If *I pass my exams* then *my father will buy me a new surfboard*.

        ↑   ↑

    Proposition 1   Proposition 2

Suppose p: I pass my exams.
and q: My father will buy me a new surfboard.

The original statement: If I pass my exams then my father will buy me a new surfboard.
Can be written: $p \rightarrow q$

Consider the truth table for this statement:

p	q	Explanation	$p \rightarrow q$
T	T	Since I have passed my exams my father will buy me a new surfboard. This supports the original statement so $p \rightarrow q$ is true here.	T
T	F	This states that even though I passed my exams, my father did not buy me a surfboard. This does not support the original statement, so $p \rightarrow q$ cannot be true here.	F
F	T	Even though I didn't pass my exams, my father can buy me a new surfboard anyway, so $p \rightarrow q$ can still be true here.	T
F	F	This states that if I do not pass my exams then my father will not buy me a new surfboard. This supports the original statement so $p \rightarrow q$ is true here.	T

For a conditional statement then the truth table looks like:

p	q	$p \rightarrow q$
T	T	T
T	F	F
F	T	T
F	F	T

worked example

1   m: It will rain today.
     n: My golf game will be postponed.
    a Translate the conditional statement $m \rightarrow n$ into words.
    b Complete a truth table for this conditional statement.

Solution

a *If* it rains today *then* my golf game will be postponed.

b

m	n	m → n	
T	T	T	Here it is raining and the game is to be postponed. This supports m → n so it is true
T	F	F	Here it is raining but the game is not postponed. This does not support m → n so it is false
F	T	T	Here it is not raining but the game is still postponed. This could happen as the game could be postponed for another reason. So m → n could still be true
F	F	T	Here it is not raining and the game is not postponed. This is basically the same as the first row so m → n is still a true statement.

So the statement $p \rightarrow q$ is true unless p is true and q is false.

Exercise 17:06

1 If *p*: It is raining.

   q: I will take my umbrella.
   a Translate the conditional statement $p \rightarrow q$ into words.
   b Complete a truth table for this conditional statement.
   c Write the only false statement in the truth table in words.
   d Using this example, explain why that if $p \rightarrow q$ is true, it does not necessarily mean that $q \rightarrow p$ is true.

2 If *e*: Tony is in Europe.

   g: Tony is in Germany.
   a Translate the statement $g \rightarrow e$ into words.
   b Translate the statement $\neg g \lor e$ into words.
   c Complete the truth table below for this conditional statement.

g	*e*	¬g	g → e	¬g ∨ e
T	T			
T	F			
F	T			
F	F			

   d What can be said about the statements $g \rightarrow e$ and $\neg g \lor e$?
   e Explain why the statement $\neg g \rightarrow e$ is true but that $g \rightarrow \neg e$ is false.

3 Consider the following conditional statement:

If my grandmother is coming for dinner then we will have ice cream for dessert.

  a Write the two sub-propositions that combine to make this statement.
  b If the first of these sub-propositions is called a, and the second b, write this conditional statement in symbols.
  c Complete a truth table for this statement.
  d The *converse* of the above statement would be:

  If we have ice cream for dessert then my grandmother is coming for dinner.

  Add a column to your truth table to show that this is not equivalent to the original statement.

4 If f: The weather is fine.

  t: Hyun Ju will play tennis.

  b: Hyun Ju will go to the beach.

  a Write the compound proposition $b \lor t$ in words.
  b Write the conditional statement $f \to (b \lor t)$ in words.
  c Write the conditional statement $(f \to b) \lor (f \to t)$ in words.
  d Complete the truth table below to show that $f \to (b \lor t) \equiv (f \to t) \lor (f \to b)$.

f	t	b	$b \lor t$	$f \to b$	$f \to t$	$f \to (b \lor t)$	$(f \to b) \lor (f \to t)$
T	T	T					
T	T	F					
T	F	T					
F	T	T					
T	F	F					
F	T	F					
F	F	T					
F	F	F					

  e Explain why that if $f \to (b \lor t)$ is true, that the converse $(b \lor t) \to f$ may not be true.

5 If b: Dan is in Bangkok.

  t: Dan is in Thailand.

  s: Dan is in South East Asia.

  a Complete a truth table to show that $b \to (t \land s)$ is equivalent to $(b \to t) \land (b \to s)$.
  b Translate
  i $b \to (t \land s)$ and
  ii $(b \to t) \land (b \to s)$ into words.

Mathematical Terms 17

compound proposition
- A proposition made up of two or more separate sub-propositions.

conditional statements
- Statements written in the form If … then … .

converse
- The converse of $p \rightarrow q$ is $q \rightarrow p$.

logical equivalence
- Two statements are logically equivalent if their truth tables are equivalent.

negating
- A statement. Considering the opposite of a statement: if p is true then the negative $\neg p$ is false.

proposition
- A statement that makes some declaration and is either true or false but not both.

sub-proposition
- Two or more of these combine to make a compound proposition.

truth table
- A table usually showing all the possible combinations of true or false for sub-propositions and also whether the compound propositions formed are true or false.

validity
- Of a statement refers to whether the statement is true or false.

Mathematical terms 17

Diagnostic Test 17: | Logic — an introduction

- Each section of the diagnostic test has similar items that test a certain question type.
- Errors made will indicate areas of weakness.
- Each weakness should be treated by going back to the section listed.

	Section

1 Decide which of the following are propositions and which are true and which are false.
  a What is your name?
  b The diagonals of a rhombus are equal.
  c The diagonals of a rhombus bisect the angles at the vertices they pass through.
  d December is a summer month in the southern hemisphere.
  e The year 2001 was a leap year.
  f A rectangle is not a parallelogram.
  g Look both ways before you cross the street.
  h $2^3 = 6$
  i Australia is the only continent that is also a country.
  j $x = 3$ is the only solution to the equation $4x^2 = 36$.
	17:01

2 Write **i** $p \wedge q$ and **ii** $p \vee q$ for each of the following and state whether the compound proposition formed is true or false.

Section
17:02
17:03

   a p: The Athens Olympic Games were held in 2004.
      q: Athens is in Greece.

   b p: Parallelograms have all sides equal.
      q: The opposite sides of a parallelogram are parallel.

   c p: A square root of 16 is 4.
      q: The cubed root of 64 is 4.

3 Complete this truth table to show that $\neg(p \wedge q) \equiv \neg p \vee \neg q$.

17:04

p	q	$\neg p$	$\neg q$	$p \wedge q$	$\neg(p \wedge q)$	$\neg p \vee \neg q$
T	T					
T	F					
F	T					
F	F					

4 Show that $\neg(p \vee q) \equiv \neg p \wedge \neg q$.

17:04

5 If a: Tony is in the Antarctic for his holiday.
     c: Tony is cold.

17:05

   a Write $a \rightarrow c$ in words.
   b Write the converse of $a \rightarrow c$ in words.
   c Explain why if $a \rightarrow c$ is true its converse is not necessarily true.
   d Complete a truth table showing that $a \rightarrow c$ and its converse are not equivalent.

1 Decide which of the following are propositions and which are true and which are false.

  a A square has four right angles.

  b You should shake hands firmly.

  c $\sqrt{169} = 13$.

  d A quadratic can have only one solution.

  e $-1 < 1$.

  f A rectangle is a square.

2 Decide which of the following are propositions and which are true and which are false.

  a Every fifth year is a leap year and has 366 days.

  b Ponting is the captain of the Australian cricket team and Clarke is the vice captain.

  c Kuala Lumpur is in Malaysia and Bangkok is in Thailand.

  d A kite is a quadrilateral and a quadrilateral has 360°.

  e 8 is a factor of 29 and a multiple of 3.

  f $\left|\binom{3}{4}\right| = 5$ and $\left|\binom{6}{7}\right| = 8$.

3 Consider the propositions $p: \sqrt{(-1)} = -1$.

                              $q: \sqrt[3]{(-1)} = -1$.

  a Translate into words

    i $p \wedge q$

    ii $p \vee q$

  b Complete the truth table.

p	q	$p \wedge q$	$p \vee q$	$\neg p$	$\neg q$

  c Translate into words

    i $p \wedge \neg q$

    ii $\neg p \wedge q$

    iii $\neg(p \wedge q)$

    iv $\neg p \vee \neg q$

  d show that **iii** and **iv** are logically equivalent using a truth table, for any p and q.

Answers

Chapter 1: Basic Skills and Number — Review

Exercise 1:01A
1 a 2   b 1   c 0   d 14   e −3   f 17   g 12   h 30
   i 70   j 20   k 300   l 25   m 19   n 11   o 18
2 a 9   b 0   c 10   d 2   e $1\frac{1}{5}$ f 2   g 81   h 196   i 100

Exercise 1:01B
1 a $1\frac{3}{4}$ b $8\frac{1}{6}$ c $3\frac{3}{4}$ d $1\frac{3}{8}$ 2 a $\frac{11}{2}$ b $\frac{22}{7}$ c $\frac{35}{4}$ d $\frac{200}{3}$
3 a $\frac{3}{5}$ b $\frac{7}{15}$ c $\frac{2}{3}$ d $\frac{5}{9}$ 4 a $\frac{18}{24}$ b $\frac{20}{50}$ c $\frac{8}{28}$ d $\frac{40}{120}$
5 a $\frac{8}{15}$ b $\frac{1}{4}$ c $\frac{37}{40}$ d $\frac{9}{35}$ 6 a $9\frac{1}{10}$ b $2\frac{9}{20}$ c $10\frac{17}{20}$ d $3\frac{19}{40}$
7 a $\frac{12}{35}$ b $\frac{27}{40}$ c $\frac{2}{15}$ d $\frac{7}{15}$ 8 a $4\frac{1}{2}$ b $4\frac{1}{2}$ c 20   d 15
9 a $1\frac{7}{20}$ b $\frac{5}{8}$ c $\frac{2}{15}$ d $1\frac{5}{6}$

Exercise 1:01C
1 a {0·066, 0·6, 0·606, 0·66}   b {0·153, 1·053, 1·53}   c {0·017, 0·7, 0·77, 7}   d {3·05, 3·4, 3·45, 3·5}
2 a 9·301   b 3·45   c 3·104   d 6·32   e 1·97   f 8·105   g 4·888   h 159·3
3 a 0·036   b 0·006   c 0·585   d 0·0025   4 a 31·4   b 500   c 0·03   d 38 000
5 a 0·03   b 0·265   c 3·07   d 0·0025   6 a $0·4\dot{3}$ b $0·8\dot{2}\dot{7}$ c $1·\dot{5}$ d $0·\dot{8}5714\dot{2}$
7 a 4·804   b 0·016   c 0·0009   d 0·000 65   8 a 21   b 10·45   c 1500   d 2·8
9 a $3\frac{17}{1000}$ b $\frac{1}{25}$ c $\frac{43}{50}$ d $16\frac{1}{200}$ 10 a 0·8   b 0·035   c 0·625   d $0·\dot{7}\dot{2}$
11 a $\frac{5}{9}$ b $\frac{257}{999}$ c $\frac{8}{11}$ d $\frac{214}{333}$ 12 a $\frac{5}{6}$ b $\frac{151}{165}$ c $\frac{98}{225}$ d $\frac{1489}{1665}$

Exercise 1:01D
1 a $\frac{27}{50}$ b $\frac{203}{100}$ or $2\frac{3}{100}$ c $\frac{49}{400}$ d $\frac{91}{1000}$ 2 a 55%   b $44\frac{4}{9}$%   c 125%   d $66\frac{2}{3}$%
3 a 0·16   b 0·086   c 0·03   d 0·1825   4 a 47%   b 6%   c 37·5%   d 130%
5 a 144 m   b 7·56 g   c $2·72   d $86 360   6 a $60   b 25 kg   c $5   d 180 min or 3 h
7 a 42·5%   b 45%   c 18·75%   d 12% (to nearest whole %)

Exercise 1:01E
1 a i 3 : 5   ii 1 : 10   iii 15 : 7   iv 3 : 1   b 14 : 1   c 2 : 3   d 15 : 4
   e i 8 : 5   ii 41 : 130   f i $\frac{3}{5}$: 1   ii $\frac{2}{7}$: 1   iii $\frac{10}{3}$: 1   iv $\frac{25}{4}$: 1
   g i 1 : $\frac{5}{3}$ ii 1 : $\frac{7}{2}$ iii 1 : $\frac{3}{10}$ iv 1 : $\frac{4}{25}$
2 a $x = 50$ b 910 million   c 2·5 people per km^2 d 3·6 million
3 a Naomi gets 48, Luke gets 36   b 40°, 60°, 80°   c Tokyo, 12 million; Moscow, 10 million
   d 36 males, 24 females

Exercise 1:01F
1 a 300 km/h   b 8 m/mL   c 14·4 t/day   d 2075 cm^3/kg
2 a 6 miles per hour   b $46.20   c $4\frac{2}{3}$ minutes/book   d 10 cm^3/s

Exercise 1:01G
1 a 2   b 2   c 3   d 3   e 4   f 3   g 4   h 3   i 3   j 4   k 1   l 1
   m 2   n 1   o 1   p 2   q 3   r 3   s 5   t 3   u 5   v 1   w 3   x 2
   y ambiguous, 2   z ambiguous, 2
2 a 2   b 3   c 1   d 1   e 2   f 2   g 3   h 5

Exercise 1:01H
1 a 4·6   b 0·8   c 3·2   d 0·1   e 15·2   f 8·1   g 1·0   h 121·6
   i 0·1   j 47·4   k 0·4   l 2·8
2 a 0·54   b 2·61   c 7·13   d 1·17   e 12·02   f 8·40   g 412·68   h 0·08
   i 0·44   j 100·33   k 0·02   l 0·01

3 a i 7 ii 7·3 **b** i 80 ii 85 **c** i 0·6 ii 0·63 **d** i 3 ii 2·6 **e** i 4 ii 4·2
f i 0·007 ii 0·0073 **g** i 0·08 ii 0·083 **h** i 3 ii 3·1 **i** i 0·009 ii 0·0093 **j** i 0·01 ii 0·0098
k i 8 ii 7·5 **l** i 0·04 ii 0·036
4 a 2 **b** 14·6 **c** 2·2 **d** 0·9 **e** 4·1 **f** 7·37 **g** 0·724 **h** 6 **i** 31·69 **j** 0·007 **k** 0·8 **l** 0·0072
5 a 5·6 **b** 0·2 **c** 0·44 **d** 15·4 **e** 8·33 **f** 413·8 **g** 72·0 **h** 3·067 **i** 10·0 **j** 4·800 **k** 0·08 **l** 0·004

Exercise 1:01I

1 Answers near these are acceptable. **a** 74 **b** 120 **c** 31 **d** 7·2 **e** 110 **f** 60 **g** 18 **h** 5·8
i 7·7 **j** 1·8 **k** 0·4 **l** 52 **m** 15 **n** 21 **o** 310 **p** 1·1 **q** 7·0 **r** 17 **s** 59

Exercise 1:02

1 a $6a$ **b** $10y$ **c** $2m$ **d** x^2 **e** $8k$ **f** $5y$ **g** $8a + 2b$ **h** $7n + 7m$
i $11m + 2$ **j** $7x + y^2$ **k** $5ab - 5a$ **l** $6x^2 + 5xy$ **m** $3a + 4b + 7$ **n** $9k + 3m - 3$ **o** $x + 2y - 3z$
2 a $35y$ **b** $5q$ **c** $6xy$ **d** $20ab$ **e** $9mn$ **f** $6m^2$ **g** $10a^2b$ **h** $10m^2n^2$
i $-20x$ **j** $12y$ **k** $5p^2q^2$ **l** $42mn$ **m** $60a^2b$ **n** $30pqr$
3 a $4x$ **b** $3a$ **c** 5 **d** 3 **e** $2n$ **f** $4a$ **g** $\dfrac{3}{2}$ **h** $\dfrac{6q}{5}$
i $\dfrac{2a}{b}$ **j** $\dfrac{5m}{n}$ **k** $\dfrac{5b}{3c}$ **l** $\dfrac{3m}{2n}$

4 a $5x + 20$ **b** $50 - 10y$ **c** $2y^2 + 10y$ **d** $5a^2 - 15a$ **e** $7p^2 + 7pq$ **f** $-3x + 15$
g $-5a - 20$ **h** $-6ax + 2ay$ **i** $6x + 25$ **j** $7y - 15$ **k** $7a - 10b$ **l** $7x - 4$
m $8a - 4$ **n** $3y^2 - 4y$ **o** $3m + 3$ **p** $9x - 36$ **q** $p^2 + 37p$
5 a $5(m + 2)$ **b** $8(k - 3)$ **c** $2(4a + 3)$ **d** $5(3n - 2)$ **e** $6(3n - 4n)$ **f** $a(b + c)$
g $n(n - m)$ **h** $p(q - 1)$ **i** $3a(b + 2)$ **j** $5m(2n - 1)$ **k** $4y(2x + z)$ **l** $bc(a - d)$
m $3a(c + 3d)$ **n** $3x(2xy + 3)$ **o** $3(a + 2b + 3c)$ **p** $4(2x^2 + x - 3)$
6 a $-4(a + 2)$ **b** $-5(3x + 2)$ **c** $-3(2p - 3)$ **d** $-2(n - 8)$
e $-x(x + 2)$ **f** $-a(5 + 2b)$ **g** $-3a(a - 2)$ **h** $-3y(3z - 2x)$

7 a $2a$ **b** $\dfrac{x}{5}$ **c** $\dfrac{5a}{3}$ **d** $\dfrac{3m}{5}$

8 a $\dfrac{8x}{15}$ **b** $\dfrac{y}{12}$ **c** $\dfrac{7a}{6}$ **d** $\dfrac{n}{8}$ **e** $\dfrac{3x + 4y}{12}$ **f** $\dfrac{4a - 9b}{6}$ **g** $\dfrac{6m + 5n}{10}$ **h** $\dfrac{k - 3l}{6}$

9 a $\dfrac{xy}{6}$ **b** $\dfrac{m^2}{10}$ **c** $\dfrac{12}{am}$ **d** $\dfrac{1}{3n^2}$ **e** $\dfrac{px}{qy}$ **f** $\dfrac{1}{2}$ **g** $\dfrac{2m}{n}$ **h** $\dfrac{2}{15}$

10 a 2 **b** $\dfrac{15}{2}$ **c** $\dfrac{5}{2}$ **d** $\dfrac{1}{2}$ **e** $\dfrac{ay}{bx}$ **f** $\dfrac{3}{4}$ **g** 15 **h** $\dfrac{3}{2}$

Exercise 1:03

1 a $\frac{1}{3}$ **b** $\frac{1}{10}$ **c** $\frac{11}{30}$ **d** $\frac{7}{10}$ **2 a** $\frac{1}{6}$ **b** $\frac{1}{3}$ **c** $\frac{1}{2}$ **d** 1
3 a $\frac{1}{3}$ **b** $\frac{7}{12}$ **c** $\frac{3}{4}$ **d** 0
4 a $\frac{1}{2}$ **b** $\frac{1}{2}$ **c** $\frac{1}{13}$ **d** $\frac{12}{13}$ **e** $\frac{3}{13}$ **f** $\frac{1}{26}$ **g** $\frac{1}{4}$ **h** 0 **i** $\frac{3}{26}$ **j** $\frac{15}{52}$ **k** $\frac{1}{13}$ **l** $\frac{3}{4}$ **m** $\frac{11}{26}$ **n** $\frac{37}{52}$ **o** $\frac{4}{13}$ **p** $\frac{2}{13}$ **q** $\frac{23}{52}$

Exercise 1:04

1 a $x = 79$ (corresp. ∠s, ∥ lines) **b** $x + 76 = 180$ (co-int. ∠s, ∥ lines)
$x = 104$

c $x + 55 = 130$ (ext. ∠ of Δ) **d** $\angle ACB = b°$ (base ∠s of isos. Δ)
$x = 75$ $b + b + 36 = 180$ (∠ sum of Δ)
∴ $b = 72$

e $x = 105$ (opp. ∠s of a par'm) **f** $x = 40$ (∠ sum of a quad.)
$y = 40$ (base ∠s of isos. Δ)

2 a i 720 ii 1440 **b** i 108° ii 135° **c** 360° **d** i 72° ii 60°

Exercise 1:05

1 a a^3 **b** 2^4 **c** n^5 **d** 10^3
2 a 2^9 **b** a^5 **c** m^5 **d** 10^8 **e** a^8 **f** y **g** b^2 **h** 10^3
i m^{12} **j** a^6 **k** x^8 **l** 10^{10} **m** 3 **n** 2 **o** 6 **p** e^0 or 1
q $30a^2$ **r** $2m^3$ **s** $30a^2$ **t** $16x^8$ or 4^2x^8
3 a $30a^5b^3$ **b** $56a^5b^3$ **c** $24a^4b^7$ **d** $10a^{10}b^3$ **e** $49x^6$ **f** $16m^8$ **g** x^6y^9 **h** $625x^4y^8$
i $6a^2$ **j** $5x^3$ **k** $3a$ **l** 8
4 a $\frac{1}{4}$ **b** $\frac{1}{10}$ **c** $\dfrac{1}{x}$ **d** $\dfrac{2}{a}$ **e** $\frac{1}{25}$ **f** $\frac{1}{8}$ **g** $\dfrac{1}{m^3}$ **h** $\dfrac{5}{x^2}$
5 a 3^{-1} **b** 8^{-1} **c** a^{-1} **d** $3x^{-1}$ **e** 2^{-4} **f** 10^{-6} **g** y^{-4} **h** $5n^{-3}$

6 a 3   **b** 6   **c** 2   **d** 3   **7 a** $a^{\frac{1}{2}}$ **b** $y^{\frac{1}{3}}$ **c** $5m^{\frac{1}{2}}$ **d** $4x^{\frac{1}{2}}$

8 a $1{\cdot}48 \times 10^{8}$ **b** $6{\cdot}8 \times 10^{4}$ **c** $1{\cdot}5 \times 10^{-4}$ **d** $1{\cdot}65 \times 10^{-6}$

9 a 62 000   **b** 1 150 000   **c** 0·0074   **d** 0·000 069 1

Exercise 1:06

1 a 45·6 m   **b** 29·6 m   **c** 39·3 m   **2 a** 88·25 cm²   **b** 28·08 cm²   **c** 11·52 cm²

3 a 63·9 m²   **b** 35·7 m²   **c** 23·3 km²   **4 a** 370·88 cm²   **b** 648 m²   **c** 333·55 m² (approx.)

5 a 38·68 m²   **b** 112·17 m²

Exercise 1:07

1 a $a = 18$ **b** $m = 5$ **c** $x = 15$ **d** $y = -2$ **e** $p = 2\frac{1}{3}$ **f** $n = 12$ **g** $x = 2$ **h** $q = 2$

i $m = 2$ **j** $y = \frac{1}{5}$ **k** $x = 8\frac{1}{2}$ **l** $k = \frac{2}{3}$ **m** $x = 2$ **n** $y = 1$ **o** $q = 3\frac{1}{2}$

2 a $m = 5$ **b** $x = 4$ **c** $x = 7$ **d** $p = 4$ **e** $n = 4$ **f** $m = 2$ **g** $a = 8$ **h** $m = 4$

i $q = -1$ **j** $x = 2$ **k** $y = -1$ **l** $p = 2$ **m** $k = -5\frac{1}{2}$ **n** $z = 1\frac{1}{2}$ **o** $y = 2\frac{3}{4}$ **p** $n = \frac{2}{3}$

q $q = \frac{1}{4}$ **r** $m = -1\frac{1}{3}$

3 a $a = 2$ **b** $x = 7$ **c** $x = 3$ **d** $x = 3$ **e** $m = -\frac{1}{2}$ **f** $k = 7\frac{1}{4}$ **g** $a = -2$ **h** $x = -3$

i $m = 4\frac{1}{3}$ **j** $a = 4$ **k** $p = 8$ **l** $x = 6$ **m** $y = -9$ **n** $b = -18$ **o** $y = -1$ **p** $m = 7$

q $m = 5$ **r** $y = 2$ **s** $x = 2\frac{1}{2}$

4 a $x = 4$ **b** $a = 9$ **c** $m = 6\frac{2}{3}$ **d** $n = 9$ **e** $x = 6$ **f** $p = -1$

5 a $a = 6$ **b** $x = 15$ **c** $p = 6$ **d** $a = 6$ **e** $m = 12$ **f** $n = 20$ **g** $q = 36$ **h** $k = 24$

i $x = 60$ **j** $y = -30$ **k** $p = 1\frac{11}{13}$ **l** $a = 4\frac{4}{5}$ **m** $m = 6$ **n** $n = -1$ **o** $x = \frac{11}{13}$ **p** $x = \frac{55}{7}$

q $m = 33$ **r** $a = \dfrac{-19}{8}$

6 a $x \leqslant 1$ **b** $x \geqslant 0$ **c** $x > 6$ **d** $x < -2$

7 a $x > 4$

b $a < 8$

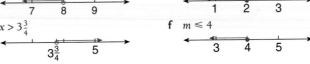

c $y \leqslant 2$

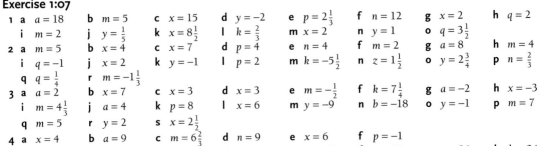

d $m \leqslant 7$

e $x > 3\frac{3}{4}$

f $m \leqslant 4$

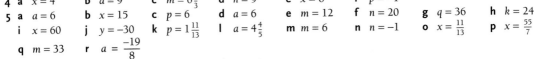

g $x > 2$

h $m \geqslant 1\frac{4}{5}$

i $n \leqslant 1$

j $x > 3$

k $x < 5\frac{1}{2}$

l $m \leqslant 10$

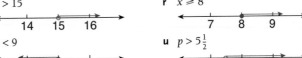

m $a \leqslant 2$

n $b \leqslant -3$

o $m < 0$

p $x < 10$

q $p > 15$

r $x \geqslant 8$

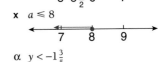

s $y \geqslant -1\frac{1}{2}$

t $p < 9$

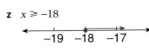

u $p > 5\frac{1}{2}$

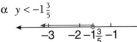

v $x \leqslant 1$

w $x > 6$

x $a \leqslant 8$

y $b < 2\frac{1}{7}$

z $x \geqslant -18$

α $y < -1\frac{3}{5}$

Exercise 1:08

1 a $96.60   **b** $238.28   **c** $350   **d** $534.90

2 a $173.47, 30·6%   **b** $8434   **c** $15 746   **d** $1336.20

3 a The 15% discount is the best, by $2.49.   **b** Jade's buy   **c** Yet tea

4 a i $7.50   **ii** $0.68   **iii** $1.88   **b i** $82.50   **ii** $7.48   **iii** $20.63   **c i** $20   **ii** $0.75   **iii** $1.80

5 a Buying on terms is a way of having an item while spreading the payment over a period of time. Interest is charged.

   b He pays $143.56. Interest is $56.56.   **c** $220   **d** $545 700   **e** $30.60

6 a i $33\frac{1}{3}\%$ **ii** 25%   **b i** 25%   **ii** $33\frac{1}{3}\%$

Exercise 1:09

1 **a** (0, 0) **b** y-axis **c** x-axis **d** 3rd

2

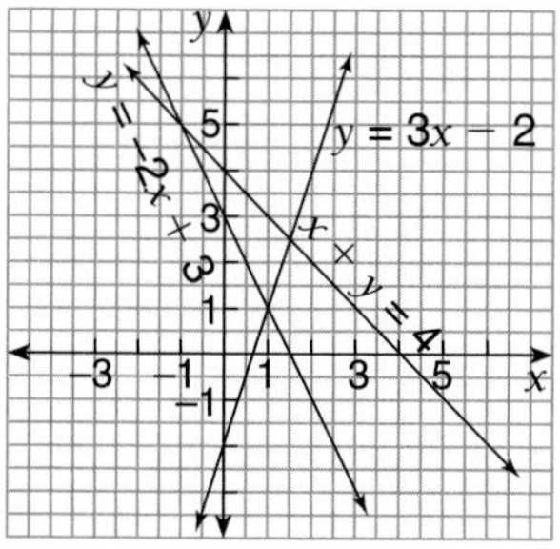

3 **a** (3, −2) and (5, 4) **b** $y = x + 2$, $y = 5x + 2$, $x + y = 2$

4 **a** **i** $y = 2$ **ii** $y = -3$ **iii** $y = 0$ **iv** $x = 2$ **v** $x = -1$ **vi** $x = 0$

b

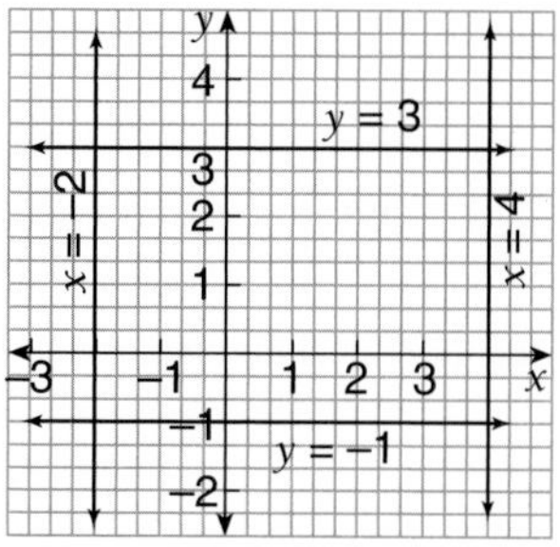

5 **a** In any right-angled triangle, the square on the hypotenuse is equal to the sum of the squares on the other two sides.

b **i** 5 **ii** $\sqrt{61}$ **iii** $\sqrt{51}$

6 **a** $\sqrt{20}$ **b** $\sqrt{53}$ **c** $\sqrt{68}$ **d** 10

7 **a** (6, 8) **b** (1, 3) **c** $(3\frac{1}{2}, 5\frac{1}{2})$

8 **a** **i** 5 **ii** $\frac{1}{2}$ **iii** $-1\frac{1}{5}$ **b** **i** $\frac{1}{3}$ **ii** $\frac{1}{5}$ **iii** $-2\frac{1}{2}$

9 **a** $m = 4, b = 7$ **b** $m = 1, b = -3$ **c** $m = -2, b = 5$

10 **a** $y = 4x + 5$ **b** $y = -\frac{1}{2}x + 3$ **c** $y = 2x - 4$ **d** $y = -7x - 3$

Exercise 1:10

1

Number	*Tally*	*Frequency*
1	𝍸 III	8
2	𝍸 𝍸 II	12
3	𝍸 II	7
4	𝍸 𝍸	10
5	𝍸 I	6
6	𝍸 II	7

$\Sigma f = 50$

a 2 **b** 5 **c** 7 **d** 21 **e** 23

2 **a**

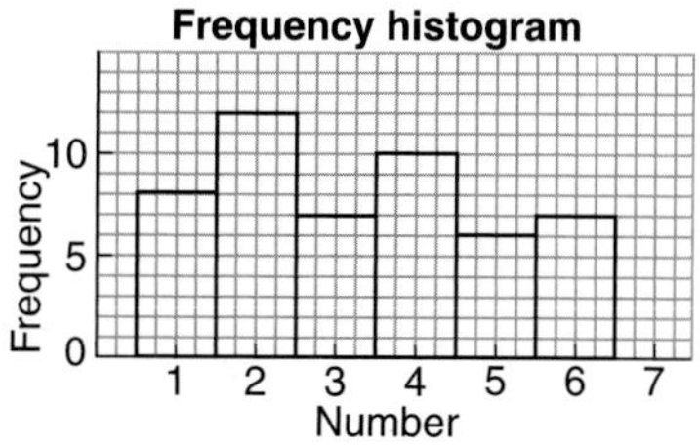

b

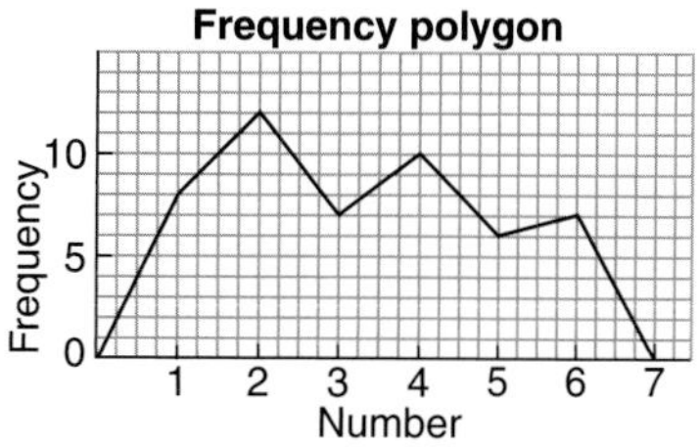

3 **a** **i** 7 **ii** 5 **iii** $4\frac{1}{9}$ **iv** 4 **b** **i** 5 **ii** 2 **iii** 3·3 **iv** 3

c

Number	*Frequency*	*Cumulative frequency*
1	8	8
2	12	20
3	7	27
4	10	37
5	6	43
6	7	50

$\Sigma f = 50$

i 37 **ii** 27 **iii** yes

4

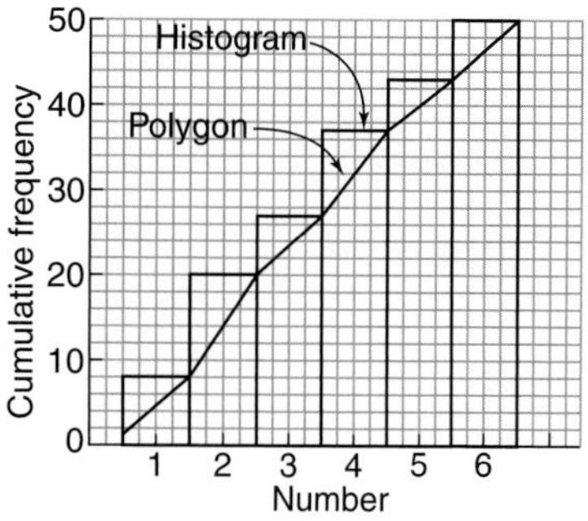

5 a

Class	Class centre	Tally	Frequency	Cumulative frequency
16–22	19	JHT III	7	7
23–29	26	JHT JHT JHT III	18	25
30–36	33	JHT JHT JHT III	18	43
37–43	40	JHT JHT JHT	15	58
44–50	47	JHT III	8	66
51–57	54	IIII	4	70

$$\Sigma f = 70$$

b 34·1 using table (34·6 using the individual numbers)

c

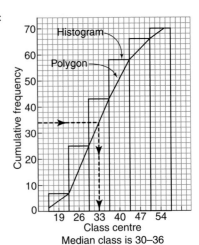

Median class is 30–36

d 23–29 and 30–36   **e** 70

Exercise 1:11

1 a $3a + 4b$ **b** $12ab$ **c** $k - m$ **d** $\dfrac{x + y + z}{3}$ **e** $2(m + 5)$

f $(a - b)^2$ **g** $\sqrt{5m + 4n}$ **h** $3m + 3$

2 a -3 **b** 21 **c** 2 **d** 18 **e** -43 **f** 45 **g** $3\frac{1}{2}$ **h** 3 **i** 3

3 a 14·7 **b** 2 **c** -7 **4 a** 92 **b** 5·81 **c** 15·7

5 a 2 **b** 10 **c** 11·5 **d** 12

6 a 4 **b** 10 **c** 25 **d** 3·08̇3 **e** 5·2̇6̇

7 a i $8n + 11 = 39$ **ii** $2n + 7 = 5$ **iii** $\dfrac{n + 4}{10} = 7$ or $(n + 4) \div 10 = 7$

b i 11   **ii** 8   **iii** width = 34 m, length = 136 m

Exercise 1:12

1 a 10 km **b** 20 km **c** 11.30 am **d** Callum **e** 11.30 am **f** 50 km **g** 30 km **h** 90 km

2 a 3000 g **b** 4400 g **c** 900 g **d** 500 g **e** 0–2 weeks

3 a D **b** C **c** A **d** B

1 Working Mathematically

1 a

t	1	3	5
m	3	7	11

, $m = 4t - 1$ **b**

t	2	4	6
m	5	10	15

, $m = \dfrac{5t}{2}$ **c**

t	1	3	6
m	3	9	18

, $m = 3t$

2 Cut along lines as shown

3 a 185   **b** 37   **4** 16 min 15 s   **5** 32

6 a 617 600   **b** 10 290 000   **c** 10 300 (to 3 sig. figs.)

Chapter 2: Proportion

Exercise 2:01

1 $1170   **2 a** €92.16   **b** 868 km   **3 a** 9 days   **b** 390 km

4 a 15   **b** 6 people   **5 a** 66 500 kJ   **b** 10·5 days   **c** 12

6 a 48 m²   **b** 13   **7 a** $7.75   **b** 6 minutes

8 a 3·75 L   **b** 6 hours 40 minutes   **9 a** 4·5 days   **b** 42 cans   **c** 21 cans

10 a 350   **b** 2   **c** 12·5

Exercise 2:02

1 a $h \propto d$ or $h = kd$ b i $\frac{80}{3}$ ii $133\frac{1}{3}$ cm   2 a $v \propto m$ or $v = km$ b i $\frac{4}{11}$ ii $11\frac{1}{4}$ litres

3 a $a \propto v$ or $a = kv$ b i $\frac{37}{5}$ ii $66\frac{3}{5}$ m^2 4 a $n \propto t$ or $n = kt$ b i $\frac{19}{5}$ ii 45

5 a $l \propto m$, $l \propto t$ b 15 m   c 3:2:5, they are the same.

Investigation 2:02   A proportional flip

1 a 75 hours   b 25 hours
2 a 12 hours   b 4 hours
3 a 15 days   b 3 days
4 a 12 days   b 0·8 days (19.2 hours)
5 i time increases   ii time decreases

Exercise 2:03

1 8 cm   2 16 days   3 2 days   4 42·5 minutes   5 14 hours 31 minutes
6 a 5 days   b 35   7 40 words per minute   8 5 days   9 4 boys   10 16 metres

Diagnostic Test 2   Proportion

1 a Direct   b Inverse   c Inverse   d Direct   e Direct
2 65 km   3 45 pieces   4 $13\frac{1}{3}$ minutes   5 $33\frac{2}{3}$ L
6 a $\frac{13}{100}$, kilograms of CO_2 per kilometre flown   b 975 kg
7 a 440 km   b 30 km/h   c How long she has been travelling
8 a 6 minutes   b 48 metres/minute   c the distance left to swim

2A Revision Assignment

1   Water : Rice
      4 : 3
      n : 500
   $n = 500 \times \frac{4}{3}$
   $n = 666\cdot7$
   Required water is 667 mL.

2   New : Old
      9 : 7
      n : 550
   $n = 550 \times \frac{9}{7}$
   $n = 707\cdot14$
   New weekly wage is $707.14.

3   $A = kn$
   $18 = 4k$
   $k = 4.5$
   $\therefore A = 4\cdot5n$
   If $A = 40.5$
   $40.5 = 4.5n$
     $n = 9$ litres

4 a Time : Speed
      5 : 49
      8 : a
    $a = 8 \times \frac{49}{5}$
    $a = 78\cdot4$
   After 8 seconds speed is 78·4 m/s.
 b Time : Speed
      5 : 49
      b : 100
    $b = 100 \times \frac{5}{49}$
    $b = 10\cdot2$
   Reaches 100 m/s at 10·2 seconds.

5 a US$50.00 ÷ 0·7370 = AU$67.84
     30.00 yuan ÷ 6·03 = AUD$4.98
     2000 yen ÷ 78·14 = AUD$25.60
 b AU$100.00 × 0·737 = US$73.70
     AU$100.00 × 6·03 = 603 yuan
     AUD$100.00 × 78·14 = 7814 yen

6   $t = \frac{k}{s}$ (inversely proportional)
   $2 = \frac{k}{80}$
   $\therefore k = 160$
   $t = \frac{160}{100} = 1.6$
   100 km/h would take 1·6 hrs.

7 a 1 man: $35 \times 5 = 175$ days
     20 men $= \frac{175}{20} = 8\frac{3}{4}$ days
     or
     $d = \frac{k}{w}$ (inversely proportional)
     $5 = \frac{k}{35}$
     $\therefore k = 175$
     $d = \frac{175}{20} = 8\frac{3}{4}$ days
 b 1 man: $35 \times 5 = 175$ days
     3 days: $\frac{175}{3} = 58\frac{1}{3}$ which means
     59 workers would be needed.

Chapter 3: Consumer Arithmetic

Exercise 3:01

1 a See page 30. **b** See page 30. **c** See page 30. **d** commission **e** See page 30.
 f See page 30. **g** See page 30. **h** commission and piece work **i** See page 30.
 j wages and commission
2 a $647.50 **b** $73.20 **c** $19.25 per hour **d** Luke, by €36.75
 e Shireen by $0.50 a hour **f** £782.80 **g** $883 per week
 h i €824.10 per week **ii** $505.96 per week **iii** ¥74 648.32 per week **iv** $1154.41 per week
 i i €55 200 **ii** $37 806 **iii** $63 660 **iv** CNY 2 337 000
 j The second salary is greater by $28.72 per week. **k** The second income is higher by $9.56 per week.
3 a i no **ii** no **iii** no **iv** (1) €69 (2) €170.89 (3) €381.34 (4) €21.16
 b i (1) $196 (2) $385 (3) $480.55 (4) $504.91 **ii** $581 **iii** no
 c i $300 **ii** $370 **iii** $642.40 **iv** $412.95
4 a £259.83 **b** £576.50 **c** £89.50
5 a $518.40 **b** $1125, $782 profit **c** $395.50
 d i $285.76 **ii** $190 **iii** $553.28 **iv** $478.80 **e** €377.95, €9.69 per hour

Exercise 3:02

1 a $408 **b** $565.15 **c i** $108.60 **ii** $181 **iii** $167.43 (to the nearest cent) **iv** $253.40
 d i €672 **ii** €851.20 **iii** €1002.40 **iv** €1136.80 **e** $295.80 **f** $39.20, 1·5 hours

g

No. 53 Name: Tom McSeveny	Time Card Summary		Whit. Pty Ltd Rate: $16.20 p.h.
Week Ending	Number of hours at:		Wage
	normal rates	time-and-a-half	double time	

Week Ending	normal rates	time-and-a-half	double time	Wage
21 Jan	35	0	0	$567
28 Jan	35	3	0	$639.90
4 Feb	35	2	0	$615.60
11 Feb	34	5·5	1	$716.85
18 Feb	35	7·5	0·5	$765.45

2 a i $700 **ii** $287.70 **iii** $346.50 **iv** $485.10 **b** €2006.90 **c** $431.20 **d** $102 400
 e $2532, $58 932 **f** $924.80 **g** $578.95 **h i** $500 **ii** $460 **i** £520, 1·35%
3 a €48 246 **b** €49 210.92 **c i** €52 223.02 **ii** €57 658.44

Exercise 3:03

1 a €200.60 **b** $303 **c** $184.95 **d** £503.65 **e** $332.95
2 a i $615.10 **ii** $98.42 **iii** $30.76 **iv** $399.92

b

Turner, Vicki	Serial no.	Gross salary	Super units		Week ended	Net pay	Pay advice no.
			Entld	Held			
	6841672	$32 096	98	98	18/11/02	$399.92	11364

Deductions this week				Pay this week			
Tax.	Super.	M'laneous	Total	Normal pay	Adjust.	Overtime	Gross earnings
$98.42	$30.76	$86.00	$215.18	$615.10	—	—	$615.10

3 a $329.30, 14·6% **b** $949.25, 34·5% **c** $682.35, 28·0% **d** $466.95, 21·1%
4 a €42 568 **b** €2137.02 **c** €404.75 **d i** €44 004 **ii** €39 600
 iii Answers will differ, however the 'lump sum' option is attractive since you have the money as well.
 iv €24 289.20 **e** 1333, 1234
5 a $122.39 **b** 952·88 **c** $4.90

Exercise 3:04

1 a Nil   **b** $1119.79   **c** $5818   **d** $19 032.62   **e** $121 289.58
2 a $33 942   **b** $33 287   **c** $6366.10   **d** Balance payable $203.90
3 $3927.70   **4 a** $57 006   **b** $54 910   **c** $13 442.20   **d** $332.20
5 a $2000   **b** $1660   **c** $1660   **d** $1400   **e** $1400
    f $1160   **g** $1060   **h** $1060

Exercise 3:05

1 a

Income	$	Fixed expenses	$	Variable expenses	$
Jobs	200	Food	50	Clothes	48
Allowance	42	Loan	36	Entertainment	48
Other	24	School Needs	16	Gifts	48
		Savings	20		
Total $	266	Total $	122	Total $	144

Total expenses = $266

b 7·5% (to one decimal place).

2 a

Income	€	Fixed expenses	€	Variable expenses	€
Monthly income after tax	1482	rent	608	food	182
		elec./tel/water	86	fares	72
		medical	164	clothing	44
				ent./sport	84
				other	50
		Total €	858	Total €	432

Total expenses = €1290

b €192, 12·96% (to 2 decimal places)   **c** No, it is not possible unless he reduces his expenses by at least €12 per month. He could reduce food, clothing, entertainment/sport or other.
3 Each answer will be different.   **4** Each answer will be different.

Exercise 3:06

1 a (a) €68.50   (b) €131   (f) €411 for 4   (k) €109.60   (v) €82.20   (q) From €117 to €137
   b 14% discount, €1.25   **c i** €1.80   **ii** 15%   **d** The first 'direct buy' price by €9 per 60 L. The second 'sale' price if 1 hour of time and wear and tear on the car is valued at more than €4.40   **e** Robyn's for €130.
2 a 'Nap' peas   **b** Corn Flakes at 0.52c/g   **c** 6 L of Vanilla, $10   **d** 'Yet' tea   **e** 'Barbeque' is most expensive
3 a i $17.05   **ii** $12.20   **iii** $7.85   **iv** $2.90   **v** $11.95   **vi** $15.70
   b i $21.55, $78.45   **ii** $30.80, $69.20   **c** $63.40, $36.60

Prep Quiz 3:07

1 $2   **2** 35c   **3** 71c   **4** $1.44   **5** $6   **6** 84c   **7** $6.16   **8** $139.70   **9** $60   **10** $8.40

Exercise 3:07

1 a $7   **b** $12   **c** $4.62   **d** $5.97   **e** $86.30   **f** $1274   **g** $9.76   **h** $14.24
   i $12.46   **j** $74.22
2 a €66   **b** €165   **c** €242   **d** €814   **e** €82.50   **f** €123.20   **g** €377.30   **h** €1041.70
   i €9.46   **j** €30.14   **k** €62.10   **l** €21.59
3 a $2   **b** $10   **c** $15   **d** $26   **e** $5.60   **f** $5.20   **g** $1.20   **h** $78.20
   i $4.25   **j** $31.80   **k** $91.30   **l** $112.50
4 a $70   **b** $120   **c** $180   **d** $250   **e** $14   **f** $26   **g** $97   **h** $115
   i $12.60   **j** $37.50   **k** $215.50   **l** $1125.80
5 $0.58   **6 a** $0.82   **b** $0.96   **c** $1.44
7 a €10.56   **b** €5.60 and €9.30   **c** €20.90, €61.60 and €45.10

Exercise 3:08

1 a See page 317.   **b** See page 317.   **c** See page 317.   **d** See page 317.
2 a $143.80, $56.80   **b** $1866, $576   **c** $1138.40, $536.80
   d i $874, $144   **ii** $1019.20, $289.20   **iii** $1165.60, $435.60   **iv** $1309.60, $579.60
   v $1456, $726   **vi** $2182, $1452   **e** $17 180, $2566.70
3 a £17.60   **b** £79.05   **c** £80 discount, 25%   **d** 30%   **e** £650   **f** £62   **g** 11%   **h** £198
4 $72   **5** $1338.75   **6 a** $405   **b** $459   **c** $197.60   **d** $717.72   **e** $1701.77

7 a £45.50, 43% **b** £22 458, £127.3% (The amount borrowed was £10 050 – £300.) **c** 9% **d** £14.76
8 a $359.04 **b** $359.04 **c** Yes **d** No **e** 25·2% **f** 28%
9 a 18·12% **b** 31·2544% **c** 22·195% **d** 17·978 156 25%

Exercise 3:09

1

	Selling price	Cost price	Profit (or loss)
a	$ 2146	$ 1645	$ 501
b	$ 468	$ 647	−$ 179
c	$ 58.75	$ 95.50	−$ 36.75
d	$ 27 940	$13 650	$14 290
e	$121 610	$85 420	$36 190

	Money received	Expenses	Profit (or loss)
f	€ 3 816.50	€ 1 308.50	€ 2 508
g	€ 491.80	€ 846.60	−€ 354.80
h	€ 9 339	€ 916	€ 8 423
i	€27 648	€25 154	€ 2 494
j	€23 370	€ 7 684	€15 686

2 a 30.5% profit **b** 27.7% loss **c** 38·5% loss **d** 104.7% profit **e** 42.4% profit
3 f 65·7% profit **g** 72·1% loss **h** 90·2% profit **i** 9·0% profit **j** 67·1% profit
4 i 9.9% profit **j** 204·1% profit
5 a $22 **b** 78·6% **c** 44%
6 a £38.40 **b** £21 **c** £12.47
7 $29 574 **8** The discount price is $40.32 in each case.
9 C : S.P. = 100:140 ∴ cost = $220, profit = $88 **10 a** $300, $330 **b** $4, $4.40 **c** $60.50, $66.55
11 $180, loss = $36 **12** ¥1 560 000, loss = ¥468 000 **13** $104 **14** $102.03 **15** $457.60
16 $726 **17 a** €1485 **b** €1080 **c** 137·5%

Diagnostic Test 3 Consumer arithmetic

1 a i $310 **ii** $580 **b** $124.95 **2 a** €567 **b** €301 **3 a** £355.95 **b** 18.4%
4 a $39 430 **b** $36 626 **c** $7367.80 **d** Refund of $6432.70 **e** $70
5 a 50 kg size **b** 660 mL for $3.75
6 a $7.37 **b** $59.29 **c** $2.95 **d** $19.50
7 a €5003.20, €2003.20 **b** €980.80, €288.80 **8 a** $402.50 **b** $588, 14% **c** $32 000
9 a $526.50 **b** $850 **10 a** 130% **b** $3640.90, 72·5%

3A Revision Assignment

1 a i $672 **ii** $798 **b** $635 **c** $1090 **d** $2124.40
2 a i 21 kg for $59.60 **ii** 21 kg pack for $59.60 **b** $140.64 **c** 141·82
3 a $52 010 **b** $12 224.20 **c** $507.80 (without considering Medicare)
4 a $32.89 **b** $29.60 **c** No **d** approx. 9·1% **5 a** 40% **b** approx. 34%

3B Working Mathematically

1 a *four cubed* **b** *the cube root of 2* **c** *per cent* **d** *therefore* **e** *for example*
  f *that is* **g** *pi* **h** *the sum of* **i** *the mean* **j** *probability of event E*
2 a *square* **b** *rectangle* **c** *parallelogram* **d** *rhombus* **e** *trapezium*
  f *pentagon* **g** *hexagon* **h** *octagon* **i** *kite* **j** *circle*
3 15° **4** $31.63
5 a 10 km **b** 20 km **c** 11:30 am **d** Bill **e** 11:30 am **f** 50 km **g** 30 km **h** 90 km
6 a $1800 **b** $1400 **c** $37.50

Chapter 4 Algebraic expressions

Prep Quiz 4:01

1 $7 + 5 = 12$ **2** $9 - 2 = 7$ **3** $25 - 8 = 17$ **4** $48 \div 6 = 8$ **5** $7 \times 3 = 21$
6 $8 + 12 = 20$ **7** $(41 + 47) \div 2 = 44$ **8** $13 + 21 = 34$ **9** $138 \div 23 = 6$ **10** $4 \times 5 - 8 = 12$

Exercise 4:01

1 a C **b** F **c** A **d** D **e** B **f** E

2 a $2n$ **b** $n + 3$ **c** $8 - n$ **d** $2n + 3$ **e** $\frac{n}{2}$ or $\frac{1}{2}n$ **f** $2n - 5$

3 a $5 + 7$ **b** $5 + y$ **c** $x + y$ **4 a** 3×7 **b** $7a$ **c** ab

5 a $8 - 3$ **b** $8 - p$ **c** $q - p$ **6 a** $\frac{8 + 12}{2} = 10$ **b** $\frac{8 + x}{2}$ **c** $\frac{w + x}{2}$

7 a 5×75 cents **b** $75a$ cents **c** ab cents

8 a $\frac{30}{5}$ cm **b** $\frac{30}{t}$ cm **c** $\frac{A}{t}$ cm **9 a** 21 years old **b** $15 + y$

10 a (60×3) km = 180 km   **b** $60h$ km   **11 a** $(10 - 3 \times 2)$ m = 4 m   **b** $(X - 2x)$ m

12 a $(85x + 63y)c$ **b** $(Cx + Dy)c$ **13** $Y - 22, (Y - 22) + x$

14 a $(x + y)$ km   **b** $\dfrac{x + y}{5}$ km/h   **15** $(100 - x)c$

16 a 8   **b** $y + 2$ **c** $y - 1$ **17** $2n + 1$

18 a $76°$ **b** $180° - (a + b)°$ **19 a** hm km   **b** $\dfrac{k}{h}$ km/h   **c** $\dfrac{k}{m}$ hours

20 a $\$(R - P)$ **b** $\$(P + G)$

21 a $(a + b + 4)$ cm   **b** $(2x + 2y)$ cm   **c** $4s$ cm   **d** $(4x + 10)$ cm

22 a x^2 cm^2 **b** $x(x + 2)$ cm^2 **c** $\dfrac{xy}{2}$ cm^2 **d** $\dfrac{bh}{2}$ cm^2

23 a $4(a + 2)$ **b** $8 - (x + y)$ **c** $2(p + q)$ **d** $(2a)^2$ **e** $3a - (b + c)$

     f $(x + 2)^2$ **g** $x(y - 5)$ **h** $\sqrt{(2m + 3n)}$

24 a $(3p + 4q)c$ **b** $[500 - (3p + 4q)]c$

25 a product of x and y **b** five subtract a **c** two times p plus q

     d three times m minus two times n **e** five times the sum of x and y

     f the square of a plus b **g** divide the sum of x and y, by two

     h subtract n from m and divide the result by a **i** the square root of the sum of u and v

     j the cube root of the product of a and b

26 a the product of a, b and c; the sum of a, b and c **b** subtract b from a; subtract a from b

     c three times the sum of a and b; three times a plus b **d** x squared plus y squared; square the sum of x plus y

     e square root of a plus the square root of b; square root of the sum of a and b

     f a divided by b plus two divided by three; the sum of a and two, divided by the sum of b and 3

Prep Quiz 4:02

1 ab **2** xy^2 **3** $2x + 3y$ **4** 14   **5** 22   **6** 100   **7** -12 **8** -2 **9** 2   **10** $1\frac{1}{15}$

Exercise 4:02

1 a 7   **b** 17   **c** 2   **d** 36   **e** 49   **f** 25   **g** 56   **h** 14   **i** -12 **j** 3·5

     k 2·5   **l** 56   **m** 84   **n** -8 **o** -20 **p** -144 **q** -9 **r** -48 **s** -4 **t** $2\frac{1}{12}$

     u $\frac{7}{12}$ **v** -7 **w** 384   **x** 6

2 a -1 **b** 7   **c** -12 **d** 48   **e** 144   **f** -2 **g** -6 **h** 22   **i** $\frac{1}{12}$ **j** 1

     k $\frac{5}{6}$ **l** -7 **m** 80   **n** $2\frac{1}{4}$ **o** $7\frac{1}{4}$ **p** $-8\frac{3}{4}$ **q** $-12\frac{1}{2}$

3 a i 31   **ii** 17   **iii** -18 **b i** 24   **ii** 35   **iii** 21·93   **c i** 198·4   **ii** 19·625   **iii** 31 420

Prep Quiz 4:03

1 $9x$ **2** x **3** $6xy$ **4** $5x^2$ **5** $3x$ **6** $2b$ **7** $8a + 5b$ **8** $5x + y$ **9** $-24a^2$ **10** $-\dfrac{a}{3b}$

Exercise 4:03

1 a $5x$ **b** $13a$ **c** $31p$ **d** $8x$ **e** $3a$ **f** $6b$

     g $10q$ **h** $21e$ **i** $2p$ **j** $7x$ **k** $4x$ **l** 0

     m $a + 4p$ **n** $2m$ **o** $1 - 3x$ **p** -2 **q** $3x^2 + x$ **r** $4p^2 + 5p$

     s $2q^2 + 4q$ **t** $2y^2$ **u** $2 - p^2 + p$ **v** $3a + a^2 + 7$ **w** $x - 7 - 3x^2$ **x** $8ab - 16$

2 a $24y$ **b** $16a$ **c** $6xy$ **d** $32pq$ **e** $6ab$ **f** $5x^2$ **g** $15a^2$ **h** a^2bc

     i $6p^2q$ **j** $5m^2np$ **k** $2mn^2$ **l** $9a^2b$ **m** $-42a^3$ **n** $10x^2$ **o** $6x^2y$ **p** $-7a^2b^2$

     q ab^2c **r** $24k^3$ **s** $70xy$ **t** $-mnp$

3 a $3x$ **b** 3   **c** $3x^2$ **d** 1   **e** $\dfrac{3m}{2n}$ **f** $\dfrac{8a}{3b}$ **g** $\dfrac{1}{4a}$ **h** $8a$

     i $\frac{1}{3}$ **j** $\frac{9}{4}$ **k** -5 **l** $-\dfrac{y}{z}$ **m** -14 **n** $\dfrac{3}{y}$ **o** $-4n$ **p** $\dfrac{a}{2b}$

4 a mn^2p **b** $4m + 13$ **c** $19 - 2a$ **d** 0   **e** $6x^2y^2$ **f** $15x^2 + 5x$ **g** $60yz$ **h** $-28x^2$

     i $7ab$ **j** $-m$ **k** 0   **l** $\dfrac{2a}{c}$ **m** $\frac{1}{3}$ **n** $18p^2q^2$ **o** $5a + b - c$ **p** $15yz$

     q y **r** $2n$ **s** $6abc$ **t** $\dfrac{3a}{2x}$

5 a $20a$ **b** x **c** $12b$ **d** $3m$ **e** 4   **f** $60a^2$ **g** $3m^2$ **h** $\frac{15}{7}$

     i 35   **j** 16   **k** $6a^2$ **l** $6y^2$ **m** $14x$ **n** $25x^2$ **o** $10y$ **p** $16m$

     q $26n$ **r** $3x$ **s** x **t** $20m$ **u** $\frac{9}{5}$ **v** 1   **w** 1   **x** $\dfrac{a}{2c}$

Prep Quiz 4:04A

1 $\frac{4}{5}$ **2** $\frac{2}{5}$ **3** $\frac{7}{12}$ **4** $\frac{7}{8}$ **5** $\frac{3}{20}$ **6** $\frac{1}{4}$ **7** $11x$ **8** $4ab$ **9** x **10** $8a$

Exercise 4:04A

1 a $2a$ **b** $\frac{x}{5}$ **c** $\frac{5a}{3}$ **d** $\frac{3m}{5}$ **e** $\frac{x+y}{4}$ **f** $\frac{5a-2b}{3}$ **g** $\frac{5}{a}$ **h** $\frac{8}{x}$

i $\frac{1}{y}$ **j** $\frac{8}{m}$ **k** $\frac{7a}{x}$ **l** $\frac{-x}{y}$ **m** $\frac{4}{n}$ **n** $\frac{1}{x}$ **o** $\frac{2a}{b}$ **p** $\frac{m}{x}$

2 a $\frac{8x}{15}$ **b** $\frac{7a}{10}$ **c** $\frac{y}{12}$ **d** $\frac{m}{4}$ **e** $\frac{7a}{6}$ **f** $\frac{13x}{6}$ **g** $\frac{n}{8}$ **h** $\frac{p}{2}$

i $\frac{3x+4y}{12}$ **j** $\frac{4a-9b}{6}$ **k** $\frac{6m+5n}{10}$ **l** $\frac{k-3l}{6}$ **m** $\frac{10}{3x}$ **n** $\frac{5}{6a}$ **o** $\frac{31}{10m}$ **p** $\frac{1}{8x}$

q $\frac{13a}{6x}$ **r** $\frac{-5x}{3m}$ **s** $\frac{13m}{4n}$ **t** $\frac{8x+3y}{12a}$

Prep Quiz 4:04B

1 $\frac{3}{8}$ **2** $\frac{3}{10}$ **3** $\frac{1}{6}$ **4** $\frac{2}{3}$ **5** 2 **6** $\frac{8}{15}$ **7** $30x$ **8** $6a^2$ **9** $3a$ **10** $2a$

Exercise 4:04B

1 a $\frac{xy}{6}$ **b** $\frac{ab}{12}$ **c** $\frac{m^2}{10}$ **d** $\frac{a^2}{40}$ **e** $\frac{12}{am}$ **f** $\frac{2}{xy}$ **g** $\frac{4}{p^2}$ **h** $\frac{1}{3n^2}$

i $\frac{px}{qy}$ **j** $\frac{1}{2}$ **k** $\frac{2m}{n}$ **l** $\frac{2}{15}$ **m** $\frac{2a}{3}$ **n** 1 **o** 9 **p** $\frac{16a}{15p}$

2 a 2 **b** $\frac{5}{3}$ **c** $\frac{15}{2}$ **d** $\frac{2}{3}$ **e** $\frac{5}{2}$ **f** $\frac{9}{2}$ **g** $\frac{1}{2}$ **h** 6

i $\frac{ay}{bx}$ **j** $\frac{3}{4}$ **k** 15 **l** $\frac{3}{2}$ **m** $2x$ **n** $\frac{3}{a}$ **o** x^2 **p** $\frac{27}{4}$

3 a $\frac{4}{5}$ **b** $\frac{2}{3}$ **c** $\frac{3}{x}$ **d** $\frac{b^2}{2}$ **e** $2y$ **f** b **g** $6m^2$ **h** 4

i $\frac{4}{q^2}$ **j** $\frac{6}{ab}$ **k** $\frac{2by}{c}$ **l** $3c$ **m** $\frac{3}{2}$ **n** 1 **o** 6 **p** $\frac{2}{5}$

Fun Spot 4:04 Try this maths-word puzzle

The mystery word is 'GRAM'.

Prep Quiz 4:05

1 $10x$ **2** $3a^2$ **3** $6x+8$ **4** $x+2$ **5** $5y^2+4y$ **6** $13+2a$
7 $3x-21$ **8** $18-45y$ **9** $2a^2+6a$ **10** $-5x-35$

Exercise 4:05

1 a $5a+35, 5(a+7)$ **b** $21+3x, 3(7+x)$ **c** $7m+7n, 7(m+n)$ **d** $pq+8p, p(q+8)$
e $6x+6y, 6(x+y)$ **f** $bc+ac, c(b+a)$

2 a $3x+4$ **b** $4a+20$ **c** $3y-6$ **d** $5x-15$ **e** $6a+9$ **f** $4m+4n$
g $18x+12y$ **h** $14x-21b$ **i** x^2+5x **j** y^2-2y **k** $2g^2-2g$ **l** $3w^2+6vw$
m x^2+xt **n** $6h^2-2h$ **o** $4q-2q^2$ **p** $16x-64x^2$ **q** $ys+yt$ **r** a^2b+ab^2
s $6x^2y-30xy$ **t** $10r^2+10rs$

3 a $-3x-12$ **b** $-4a-20$ **c** $8-4a$ **d** $9-3p$ **e** $-14m-35$ **f** $35-14m$
g $14m-35$ **h** $8x-8$ **i** $3-a$ **j** $9-4m$ **k** $-3-6y$ **l** $4c-2a$
m $-2a^2-a$ **n** $-3x^2-3x$ **o** $3m-9m^2$ **p** $9hj-27h^2$

4 a $5x+7$ **b** $10x+7$ **c** $8y-3$ **d** $10a-9$ **e** $p+10$ **f** $15-m$
g $7a+20$ **h** $7x+2$ **i** $10n-7$ **j** $11h+13$ **k** $8x+7$ **l** $10y+2$
m $a+8$ **n** $5m-16$ **o** $2y+14$ **p** $x+28$ **q** $9x+21$ **r** $2a+6$
s $4m+9$ **t** $14x+7$

5 a $6x+10$ **b** $9m+24$ **c** a^2+7a+6 **d** $13m-14$ **e** $17x-12$ **f** $10x+40$
g $2x+23$ **h** $3m$ **i** $2a+66$ **j** $2n-46$ **k** x^2+6x+3 **l** $a^2+10a-21$
m m^2-m-12 **n** $t^2-9t+20$ **o** $3a^2+3ab$ **p** $x^2+2xy+y^2$

Prep Quiz 4:06

1 $12x$ **2** a **3** x^2-2x+3 **4** $2x+10$ **5** x^2-2x **6** $-3a-3$
7 $-5y+y^2$ **8** x^2+4x+3 **9** $25-a^2$ **10** $6x^2-19x-10$

Exercise 4:06

1 a $ab + 3a + 2b + 6$ **b** $xy + 4x + y + 4$ **c** $mn + 5m + 7n + 35$ **d** $ax + 2a + 3x + 6$
   e $pq + 4p + 5q + 20$ **f** $2xy + 6x + y + 3$ **g** $3ap + 2a + 18p + 12$ **h** $8xy + 12x + 2y + 3$
   i $6ab - 21a + 2b - 7$ **j** $14px + 7x + 10p + 5$ **k** $5px - 20p + 3x - 12$ **l** $2ax + 4bx + ay + 2by$

2 a $a^2 + 5a + 6$ **b** $x^2 + 6x + 5$ **c** $n^2 + 7n + 12$ **d** $p^2 + 7p + 10$
   e $m^2 - 2m - 3$ **f** $y^2 + 5y - 14$ **g** $x^2 - 5x - 6$ **h** $t^2 - 2t - 8$
   i $x^2 - 6x + 8$ **j** $n^2 - 8n + 7$ **k** $a^2 - 9a + 18$ **l** $x^2 - 19x + 90$
   m $y^2 - 4y - 77$ **n** $a^2 - a - 2$ **o** $x^2 - 16x + 64$ **p** $m^2 - 11m + 18$
   q $a^2 - 9$ **r** $x^2 - 4x - 21$ **s** $y^2 + 17y + 60$ **t** $a^2 - 64$
   u $q^2 + 10q + 25$ **v** $x^2 - 10x + 9$ **w** $t^2 + 13t + 30$ **x** $k^2 + 3k - 88$

3 a $2a^2 + 7a + 3$ **b** $2x^2 + 5x + 2$ **c** $3m^2 + 17m + 10$ **d** $4y^2 + 13y + 3$
   e $4x^2 + 8x + 3$ **f** $6n^2 + 7n + 2$ **g** $8x^2 + 18x + 9$ **h** $10t^2 + 19t + 6$
   i $10x^2 - 12x + 2$ **j** $24p^2 - 13p - 2$ **k** $10m^2 - 29m + 10$ **l** $21q^2 + q - 2$
   m $18x^2 + 6x - 4$ **n** $4n^2 - 9$ **o** $64y^2 - 1$ **p** $15k^2 - 19k + 6$
   q $49p^2 - 14p + 1$ **r** $15x^2 - 14x + 3$ **s** $25x^2 + 40x + 16$ **t** $27y^2 + 6y - 8$
   u $5p^2 - 33p - 14$ **v** $10q^2 - 101q + 10$ **w** $12a^2 + 25a + 12$ **x** $49p^2 - 25$

4 a $12 + 7x + x^2$ **b** $10 - 7a + a^2$ **c** $7 - 6m - m^2$ **d** $9 - n^2$
   e $y^2 + 9y + 20$ **f** $12x - x^2 - 35$ **g** $k^2 + 19k + 90$ **h** $2a^2 + 7a + 3$
   i $19n - 6n^2 + 7$ **j** $x^2 + 3xy + 2y^2$ **k** $2n^2 + 5mn + 2m^2$ **l** $2a^2 + ab - 3b^2$
   m $4p^2 - q^2$ **n** $6x^2 - 13xy - 5y^2$ **o** $6a^2 + 13ab + 6b^2$ **p** $81w^2 - 90wx + 25x^2$

Prep Quiz 4:07A

1 16   **2** 49   **3** 4   **4** 100   **5** $9x^2$ **6** 14   **7** 9   **8** 4   **9** 10   **10** −6

Investigation 4:07   The square of a binomial

x	y	x^2	y^2	xy	$(x + y)^2$	$x^2 + 2xy + y^2$	$(x - y)^2$	$x^2 - 2xy + y^2$
5	3	25	9	15	64	64	4	4
6	1	36	1	6	49	49	25	25
10	4	100	16	40	196	196	36	36

Exercise 4:07A

1 a 4   **b** 36   **c** 9   **d** 100   **e** $2x$ **f** $14y$ **g** $4n$ **h** $10p$ **i** q^2 **j** x^2
   k 3   **l** 9   **m** 7   **n** 11   **o** $4x^2$ **p** $25n^2$ **q** $42m$ **r** $40x$ **s** $4a$ **t** $126y$

2 a $x^2 + 6x + 9$ **b** $x^2 + 10x + 25$ **c** $x^2 + 2x + 1$ **d** $x^2 - 12x - 36$
   e $m^2 - 2m + 1$ **f** $n^2 - 10n + 25$ **g** $x^2 + 4x + 4$ **h** $n^2 - 16n + 64$
   i $m^2 + 22m + 121$ **j** $a^2 + 24a + 144$ **k** $x^2 + 20x + 100$ **l** $p^2 - 18p + 81$
   m $x^2 + 2xy + y^2$ **n** $a^2 + 2am + m^2$ **o** $x^2 + 2xt + t^2$ **p** $a^2 - 2ab + b^2$
   q $k^2 - 2km + m^2$ **r** $p^2 - 2pq + q^2$

3 a $4x^2 + 12x + 9$ **b** $4x^2 + 4x + 1$ **c** $9x^2 + 30x + 25$ **d** $16a^2 + 8a + 1$
   e $9a^2 + 42a + 49$ **f** $49t^2 + 28t + 4$ **g** $4x^2 - 4x + 1$ **h** $9a^2 - 12a + 4$
   i $25m^2 - 40m + 16$ **j** $16t^2 - 56t + 49$ **k** $36q^2 - 12q + 1$ **l** $81n^2 + 72n + 16$
   m $4x^2 + 4xy + y^2$ **n** $a^2 + 6ab + 9b^2$ **o** $9t^2 - 12xt + 4x^2$

Prep Quiz 4:07B

1 40   **2** 40   **3** 12   **4** 12   **5** 24   **6** 24   **7** 27   **8** 27   **9** 19   **10** 19

Exercise 4:07B

1 a $x^2 - 16$ **b** $a^2 - 1$ **c** $m^2 - 4$ **d** $n^2 - 49$ **e** $p^2 - 25$ **f** $q^2 - 36$
   g $x^2 - 9$ **h** $y^2 - 81$ **i** $100 - x^2$ **j** $25 - a^2$ **k** $64 - x^2$ **l** $121 - m^2$
   m $x^2 - t^2$ **n** $a^2 - b^2$ **o** $m^2 - n^2$ **p** $p^2 - q^2$

2 a $4a^2 - 1$ **b** $9x^2 - 4$ **c** $25m^2 - 9$ **d** $81q^2 - 4$ **e** $16t^2 - 9$ **f** $49x^2 - 1$
   g $64n^2 - 25$ **h** $100x^2 - 9$ **i** $4x^2 - y^2$ **j** $16a^2 - 9b^2$ **k** $25p^2 - 4q^2$ **l** $9m^2 - n^2$
   m $4m^2 - 25n^2$ **n** $4p^2 - 9q^2$ **o** $x^2 - 25y^2$ **p** $144x^2 - 25y^2$

Exercise 4:08

1 a $8x - 21$ **b** $x^2 + x - 2$ **c** $2x^2 - x - 1$ **d** $4x - x^2 + 10$
   e $9x^2 - 6x + 1$ **f** $x^2 - 25$ **g** $6x^2 - 23x + 7$ **h** $25x^2 - 1$
   i $x^2 + 6x + 7$ **j** $8x$ **k** $x^2 + 7x - 30$ **l** $81 - y^2$
   m $x^2 - 15x$ **n** $3x^2 + 9x + 6$ **o** $x^2 + 2xy + y^2$ **p** $2x^2 + 5xy + 2y^2$
   q $3x$ **r** $a^2 - 4b^2$ **s** $2a - 2x$ **t** $15a^2 + 26a - 21$
   u $4m^2 - 20mn + 25n^2$ **v** $1 - 25y^2$ **w** $21 - 4x$ **x** $81x^2 - 64y^2$

2 a $x^2 + 7x + 11$ **b** $a^2 - 9a + 6$ **c** $x^2 - 2x + 20$ **d** $x^2 + 2x + 9$
  e $2x^2 + 9x + 11$ **f** -1 **g** $12m + 37$ **h** $-14y - 98$
  i $2x^2 + 6x + 5$ **j** $2a + 5$ **k** $2x^2 + 8x + 8$ **l** $2a^2 - 4$
  m $5x + 7$ **n** $y - 17$ **o** $4x^2 - x - 14$ **p** $3x^2 + 24x + 49$
  q $9x^2 - 10x - 2$ **r** $10x$ **s** $p^2 - q^2$ **t** $2xy + 2y^2$
  u $2a^2 + 5ab + 3b^2$ **v** $2m^2 + 2n^2$ **w** $3x^2 + 11x + 8$ **x** $5x^2 + 6x + 1$
  y $12xy + 18y^2$ **z** ab
3 a $3x^2 + 12x + 14$ **b** $3x^2 + 15x + 20$ **c** $3a^2 + 1$ **d** $5x + 7$
  e $19a^2 + 13ab - 7b^2$ **f** $12x^2 + 3x + 12$ **g** $-4m + 24$ **h** $4x^2 - 3y^2 + 1$
  i $6x^2 + 4xy + 6y^2$ **j** $-4y^2$

Challenge 4:08   Patterns in products

1 $10x^2 + 110x + 385$ **2** $9x^2 + 99x + 330$ **3** $11a^2 + 110$ **4** $55m^2 - 55n^2$

Investigation 4:08   Using special products in arithmetic

Exercise A
1 a $10\,201$ **b** $42\,025$ **c** $1\,008\,016$ **d** 5184 **e** 9604 **f** $39\,601$ **g** $990\,025$ **h** 4489
Exercise B
1 a 396 **b** 840 **c** 1425 **d** $12\,920$
2 a $\sqrt{56}$ **b** $\sqrt{540}$ **c** $\sqrt{445}$ **d** $\sqrt{960}$

Diagnostic Test 4   Algebraic expressions

1 a $y = 4x$ **b** $y = 2x + 2$ **c** $y = x^2$
2 a $x + y$ **b** $\dfrac{5+m}{2}$ or $(5+m) \div 2$ **c** $\$pb$ **d** $200 - x$
3 a 13 **b** 45 **c** 310 **4 a** $4x + 4$ **b** $5q^2 + 7q$ **c** $2xy$ **d** $2m - n + 3$
5 a $-5ay$ **b** $2x^2y$ **c** $-36ab$ **d** $12x^3y$ **6 a** $3m$ **b** $6b$ **c** $2x$ **d** $\dfrac{-n}{m}$
7 a x **b** $\dfrac{-x}{6}$ **c** $\dfrac{7a}{15}$ **d** $\dfrac{9m}{8}$ **8 a** $\dfrac{n}{4}$ **b** $\dfrac{10}{ab}$ **c** $\dfrac{1}{2}$ **d** $\dfrac{6}{5}$
9 a $6m$ **b** 2 **c** 12 **d** $\dfrac{5a}{2}$ **10 a** $4x - 12$ **b** $8x + 12$ **c** $8x^2 - 12$ **d** $15a - 3a^2$
11 a $12 - 4x$ **b** $-4x^2 - 12x$ **c** $15m - 15m^2$ **d** $-12a^2 - 28a$
12 a $-x$ **b** $10n - 7$ **c** $-a^2 + 6ab$
13 a $x^2 + 7x + 12$ **b** $2a^2 - 7a + 3$ **c** $6 - y - y^2$ **d** $2x^2 - 5xy - 3y^2$
14 a $x^2 + 4x + 4$ **b** $a^2 - 14a + 49$ **c** $4y^2 + 20y + 25$ **d** $m^2 - 2mn + n^2$
15 a $x^2 - 9$ **b** $y^2 - 49$ **c** $4a^2 - 25$ **d** $x^2 - y^2$

4A   Revision Assignment

1 a $7a$ **b** $18x^2$ **c** $-4a$ **d** $2x^2$ **e** 6 **f** $\dfrac{3y}{2}$ **g** $2x + 3y$ **h** $6ab^2$
  i $2ab$ **j** $12ab$ **k** $6a^2 - a$ **l** $-x - 3y$ **m** $19 + 5x$ **n** $12x$ **o** $4x^2 - x$ **p** $10x$
2 a $x^2 + x - 2$ **b** $8x - 3$ **c** 3 **d** $2x^2 - 13x - 7$ **e** $x^2 - 25$ **f** $9x^2 + 12x + 4$
  g $x^2 - x + 2$ **h** $6 - 5x + x^2$ **i** $y^2 - x^2$ **j** $4x^2 - 4xy + y^2$ **k** $20x + 15$
  l $4x^2 + 8x + 4$
3 a $\dfrac{5x}{6}$ **b** $\dfrac{3a}{10}$ **c** $\dfrac{5ab}{4}$ **d** $\dfrac{2}{3}$ **e** $\dfrac{16x}{15}$ **f** $\dfrac{13m}{30}$ **g** $\dfrac{8n}{7}$ **h** $\dfrac{5x+11}{6}$
4 $4y$ **5 a** $y = 12 - 3x$ **b** $s = t^2 + 1$
6 $\frac{1}{2}(2x - 2)(x + 1) = x^2 - 1$ **7 a** $3x^2 + 14x - 24$ **b** $10x^2 + 12x$ **c** $x^2 + 4x + 4$

4B   Working Mathematically

1 a square   **b** rectangle   **c** parallelogram   **d** rhombus
  e trapezium   **f** pentagon   **g** hexagon   **h** octagon
  i kite   **j** isosceles triangle
2 a An octagonal prism   **b** 200 mL
3 17   **4 a** 4   **b** 10   **5 a** 40%   **b** 5%
6 a Tasmania; 60%   **b** Victoria; over 90%   **c** Queensland, just under 3000 per 10 000
  d About 50%; less than 40%. Perhaps some could read but not write, or perhaps some children were not tested.

Chapter 5: Indices and surds

Exercise 5:01

1 a 81 **b** 512 **c** 144 **d** 125 **e** 1296 **f** 81 **g** 72 **h** 512
i 531 441 **j** 390 625

2 a 5^4 **b** 4^3 **c** 10^6 **d** x^7 **e** y^2 **f** x^5 **g** a^6 **h** m^6 **i** y^5 **j** w^4

3 a x^6 **b** d^7 **c** m^7 **d** $12a^9$ **e** $-15y^7$ **f** x^6 **g** m^7 **h** a^3 **i** $4y^4$ **j** $-9d^8$
k x^9 **l** 1 **m** $9x^6$ **n** $256a^4$ **o** $216y^{15}$

4 a 4^5 **b** 5^8 **c** 7^7 **d** 2^7 **e** 10^7 **f** 5^6 **g** 3^6 **h** 10^0 **i** 3^4 **j** 3^2
k 5^6 **l** 7^{49} **m** 2^{12} **n** $4^{27} = 2^{54}$ **o** 3^{24}

5 a $8x^7$ **b** $5a^3$ **c** $4m^{10}$ **d** $8x$ **e** $5a$ **f** $4m^2$ **g** $50y^4$ **h** $32m^4$
i $32a^9$ **j** $2y^2$ **k** 8 **l** $2a$ **m** $72x^8$ **n** $27a^9$ **o** $108y^7$ **p** $2x^2$
q $3a^5$ **r** $3y^5$ **s** $3a^2$ **t** $2x^5$ **u** $2a$

6 a 6 **b** 6 **c** 1 **d** a **e** y^3 **f** m^5 **g** $8m^6$ **h** $16n^6$
i $16p^{12}$ **j** x^5y^3 **k** a^2b^9 **l** x^5y^3 **m** x^3y^4 **n** a^5b^2 **o** m^3n^4 **p** x^4y^6
q $a^2b^2c^2$ **r** p^3q^9 **s** $10x^3y^2$ **t** $28a^3b^5$ **u** $44a^5b^2$ **v** $3a^4$ **w** $-24a^3$ **x** $2c$
y $22x^2 - 5x^3$ **z** $12x^2 + 7x + 1$

7 a $30x^6$ **b** $40a^3$ **c** $5xy^4$ **d** $\dfrac{x^3}{2}$ **e** $\dfrac{y}{7}$ **f** $\dfrac{10}{x}$ **g** x^8 **h** a^{13}
i y^{26} **j** a^2 **k** m^2 **l** n^2 **m** y^{19} **n** $8a^{18}$ **o** b^2 **p** x^2
q $2a^2$ **r** $7pq^2$ **s** $2x^5$ **t** $6x^6$ **u** $\dfrac{xy^3}{16}$

8 a $x^4 - x^2$ **b** $5a^3 - a^5$ **c** $5a^3 - a^5$ **d** $x^3 + xy$ **e** $7m - m^3$ **f** $y^3 - xy^2$ **g** $6a^5 + 9a^3$ **h** $15x^3 - 5x^2$
i $2m^3n^2 - 2m^5$ **j** $5x^3 - 3x^2 + 7x$ **k** $2x^4 + 7x^3 - 14x^2$ **l** $y^3 - 7y^2 - y$
m $-7x^2$ **n** $4y^4$ **o** $-6x^2 + x$

9 a 3^{2x+1} **b** 5^{y-1} **c** 2^{4x-2} **d** e^{3x+1} **e** e^{x+1} **f** e^{x+3}

Exercise 5:02

1 a $\dfrac{1}{3}$ **b** $\dfrac{1}{5}$ **c** $\dfrac{1}{2}$ **d** $\dfrac{1}{36}$ **e** $\dfrac{1}{16}$ **f** $\dfrac{1}{1000}$ **g** $\dfrac{1}{16}$ **h** $\dfrac{1}{10\,000}$ **i** $\dfrac{1}{25}$

2 a 11^{-1} **b** 3^{-1} **c** 5^{-1} **d** 7^{-1} **e** 3^{-3} **f** 5^{-4} **g** 2^{-8} **h** 7^{-2} **i** 10^{-2}
j 10^{-3} **k** 10^{-6} **l** 10^{-5}

3 a true **b** false **c** true **d** false **e** false **f** false **g** true **h** false

4 a x **b** a^3 **c** m^3 **d** 1 **e** $3a$ **f** $30x^2$ **g** $5a$
h $30m^2$ **i** $\dfrac{1}{x^3}$ **j** $\dfrac{2}{a^5}$ **k** $\dfrac{8}{y}$ **l** $\dfrac{30}{m^5}$

5 a m^5 **b** x^4 **c** y^2 **d** x^4 **e** $\dfrac{1}{a^4}$ **f** $\dfrac{1}{y^4}$ **g** $\dfrac{1}{y^3}$
h $\dfrac{1}{x^2}$ **i** $3x^3$ **j** $\dfrac{2}{a^4}$ **k** $\dfrac{24}{a^5}$ **l** $2n$

6 a a^6 **b** $\dfrac{1}{x^2}$ **c** $\dfrac{1}{y^6}$ **d** m^4 **e** $\dfrac{1}{2x^2}$ **f** $\dfrac{1}{9x^2}$ **g** $\dfrac{25}{x^2}$
h $\dfrac{49}{x^4}$ **i** $\dfrac{1}{abc}$ **j** $\dfrac{1}{a^2b^2c^2}$ **k** $\dfrac{1}{2a^2b}$ **l** $\dfrac{2}{a^2b}$

7 a $\dfrac{5}{6}$ or $0.8\dot{3}$ **b** $\dfrac{1}{6}$ or $0.1\dot{6}$ **c** 1 **d** $\dfrac{1}{12}$ or $0.08\dot{3}$

8 a 3^{2x} **b** 5^{2y-2} **c** e^{2x} **d** e^{x+1}

Prep Quiz 5:03

1 $\sqrt{25} = 5$ **2** $\sqrt{49} = 7$ **3** $\sqrt[3]{8} = 2$ **4** $\sqrt[3]{125} = 5$ **5** $n = \dfrac{1}{2}$
6 $n = \dfrac{1}{2}$ **7** $n = \dfrac{1}{2}$ **8** $n = \dfrac{1}{2}$ **9** $n = \dfrac{1}{3}$ **10** $n = \dfrac{1}{3}$

Exercise 5:03

1 a $\sqrt{5}$ **b** $\sqrt{10}$ **c** $\sqrt{2}$ **d** $3\sqrt{2}$ **e** $4\sqrt{3}$ **f** $7\sqrt{6}$

2 a $3^{\frac{1}{2}}$ **b** $3 \times 2^{\frac{1}{3}}$ **c** $11^{\frac{1}{3}}$ **d** $7 \times 3^{\frac{1}{2}}$

3 a 2 **b** 7 **c** 2 **d** 2 **e** 4 **f** 10 **g** 12 **h** 1 **i** 11 **j** 2 **k** 9 **l** 3

4 a x **b** a **c** m **d** $12x$ **e** $6y$ **f** $18n$ **g** x **h** y^2 **i** $2a^3$ **j** ab^2 **k** $3x^2y^3$ **l** $2xy$

5 a $\dfrac{1}{3}$ **b** $\dfrac{1}{5}$ **c** $\dfrac{1}{2}$ **d** 27 **e** 8 **f** 32 **g** 8 **h** 25 **i** $\dfrac{1}{4}$ **j** 243 **k** 16 **l** $\dfrac{1}{8}$

6 a 15 **b** 28 **c** 32 **d** 9 **e** 15 **f** 20 **g** 3375 **h** 81 **i** $3\,200\,000$
j 4 **k** 32 **l** 1000

7 a 4 **b** 2 **c** 54 **d** 3 **e** 1 **f** $\dfrac{1}{2}$ **g** $\dfrac{1}{2}$ **h** 4

8 a $9a^2$ **b** x^4y^8 **c** $4m^6$ **d** $\dfrac{a^2}{b^2}$ **e** $\dfrac{8}{x^3}$ **f** $\dfrac{y^9}{125}$

Investigation 5:03   Reasoning with fractional indices

- $x^{\frac{1}{2}}, x^1, x^{\frac{3}{2}}, x^2, x^{\frac{5}{2}} \dots$ The power of x is increasing by $\frac{1}{2}$ each time.
- $x^{3b} = x^1, \therefore 3b = 1, \therefore b = \frac{1}{3}$
- $\sqrt{8} = \sqrt{2^3} = (2^3)^{\frac{1}{2}} = 2^{\frac{3}{2}} = 2^{\frac{2}{2}} \times 2^{\frac{1}{2}} = 2\sqrt{2} = (\sqrt{2})^2 \times (\sqrt{2})^1 = (\sqrt{2})^3$
- Some values are: $(x = 4, p = 1, q = 2), (x = 8, p = 1, q = 3), (x = 16, p = 1, q = 4)$

Investigation 5:04   Multiplying and dividing by powers of 10

1 a 18   b 180   c 1800   d 40·5   e 405   f 4050   g 62 000   h 620 000
   i 6 200 000 j 314·16 k 3141·6 l 31 416. To multiply by 10^n move the decimal point n places to the right.
2 a 0·18   b 0·018   c 0·0018   d 9·685   e 0·9685   f 0·09685. To divide by 10^n move the
   decimal point n places to the left.

Exercise 5:04

1 a $2 \times 10^4 = 2 \times 10 \times 10 \times 10 \times 10 = 20\,000$, $2^4 = 2 \times 2 \times 2 \times 2 = 16$

   b $5 \times 10^{-2} = 5 \times \dfrac{1}{10^2} = 5 \times \dfrac{1}{100} = \dfrac{5}{100}$, $5^{-2} = \dfrac{1}{5^2} = \dfrac{1}{25}$

   c $1\cdot577\,88 \times 10^{12}$ or $1\,577\,800\,000\,000$ (taking 1 year = 365·25 days). However, since years that are multiples of 100 are not leap years unless they are multiples of 400, the answer could be $1\,577\,847\,600\,000$ or $1\cdot577\,847\,6 \times 10^{12}$.
   d Yes (if you are older than 9 years 4 months 8 days)
   e $9\cdot8 \times 10^{-5}, 0\cdot0034, 5\cdot6 \times 10^{-2}, 2\cdot04, 6, 5\cdot499 \times 10^2, 3\cdot24 \times 10^3, 1\cdot2 \times 10^4$
   f $7\cdot6 \times 10^{-3}$ cm   g Answers may vary. It would be about 0·5 mm, or 5×10^{-1} mm, or 5×10^{-2} cm.
2 a 21   b 0·21   c 0·21   d 704   e 0·0704
   f 0·0704   g 1375   h 0·001 375   i 0·001 375
3 a $4\cdot7 \times 10^2$ b $2\cdot6 \times 10^3$ c $5\cdot3 \times 10^4$ d 7×10^2 e 5×10^4
   f 7×10^5 g $6\cdot5 \times 10^1$ h $3\cdot42 \times 10^2$ i 9×10^1 j $4\cdot97 \times 10^3$
   k $6\cdot35 \times 10^4$ l $2\cdot941 \times 10^6$ m $2\cdot971 \times 10^2$ n $6\cdot93 \times 10^1$ o $4\cdot9765 \times 10^3$
   p $9\cdot31 \times 10^6$ q $6\cdot7 \times 10^7$ r $1\cdot901 \times 10^5$ s 6×10^5 t $5\cdot017 \times 10^5$
   u 1×10^5
4 a $7\cdot5 \times 10^{-2}$ b $6\cdot3 \times 10^{-3}$ c $5\cdot9 \times 10^{-1}$ d 8×10^{-2} e 3×10^{-4}
   f 9×10^{-3} g 3×10^{-1} h $3\cdot01 \times 10^{-2}$ i $5\cdot29 \times 10^{-4}$ j $4\cdot26 \times 10^{-1}$
   k 1×10^{-3} l $9\cdot7 \times 10^{-6}$ m 6×10^{-5} n $9\cdot07 \times 10^{-4}$ o 4×10^{-9}
5 a 230   b 94 000   c 3700   d 295   e 87·4
   f 763 000   g 1075   h 20 000   i 80   j 0·029
   k 0·001 9   l 0·95   m 0·003 76   n 0·000 463   o 0·0107
   p 0·07   q 0·80   r 0·000 005   s 973 000   t 0·0063
   u 47 000 000   v 914·2   w 0·010 32   x 100 000 000

Prep Quiz 5:05

1 $6\cdot9 \times 10^2$ 2 4×10^3 3 $9\cdot632 \times 10^2$ 4 $7\cdot3 \times 10^{-2}$ 5 3×10^{-4}
6 2900   7 800 000   8 0·046   9 0·000 000 5   10 0·814

Exercise 5:05

1 a 15 / 6.3   b −12 / 1.4   c 11 / 9.2

2 a $3\cdot02 \times 10^5$ b $4\cdot631 \times 10^9$ c $1\cdot37 \times 10^{15}$ d $1\cdot31 \times 10^{-4}$ e $6\cdot9 \times 10^{-8}$
   f $4\cdot6327 \times 10^{-10}$ g $7\cdot6514 \times 10^8$ h $1\cdot031\,24 \times 10^{-12}$ i $6\cdot9333 \times 10^{-5}$

   A calculator readout of $\boxed{2.\,^{04}}$ = $2 \times 10^4 = 20\,000$; $2^4 = 16$.

3 $1\cdot031\,24 \times 10^{-12}, 4\cdot6327 \times 10^{-10}, 6\cdot9 \times 10^{-8}, 6\cdot9333 \times 10^{-5}, 1\cdot31 \times 10^{-4}, 3\cdot02 \times 10^5, 7\cdot6514 \times 10^8, 4\cdot631 \times 10^9, 1\cdot37 \times 10^{15}$
4 a $2\cdot1160 \times 10^{14}$ b $5\cdot6689 \times 10^{-12}$ c $1\cdot6807 \times 10^{-16}$ d $7\cdot1538 \times 10^{11}$ e $1\cdot6687 \times 10^{14}$
   f $1\cdot3158 \times 10^{-12}$ g $3\cdot9366 \times 10^{12}$ h $4\cdot0459 \times 10^{19}$
5 a 318 600   b 0·006 626   c 0·2442   d 0·000 014 44   e 0·008 424
   f 771 000   g 86 310   h 0·004 498   i 0·000 188 7
6 a $1\cdot393 \times 10^6, 12\,800$ km or $1\cdot28 \times 10^4$ km   b 5 000 000 km or 5×10^6 km   c 8 min   d 2×10^{27} tonnes
   e 2×10^{38}

Exercises 5:06

1 a rational   b irrational   c rational   d rational   e rational   f irrational
   g irrational   h rational   i rational   j rational   k rational   l rational
   m rational   n rational   o rational   p irrational   q rational   r irrational
   s rational   t rational   u rational   v rational   w irrational   x irrational
   y rational   z irrational

2 a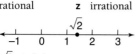
$\sqrt{2} \doteqdot 1\cdot4$

b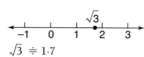
$\sqrt{3} \doteqdot 1\cdot7$

c
$\sqrt{5} \doteqdot 2\cdot2$

d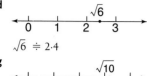
$\sqrt{6} \doteqdot 2\cdot4$

e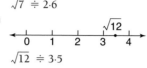
$\sqrt{7} \doteqdot 2\cdot6$

f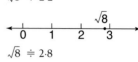
$\sqrt{8} \doteqdot 2\cdot8$

g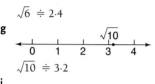
$\sqrt{10} \doteqdot 3\cdot2$

h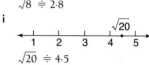
$\sqrt{12} \doteqdot 3\cdot5$

i
$\sqrt{20} \doteqdot 4\cdot5$

j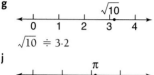
$\pi \doteqdot 3\cdot1$

3 a 3, 4   b 4, 5   c 6, 7   d 8, 9   e 9, 10   f 11, 12   g 13, 14   h 15, 16   i 19, 20   j 30, 31

4 a $\sqrt{3}, 2, \sqrt{5}$ b $\sqrt{8}, 3, \pi$ c 3, $\sqrt{10}, \sqrt{12}$ d $\sqrt{40}, 6\cdot5, 7, \sqrt{50}$
   e $\sqrt{2}, 2\cdot1, \pi, \sqrt{12}$ f $\sqrt{26}, \sqrt{30}, 5\cdot6, 6$ g $\sqrt{60}, 7\cdot9, \sqrt{65}, 8\cdot1$ h $\sqrt{98}, 10, \sqrt{102}, 10\cdot1$
   i $\sqrt{9}, 3\cdot1, \pi, 3\cdot2$ j $4\cdot1, \sqrt{20}, 4\cdot5, \sqrt{21}$ k $\sqrt{390}, 20, \sqrt{420}, 21$ l $24, \sqrt{600}, \sqrt{610}, 25$

Prep Quiz 5:07

1 4   2 3   3 6   4 5   5 7   6 12   7 12   8 2   9 2   10 16

Exercise 5:07

1 a $\sqrt{15}$ b $\sqrt{15}$ c $\sqrt{42}$ d $\sqrt{42}$ e $\sqrt{30}$ f $\sqrt{46}$ g $\sqrt{65}$ h $\sqrt{33}$
  i $\sqrt{10}$ j $\sqrt{14}$ k $\sqrt{110}$ l $\sqrt{91}$ m $\sqrt{13}$ n $\sqrt{11}$ o $\sqrt{7}$ p $\sqrt{2}$
  q $\sqrt{19}$ r $\sqrt{19}$ s $\sqrt{6}$ t $\sqrt{2}$

2 a 16   b 9   c 1   d 100   e 5   f 8   g 15   h 73
  i 8   j 45   k 12   l 75   m 147   n 28   o 891   p 180
  q 1000   r 1620   s 1800   t 3375

3 a $2\sqrt{2}$ b $2\sqrt{5}$ c $2\sqrt{3}$ d $5\sqrt{2}$ e $2\sqrt{6}$ f $4\sqrt{2}$ g $3\sqrt{5}$ h $3\sqrt{6}$
  i $2\sqrt{7}$ j $3\sqrt{10}$ k $2\sqrt{14}$ l $3\sqrt{7}$ m $2\sqrt{11}$ n $2\sqrt{13}$ o $6\sqrt{3}$ p $2\sqrt{10}$
  q $3\sqrt{11}$ r $2\sqrt{15}$ s $4\sqrt{6}$ t $2\sqrt{19}$ u $2\sqrt{17}$ v $3\sqrt{14}$ w $10\sqrt{2}$ x $9\sqrt{2}$

4 a 4·2   b 5·2   c 2·8   d 3·5   e 5·6   f 6·9   g 7·1   h 12·7

5 a $4\sqrt{3}$ b $6\sqrt{2}$ c $10\sqrt{2}$ d $12\sqrt{2}$ e $10\sqrt{5}$ f $10\sqrt{3}$ g $30\sqrt{3}$ h $6\sqrt{14}$
  i $10\sqrt{5}$ j $12\sqrt{5}$ k $6\sqrt{6}$ l $6\sqrt{6}$ m $14\sqrt{14}$ n $18\sqrt{2}$ o $6\sqrt{11}$ p $15\sqrt{10}$
  q $60\sqrt{2}$ r $35\sqrt{2}$ s $54\sqrt{3}$ t $10\sqrt{17}$

6 a $\sqrt{12}$ b $\sqrt{18}$ c $\sqrt{20}$ d $\sqrt{54}$ e $\sqrt{32}$ f $\sqrt{75}$ g $\sqrt{63}$ h $\sqrt{50}$
  i $\sqrt{72}$ j $\sqrt{150}$ k $\sqrt{90}$ l $\sqrt{112}$ m $\sqrt{252}$ n $\sqrt{250}$ o $\sqrt{98}$ p $\sqrt{200}$
  q $\sqrt{243}$ r $\sqrt{256}$ s $\sqrt{441}$ t $\sqrt{432}$

Prep Quiz 5:08

1 $2\sqrt{3}$ 2 $2\sqrt{5}$ 3 $4\sqrt{2}$ 4 $5\sqrt{2}$ 5 5   6 3·6   7 2   8 3·5   9 11   10 7·8

Exercise 5:08

1 a $5\sqrt{2}$ b $11\sqrt{3}$ c $7\sqrt{6}$ d $3\sqrt{3}$ e $3\sqrt{5}$ f $\sqrt{2}$ g $5\sqrt{7}$ h $6\sqrt{3}$
  i $8\sqrt{6}$ j $14\sqrt{5}$ k $9\sqrt{10}$ l $6\sqrt{3}$ m $3\sqrt{2}$ n $3\sqrt{3}$ o 0

2 a $6\sqrt{5}+3\sqrt{7}$ **b** $4\sqrt{7}+2\sqrt{5}$ **c** $4\sqrt{3}+8\sqrt{5}$ **d** $2\sqrt{3}+5\sqrt{2}$ **e** $\sqrt{10}+4\sqrt{7}$ **f** $2\sqrt{3}+2\sqrt{5}$

   g $8\sqrt{11}+3\sqrt{7}$ **h** $\sqrt{2}+12\sqrt{3}$ **i** $\sqrt{5}-\sqrt{2}$ **j** $2\sqrt{7}-5\sqrt{5}$

3 a $3\sqrt{2}$ **b** $4\sqrt{3}$ **c** $5\sqrt{2}$ **d** $4\sqrt{5}$ **e** $5\sqrt{3}$ **f** $5\sqrt{6}$ **g** $3\sqrt{2}$ **h** $\sqrt{5}$

   i $\sqrt{2}$ **j** $7\sqrt{2}$ **k** $5\sqrt{5}$ **l** $2\sqrt{3}$ **m** $\sqrt{3}$ **n** $22\sqrt{2}$ **o** $23\sqrt{2}$ **p** $16\sqrt{7}$

   q $8\sqrt{5}$ **r** $-2\sqrt{3}$

4 a $4\sqrt{2}$ **b** $3\sqrt{5}$ **c** $6\sqrt{3}$ **d** $6\sqrt{7}$ **e** $3\sqrt{3}+5\sqrt{2}$ **f** $8\sqrt{5}+4\sqrt{2}$

   g $18\sqrt{2}+3\sqrt{3}$ **h** $21\sqrt{2}-5\sqrt{3}$

Exercise 5:09

1 a $\sqrt{6}$ **b** $\sqrt{35}$ **c** $\sqrt{33}$ **d** $\sqrt{10}$ **e** $\sqrt{21}$ **f** $\sqrt{70}$ **g** 4 **h** 6

   i 10 **j** $3\sqrt{2}$ **k** $5\sqrt{2}$ **l** $2\sqrt{5}$ **m** $2\sqrt{15}$ **n** $12\sqrt{10}$ **o** $14\sqrt{6}$ **p** 20

   q 18 **r** 20 **s** $24\sqrt{5}$ **t** $8\sqrt{3}$ **u** $24\sqrt{5}$ **v** $6x$ **w** $4\sqrt{x}$ **x** a^2x

2 a $\sqrt{5}$ **b** $\sqrt{3}$ **c** $\sqrt{2}$ **d** 3 **e** 2 **f** 3 **g** 5 **h** 6

   i 2 **j** $4\sqrt{2}$ **k** $3\sqrt{5}$ **l** $\sqrt{7}$ **m** $6\sqrt{2}$ **n** $3\sqrt{2}$ **o** $2\sqrt{3}$ **p** $\sqrt{5}$

   q $\sqrt{3}$ **r** $\sqrt{2}$ **s** $\sqrt{x}$ **t** $\sqrt{5}$ **u** $\sqrt{5}$

3 a $3\sqrt{2}$ **b** $8\sqrt{3}$ **c** $\sqrt{2}$ **d** 1 **e** $\sqrt{6}$ **f** $6\sqrt{2}$ **g** $\sqrt{2}$ **h** 3

   i $\dfrac{9}{4\sqrt{3}}$

4 a $\sqrt{6}+2$ **b** $5+\sqrt{10}$ **c** $14-\sqrt{14}$ **d** $5\sqrt{3}-3$ **e** $2\sqrt{6}-\sqrt{2}$ **f** $10\sqrt{5}-4\sqrt{10}$

   g $4+2\sqrt{2}$ **h** $15+6\sqrt{5}$ **i** $4\sqrt{6}-12$ **j** $3\sqrt{30}+18$ **k** $14-2\sqrt{14}$ **l** $7\sqrt{3}-9$

   m $2\sqrt{6}+8$ **n** $4\sqrt{10}-40$ **o** $60-30\sqrt{3}$ **p** $a+\sqrt{a}$ **q** $2x+3\sqrt{x}$ **r** $6y+4\sqrt{xy}$

Prep Quiz 5:10

1 $\sqrt{15}$ **2** 6 **3** 5 **4** 18 **5** $10\sqrt{2}$ **6** $8\sqrt{3}$ **7** 0 **8** $5\sqrt{7}-20$ **9** $10+\sqrt{30}$ **10** $6\sqrt{6}-6$

Exercise 5:10

1 a $5+4\sqrt{2}$ **b** $4\sqrt{3}-2$ **c** $17-7\sqrt{7}$ **d** $2+\sqrt{6}+\sqrt{10}+\sqrt{15}$

   e $\sqrt{35}-\sqrt{10}-\sqrt{14}+2$ **f** $5\sqrt{2}+\sqrt{10}+\sqrt{30}+\sqrt{6}$ **g** $5\sqrt{3}+5\sqrt{2}+\sqrt{6}+2$ **h** $4-2\sqrt{5}-2\sqrt{3}+\sqrt{15}$

   i $5\sqrt{6}-6-5\sqrt{2}+2\sqrt{3}$ **j** $4+\sqrt{2}+2\sqrt{6}+\sqrt{3}$ **k** $13+3\sqrt{15}$ **l** $10+5\sqrt{6}$

   m $7\sqrt{14}-27$ **n** $9\sqrt{15}-5$ **o** $26\sqrt{14}-45$ **p** $-21\sqrt{21}-40$

   q $114+21\sqrt{70}$ **r** $77+39\sqrt{6}$ **s** $66+14\sqrt{6}$ **t** $42-27\sqrt{7}$

   u $32\sqrt{3}-1$ **v** $x+5\sqrt{x}+6$ **w** $2m+3\sqrt{mn}+n$ **x** $6a+5\sqrt{ab}-6b$

2 a $3+2\sqrt{2}$ **b** $28-10\sqrt{3}$ **c** $9+4\sqrt{5}$ **d** $5+2\sqrt{6}$ **e** $7-2\sqrt{10}$ **f** $13+2\sqrt{30}$

   g $13+4\sqrt{3}$ **h** $34-24\sqrt{2}$ **i** $45+20\sqrt{5}$ **j** $15+4\sqrt{14}$ **k** $55+30\sqrt{2}$ **l** $52-6\sqrt{35}$

   m $83+20\sqrt{6}$ **n** $167-28\sqrt{15}$ **o** $550-100\sqrt{30}$ **p** $x+2\sqrt{xy}+y$ **q** $4m+20\sqrt{m}+25$

   r $9p-12\sqrt{pq}+4q$

3 a 1 **b** 22 **c** -39 **d** 14 **e** -1 **f** 2 **g** 2 **h** 4

   i -13 **j** 18 **k** -5 **l** 42 **m** 38 **n** -6 **o** $x-y$ **p** $4a-9b$

Prep Quiz 5:11

1 5 **2** 10 **3** 6 **4** 10 **5** 12 **6** 1 **7** 1 **8** 23 **9** 10 **10** 23

Exercise 5:11

1 a $\dfrac{\sqrt{2}}{2}$ **b** $\dfrac{\sqrt{5}}{5}$ **c** $\dfrac{2\sqrt{3}}{3}$ **d** $\dfrac{\sqrt{10}}{2}$ **e** $\dfrac{3\sqrt{2}}{2}$ **f** $2\sqrt{3}$ **g** $2\sqrt{5}$ **h** $\dfrac{2\sqrt{11}}{11}$

   i $\dfrac{\sqrt{6}}{3}$ **j** $\dfrac{\sqrt{15}}{5}$ **k** $\dfrac{\sqrt{2}}{2}$ **l** $\dfrac{\sqrt{5}}{5}$ **m** $\dfrac{\sqrt{2}}{4}$ **n** $\dfrac{2\sqrt{3}}{15}$ **o** $\dfrac{7\sqrt{5}}{10}$ **p** $\dfrac{5\sqrt{3}}{3}$

   q $\dfrac{\sqrt{2}}{2}$ **r** $\dfrac{\sqrt{10}}{10}$ **s** $\dfrac{\sqrt{6}}{3}$ **t** $\dfrac{\sqrt{35}}{3}$ **u** $\dfrac{2\sqrt{3}+3}{3}$ **v** $\dfrac{\sqrt{2}+\sqrt{10}}{2}$ **w** $\dfrac{7+\sqrt{21}}{14}$ **x** $\dfrac{2-\sqrt{2}}{10}$

2 a $0.894, \dfrac{2\sqrt{5}}{5}$ **b** $1.13, \dfrac{3\sqrt{7}}{7}$ **c** $0.612, \dfrac{\sqrt{6}}{4}$ **d** $0.394, \dfrac{\sqrt{35}}{15}$

3 a $\dfrac{3\sqrt{2}+2\sqrt{3}}{6}$ **b** $\dfrac{2\sqrt{5}-5\sqrt{2}}{10}$ **c** $\dfrac{5\sqrt{6}+6\sqrt{5}}{30}$ **d** $\dfrac{\sqrt{10}-3\sqrt{5}}{5}$ **e** $\dfrac{13\sqrt{2}}{4}$ **f** $\dfrac{2\sqrt{3}-\sqrt{2}}{6}$

g $\dfrac{2\sqrt{2}+5\sqrt{10}}{10}$ **h** $\dfrac{3\sqrt{10}+2\sqrt{15}}{6}$ **i** $\dfrac{2\sqrt{10}-5\sqrt{6}}{10}$

Challenge 5:11   Rationalising binomial denominators

1 a $\dfrac{1-\sqrt{2}}{-1}=\sqrt{2}-1$ **b** $\dfrac{\sqrt{3}+1}{2}$ **c** $\dfrac{\sqrt{7}+\sqrt{5}}{2}$ **d** $\dfrac{\sqrt{10}-\sqrt{2}}{8}$ **e** $\dfrac{3\sqrt{3}-6}{-1}=-3\sqrt{3}+6$

f $\dfrac{25+5\sqrt{2}}{23}$ **g** $\dfrac{10\sqrt{5}+10\sqrt{2}}{3}$ **h** $3\sqrt{7}+3\sqrt{3}$ **i** $\dfrac{2\sqrt{3}-5}{-13}$ **j** $\dfrac{10+4\sqrt{2}}{17}$

k $\dfrac{3\sqrt{2}-2\sqrt{3}}{2}$ **l** $\dfrac{4\sqrt{3}+3\sqrt{2}}{30}$ **m** $\dfrac{27+10\sqrt{2}}{23}$ **n** $\dfrac{19+8\sqrt{3}}{13}$ **o** $4-\sqrt{15}$

p $\dfrac{7-2\sqrt{6}}{5}$

2 a 4 **b** $\dfrac{2\sqrt{5}+\sqrt{3}-\sqrt{7}}{2}$ **c** $\dfrac{105+\sqrt{3}}{66}$

Diagnostic Test 5   Indices and surds

1 a 3^4 **b** 5^2 **c** m^3
2 a 9 **b** 16 **c** 1000
3 a 3^7 **b** x^5 **c** $6m^3n^5$ **4 a** x^5 **b** $5a^3$ **c** $2a^2b$
5 a a^8 **b** x^{12} **c** $8a^{12}$ **6 a** 1 **b** 5 **c** 3
7 a $\frac{1}{9}$ **b** $\frac{1}{5}$ **c** $\frac{27}{8}$ or $3\frac{3}{8}$ **8 a** x^4 **b** $\dfrac{2}{x^2}$ **c** $\dfrac{9}{x^2}$
9 a 5 **b** 3 **c** 2 **10 a** $12x$ **b** $7m^3$ **c** $2x$
11 a 2.43×10^2 **b** 6.7×10^4 **c** 9.38×10^7
12 a 130 **b** 243.1 **c** $46\,300\,000$
13 a 4.3×10^{-2} **b** 5.97×10^{-5} **c** 4×10^{-3}
14 a 0.029 **b** $0.000\,093\,8$ **c** $0.001\,004$
15 a 9.61×10^{16} **b** 4.64×10^7 **c** 1.4×10^{12} **d** 1.2×10^{-3}
16 a irrational **b** rational **c** irrational **d** rational
17 a 2.236 **b** 3.606 **c** 4.583 **d** 6.856 **18 a** $2\sqrt{5}$ **b** $3\sqrt{3}$ **c** $6\sqrt{2}$ **d** $10\sqrt{3}$
19 a $\sqrt{20}$ **b** $\sqrt{18}$ **c** $\sqrt{175}$ **d** $\sqrt{80}$ **20 a** $6\sqrt{3}$ **b** $5\sqrt{5}$ **c** $\sqrt{2}$ **d** $5\sqrt{3}$
21 a $\sqrt{30}$ **b** 6 **c** $2\sqrt{15}$ **d** 24 **22 a** $\sqrt{6}$ **b** 2 **c** 5 **d** $5\sqrt{2}$
23 a $11+5\sqrt{5}$ **b** $-5\sqrt{6}$ **c** $10+2\sqrt{21}$ **d** 22 **24 a** $\dfrac{3\sqrt{2}}{2}$ **b** $\sqrt{5}$ **c** $\dfrac{3+\sqrt{3}}{6}$ **d** $\dfrac{5\sqrt{2}-2}{10}$

5A Revision Assignment

1 a a^5 **b** $12a^5$ **c** a^3b^2 **d** $12a^3b^3$ **e** 3^5 **f** a^3 **g** $7m$ **h** $4y^4$ **i** $2a^2b$ **j** 4^4
k 3^8 **l** x^6 **m** a^{11} **n** m **o** $2x$ **p** $\dfrac{a^2}{2}$

2 a 1 **b** 6 **c** $125x^9$ **d** $1000a^6$ **e** $8x$

3 a 2.16×10^4 **b** 1.25×10^2 **c** 7.0×10^{-5} **d** 1.56×10^{-4}
4 a $810\,000$ **b** 1267 **c** 0.035 **d** $0.000\,106$
5 a 1024 **b** $531\,441$ **c** $145\,800\,000$ **d** $351\,232$
6 a 7 **b** 5 **c** 8 **7 a** $3^7=2187$ **b** $10^3=1000$ **c** $2^8=256$
8 a m^3 **b** $72a^{17}$ **c** 2 **9 a** 8 **b** 4 **c** 27 **d** $100\,000$
10 a $20x$ **b** $2x^{-2}$ or $\dfrac{2}{x^2}$ **c** $6m^2n^3$

11 a $10\sqrt{5}$ **b** $5\sqrt{7}$ **c** 0 **d** $6\sqrt{14}$ **e** 20 **f** 6 **g** $3+3\sqrt{5}$
h $9+2\sqrt{14}$ **i** $5+\sqrt{10}+2\sqrt{3}+\sqrt{30}$ **j** $\sqrt{mn}$ **k** $m+2\sqrt{mn}+\sqrt{n}$ **l** $m-n$

12 a $\dfrac{\sqrt{5}}{2}$ **b** $\dfrac{\sqrt{6}}{3}$ **c** $\dfrac{2\sqrt{3}+3\sqrt{2}}{6}$ **d** $\dfrac{9\sqrt{2}-4\sqrt{5}}{6\sqrt{10}}$

13 a $\dfrac{2\sqrt{5}+2}{4}$ **b** $\dfrac{\sqrt{7}-\sqrt{2}}{5}$ **c** $9-4\sqrt{5}$ **d** $-5-2\sqrt{6}$

14 a $\dfrac{2\sqrt{3}-3}{3}$ **b** $\dfrac{21-9\sqrt{5}}{2}$ **c** $\dfrac{84-36\sqrt{3}+21\sqrt{7}-9\sqrt{21}}{22}$

5B Working Mathematically

1 a *hectare*   **b** *cross-section*   **c** *coordinates*   **d** *tally*
    e *picture* graph   **f** *column* graph   **g** *line* graph   **h** *sector* (or *pie*) graph
    i *bar* graph   **j** *scatter* diagram
2   (1) *parallel* lines   (2) *perpendicular* lines   (3) *vertical, horizontal*   (4) *concurrent* lines
    (5) *angle ABC* or *CBA*   (6) *acute* angle   (7) *right* angle   (8) *obtuse* angle
    (9) *straight* angle   (10) *reflex* angle   (11) *revolution*   (12) *adjacent* angles
3 a   3, 6   **b i** 20   **ii** 35   **iii** 405   **4** $31.63
5 a   60 dB   **b**   120 dB   **c** 10^6 or 1 000 000   **d** 10^5 or 100 000
    e i 4 times   **ii** 64 times   **iii** 32 times

Chapter 6:   Equations, Inequations and Formulae

Exercise 6:01

1 a 1042   **b** 1·9   **c** 8·8   **d** 8   **e** 4·9   **f** −13   **g** −6   **h** −2
    i −3   **j** 6   **k** −0·7   **l** 4·7   **m** −6   **n** 3·4   **o** 0·3   **p** 5
    q 0·1   **r** 5   **s** 36   **t** −14   **u** 3·52
2 a 5   **b** 7   **c** 15   **d** 24   **e** 3   **f** 7   **g** 1   **h** −3
    i −3   **j** −3   **k** −4   **l** 8
3 a $3\frac{2}{3}$ **b** $7\frac{3}{4}$ **c** $89\frac{4}{9}$ **d** $23\frac{2}{3}$ **e** 11   **f** $5\frac{5}{11}$ **g** $6\frac{2}{3}$ **h** 6
    i 3   **j** $4\frac{1}{2}$ **k** $-3\frac{2}{3}$ **l** $1\frac{1}{5}$ **m** $-1\frac{3}{7}$ **n** $-5\frac{2}{3}$ **o** $4\frac{1}{6}$ **p** −5
    q 1·2   **r** 6·5   **s** 1·5   **t** 3
4 a 1   **b** −1   **c** −1   **d** 2   **e** 4   **f** −3   **g** −5   **h** 6
    i 9   **j** 5   **k** −2   **l** −7   **m** −8   **n** −3   **o** 0   **p** 1
    q 2   **r** 2   **s** 4   **t** 1   **u** 3   **v** −1   **w** 25   **x** 3
5 a Yes   **b** No   **c** Yes   **d** Yes   **e** Yes   **f** No   **g** Yes   **h** Yes
    i Yes   **j** Yes   **k** No   **l** No
6 a $a=-2$ **b** $m=2\frac{1}{3}$ **c** $x=1\frac{2}{5}$ **d** $y=-\frac{1}{5}$ **e** $t=-5$ **f** $x=-5$ **g** $x=\frac{10}{11}$ **h** $d=1$
    i $t=2\frac{1}{2}$ **j** $m=2\frac{2}{5}$ **k** $x=1\frac{1}{7}$ **l** $y=1\frac{4}{5}$ **m** $a=-6\frac{1}{2}$ **n** $b=-1\frac{1}{7}$ **o** $s=-2$ **p** $x=-13$
    q $g=3$ **r** $x=-8$ **s** $x=-6$ **t** $y=0$ **u** $d=1$

Prep Quiz 6:02

1 $7x+28$ **2** $2a-6$ **3** $20a+45$ **4** $12p-42$ **5** $12-3x$ **6** −5   **7** 6   **8** −9   **9** $\frac{1}{2}$ **10** −7

Exercise 6:02

1 a $x=4$ **b** $a=4$ **c** $y=6$ **d** $x=3$ **e** $m=-3$ **f** $b=-15$ **g** $a=2$ **h** $x=10$
    i $x=7$ **j** $x=1$
2 a $x=17$ **b** $a=-2$ **c** $y=3$ **d** $t=5$ **e** $x=32$ **f** $x=-2\frac{1}{3}$ **g** $x=16\frac{2}{3}$ **h** $m=-1\frac{4}{7}$
    i $a=-2$ **j** $t=\frac{1}{3}$ **k** $a=1\frac{1}{8}$ **l** $y=5$ **m** $a=\frac{1}{11}$ **n** $n=10$ **o** $y=3$ **p** $x=-1\frac{3}{5}$
    q $t=-3\frac{1}{9}$ **r** $a=-1$
3 a 1   **b** 1   **c** 1   **d** 2   **e** 1   **f** 2   **g** 2   **h** 2   **i** 2
4 a $x=-8$ **b** $a=-6$ **c** $t=2$ **d** $y=2$ **e** $b=0$ **f** $q=1\frac{1}{3}$ **g** $w=2\frac{1}{2}$ **h** $x=1\frac{1}{2}$
    i $x=2\frac{1}{2}$ **j** $4\frac{7}{8}$
5 a 2   **b** 3   **c** 2   **d** 2   **e** 1   **f** 2

Exercise 6:03

1 a $m=12$ **b** $a=-15$ **c** $t=36$ **d** $x=-6$ **e** $p=15$ **f** $m=-8\frac{2}{5}$ **g** $y=11\frac{1}{3}$ **h** $b=3$
    i $x=-\frac{1}{3}$ **j** $q=8$
2 a Incorrect   **b** Correct   **c** Correct   **d** Correct   **e** Incorrect   **f** Incorrect

3 a B **b** A **c** correct

4 a $m = 8$ **b** $x = \frac{7}{11}$ **c** $q = 9$ **d** $a = 2$ **e** $p = 4$ **f** $t = \frac{1}{3}$ **g** $y = 13$ **h** $x = 3$

  i $d = -2\frac{1}{2}$ **j** $y = \frac{1}{3}$

Prep Quiz 6:04

1 2, 4, 6 **2** 5, 10, 15 **3** 6 **4** 60 **5** $3x$ **6** a **7** $15x$ **8** $2x + 1$ **9** $4x - 2$ **10** $6x - 3$

Exercise 6:04

1 a 6 **b** 12 **c** 48 **d** 12 **e** 20 **f** 30 **g** 8 **h** 15 **i** 6 **j** 30

  k 12 **l** 5 **m** 24 **n** 20 **o** 20 **p** 8 **q** 6 **r** 9

2 a $7\frac{6}{7}$ **b** $14\frac{3}{7}$ **c** $14\frac{4}{7}$ **d** $3\frac{1}{8}$ **e** $\frac{7}{8}$ **f** $\frac{4}{11}$ **g** -62 **h** $-\frac{1}{13}$ **i** $-5\frac{4}{5}$

Challenge 6:04 Equations with pronumerals in the denominator

1 a 2 **b** $\frac{1}{6}$ **c** $\frac{3}{8}$ **d** $\frac{3}{11}$ **e** $\frac{4}{21}$ **f** -1 **g** $\frac{1}{7}$ **h** $3\frac{1}{4}$ **i** $-4\frac{2}{3}$ **j** -1

  k $-\frac{7}{13}$ **l** $\frac{16}{31}$

2 a -4 **b** 2 **c** 3 **d** 8 **e** 3 **f** 4 **g** $1\frac{1}{6}$ **h** $-4\frac{1}{5}$ **i** $1\frac{2}{3}$ **j** $1\frac{1}{24}$

  k $-\frac{4}{7}$ **l** $\frac{3}{4}$

Prep Quiz 6:05

1 7 **2** $x + 3$ **3** $x + y$ **4** 12 **5** $3x$ **6** xy **7** $\$(50 - x)$ **8** $\$5x$ **9** xy **10** $x + 5$ years

Exercise 6:05

1 a $x + 5 = 22$; 17 **b** $x - 3 = 10$; 13 **c** $8x = 32$; 4 **d** $\frac{x}{8} = 7$; 56 **e** $2x + 6 = 14$; 4 **f** $3x + 5 = 20$; 5

  g $5x - 8 = 22$; 6 **h** $4(x + 5) = 56$; 9 **i** $\frac{x}{2} - 5 = 3$; 16

2 a $2x + 3 = 33$; 15 **b** $4x - 3 = 25$; 7 **c** $2(x + 3) = 22$; 8 **d** $\frac{x}{4} - 7 = 1$; 32 **e** $\frac{x+4}{3} = 8$; 20

3 a 11 **b** 7 **c** 17 **d** 8

4 a 13 yrs, 39 yrs **b** $480, $80 **c** Mina $25, Jalena $18 **d** Zarko $165, Alex $335 **e** 40 yrs

5 a 13 **b** 19 cm by 13 cm **c** 4 kg **d** 24 km

6 a $2 **b** They meet at 2:48 pm when X has travelled 24 km and Y has travelled 16 km.

  c The son is 28 yrs old and his father is 56 yrs old. **d** 3600 litres

7 a Alejandro is 20 yrs old and Franco is 45 yrs old. **b** 16 five-cent coins, 34 ten-cent coins

  c 12 **d** small tank 900 L; large tank 1200 L **e** 50 km

8 a 200 L/min, 400 L/min **b** 25 km **c** 120 km/h **d** $4800 **e** 9·6 cm by 2·4 cm and 3·2 cm by 0·8 cm

Exercise 6:06

1 a $x < 2$ **b** $y \geqslant -\frac{2}{3}$ **c** $a > 3$ **d** $t \leqslant 98$ **e** $q < -2$ **f** $n < 6\frac{1}{2}$ or $6\frac{1}{2} > n$ **g** $m \geqslant 4$

  h $x < 19$ **i** $y > 25$ **j** $q \geqslant 21$

2 a $a < 2\frac{1}{2}$ **b** $x \leqslant -3$ **c** $b < -2$ **d** $y \geqslant -2$ **e** $x \leqslant 22$ **f** $m < 11$ **g** $t \leqslant -5$ **h** $n > -6$

  i $x \geqslant 8$ **j** $x \geqslant -3$

3 a $x < 13$ **b** $a \leqslant -2$ **c** $t > 21$ **d** $w \geqslant -6$ **e** $w < -9$ **f** $d \leqslant 3$ **g** $q \leqslant 10$ **h** $b < 6$

  i $z > 5$ **j** $y > -16$ **k** $x \leqslant 5$ **l** $m \leqslant 7\frac{1}{2}$

4 a $m > 7$

  b $p \leqslant 7$

  c $m < 2$

  d $y \geqslant -8\frac{2}{5}$

  e $x < 3\frac{3}{4}$

  f $x > -2$

  g $x < 15$

  h $y > 12$

  i $m \geqslant 4$

  j $x < -50$

  k $x < 6$

  l $x > -12$

5 a $3m > -24$
$m > -8$

−8

b $4x < -16$
$x < -4$

−4

c $5p \geqslant -20$
$p \geqslant -4$

−4

d $6x > 12$
$x > 2$

2

e $6x < -15$
$x < -2\frac{1}{2}$

$2\frac{1}{2}$

f $3x \geqslant 10$
$x \geqslant 3\frac{1}{3}$

$3\frac{1}{3}$

g $x < -4$

−4

h $x > -3$

−3

i $x \geqslant -5$

−5

j $x < -6$

−6

k $x < -5$

5

l $x \leqslant -8$

−8

m $x > -2$

−2

n $x < -6$

−6

o $x < -12$

−12

6 a $2x > 6$
$x > 3$

b $4m < 16$
$m < 4$

c $2p \geqslant 6$
$p \geqslant 3$

d $3p \leqslant -3$
$p \leqslant -1$

e $5p \geqslant 6$
$p \geqslant 1\frac{1}{5}$

f $2x < -7$
$x < -3\frac{1}{2}$

g $3x \leqslant 12$
$x \leqslant 4$

h $5p \geqslant 10$
$p \geqslant 2$

i $4y < 5$
$y < 1\frac{1}{4}$

j $15 > 5x$
$x < 3$

k $4 < 2x$
$x > 2$

l $12 \geqslant 8x$
$x \leqslant 1\frac{1}{2}$

m $2x + 6 < 14$
$2x < 8$
$x < 4$

n $3m + 6 > 15$
$3m > 9$
$m > 3$

o $6x - 15 \leqslant 6$
$6x \leqslant 21$
$x \leqslant 3\frac{1}{2}$

p $4x - 12 \geqslant 5$
$4x \geqslant 17$
$x \geqslant 4\frac{1}{4}$

q $4 < 4m - 6$
$10 < 4m$
$m > 2\frac{1}{2}$

r $10p - 8 > 22$
$10p > 30$
$p > 3$

7 a $-3m > 6$
$3m < -6$
$m < -2$

b $-2y < 4$
$2y > -4$
$y > -2$

c $6 \leqslant -4x$
$-4x \geqslant 6$
$4x \leqslant -6$
$x \leqslant -1\frac{1}{2}$

d $-x \leqslant 2$
$x \geqslant -2$

e $-m \geqslant -6$
$m \leqslant 6$

f $-2m \leqslant -16$
$m \geqslant 8$

g $-4p < -2$
$p > \frac{1}{2}$

h $2 - 2x < 6$
$-2x < 4$
$x > -2$

i $12 - 3y > 15$
$-3y > 3$
$y < -1$

j $12 - 6x \geqslant 18$
$-6x \geqslant 6$
$x \leqslant -1$

k $6 - 10y \leqslant -4$
$-10y \leqslant -10$
$y \geqslant 1$

l $6 - 4p > 8$
$-4p > 2$
$p < -\frac{1}{2}$

m $4m \geqslant 3 - 6x$
$1 \geqslant -6x$
$-6x \leqslant 1$
$x \geqslant -\frac{1}{6}$

n $10 - 4a \leqslant -5$
$-4a \leqslant -15$
$a \geqslant 3\frac{3}{4}$

o $3 - 6x > 2$
$-6x > -1$
$x < \frac{1}{6}$

8 a $4x > 12$
$x > 3$

b $2x < 11$
$x < 5\frac{1}{2}$

c $-m \geqslant -10$
$m \leqslant 10$

d $a \leqslant 2$

e $-3b \geqslant 9$
$b \leqslant -3$

f $3m + 12 < 2m + 12$
$m < 0$

g $\frac{x}{2} < 5$
$x < 10$

h $\frac{p}{3} > 5$
$p > 15$

i $\frac{3x}{4} > 6$
$3x > 24$
$x > 8$

j $-\frac{2y}{3} < 1$
$2y > -3$
$y > -\frac{3}{2}$

k $p - 1 < 8$
$p < 9$

l $2p + 3 > 14$
$2p > 11$
$p > 5\frac{1}{2}$

m $4 - x > 3$
$-x > -1$
$x < 1$

n $\frac{3x + 2x}{6} > 5$
$5x > 30$
$x > 6$

o $\frac{a + 2a}{4} < 6$
$3a < 24$
$a < 8$

p $9b - 2b < 15$
$7b < 15$
$b < 2\frac{1}{7}$

q $\frac{3x - 4x}{6} < 3$
$-x < 18$
$x > -18$

r $y - 6y > 8$
$-5y > 8$
$y < -1\frac{3}{5}$

s $-\frac{3a}{2} > -4$
$3a < 8$
$a < 2\frac{2}{3}$

t $1 - 2x < 18$
$-2x < 17$
$x > -8\frac{1}{2}$

u $3(1 - 3x) < 8(1 - x)$
$3 - 9x < 8 - 8x$
$-x < 5$
$x > -5$

9 a $3x < 8; x < 2\frac{2}{3}$

b $2x - 4 > 9; x > 6\frac{1}{2}$

c $100 - 4x < 25; x > 18\frac{3}{4}$

d $\frac{94 + 2x}{12} > 16 ; x > 49$

e $25x - 540 > 2000; x > 101\frac{3}{5}$

Exercise 6:07

1 a $y = 9$
b $T = 217$
c $A = 2518$
d $T = -177\,147$
e $T = 57 \cdot 6$
f $S = 4032$
g $x = 3$
h $m = \frac{1}{2}$

2 a $s = 9$
b $14 \cdot 7 \text{ cm}^2$

3 a $184 \cdot 4$ (to 1 dec. pl.)
b $27 \cdot 9$ (to 1 dec. pl.)
c $M = 539, N = 485$
d $40\,117$

Exercise 6:08

1 **a** $v = 31$ **b** $a = -3$ **c** $v = 18$ **d** $a = -2$ **e** $a = \frac{1}{2}$ **f** $t = 36$

2 **a** $h = 12$ **b** $h = 6\frac{2}{5}$ **c** $a = 9$ **d** $a = 2\frac{2}{5}$ **e** $b = 7$ **f** $b = 5$

3 **a** $m = 25$ **b** $m = 11\frac{1}{5}$ **c** $r = 45$ **d** $r = 14.7$ **e** $v = 7$ **f** $v = 6$

4 **a** $R = 4\frac{2}{7}$ **b** $g = 10$ **c** $S = 16$ **d** $T = 13\frac{1}{3}$ **e** $F = 35$

5 **a** $B = \frac{15}{2} = 7\frac{1}{2}$ **b** $x_2 = 3$ **c** $x = 8$ **d** $m = 8$ **e** $P = 3000$

6 **a** $A = -10$ **b** $X = 3$ **c** $n = 16$ **d** $H = 2.67$ **e** $x = -23$

Prep Quiz 6:09

1 25 **2** a **3** 27 **4** m **5** 5 **6** a **7** 5 **8** m **9** $a = 1$ **10** $x = 8\frac{1}{3}$

Exercise 6:09

1 **a** $x = p - m$ **b** $x = m - np$ **c** $x = pq - n$ **d** $x = \dfrac{b}{a}$ **e** $x = \dfrac{y}{3}$ **f** $x = \dfrac{b+c}{a^2}$

g $x = \dfrac{b - 2d}{a}$ **h** $x = \dfrac{b+c}{a}$ **i** $x = \dfrac{c - 3b}{a}$ **j** $x = ay$ **k** $x = \dfrac{a}{y}$ **l** $x = by$

m $x = \dfrac{25}{a}$ **n** $x = \dfrac{bc}{a}$ **o** $x = \dfrac{pL}{2}$

2 **a** $x = \dfrac{a - 2y}{2}$ **b** $x = \dfrac{p - 5t}{5}$ **c** $x = \dfrac{y + 21}{3}$ **d** $x = \dfrac{p + qr}{q}$ **e** $x = \dfrac{6a - b}{6}$ **f** $x = \dfrac{tv - w}{t}$

g $x = \dfrac{R - 4r}{2r}$ **h** $x = \dfrac{p + 5qy}{5q}$ **i** $x = \dfrac{\pi r^2 - A}{\pi r}$

3 **a** $y = A - x$ **b** $L = \dfrac{P - 2B}{2}$ **c** $d = \dfrac{C}{\pi}$ **d** $u = v - at$ **e** $a = \dfrac{V - u}{t}$ **f** $m = \dfrac{E}{c^2}$

g $D = ST$ **h** $V = RI$ **i** $P = \dfrac{100I}{RT}$ **j** $R = \dfrac{P}{I^2}$ **k** $s = \dfrac{v^2 - u^2}{2a}$ **l** $a = \dfrac{F - p}{c}$

m $n = \dfrac{P - ma}{a}$ **n** $p = \dfrac{x - 2aq}{2a}$ **o** $m = \dfrac{2K}{v^2}$ **p** $u = \dfrac{mv - P}{m}$ **q** $H = \dfrac{3V}{A}$ **r** $h = \dfrac{3V}{\pi r^2}$

s $h = \dfrac{S - \pi r^2}{\pi r}$ **t** $h = \dfrac{E - \frac{1}{2}mv^2}{mg}$ **u** $k = \dfrac{2ab - P}{2a}$ **v** $a = 2A - b$ **w** $b = \dfrac{2A - ha}{h}$ **x** $r = \dfrac{q_1 q_2}{F}$

y $d = \dfrac{T - a}{n - 1}$ **z** $a = \dfrac{S(r - 1)}{r^n - 1}$

Prep Quiz 6:10

1 15 **2** 6 **3** 13 **4** ± 3 **5** 25 **6** 2 or -8 **7** 7 **8** $3(x + 4)$ **9** $x(x - 2)$ **10** $5a(a + 2b)$

Exercise 6:10

1 **a** $x = \pm\sqrt{\dfrac{n}{m}}$ **b** $x = \pm\sqrt{\dfrac{a}{b}}$ **c** $x = \pm\sqrt{a + b}$ **d** $x = \pm\sqrt{k - h}$ **e** $x = \pm\sqrt{ay}$ **f** $x = \pm\sqrt{\dfrac{3m}{n}}$

g $x = \pm\sqrt{L + y^2}$ **h** $x = \pm\sqrt{\dfrac{B}{A}}$

2 **a** $a = \dfrac{c^2}{b}$ **b** $a = \dfrac{u^2}{3}$ **c** $a = c^2 + b$ **d** $a = (c + b)^2$ **e** $a = \left(\dfrac{P - L}{M}\right)^2$

f $a = \left(\dfrac{M - L}{N}\right)^2$ **g** $a = \dfrac{L^2 + 1}{3}$ **h** $a = \dfrac{b - P^2}{2}$

3 **a** $N = \dfrac{2a}{3}$ **b** $N = \dfrac{2L - 2a}{3}$ **c** $N = \dfrac{2x + 6}{3}$ **d** $N = \dfrac{6L - 2M}{3}$ **e** $N = 3x - a$

f $N = \dfrac{6x + 1 - 2M}{3}$ **g** $N = \dfrac{3m - u}{4}$ **h** $N = \dfrac{a^2 + b^2 + bL}{a}$

4 **a** $x = \dfrac{b - a}{2}$ **b** $x = \dfrac{q}{a - p}$ **c** $x = \dfrac{a - b}{a - 1}$ **d** $x = \dfrac{n - m}{m - n}$ or -1 **e** $x = \pm\sqrt{\dfrac{2}{p - q}}$

f $x = \dfrac{L}{A + B + 1}$ **g** $x = \dfrac{15a}{8}$ **h** $x = \dfrac{2a}{1 - a}$ **i** $x = \dfrac{5y}{y - 1}$ **j** $x = \dfrac{3 - m}{m - 1}$

k $x = \dfrac{a - A}{A - b}$ **l** $x = \dfrac{Ba + a}{B - 1}$

5

	A	**B**	**C**
a	$B = \dfrac{A}{L}$	$X = A + Y$	$t = \dfrac{V - u}{a}$
b	$V = \dfrac{M}{D}$	$S = DT$	$I = \pm\sqrt{\dfrac{P}{R}}$
c	$h = \dfrac{3V}{A}$	$r = \pm\sqrt{\dfrac{3V}{\pi h}}$	$r = \pm\sqrt{\dfrac{S}{4\pi}}$
d	$b = 2M - a$	$y = \dfrac{2A - xh}{h}$	$s = \dfrac{v^2 - u^2}{2a}$
e	$a = \dfrac{x^2 + y^2}{y}$	$h = \dfrac{S}{2\pi r} - r$	$d = \dfrac{2T - 2an}{n(n - 1)}$
f	$c = \dfrac{a^2}{b}$	$X = \dfrac{Y^2}{a^2}$	$a = \dfrac{X^2 + 4b}{4}$
g	$Y = aX^2$	$x = \dfrac{bR^2}{a}$	$b = m^2n - a$
h	$l = \dfrac{gT^2}{4\pi^2}$	$u = \dfrac{4x^2t}{A^2}$	$s = \dfrac{v^2 - u^2}{2a}$
i	$a = \dfrac{6y - 3b}{2}$	$X = \dfrac{12Z - 4Y}{3}$	$c = b - 5A$
j	$A = 2x - 3y$	$N = \dfrac{6L + 1}{5}$	$X = \dfrac{a^2}{a - b}$
k	$k = \dfrac{h}{1 - 2h}$	$a = \dfrac{2y}{1 - y}$	$x = \dfrac{3z}{z - 1}$

Exercise 6:11

1 a 17.64 m^2 **b** 1250 cm^2 **2 a** $A = \pi r^2$ **b** 7 cm
3 a 149 **b** 40   **4** 12 cm   **5 a** 6·14 m **b** 2·34 m
6 1·9 cm   **7** $P = 2x + D\pi$; **a** 76·39 m (correct to 2 decimal places)   **b** 63·66 m (correct to 2 decimal places)
8 a 7·08 m/s **b** 4·8 m/s² **c** 6·5 s   **9 a** 2·5 kg **b** 2·7 m/s
10 60 cm   **11 a** $4609 **b** $4000 **c** 14%
12 a $A = \pi(R^2 - r^2)$ **b** 96·8 cm² **c** 3·6 cm **d** 6·3 cm
13 a $V = \pi r^2 h + \frac{2}{3}\pi r^3$ or $V = \pi r^2(h + \frac{2}{3}r)$ **b** 145 m³ **c** 6·88 m
14 a 5.6×10^{-18} (correct to 2 significant figures) **b** 6.2×10^{-22} m
15 3.3×10^{-8} coulombs (correct to 2 significant figures)

Diagnostic Test 6   Equations, inequations and formulae

1 a $p = 7$ **b** $m = 12$ **c** $m = -10$ **2 a** $x = -4$ **b** $a = 3$ **c** $b = -5$
3 a $x = 2$ **b** $a = 9$ **c** $x = 2.6$ **4 a** $x = -18$ **b** $a = 1$ **c** $m = -14$
5 a $y = 12$ **b** $m = 12$ **c** $p = 18$ **d** $m = 10$ **6 a** $m = 5$ **b** $m = 9$ **c** $p = 7$ **d** $x = 6\frac{2}{3}$
7 a $m = \dfrac{5}{2}$ **b** $x = -2$ **c** $n = 1$ **d** $a = \dfrac{11}{8}$ **8 a** $a = 12$ **b** $m = 24$ **c** $x = -60$ **d** $y = \dfrac{19}{6}$
9 a $2a + 7 = 10$ **b** $\dfrac{a}{3} - 4 = 4$ **c** $3(a + 6) = 32$
10 a $x + (x + 5) = 57$; 26, 31   **b** $3x + x + 3x + x = 48$; 6, 18   **c** $3x + 10 = 2(x + 10)$; 10, 30

11 a   [number line 1 to 5, open circle at 3, arrow right]
b   [number line −3 to 1, closed circle at −1, arrow left]
c   [number line −2 to 2, closed circle at 0, arrow left]
d   [number line 3 to 7, open circle at 5, arrow right]

12 a $x \geqslant \frac{1}{2}$ **b** $x < 9\frac{1}{2}$ **c** $x > 5$ **13 a** $x < -2$ **b** $x < -63$ **c** $a < \frac{1}{3}$
14 a 36·2 **b** 3·7268 **c** 33·54   **15 a** 8 **b** 15·075 **c** 3·5
16 a $a = \dfrac{x + 2b}{3}$ **b** $a = \dfrac{V^2 - u^2}{2s}$ **c** $a = \dfrac{Ah}{D} - b$
17 a $y = \pm\sqrt{\dfrac{x}{a}}$ **b** $y = \dfrac{A^2B}{T^2}$ **c** $y = \dfrac{P}{1 - P}$

6A Revision Assignment

1 a $m = 3$ **b** $y = -1$ **c** $m = 3$ **d** $n = -2$ **e** $x = \frac{11}{2}$ **f** $x = \frac{-8}{5}$ **g** $x = -11$ **h** $x = \frac{1}{5}$
   i $x = 1$

2 a $x = -1$ **b** $a = 6$ **c** $m = 1\frac{1}{2}$ **d** $x = -6$ **e** $n = 11$ **f** $x = 0$ **g** $a = \frac{2}{11}$ **h** $n = \frac{-23}{11}$
   i $m = -3$ **j** $x = -9$

3 a $x = 8$ **b** $m = 15$ **c** $x = 9$ **d** $a = 17$ **e** $y = 8$ **f** $p = 3$ **g** $m = -3$ **h** $m = -\frac{1}{3}$
   i $n = \frac{-16}{5}$ **j** $x = -13$ **k** $a = \frac{-70}{3}$ **l** $q = \frac{-6}{29}$

4 a $m = -2$,
   b $x < 4$,
   c $n > \frac{2}{5}$,
   d $x \le \frac{3}{2}$,
   e $y < \frac{3}{2}$,
   f $n \le \frac{11}{3}$,
   g $x < -4$,
   h $x \le -9$,
   i $a \ge \frac{3}{2}$,

5 a $3x + 7 = 15, x = \frac{8}{3}$ **b** $5(x - 9) = 30, x = 15$ **c** $8x + 10 = 12x - 7, x = \frac{17}{4}$
   d $x + 4 = 2[(x - 12) + 4]$, ages are 20 and 8   **e** $12 + x = \frac{3}{2}[2 + x], x = 18$

6 a 66 **b** 8 **c** $4 \cdot 1$ **7 a** $\frac{1}{3}$ **b** $\frac{-30}{73}$ **c** $\frac{2}{3}$

8 a $P = \frac{100A}{RT}$ **b** $P = \pm\sqrt{\frac{V}{R}}$ **c** $P = \frac{RT^2}{3}$ **d** $P = \frac{Q}{QX + 1}$

9 a $x = \frac{3}{5}$ **b** $x = 1\frac{2}{3}$ **c** $x = -1\frac{1}{3}$ **d** $x = -\frac{2}{15}$ **e** $x = \frac{13}{22}$ **f** $p = \frac{5}{8}$

6B Working Mathematically

1 a reflection   **b** translation   **c** rotation   **d** tessellation   **e** picture   **f** column   **g** line
   h pie   **i** bar   **j** scatter diagram

2 a (1) $15x^2$ (2) $15x^3$ (3) $-80x^2$ (4) $60x^5$ (5) $14x^4$
   (6) $9x^3$ (7) $-30x^3$ (8) $-48x^4$ (9) $-15x^6$ (10) $21x^6$
   (11) $4x^4$ (12) $-7x^{11}$

b (1) $6x + 3$ (2) $-4x - 2$ (3) $30x + 10$ (4) $-6x - 6$ (5) $-24x - 64$
   (6) $30x + 10$ (7) $-6x - 48$ (8) $60x + 24$ (9) $14x + 28$ (10) $-25x - 20$
   (11) $-22x - 77$ (12) $8x + 12$

c (1) $25m^4$ (2) $4m^6$ (3) $64m^{10}$ (4) $36m^4$ (5) m^4
   (6) $81m^6$ (7) $4m^{12}$ (8) $9m^6$ (9) m^{14} (10) $64m^8$
   (11) $16m^2$ (12) $49m^4$

d (1) $-15x^2 + 40x$ (2) $3x^2 - 3x$ (3) $10x^2 - 50x$ (4) $-30x^2 - 60x$ (5) $21x^2 + 7x$
   (6) $9x^2 + 63x$ (7) $-12x + 30x$ (8) $-12x^2 + 120x$ (9) $10x^2 - 20x$ (10) $-3x^2 - 21x$
   (11) $-4x^2 + 24x$ (12) $-14x^2 - 21x$

3 a 10 minutes   **b** 55 minutes   **4** $\frac{9}{10}$

5 a i 2^{20} **ii** 2^{30} **b i** $2^{20} = 1\,048\,576$ **ii** $2^{30} = 1\,073\,741\,824$

6 a $2\frac{1}{2}$ minutes   **b** $46°$ **c** $27°$ **d** $73°$

Chapter 7: Factorising algebraic expressions

Exercise 7:01

1 a $5(x + y)$ **b** $-m(3 + m)$ **c** $2x(3y - 1)$ **d** $5(3p - 4q)$ **e** $5q(3p - 4)$
   f $3st(4t + 5)$ **g** $-6x(3y + 1)$ **h** $at(1 - t)$ **i** $xy(7x + 1)$ **j** $a(a + b)$

2 a $a(a + b + 3)$ **b** $x(y - 3x + 2)$ **c** $4t(3s - t + 2)$ **d** $6(6 - 2ab + 3b)$ **e** $ab(3 - 9a + 4b + ab)$
   f $4(m - 2n - 3mn)$ **g** $1(3 + 5m - 2n)$ **h** $-n(3 + 5m - 2n)$ **i** $4(3x^2 + 2x - 1)$ **j** $4y^2(3x^2 + 2x - 1)$

3 a $(x + y)(x + 4)$ **b** $(4 - b)(a + 2)$ **c** $(m - 3)(m - 1)$ **d** $(2 + s)(s - 3)$ **e** $(2a - 1)(a - 1)$
   f $(3m + 2)(9 - 2m)$ **g** $(x + 6)(x - 5)$ **h** $(y - 2)(y + 5)$ **i** $(x - 5)(3 - x)$ **j** $(ab + 2)(9 - a)$

Prep Quiz 7:02

1 $3(a + 6)$ **2** $x(5 + a)$ **3** $p(q - x)$ **4** $3x(a - 3b)$ **5** $x(x - 2)$ **6** $a^2(a + 1)$ **7** $3(3 - a)$ **8** $-5(m + 2)$
9 $(a + 1)(9 + x)$ **10** $(x + y)(x - 1)$

Exercise 7:02

1 a $(a + b)(2 + x)$ **b** $(x + 7)(a + p)$ **c** $(x - y)(m + x)$ **d** $(m + n)(x - y)$ **e** $(2 - x)(a^2 + 7)$
   f $(q - 2)(q - 2)$ **g** $(x + y)(1 + a)$ **h** $(x - 2)(1 - 3y)$

2 a $(a+b)(p+q)$ **b** $(3+x)(a+b)$ **c** $(m+3p)(n+5)$ **d** $(a+c)(a+b)$ **e** $(3x+y)(3x-4)$
  f $(3p-4)(4p+q)$ **g** $(b+3)(a+c)$ **h** $(x+1)(y+4)$ **i** $(a^2+1)(a+1)$ **j** $(p+r)(q+5)$
  k $(y-1)(x+1)$ **l** $(2+y)(4a-1)$ **m** $(m+1)(n+1)$ **n** $(x+m)(x+y)$ **o** $(x+w)(x-y)$
  p $(x+z)(x+y)$ **q** $(a+4)(11+c)$ **r** $(a-1)(a^2+1)$
3 a $(y+z)(x-w)$ **b** $(a+c)(b-d)$ **c** $(a+3)(5-b)$ **d** $(x-4)(6-y)$ **e** $(y+2)(11-x)$
  f $(ax-1)(x-1)$

Prep Quiz 7:03

1 4 **2** 7 **3** 11 **4** x **5** $3x$ **6** $8x$ **7** x^2-4 **8** x^2-25 **9** $49-a^2$ **10** $9m^2-4n^2$

Exercise 7:03

1 a $(x-2)(x+2)$ **b** $(a+4)(a-4)$ **c** $(m+5)(m-5)$ **d** $(p-9)(p+9)$
  e $(y-10)(y+10)$ **f** $(x-11)(x+11)$ **g** $(3-x)(3+x)$ **h** $(1-n)(1+n)$
  i $(7-y)(7+y)$ **j** $(a-b)(a+b)$ **k** $(x-a)(x+a)$ **l** $(y+a)(y-a)$
  m $(3a-2)(3a+2)$ **n** $(4x-1)(4x+1)$ **o** $(5p-3)(5p+3)$ **p** $(7-2a)(7+2a)$
  q $(5p-a)(5p+a)$ **r** $(m-9n)(m+9n)$ **s** $(10a-3b)(10a+3b)$ **t** $(9x+11y)(9x-11y)$
2 a $2(x-4)(x+4)$ **b** $3(x-6)(x+6)$ **c** $4(a-5)(a+5)$ **d** $5(y-2)(y+2)$
  e $6(2a-b)(2a+b)$ **f** $3(x-3y)(x+3y)$ **g** $8(y-4)(y+4)$ **h** $5(4p-q)(4p+q)$
  i $4(x-4)(x+4)$ **j** $3(x-1)(x+1)$ **k** $2(6p-1)(6p+1)$ **l** $2(1-3x)(1+3x)$
  m $2(2a-3m)(2a+3m)$ **n** $5(5-2a)(5+2a)$ **o** $2(10x-3y)(10x+3y)$ **p** $2(7m-2n)(7m+2n)$

Challenge 7:03   The difference of two cubes (Extension)

Volume of part ①	Volume of part ②	Volume of part ③	Volume of part ④
$b \times b \times b$	$(a-b) \times b \times b$	$(a-b) \times a \times b$	$a \times a \times (a-b)$

$\therefore a^3 = b^3 + (ab^2 - b^3) + (a^2b - ab^2) + (a^3 - a^2b)$
$a^3 - b^3 = (a-b)b^2 + (a-b)ab + (a-b)a^2$
$\qquad = (a-b)(a^2 + ab + b^2)$

1 $(m-n)(m^2+mn+n^2)$ **2** $(x-y)(x^2+xy+y^2)$ **3** $(a-2)(a^2+2a+4)$
4 $(m-3)(m^2+3m+9)$ **5** $(x-10)(x^2+10x+100)$ **6** $(y-5)(y^2+5y+25)$
7 $(4-n)(16+4n+n^2)$ **8** $(3-k)(9+3k+k^2)$ **9** $(2m-3)(4m^2+6m+9)$
10 $(4x-5y)(16x^2+20xy+25y^2)$ **11** $(5x-2y)(25x^2+10xy+4y^2)$ **12** $(3m-7n)(9m^2+21mn+49n^2)$

Prep Quiz 7:04

1 x^2+5x+6 **2** a^2+2a-3 **3** $m^2-9m+14$ **4** $x^2+10x+25$ **5** a^2-4a+4 **6** $3, 2$
7 $4, 5$ **8** $-5, 3$ **9** $4, -1$ **10** $9, -2$

Exercise 7:04

1 a $(x+3)(x+1)$ **b** $(x+2)(x+1)$ **c** $(x+5)(x+1)$ **d** $(x+6)(x+1)$ **e** $(x+5)(x+4)$
  f $(x+5)(x+5)$ **g** $(x+6)(x+6)$ **h** $(x+7)(x+3)$ **i** $(x+6)(x+3)$ **j** $(x+10)(x+4)$
  k $(x+6)(x+9)$ **l** $(x+9)(x+4)$ **m** $(x-2)(x-2)$ **n** $(x-6)(x-6)$ **o** $(x-4)(x-3)$
  p $(x-5)(x-4)$ **q** $(x+3)(x-1)$ **r** $(x+4)(x-3)$ **s** $(x+6)(x-2)$ **t** $(x+10)(x-3)$
  u $(x-2)(x+1)$ **v** $(x-12)(x+2)$ **w** $(x-10)(x+3)$ **x** $(x-8)(x+7)$
2 a $(a+4)(a+2)$ **b** $(m+6)(m+3)$ **c** $(y+6)(y+7)$ **d** $(p+3)(p+4)$ **e** $(x+2)(x+10)$
  f $(n+14)(n+3)$ **g** $(s+18)(x+3)$ **h** $(a+4)(a+14)$ **i** $(x-4)(x+1)$ **j** $(a-4)(a+2)$
  k $(p-8)(p+3)$ **l** $(y+3)(y-2)$ **m** $(x+8)(x-1)$ **n** $(q+8)(q-3)$ **o** $(m+15)(m-3)$
  p $(a+21)(a-3)$ **q** $(y+11)(y-5)$ **r** $(x-1)(x-1)$ **s** $(k-3)(k-2)$ **t** $(x-9)(x-4)$
  u $(a-18)(a-4)$ **v** $(p+6)(p+16)$ **w** $(q-15)(q+3)$ **x** $(m-11)(m+7)$
3 a $2(x+2)(x+1)$ **b** $3(x-3)(x+1)$ **c** $5(x-4)(x+2)$ **d** $2(x+4)(x+4)$ **e** $3(x-11)(x+1)$
  f $3(x+3)(x+4)$ **g** $4(a-5)(a+2)$ **h** $2(n+3)(n+1)$ **i** $5(x-4)(x-2)$ **j** $3(x-3)(x-4)$
  k $3(a-9)(a+4)$ **l** $5(x+10)(x-7)$

Exercise 7:05

1 a iii   **b** iv   **c** ii   **d** iv
2 a $(2x+1)(x+3)$ **b** $(3x+2)(x+2)$ **c** $(2x+3)(x+2)$ **d** $(2x+1)(x+5)$ **e** $(3x+2)(x+1)$
  f $(2x+5)(x+3)$ **g** $(x+3)(4x+1)$ **h** $(5x+2)(x+3)$ **i** $(2x+3)(x+5)$ **j** $(2x-1)(x-2)$
  k $(3x-2)(x-3)$ **l** $(5x-2)(x-3)$ **m** $(x-2)(4x-3)$ **n** $(5x-3)(2x-3)$ **o** $(5x-7)(x-3)$
  p $(2x+5)(x-2)$ **q** $(3x-5)(x+3)$ **r** $(x+3)(4x-1)$ **s** $(2x+3)(x-2)$ **t** $(2x+1)(x-3)$
  u $(3x-10)(x+3)$ **v** $(2x+3)(3x-7)$ **w** $(2x+3)(x-4)$ **x** $(x+2)(4x-9)$

3 a $(3x + 1)(4x + 1)$ **b** $(3a + 1)(2a + 1)$ **c** $(3p + 2)(2p + 1)$ **d** $(5y - 2)(2y - 1)$ **e** $(3x - 1)(4x - 1)$
  f $(3a - 2)(3a - 5)$ **g** $(2m + 5)(4m - 1)$ **h** $(2n - 3)(3n + 1)$ **i** $(7q - 2)(3q - 2)$ **j** $(4x - 1)(5x + 1)$
  k $(2m - 3)(4m + 5)$ **l** $(6y - 5)(3y + 2)$ **m** $(2a + 3)(3a - 2)$ **n** $(3k + 4)(5k + 2)$ **o** $(2x + 3)(4x + 3)$
  p $(4 + a)(1 - a)$ **q** $(2 + 5m)(1 - 2m)$ **r** $(3x + 2)(3 - x)$ **s** $(2 - 3x)(x + 3)$ **t** $(5 - 7x)(4x + 3)$
  u $(2 - 5n)(1 + 7n)$ **v** $(3x + 4y)(x + 2y)$ **w** $(2x - y)(x - 2y)$ **x** $(5m - 7n)(m + n)$
4 a $2(3x - 1)(x + 2)$ **b** $2(3a + 2)(a - 1)$ **c** $3(2a - 3)(a + 3)$ **d** $4(2x - 3)(x + 3)$ **e** $2(3x + 2)(x + 4)$
  f $3(2p - 1)(2p + 3)$ **g** $5(3q + 7)(2q - 1)$ **h** $2(5m - 3)(m - 4)$ **i** $5(5a - 1)(2a + 1)$ **j** $2(2 - 5x)(1 + x)$
  k $3(3 - t)(t + 4)$ **l** $3(3 + 2x)(1 + 2x)$
5 a $(x + 3)(x + 5) = x^2 + 8x + 15$; $(x - 3)(x + 5) = x^2 + 2x - 15$; $(x + 3)(x - 5) = x^2 - 2x - 15$;
  $(x - 3)(x - 5) = x^2 - 8x + 15$; $(x + 1)(x + 15) = x^2 + 16x + 15$; $(x - 1)(x + 15) = x^2 + 14x - 15$;
  $(x + 1)(x - 15) = x^2 - 14x - 15$; $(x - 1)(x - 15) = x^2 - 16x + 15$
  b $(x - 1)(x + 12) = x^2 + 11x - 12$; $(x - 12)(x + 1) = x^2 - 11x - 12$; $(x - 3)(x + 4) = x^2 + x - 12$;
  $(x - 4)(x + 3) = x^2 - x - 12$; $(x - 6)(x + 2) = x^2 - 4x - 12$; $(x - 2)(x + 6) = x^2 + 4x - 12$
  c $(x - 1)(x - 4) = x^2 - 5x + 4$; $(x + 1)(x + 4) = x^2 + 5x + 4$; $(x - 2)(x - 3) = x^2 - 5x + 6$; $(x + 2)(x + 3) = x^2 + 5x + 6$
  d $(5x + 1)(x + 2) = 5x^2 + 11x + 2$; $(5x + 1)(x - 2) = 5x^2 - 9x - 2$; $(5x - 1)(x + 2) = 5x^2 + 9x - 2$;
  $(5x - 1)(x - 2) = 5x^2 - 11x + 2$

Challenge 7:05 Another factorising method for harder trinomials

1 $(2x + 3)(x + 2)$ **2** $(4x + 1)(x - 5)$ **3** $(3x - 4)(x - 3)$ **4** $(2x + 1)(3x + 2)$ **5** $(5x - 1)(x + 2)$ **6** $(4x - 3)(3x - 4)$

Exercise 7:06

1 a $(x - 5)(x - 1)$ **b** $(x - 3)(x + 3)$ **c** $(x + 2)(y + 9)$ **d** $a(a - 9)$
  e $(a - 3)(a - 3)$ **f** $(2x - 1)(2x + 1)$ **g** $(4x - 7)(3x + 5)$ **h** $(a - 5)(a - 8)$
  i $5ab(a - 2b^2)$ **j** $(p - q)(p + q)$ **k** $(p + 10)(q - 3)$ **l** $(7x - 3)(x + 2)$
  m $a(a + 3 - b)$ **n** $(4 - 5a)(4 + 5a)$ **o** $(1 + 4a)(1 - 6a)$ **p** $(m + n)(4 - a)$
  q $5y(a - 2 + 3x)$ **r** $(5x - 7)(3x + 4)$ **s** $(xy - 1)(xy + 1)$ **t** $(x - 8)(x + 7)$
  u $(2m + 3p)(n + 2)$ **v** $(10a - 7x)(10a + 7x)$ **w** $(2 + x)(1 - 3x)$ **x** $(k + 8)(k - 6)$
2 a $2(1 - 2x)(1 + 2x)$ **b** $5(x - y)(x - 2)$ **c** $2(a - 8)(a - 3)$ **d** $3(m - 3)(m - 3)$
  e $(x - 1)(x + 1)(x^2 + 1)$ **f** $(p - 4)(p - 1)(p + 1)$ **g** $4(x - 3)(x + 3)$ **h** $a(a - 1)(a + 1)$
  i $3(a - 8)(a - 5)$ **j** $9(1 - p)(1 + p)$ **k** $3(k + 3)(k - 2)$ **l** $3(2a - 3)(4a - 1)$
  m $a(x + y)(x + 3)$ **n** $(x + y)(x + y + 3)$ **o** $5x(y - 2z)(y + 2z)$ **p** $a(3x - 2)(2x + 3)$
  q $(x - y)(x + y + 5)$ **r** $3(x - 2)(x - 2)$ **s** $7(3x - 2y)(3x + 2y)$ **t** $(a^2 + 4)(a - 2)(a + 2)$
  u $a(a - 4)$ **v** $(1 + p)(1 + p^2)$ **w** $4(2t + 3)(t - 5)$ **x** $2(2 + x)(2 - 3x)$

Prep Quiz 7:07

1 $\dfrac{a}{2}$ **2** $\dfrac{3y}{2x}$ **3** 4 **4** $\dfrac{3}{2}$ **5** $3x(2x + 3)$ **6** $(x + 3)(x + 4)$ **7** $(x - 7)(x + 7)$ **8** $3(x + 1)^2$ **9** $(x + y)(3 + a)$
10 $(2x - 1)(x + 5)$

Exercise 7:07

1 a $x + 2$ **b** $\dfrac{2}{x + 3}$ **c** $\dfrac{4}{x - 3}$ **d** 2 **e** $\dfrac{1}{3}$ **f** $\dfrac{5}{8}$ **g** $\dfrac{1}{2}$ **h** $\dfrac{7}{3}$
  i $\dfrac{x + 1}{x - 1}$ **j** $x + 2$ **k** $\dfrac{1}{a - 1}$ **l** $\dfrac{2y - 3}{2}$ **m** $\dfrac{a - 4}{3 - a}$ **n** $x + 1$ **o** $\dfrac{x + 6}{3}$ **p** $a - 4$
  q $x - 3$ **r** $\dfrac{x - 2}{x + 1}$ **s** $\dfrac{x + 1}{x + 3}$ **t** $\dfrac{m + 8}{m - 4}$ **u** $\dfrac{t + 4}{t - 3}$ **v** $\dfrac{a - x}{a + 3}$ **w** $\dfrac{x - 1}{2x - 1}$ **x** $\dfrac{2(3a - 2)}{2a - 1}$
2 a $4x$ **b** $\dfrac{y - 3}{4}$ **c** $\dfrac{10}{21}$ **d** $\dfrac{15}{2}$ **e** $\dfrac{1}{3}$ **f** $\dfrac{3(1 + 2a)}{5(1 - 2a)}$ **g** $\dfrac{y(2y + 3)}{3(y + 4)}$ **h** $\dfrac{2x + 5}{9}$
  i $\dfrac{1}{x + 1}$ **j** $\dfrac{x + 7}{x - 5}$ **k** $\dfrac{a + 3}{a - 1}$ **l** 1 **m** $\dfrac{x + 3}{x + 7}$ **n** $\dfrac{m + 1}{m + 5}$ **o** $\dfrac{(a + 2)(a - 4)}{(a + 4)(a - 1)}$
  p $\dfrac{x + 4}{2}$ **q** 1 **r** $\dfrac{a}{2a - 1}$ **s** 2 **t** $\dfrac{(a + b - c)(a - c)}{a + c}$
3 a 6 **b** $\dfrac{2}{7}$ **c** 5 **d** $\dfrac{9}{2}$ **e** $\dfrac{3}{5(x + 1)}$ **f** 16 **g** $\dfrac{m}{2}$ **h** $\dfrac{5k}{k - 1}$
  i $\dfrac{n - 3}{n + 2}$ **j** $\dfrac{y}{y - 7}$ **k** $\dfrac{a + 1}{a - 3}$ **l** 1 **m** $\dfrac{x + 2}{x - 3}$ **n** $\dfrac{p + 4}{p - 4}$ **o** $\dfrac{(n - 7)(n - 3)}{(n + 1)(n + 7)}$
  p 2 **q** $3(x - 1)$ **r** 1 **s** 2 **t** $\dfrac{(p + q + r)(p - q)}{p + q}$

Prep Quiz 7:08

1 $1\frac{1}{10}$ **2** $1\frac{1}{8}$ **3** $\frac{3}{10}$ **4** $\frac{19}{60}$ **5** $\frac{12}{x}$ **6** $\frac{5}{2a}$ **7** $\frac{13}{6a}$ **8** $\frac{3}{4x}$ **9** $\frac{5a}{2x}$ **10** $\frac{7m}{6n}$

Exercise 7:08

1 a $\dfrac{2x}{(x+1)(x-1)}$ **b** $\dfrac{2a+8}{(a+5)(a+3)}$ **c** $\dfrac{8}{(y-7)(y+1)}$ **d** $\dfrac{5x+19}{(x+3)(x+5)}$ **e** $\dfrac{2m-13}{(m+1)(m-2)}$

f $\dfrac{3t-18}{(t+10)(t+2)}$ **g** $\dfrac{7x-4}{(2x-1)(x-1)}$ **h** $\dfrac{-3x+31}{(3x+2)(2x+5)}$ **i** $\dfrac{59x-1}{(5x-1)(3x+1)}$ **j** $\dfrac{13x+21}{2x(x+7)}$

k $\dfrac{17x-25}{3x(2x+5)}$ **l** $\dfrac{1-4a}{21(2a+1)}$ **m** $\dfrac{2x^2+4x}{(x+3)(x+1)}$ **n** $\dfrac{-3a}{(2a+1)(4a-1)}$ **o** $\dfrac{2x^2+6x+5}{(x+2)(x+1)}$

2 a $\dfrac{x+3}{(x+1)(x+2)}$ **b** $\dfrac{1+x}{x(x+2)}$ **c** $\dfrac{x-1}{x(x+3)}$ **d** $\dfrac{x+1}{(x-5)(x+2)}$

e $\dfrac{4x+15}{(x+2)(x+3)}$ **f** $\dfrac{5x+2}{(x+1)(x+4)}$ **g** $\dfrac{2}{(x+1)(x+3)}$ **h** $\dfrac{6x-10}{(x-3)(x+3)(x+1)}$

i $\dfrac{8x-2}{(x+7)(x-1)(x+1)}$ **j** $\dfrac{2x-72}{(x+9)(x+3)(x-1)}$ **k** $\dfrac{7x+5}{(2x+1)(x+5)(x+2)}$

l $\dfrac{-13x-12}{x(2x-1)(3x+2)}$ **m** $\dfrac{2x^2+2}{(x+3)(x+1)(x-1)}$ **n** $\dfrac{2x+7}{x(x+3)(x+2)}$

3 a $\dfrac{(1+x)}{x(x+1)} = \dfrac{1}{x}$ **b** $\dfrac{-2}{3(x+3)}$ **c** $\dfrac{7}{2(2x+3)}$ **d** $\dfrac{3x+8}{(x+1)(x-1)}$

e $\dfrac{x+5}{2(x-3)(x+3)}$ **f** $\dfrac{-1}{x(x+1)(x-1)}$ **g** $\dfrac{2x}{(x+1)^2(x-1)}$ **h** $\dfrac{2x+7}{(x+3)(x+4)^2}$

i $\dfrac{6x+22}{(x+2)(x+4)(x+3)}$ **j** $\dfrac{6x+14}{(x+3)(x+4)(x+1)}$ **k** $\dfrac{-x-1}{(x-2)(x+1)(x-3)}$

l $\dfrac{x-1}{(x-3)(x+2)(x+1)}$ **m** $\dfrac{2x+2}{(x-4)(x+1)(x-2)} = \dfrac{2}{(x-4)(x-2)}$

n $\dfrac{x+10}{(2x-1)(x+4)(3x+2)}$ **o** $\dfrac{6x+34}{(x-7)(x+7)(x+3)}$ **p** $\dfrac{2x-3}{(2x-1)(x+1)(x-1)}$

q $\dfrac{2x^2-x-5}{(x+2)(x+3)(x-3)}$ **r** $\dfrac{-3x-8}{x(x-4)(x+4)}$ **s** $\dfrac{7x^2-x-10}{5(x-2)(x+2)^2}$

t $\dfrac{7x^2+9x-5}{(2x+1)(x-3)(2x-1)}$

Diagnostic Test 7   Factorising algebraic expressions

1 a $3(x-4)$ **b** $a(x+y)$ **c** $-2(x+3)$ **d** $x(a+b-c)$

2 a $(a+b)(x+2)$ **b** $(6+a)(m+n)$ **c** $(x+1)(y-1)$ **d** $(a+c)(b+4)$

3 a $(x-5)(x+5)$ **b** $(a-x)(a+x)$ **c** $(2-m)(2+m)$ **d** $(3x-1)(3x+1)$

4 a $(x+3)(x+4)$ **b** $(x-2)(x-3)$ **c** $(x-5)(x+2)$ **d** $(x+5)(x-4)$

5 a $(2x+1)(x+5)$ **b** $(3x-2)(x-3)$ **c** $(4x-9)(x+2)$ **d** $(3x+1)(2x+1)$

6 a $x+2$ **b** $\frac{6}{7}$ **c** $\frac{x}{a}$ **d** $\frac{x+5}{x+2}$ **7 a** $6x$ **b** $\frac{a-1}{a-3}$ **c** $\frac{9}{5}$ **d** $\frac{x+2}{x-3}$

8 a $\dfrac{3x+1}{(x+3)(x-1)}$ **b** $\dfrac{1}{x(x+2)(x+1)}$ **c** $\dfrac{3x+19}{2(x-3)(x+3)}$ **d** $\dfrac{-7x-8}{(x+3)(x+4)(x-1)}$

7A Revision Assignment

1 a $(a+4)(a+5)$ **b** $2(p-2q)$ **c** $(m-9)(m+5)$ **d** $(5x^2+1)(x+2)$ **e** $(2x-1)(2x+1)$

f $xy(x-1)$ **g** $(3a+1)(2a-5)$ **h** $(x+6)(x-5)$ **i** $(3a+5)(a-3)$ **j** $(x+p)(y+z)$

k $(2x-1)(x+1)$ **l** $(x^2+2)(x-3)$ **m** $-5ab(1+2ab)$ **n** $(x-y)(x+y+2)$ **o** $(2+3x)(1-3x)$

2 a $2(y-3)(y+3)$ **b** $3(r+7)(r-4)$ **c** $2(x+1)(2x^2+3)$ **d** $2(1-3x)(1+3x)$ **e** $a(a-8)(a+9)$

f $3(11+a)(1+a)$ **g** $(x-y)(x+y+1)$ **h** $x(x-4)$

3 a $\dfrac{x+12}{x+3}$ **b** $\dfrac{5(2x+1)}{x+3}$ **c** $\dfrac{5x+13}{(x+2)(x+3)}$ **d** $\dfrac{x^2}{(x-1)(x-2)}$ **e** $\dfrac{x-1}{5}$ **f** $\dfrac{1}{x-2}$

g $\dfrac{-2x-3}{(x+2)(x+1)}$ **h** $\dfrac{6x-1}{(3x-1)^2}$ **i** $\dfrac{2x+3}{(3+2x)(2x+3)}$ **j** $\dfrac{x+2}{5(x-7)}$

7B Working Mathematically

1 a *collinear* points **b** *vertices* **c** *hypotenuse* **d** $\alpha + \beta$ **e** 360°
f $3 \times 180° = 540°$ **g** AB is a *diameter*, OC is a *radius* **h** *circumference* **i** *semicircle*
j AB is a *tangent*. CD is an *arc*. EF is a *chord*.
2 a *concurrent* lines **b** *adjacent* angles **c** *complementary* angles **d** *supplementary* angles
e *vertically opposite* angles **f** *transversal* **g** *bisecting* an interval **h** *bisecting* an angle
i $\angle CAB = 60°$ **j** CD is *perpendicular* to AB
3 $84:60:36$ or $7:5:3$ **4** 17
5 a 10% **b** This would include those who were car passengers $(12\frac{1}{2}\%)$ as well as those who went by bus $(11\frac{1}{9}\%)$ and those who went by train (10%). Answer $= 33\frac{11}{18}\%$ **c** 23° **d** 62·5%
6 a Man **b** Woman **c** Heart diseases **d** Depends on the number of men or women still living.

Chapter 8:   Coordinate geometry

Prep Quiz 8:01
1 C **2** 5 **3** 13 **4** $\sqrt{20} = 2\sqrt{5}$ **5** 4 **6** 3 **7** 4 **8** 3 **9** 5 units **10** 5 units

Exercise 8:01
1 a 10 **b** 5 **c** $\sqrt{34}$ **d** $\sqrt{29}$ **e** 13

2

	a	b	c	d	e	f
BC	4	3	2	7	6	6
AC	5	3	6	6	4	3
AB	$\sqrt{41}$	$\sqrt{18}$	$\sqrt{40}$	$\sqrt{85}$	$\sqrt{52}$	$\sqrt{45}$

3 a $\sqrt{20} = 2\sqrt{5}$ **b** $\sqrt{58}$ **c** $\sqrt{53}$ **d** $\sqrt{29}$ **e** $\sqrt{41}$ **f** $\sqrt{40} = 2\sqrt{10}$
4 a 5 **b** 10 **c** 5 **d** 10 **e** 13 **f** 13
g $\sqrt{20}$ **h** $\sqrt{5}$ **i** $\sqrt{89}$ **j** $\sqrt{17}$ **k** $\sqrt{26}$ **l** $\sqrt{2}$
5 a $\sqrt{20} = 2\sqrt{5}$ units **b** $(-1, 2)$ **c** $\sqrt{106}$ units **d** $(7, 2)$
6 a AB = 5 units; BC = $\sqrt{50}$ units = $5\sqrt{2}$ units; AC = $\sqrt{41}$ units
b AB = $\sqrt{13}$ units; DC = $\sqrt{13}$ units; AD = $\sqrt{5}$ units; BC = $\sqrt{5}$ units
c BD = $\sqrt{32}$ units; AC = 2 units **d** EF = FG = GH = HE = $\sqrt{10}$ units **e** 5
f AB = $\sqrt{40}$ units = $2\sqrt{10}$ units; BC = $\sqrt{40}$ units = $2\sqrt{10}$ units. Since two sides are equal the triangle is isosceles.
g 13 units

Prep Quiz 8:02
1 7 **2** 1 **3** 7 **4** 1 **5** 7 **6** 1 **7** 3 **8** 3 **9** 1 **10** 1

Exercise 8:02
1 a $(3, 3)$ **b** $(-1, -1)$ **c** $(0, 1)$ **d** $(1, -3)$ **e** $(1\frac{1}{2}, 0)$
2 a $(2\frac{1}{2}, 2\frac{1}{2})$ **b** $(3\frac{1}{2}, 7)$ **c** $(-4, 3)$ **d** $(0, -2\frac{1}{2})$ **e** $(-4, -6)$ **f** $(4\frac{1}{2}, -5\frac{1}{2})$
g $(\frac{1}{2}, -5)$ **h** $(-\frac{1}{2}, 2\frac{1}{2})$ **i** $(-1\frac{1}{2}, -7\frac{1}{2})$
3 a $(4, 7)$ **b** $(3, 7)$ **c** $(6, 4)$ **d** $(-2, 1)$ **e** $(2, 2)$ **f** $(1, -2)$
g $(-4, -8)$ **h** $(-3, -1)$ **i** $(-4, -5\frac{1}{2})$
4 a $(-\frac{1}{2}, -3)$ **b** $(7\frac{1}{2}, -1)$ **c** $(5, 0)$ **d** $(-\frac{1}{2}, -\frac{1}{2})$ **e** $(-2, -2)$ **f** $(5\frac{1}{2}, -5\frac{1}{2})$
g $(87, 70)$ **h** $(70, -26)$ **i** $(262, 76)$
5 a i $(2\frac{1}{2}, 2)$ **ii** $(2\frac{1}{2}, 2)$ **iii** Yes **iv** The diagonals bisect each other.
b $(3, 8)$ **c i** $(4, 3)$ **ii** $(4, 3)$ **iii** Yes **iv** The diagonals bisect each other.
6 a $k = 0$ **b** $d = 15, e = -6$ **c** $(-16, 0)$ **d** $(7, 2)$
7 a C is $(4\frac{1}{2}, 5\frac{1}{2})$; D is $(8, 7)$; E is $(11\frac{1}{2}, 8\frac{1}{2})$ **b** B is $(29, 16)$; C is $(8, 7)$; E is $(22, 13)$
8 a AC and BD are the diagonals.
Midpoint of BD is $(-4, 2)$
Midpoint of AC is $(-4, 2)$
∴ Diagonals have the same midpoint.
∴ Diagonals bisect each other.
∴ ABCD is a parallelogram.
b Length of both diagonals = $\sqrt{80}$ units.
Midpoint of both diagonals = $(\frac{1}{2}, -1)$
∴ Diagonals bisect each other.
∴ Figure has equal diagonals that bisect each other.
∴ The figure is a rectangle.

Prep Quiz 8:03

1 EF **2** A and B **3** C and D **4** E and F **5** B and C **6** D and E **7** F and G **8** up **9** down **10** not at all

Exercise 8:03

1 a positive **b** positive **c** negative **d** negative **e** positive

2 a 5 **b** $-\frac{4}{3}$ **c** -3 **d** 3 **e** -1 **f** 2

3 a

Line	AB	CD	EF	GH
Gradient	2	2	$-\frac{1}{2}$	$-\frac{1}{2}$

b AB and CD; EF and GH

c AB and CD; EF and GH

4 a and b

c Yes

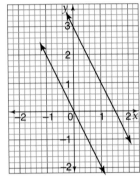

5 a $\frac{1}{3}$ **b** 4 **c** $\frac{1}{2}$ **d** $\frac{2}{5}$
e $\frac{1}{6}$ **f** 3 **g** $\frac{1}{4}$ **h** $\frac{1}{2}$
i $\frac{5}{6}$ **j** $\frac{1}{5}$ **k** $\frac{8}{3}$ **l** -4
m -1 **n** $-2\frac{1}{2}$ **o** -4 **p** 2
q 0 **r** 0

6 a 5 **b** 2 **c i** $-\frac{1}{2}$ **ii** $-\frac{1}{2}$ **iii** $-\frac{1}{2}$ **iv** $-\frac{1}{2}$

d If three points lie on the same straight line, then the intervals joining one of the points to the other two must have the same gradients. Using $(-2, 5)$ and $(2, 13)$, $m = \dfrac{13-5}{2--2} = 2$; Using $(2, 13)$ and $(6, 21)$, $m = \dfrac{21-13}{6-2} = 2$

As the intervals joining $(2, 13)$ to the other two points have the same gradient, the points are collinear.

7 a i $\frac{1}{4}, \frac{1}{4}$ **ii** $2\frac{1}{2}, 2\frac{1}{2}$ **iii** ABCD is a parallelogram since it has opposite sides parallel.

b AB and DC have a gradient of $\frac{2}{7}$ and, hence, are parallel. AD and BC have a gradient of 1 and, hence, are parallel. Since there are two pairs of parallel sides, ABCD is a parallelogram.

8 AB and CD have a slope of $\frac{1}{4}$ and hence are parallel. AD and BC have a slope of 4 and hence are parallel. Since there are two pairs of parallel sides, ABCD is a parallelogram. Also AB $=$ AD $= \sqrt{153}$ units. Hence ABCD is a parallelogram with a pair of adjacent sides equal. ABCD is a rhombus.

Investigation 8:03 Gradients in building

1 a C **b** B **c** A **2 a** 8 m **b** 5·6 m **c** 12·8 m

3 a $1\frac{1}{2}$ m **b** $\frac{1}{2}$ m

4 No, he would need a run of 11·2 m. He could curve the rampway across the slope.

Exercise 8:04

1 a

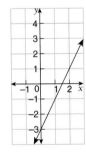

b

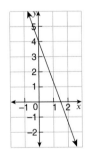

c

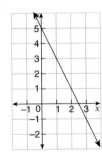

d

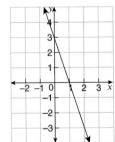

2 a

b

c

d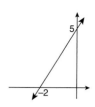

e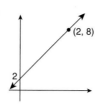

f

g

h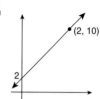

3 b, c, f   **4** a, b, d

5 a A: $x = -4$, B: $x = -1$, C: $x = 3$, D: $y = 3$, E: $y = 1$, F: $y = -4$

  b A: $x = -3$, B: $x = 2$, C: $x = 4$, D: $y = 4$, E: $y = 2$, F: $y = -2$

6 a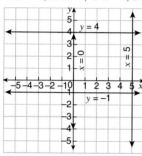

b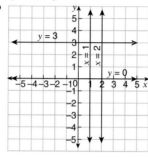

c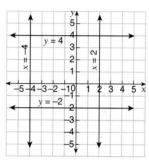

d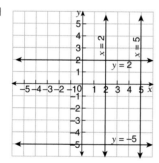

e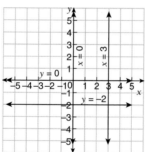

The lines in **a** and **c** enclose square regions.

7 A: $y = x$, B: $y = x - 2$, C: $y = 2x$, D: $x + y = 3$, E: $2x + y = 2$, F: $2x + y = 0$

8 a C   **b** D   **c** A   **d** B

9 a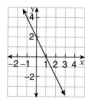

x-intercept is 1
y-intercept is 2

b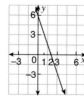

x-intercept is 2
y-intercept is 6

c

x-intercept is 2
y-intercept is 4

d

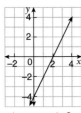

x-intercept is 2
y-intercept is −4

e

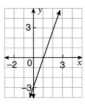

x-intercept is 1
y-intercept is −3

f

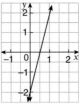

x-intercept is $\frac{1}{2}$
y-intercept is −2

10 a

b

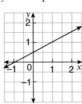

c

d

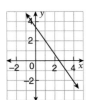

e

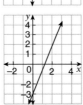

f

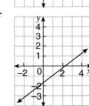

Prep Quiz 8:05

1 0　　**2** b　　**3** 2　　**4** −1　　**5** 2　　**6** $\frac{1}{2}$　　**7** (0, 2)　　**8** (0, −1)　　**9** Yes　　**10** Yes

Investigation 8:05　What does y = mx + c tell us?

2

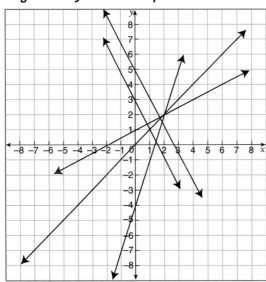

3 The gradient of the line is the same as the coefficient of x.
The y-intercept of the line is the same as the constant.

Line	Equation	Gradient	y-intercept
1	$y = 3x - 4$	3	−4
2	$y = 5 - 2x$	−2	5
3	$y = \frac{1}{2}x + 1$	$\frac{1}{2}$	1
4	$y = x$	1	0
5	$y = 3 - 2x$	2	3

4

Line	Gradient	y-intercept	Equation
A	3	$3\frac{1}{2}$	$y = 3x + 3\frac{1}{2}$
B	3	$-6\frac{1}{2}$	$y = 3x - 6\frac{1}{2}$
C	$-\frac{1}{4}$	$-2\frac{1}{2}$	$y = -\frac{1}{4}x - 2\frac{1}{2}$
D	$-\frac{1}{4}$	$7\frac{1}{2}$	$y = -\frac{1}{4}x + 7\frac{1}{2}$
E	−1	$1\frac{1}{2}$	$y = -x + 1\frac{1}{2}$
F	−1	$9\frac{1}{2}$	$y = -x + 9\frac{1}{2}$

5 It tells us that m is the gradient and b is the y-intercept.
6 Lines of the same colour have the same slope or gradient.

Exercise 8:05

1 a $4, -5$ **b** $3, 2$ **c** $-1, 9$ **d** $\frac{5}{7}, 3$ **e** $\frac{3}{2}, -\frac{5}{2}$

2 a $3, 4$ **b** $3, 5$ **c** $-\frac{3}{4}, 2\frac{1}{2}$ **d** $-\frac{3}{2}, 3$ **e** $-\frac{1}{2}, \frac{3}{2}$

  f $-2, 5$ **g** $\frac{5}{3}, \frac{1}{3}$ **h** $2, 1\frac{1}{3}$ **i** $1, -1$ **j** $-5, 6$

3 a $3, 7, 3x - y + 7 = 0$ **b** $-\frac{1}{5}, 3, x + 5y - 15 = 0$ **c** $-\frac{4}{3}, -1, 4x + 3y + 3 = 0$

  d $2, 0, 2x - y = 0$ **e** $0, -5, y + 5 = 0$

4

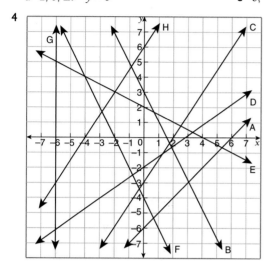

Prep Quiz 8:06

1 3 **2** 5 **3** 11 **4** 0 **5** 4 **6** 5 **7** 1 **8** 2 **9** 3 **10** 0

Exercise 8:06

1 a 1 **b** 2 **c** 5 **d** -5 **e** -2 **f** -11

2 a $y = 2x + 1$ **b** $y = 5x$ **c** $y = 3x - 4$ **d** $y = 4x + 10$ **e** $y = -x + 6$ **f** $y = -2x + 7$

  g $y = -5x + 5$ **h** $y = \frac{1}{2}x + 3$ **i** $y = \frac{1}{4}x + 2$ **j** $y = -\frac{1}{2}x - 3$

3 a $y = 2x - 4$ **b** $y = -x + 3$ **c** $y = 3x + 6$ **d** $y = -3x + 1$ **e** $y = 3x$ **f** $y = 4x + 2$

  g $y = 4x$ **h** $y = -2x - 8$ **i** $y = 2x - 2$ **j** $y = \frac{1}{2}x + 3\frac{1}{2}$

Exercise 8:07

1 a 4 **b** 1 **c** -2 **d** 5 **e** $\frac{1}{4}$ **f** -1 **g** 3 **h** 1 **i** -5 **j** -3

2 a $y = 4x - 8$ **b** $y = x + 4$ **c** $y = -2x + 7$ **d** $y = 5x + 9$ **e** $y = \frac{1}{4}x + 1\frac{1}{2}$ **f** $y = -x + 7$

  g $y = 3x$ **h** $y = x$ **i** $y = -5x + 3$ **j** $y = -3x$

3 a $y = 2x + 2$ **b** $y = -3x + 15$ **c** $y = 4x + 4$ **d** $y = 2x + 4, 10 = 2(3) + 4$ **e** $y = x + 1$

4 a m of AB $= 1$, m of BC $= -3$, m of AC $= -\frac{3}{5}$ **b** $y = x + 3, y = -3x + 7, y = -\frac{3}{5}x - \frac{1}{5}$

  c $3, 7, -\frac{1}{5}$ **d** $y = 1$ **e** $m = 0, b = 1$

5 a $y = -2x + 4, -2 = -2(3) + 4$ **b** Equation of AB is $y = -2x - 2$. Substitute C $(3, -8)$: $-8 = -2(3) - 2$. $\therefore$ C lies on AB
  c Equation of line joining $(-2, -11)$ and $(3, 4)$ is $y = 3x - 5$. Substitute $(4, 7)$: $7 = 3(4) - 5$. $\therefore$ the points are collinear.

6 a $3x + 7y + 5 = 0$ **b** $6x - 5y - 8 = 0$ **c** $470x + 270y + 91 = 0$ **d** $42x + 138y + 29 = 0$

Prep Quiz 8:08

1 $\frac{1}{2}$ **2** yes   **3** $\frac{1}{2}$ **4** no   **5** $m_1 = -\frac{1}{3}$ **6** $m_2 = 3$ **7** $m_1 m_2 = -1$ **8** $m_3 = -2$ **9** $m_4 = \frac{1}{2}$ **10** $m_3 m_4 = -1$

Exercise 8:08

1 a yes   **b** no   **c** yes   **d** yes   **e** yes   **f** yes   **g** yes   **h** yes

2 a yes   **b** yes   **c** yes   **d** yes   **e** no   **f** yes   **g** yes   **h** yes

3 a $2x - y + 6 = 0$ and $y = 2x - 3$ **b** $x + y = 3$ and $y = -x + 8$ **c** AB and CD

4 a $x + 2y = 4, y = -0.5x + 5$ **b** $y = -1\frac{1}{2}x + 2, y = \frac{2}{3}x$

  c m of AB is -1; m of BC is 1 $\therefore$ AB $\perp$ BC (since $m_1 m_2 = -1$)

5 a $y = 5x + 3$ **b** $y = 3x - 1$ **c** $y = x + 3$ **d** $y = -x + 10$

6 a $y = 3x + 5$ **b** $y = x + 3$ **c** $y = 2x$ **d** $y = \frac{1}{2}x + 1 \cdot 5$

7 a $y = 5x - 7$ **b** $y = -3x + 3$ **c** $y = 3x + 5$ **d** $y = -3$ **e** $y = -3$

8 a $x + 2y - 8 = 0$ **b** $x - 3y - 1 = 0$ **c** $x + 3y - 15 = 0$ **d** $y = -3$ **e** $x = 3$

9 a $2x - 3y - 18 = 0$ **b** $3x - 4y + 11 = 0$ **c** $2x - 3y - 1 = 0$ **d** $a = \frac{29}{3}$

10 a A $(-1 \cdot 48, 1 \cdot 2)$; B $(2, 1 \cdot 2)$; C $(0, -2 \cdot 5)$; D $(2, -1 \cdot 7)$; E $(-1, 0)$

Prep Quiz 8:09

1 $x = 3$ **2** $x > 3$ **3** $x < 3$ **4** $x = 0$ **5** $x < 0$ **6** $x \geqslant 0$ **7** $x = -1$ **8** $x > -1$ **9** $x < -1$

10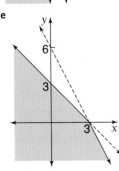

Exercise 8:09

1 a $x < -1$ **b** $y \leqslant 3$ **c** $y \leqslant -2x + 6$ **d** $x + y \leqslant 3$ **e** $y < 2x$

2 a 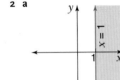 **b** 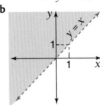 **c** 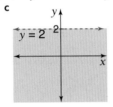 **d**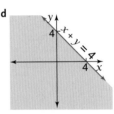

e 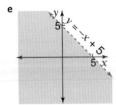 **f** 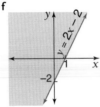 **g** 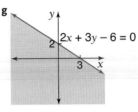 **h**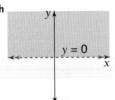

3 a 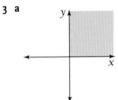 **b** 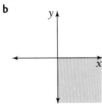 **c** 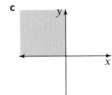 **d**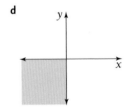

4 a 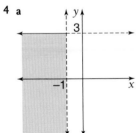 **b** 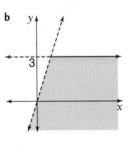 **c** 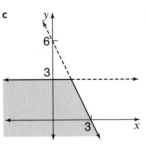 **d**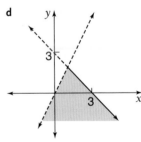

e 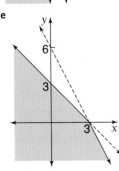 **f**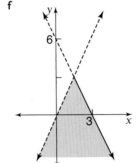

5 a 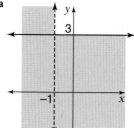 **b** 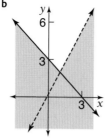 **c** 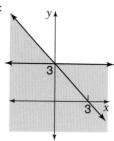 **d**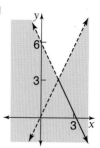

6 a $y > 1 \cup x > -1$ **b** $x + y > 3 \cap x \le 2$ **c** $y \le x \cup y \le -x$

7 a 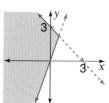 **b** 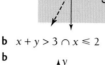 **c** 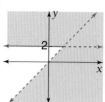 **d**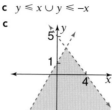

8 a 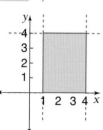 **b**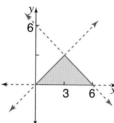

9 a $y \ge -2 \cap x \le 2 \cap y \le x$ **b** $y \le -x + 2 \cap y \ge -x - 2 \cap y \le x + 2 \cap y \ge x - 2$
c $y \le -\frac{1}{2}x + 1 \cap y \le \frac{1}{2}x + 1 \cap y \ge 2x - 4 \cap y \ge -2x - 4$

Diagnostic Test 8   Coordinate geometry

1 a $\sqrt{45} = 3\sqrt{5}$ **b** $\sqrt{61}$ **c** $\sqrt{34}$ **2 a** 10   **b** $\sqrt{13}$ **c** $\sqrt{17}$
3 a $(4, 6)$ **b** $(4, 1\frac{1}{2})$ **c** $(-1, -2\frac{1}{2})$ **4 a** 1   **b** -2 **c** $\frac{1}{2}$
5 a 4   **b** $-\frac{1}{2}$ **c** $\frac{2}{3}$ **6 a** yes   **b** no   **c** yes
7 a

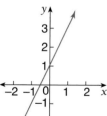 **b** 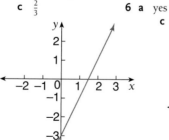 **c**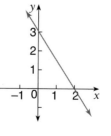

8 a x-int. $= 1\frac{1}{2}$ **b** x-int. $= 6$ **c** x-int. $= 4$
  y-int. $= -3$ y-int. $= 2$ y-int. $= 2$

9 a 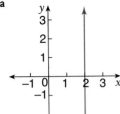 **b** 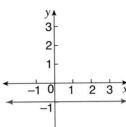 **c**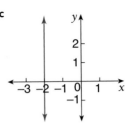

10 a $y = 3x + 2$ **b** $y = \frac{1}{2}x - 3$ **c** $y = 3 - x$

11 a $3x - y + 2 = 0$ **b** $x - 2y - 6 = 0$ **c** $x + y - 3 = 0$

12 a grad. = 2; y-int. = 3   **b** grad. = −2; y-int. = 3   **c** grad. = −1; y-int. = 4

13 a $y = 4x + 6$ **b** $y = -\frac{2}{3}x + 1$ **c** $y = -\frac{5}{2}x - \frac{1}{2}$

14 a $y = 2x + 2$ **b** $y = -3x + 6$ **c** $y = \frac{1}{2}x + 1$

15 a $y = 2x - 1$ **b** $y = -3x - 1$ **c** $y = \frac{4}{3}x$

16 a $y = 4x + 2$ **b** $y = -3x + 10$ **c** $y = -\frac{3}{2}x + \frac{5}{2}$ (or $3x + 2y - 5 = 0$)

     d $y = \frac{1}{2}x + 4\frac{1}{2}$ (or $x - 2y + 9 = 0$)

17 a $x \geqslant -1$ **b** $y \leqslant -2x$ **c** $2x - y + 2 \geqslant 0$

18 a 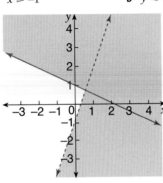   **b**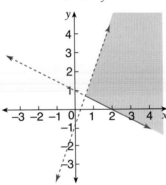

8A Revision Assignment

1 a $\sqrt{65}$ **b** $\frac{7}{4}$ **c** $(4, 1\frac{1}{2})$ **2 a** 13   **b** $\frac{12}{5} = 2 \cdot 4$ **c** $(4\frac{1}{2}, 11)$

3 a $7x - 4y - 22 = 0$ **b** $169\frac{1}{2}$ **c** $4x + 7y - 59 = 0$

4 a $(0, -3); y = x - 3$ **b** $y = -\frac{1}{2}x + 6; 12$ **c** $y = -2x + 6$

5 XY = YZ = $\sqrt{20}$ **6** $9x + 6y - 8 = 0$

   ∴ △XYZ is isosceles

   slope of YZ = 2   **7** $2x - 7y + 22 = 0$

   slope of YX = $-\frac{1}{2}$

   slope of YZ × slope of YX = −1   **8** $x \geqslant 0 \cap y \leqslant -x + 2 \cap y \geqslant x$

   ∴ YZ is perp. to YX

   ∴ ∠XYZ = 90°

   ∴ △XYZ is right-angled and isosceles.

8B Working Mathematically

1 a 1   **b** 31, 35, 39, 43, 47, 51, 55, 59 minutes   **2** 4

3 a 53%   **b** 12 cm   **c** 68%, 46%, 31%, 21%   **4 a** 6   **b** 3

5 126 984   **6 a**

1	2	3	4
3	4	1	2
4	3	2	1
2	1	4	3

b

1	2	3	4
2	1	4	3
3	4	1	2
4	3	2	1

Another solution is possible.

Chapter 9: Simultaneous equations

Investigation 9:01A   Solving problems by 'guess and check'
1 34 and 52   **2** 236 girls, 184 boys   **3** 23 fours, 6 sixes   **4** 216 BHP; 425 ICI

Prep Quiz 9:01
1 1   **2** −1   **3** −3   **4** −11   **5** $-2\frac{1}{2}$ **6** −2   **7** $-1\frac{1}{2}$ **8** $-4\frac{1}{2}$

9

x	0	1	2
y	−2	1	4

10
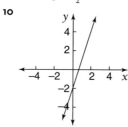

Exercise 9:01
1 a $x=1, y=2$ **b** $x=-2, y=-1$ **c** $x=-1, y=2$ **d** $x=0, y=3$ **e** $x=4, y=-1$ **f** $x=3, y=0$
  g No solution, since the lines are parallel.
  h An infinite number of solutions exist, eg (−1, 0), (0, 1), $(\frac{1}{2}, 1\frac{1}{2})$ etc. These two equations represent the same line.

2 a $x=0.2, y=1.2$ **b** $x=-3.3, y=-0.3$ **c** $x=1.3, y=-2.6$ **d** $x=2.8, y=-0.3$
3 a $x=2, y=-1$ **b** $x=2, y=-1$ **c** $x=1, y=-2$ **d** $x=2, y=4$ **e** $a=-1, b=-2$
  f $p=-2, q=2$ **g** $a=1, b=1$ **h** $p=6, q=2$

4 a
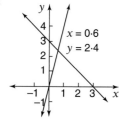

b
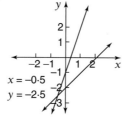

c
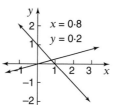

5 a
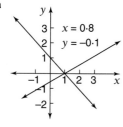

b
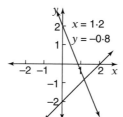

c
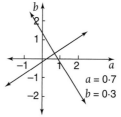

6 after $2\frac{1}{2}$ hours and 150 km

7 6 machines, $1080

8
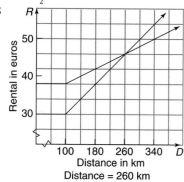
Distance = 260 km

9
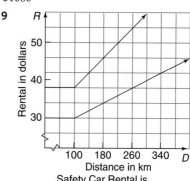
Safety Car Rental is always cheaper.

Exercise 9:02A

1 a $x = -1, y = 4$ b $x = 2, y = 5$ c $x = -2, y = -1$ d $x = 3, y = -2$ e $x = 4, y = 1$
 f $x = 4, y = 0$ g $x = 4, y = -2$ h $x = 3, y = 3$ i $x = 6, y = 2$ j $x = 1, y = 5$

2 a $x = 6, y = -1$ b $x = 2\frac{3}{4}, y = \frac{1}{2}$ c $x = -12, y = 10$ d $x = 5, y = 3$ e $x = -2, y = 4$
 f $x = 2, y = 3$ g $x = 3, y = 4$ h $x = 5, y = -2$ i $x = -2, y = 4$

3 a $x = \frac{7}{8}, y = \frac{3}{4}$ b $a = -3\frac{2}{3}, b = 17$ c $m = \frac{5}{6}, n = -1\frac{1}{12}$ d $x = \frac{1}{14}, y = -\frac{5}{14}$

4 a $a = 1\frac{1}{16}, b = \frac{3}{8}$ b $x = \frac{12}{17}, y = 1\frac{8}{17}$ c $m = 1\frac{2}{17}, n = \frac{10}{17}$ d $x = -2\frac{1}{3}, y = -4\frac{8}{9}$

Exercise 9:02B

1 a $x = 5, y = 4$ b $x = 5, y = 9$ c $x = 3, y = 1$ d $x = 5, y = -1$ e $x = 3, y = 2$
 f $x = 1, y = 2$ g $x = -2, y = 4$ h $x = -8, y = 2$ i $x = 1\frac{1}{3}, y = 7$ j $x = 7, y = -1\frac{2}{7}$
 k $x = 1, y = 2\frac{1}{2}$ l $x = 2, y = -3\frac{2}{5}$

2 a $x = 2, y = 1$ b $x = 3, y = -8$ c $x = 1, y = -4$ d $x = -2, y = -3$ e $x = 4, y = 6$
 f $x = 4, y = 1$ g $x = 3, y = 4$ h $x = 2\frac{1}{4}, y = \frac{1}{2}$ i $x = 4, y = 4$ j $x = 2, y = 1$
 k $x = -3, y = 5\frac{1}{5}$ l $x = -1, y = -4$

3 a $x = 1, y = 5$ b $x = 2, y = 3$ c $x = 5, y = -7$ d $x = -2, y = 4$ e $x = 2, y = 3$
 f $x = -2\frac{1}{3}, y = 1\frac{1}{2}$ g $x = 1, y = -2$ h $x = 1, y = -8$ i $x = 3, y = -5$

4 a $x = 4, y = 3$ b $x = 1, y = 5$ c $x = 2, y = 2$ d $x = 3, y = 2$ e $x = 1, y = -2$
 f $x = -2, y = 3$ g $x = 1, y = -2$ h $x = 3, y = 1$ i $x = 1, y = 2$ j $x = 0, y = 5$
 k $x = 2, y = 9$ l $x = -3, y = 2$ m $x = 1, y = -1$ n $x = 7\frac{8}{11}, y = 4\frac{4}{11}$

Exercise 9:03

1 a 7 and 18 b 32 and 65 c 3 and 9 d 11 and 2 e 5 and 22
2 a length = 8 cm, width = 3 cm b pen = 35c, pencil = 22c c maths = 72, science = 57
 d chocolate = 25c, drink = 45c e Bill = \$1, Jim = 50c
3 a $x = 5, y = 2$ b $x = 3, y = 2$ c $x = 15, y = 30$ d $x = 35, y = -35$ e $x = 7, y = 2$ f $x = 4, y = -2$
4 a length = $10\frac{1}{2}$ cm, width = $6\frac{1}{2}$ cm b box A = $28\frac{1}{3}$ kg, box B = 50 kg
 c 36 rows of 45 seats and 12 rows of 40 seats d 15 seniors and 75 juniors
5 a 8 aprons b 5 weeks

Reading Mathematics 9:03

1 30 g 2 837 3 $\frac{1}{2}$ cup 4 4·9 g 5 5·5 6 calcium 7 a 1·6 b 696 8 150 g

Diagnostic Test 9 Simultaneous equations

1 a $x = -2, y = -1$ b $x = 2, y = 3$ c $x = -4, y = 1$
2 a $x = 3, y = 1$ b $x = 3\frac{2}{5}, y = -1\frac{3}{5}$ c $a = 1\frac{3}{7}, b = 2\frac{5}{7}$
3 a $x = 2, y = 1$ b $x = 2\frac{3}{5}, y = -\frac{1}{5}$ c $a = 2, b = 0$

9A Revision Assignment

1 a $x = 3, y = 0$ b $x = 1\frac{1}{3}, y = 2\frac{1}{3}$ c $a = 1\frac{18}{33}, b = -\frac{6}{33}$ d $a = -2, b = -5\frac{1}{3}$ e $a = 1\frac{7}{16}, b = -1\frac{3}{16}$
 f $x = \frac{3}{5}, y = -\frac{8}{5}$ g $p = -1, q = 3$ h $x = \frac{1}{4}, y = -2$ i $m = 1\frac{3}{19}, n = \frac{10}{19}$
2 father is 54 years old, daughter is 18 yrs old 3 no. of adults = 59, no. of children = 141
4 share A = \$1.80, share B = \$1.20 5 length = 15 cm, width = 10 cm
6 length = 15 cm width = 5 cm 7 4 km/h

9B Working Mathematically

1 Answers will vary. a Answers will vary. b Overestimate
 c Estimate to the nearest metre, then add a few metres to the estimate.
2 1 3 $x = 72$ 4 a 3 b 6 c 10 d 28
5 10 6 Dixon-Fly, Wynn-Free, Goad-Back, McCully-Breast with a time of 147·65 seconds

Chapter 10: Graphs of physical phenomena

Prep Quiz 10:01A

1 200 km 2 450 km 3 25 km 4 4 h 5 10 h 6 70 km/h 7 500 km/h 8 A 9 B 10 B

Exercise 10:01A

1 a Tamara b Louise c Louise d After 2 hours and 5·5 hours e 100 km/h

2 a After 7 hours, 30 km/h **b** Yes, 2 h **c** 180 km
d 18 km/h **e** Shown on the graph in green
3 a **b** 85 km/h

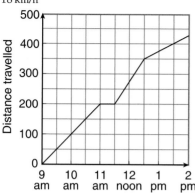

4 a 40 km **b** No, Day 2 **c** Day 4 **d** 8 km/day **e** 12 km
5 a Yes, blue **b** Blue: 28·6 km/h; Red 33·3 km/h **c** Red **d** The same **e** Red

Exercise 10:01B

1 a 15 km/h **b** 20 km/h **c** 10 km/h **d** 40 km/h
2 a 50 km/h **b** faster at point P than Q **c** faster at point R than Q **d** 100 km/h **e** 50 km/h
3 a 40 km/h **b** Benny (blue) **c** Robyn (red) **d** 1:30 pm and 2:15 pm
4 a approx 67 km/h **b i** A is less **ii** B is greater **c** F **d** B and C
5 a 30 m/s **b** 20 m/s **c** 40 m/s **d** decreasing **e** increasing
6 a i 15·6 m **ii** 9·1 m **b** increases at a decreasing rate **c i** 2·4 m/min **ii** 1·5 m/min

Prep Quiz 10:02

1 *A* **2** *B* **3** *C* **4** I **5** II **6** I **7** II **8** *Y* **9** *Z* **10** *X*

Exercise 10:02

1 a *E* **b** *D* **c** *A* **d** *C* **e** *F* **f** *B* **2** *C* **3** *B*
4 The tank is empty at the start. It is then filled at a steady rate until the water level is 3 m. This takes 20 mins.
The water level remains at 3 m for 20 mins. The tank is then emptied at a steady rate in 10 mins.
The tank remains empty for 10 mins. This cycle is then repeated.
5 a Jill is resting, then does some exercise requiring a steady application after which she rests, and her pulse rate
returns to normal.
b A balloon is blown up by mouth; it remains blown up for a short time until it bursts.
c A car is travelling at a steady rate and then stops. It is stationary for a while with the engine running, after which it
starts moving again but fuel is being used at a faster rate — maybe it is going up hill. It then begins to travel at a
more economical rate — maybe it is travelling on a flatter surface.
d Sam eats four pieces of pizza before being sick!
6 *B* **7** *I* **8** *A* — graph II, *B* — graph I, *C* — graph III, *D* — graph IV
9 salt *A* IV, salt *B* III, salt *C* I, salt *D* II **10 a** III **b** I **c** IV

11  **12** **13**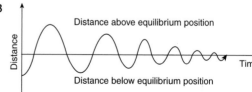

14 a **b** **c** **d**

e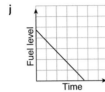

f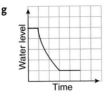

g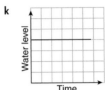

h

i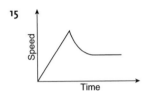

j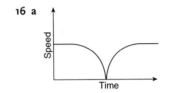

k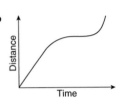

l

[Your graph for part (l) might be different, but hopefully it looks like this.]

15

16 a

b

17 a She would turn to the right, as in the picture shown in the question.
  b As the difference in steps increases, the radius of the circle decreases.
  c The curve of best fit is drawn to the right.
  d Since the product of d and t is always 180;

  $$dr = 180 \text{ or } r = \frac{180}{d}$$

  e When $d = 1.5$, $r = \dfrac{180}{1.5}$

  $$= 120$$

  ∴ the radius of the circle would be 120 metres.

  f When $d = 0$, $r = \dfrac{180}{0}$

  As $\dfrac{180}{0}$ cannot exist, there is no circle.

  The person walks in a straight line.

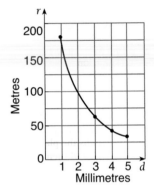

18 a 18 000 litres
  b

t	0	5	10	20	25	30
V	18 000	12 500	8000	2000	500	0

  d 9 minutes (approx.)
  e No. From the graph the pool drains rapidly at the beginning (perhaps high pressure) but decreases as it nears empty.

  c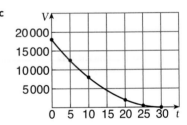

Fun Spot 10:02 Make words with your calculator

	¹G	L	O	²B	E			³G			⁴I
⁵H	O			L		⁶S	O	I	⁷L	S	
	O		⁸B	E		S		H	O		
		⁹H	O	S	¹⁰E		O		¹¹G	O	B
¹²G	O	O	S	E		E			S		
¹³L	E	G		¹⁴L	¹⁵O	S	¹⁶S		E		
	L				¹⁷H		I			¹⁸I	
	¹⁹S	²⁰H	E	L	L		O	²¹B	²²I	L	L
		I					G		L	L	
²³S	E	E	S		²⁴S	E	L	L			
H		²⁵S	I	L	O		O				
E					L		²⁶B	O	²⁷S	S	
	²⁸G	E	E	S	E				O		

Diagnostic Test 10   Graphs of Physical Phenomena

1 a 10 am **b** 35 km **c** 45 km **d** 11 am; $\frac{1}{2}$ hr **e** 60 km
2 a 60 km **b i** 10 km/h **ii** 40 km/h **iii** 80 km/h **c** 12 km/h **d** 30 km/h, between 2 pm and 3 pm
3 a 40 km/h **b** Q **c** 50 km/h
4 a Speed was decreasing since the slope of the curve was decreasing.
  b Speed $= \dfrac{\text{dist}}{\text{time}} = \dfrac{80}{2} = 40$ m/s.
  c Since tangent at H is horizontal, speed is 0 m/s, ball is stationary at this point, the ball has stopped increasing in height and is about to start moving down.
  d Assume tangent passes through (3, 60) and (4, 20) (or similar)
    so speed $= \dfrac{60-20}{4-3} = \dfrac{40}{1} = 40$ m/s
5 a 2·5 min **b** 45°C **c** 25°C **d** approx. 75°C **6 a** 60 g **b** approx. 80°C **c** I **d** No

7 a

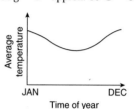

b

c

10A   Revision Assignment

1 a 20 km
  b 40 km
  c 10:30 am
  d Travers
  e 60 km, 8 km
3 a *E* **b** *C* **c** *A* **d** *D*
4 a In plane, then jump, parachute opens, slower descent to ground.
  b Kite gradually rising and dipping with the wind.
  c Initial cast, then below water, grabbed by a fish, reeled in to land.
  d Initial run, then jump over bar, landing on mat, then stand up.
5 Andrew climbs the platform but fails to jump and climbs back down. Helen jumps and then hauled back to platform.

2

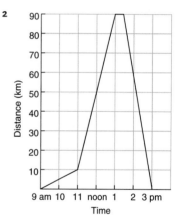

10B   Working Mathematically

1 a *collinear* points **b** *vertices* **c** *hypotenuse* **d** $a + b$ **e** 360°
  f $3 \times 180° = 540°$ **g** *AB* is a *diameter*, *OC* is a *radius* **h** *circumference* **i** *semicircle*
  j *AB* is a *tangent*. *CD* is an *arc*. *EF* is a *chord*.
2 a $2580 **b** $280 **c** 20·3% **3 a** 124·7 cm² **b** 593·8 cm² **c** 843·2 cm² **4** $545
5 a Jan **b** July **c** Feb **d** 110 mm **e** 1860 mm **f** 270 mm **g** 180 mm
6 a The first stands for 3 months, the second for 3 years.
  b i 5·9 kg **ii** 10 kg **iii** 11·7 kg **iv** 12·9 kg **v** 10·6 kg
  c 40% **d** From 4·3 kg to 6·2 kg **e** From about 2·5 kg to 4 kg

Chapter 11:   Deductive geometry

Prep Quiz 11:01

1 vertically opposite angles **2** supplementary angles **3** complementary angles
4 angles at a point **5** corresponding angles **6** alternate angles
7 co-interior angles **8** angle sum of a triangle = 180° **9** angle sum of a quadrilateral = 360°
10 base angles of an isosceles triangle are equal; (α = β)

Exercise 11:01A

1 a $\angle HEB = 55°$ (adj. angles on straight line) **b** $\angle EFB = 93°$ (vert. opp. $\angle HFG$)
  $\angle ABC = 55°$ (corresp. to $\angle HEB$, *DC* ∥ *GH*) $\angle ABC = 93°$ (corresp. to $\angle EFB$, *AD* ∥ *EG*)
  c $\angle BDG = 106°$ (supp. adj. angles)
  $\angle ABC = 106°$ (corresp. to $\angle BDG$, *HC* ∥ *FG*)

2 a ∠CBE = 39° (alt. to ∠DEB, AC ∥ DF)
$x = 141$ (adj. angles on a straight line)
c ∠EBC = 70° (corresp. to ∠GCD, EF ∥ GH)
$x = 70$ (vert. opp. ∠EBC)
e ∠DCH = 125° (corresp. to ∠CBF, EF ∥ GH)
$x = 35$ (since $x° + 90° = 125°$)
3 a ∠BCE = 82° (alt. to ∠ABC, AB ∥ ED)
$x = 98$ (co-int. to ∠BCE, BC ∥ FG)

c ∠BCF = 152° (co-int. to ∠ABC, AB ∥ FC)
∠DCF = 120° (co-int. to ∠CDE, FC ∥ ED)
$x° + 272° = 360°$ (angles at a point)
$x = 88$
e ∠BCF = 100° (alt. to ∠ABC, AB ∥ CF)
∠DCF = 59° (∠BCF − ∠BCD)
$x = 121$ (co-int. to ∠DCF, DE ∥ CF)
g ∠ABD = 42° (co-int. to ∠CDB, AB ∥ CD)
∠ABF = 77° (co-int. to ∠EFB, AB ∥ EF)
$x = 35$ (∠ABF − ∠ABD)

i ∠BDE = 76° (co-int. to ∠DBC, AC ∥ DE)
∠FDE = 38° (∠BDF = ∠FDE, given)
$x = 142$ (co-int. to ∠FDE, FG ∥ DE)

b ∠EBC = 88° (vert. opp. ∠ABF)
$x = 88$ (corresp. to ∠EBC, EF ∥ GH)
d ∠DAB = 92° (co-int. to ∠CBA, AD ∥ BC)
$x = 62$ (since $x° + 30° = 92°$)
f ∠CBE = 48° (alt. to ∠BED, AC ∥ DF)
$x = 42$ (supp. adj. angles)
b ∠BCD = 77° (alt. to ∠ABC, AB ∥ CD)
∠CDE = 103° (co-int. to ∠BCD, BC ∥ ED)
$x = 103$ (alt. to ∠CDE, EF ∥ CD)
d ∠ACF = 45° (alt. to ∠BAC, AB ∥ FC)
∠DCF = 18° (alt. to ∠CDE, FC ∥ DE)
$x = 63$ (∠ACF + ∠DCF)
f Draw CF right from C ∥ AB and DE
∠ACF = 40° (co-int. to ∠CAB, AB ∥ CF)
∠DCF = 52° (co-int. to ∠CDE, CF ∥ DE)
$x = 92$ (∠ACF + ∠DCF)
h Draw EI up from E ∥ AB and CD.
∠GEI = 73° (co-int. to ∠CGE, CD ∥ EI)
∠FEI = 106° (co-int. to ∠AFE, AB ∥ EI)
$x = 33$ (∠FEI − ∠GEI)

Exercise 11:01B

1 a ∠DCA = 40° (alt. to ∠EDC, ED ∥ CA)
∠ABC + 60° + 40° = 180° (angle sum of a △)
∠ABC = 80°
c ∠CDE + 40° + 75° = 180° (angle sum of a △)
∠CDE = 65°
∠ABC = 115° (co-int. to ∠CDE, AB ∥ ED)
2 a ∠CDB = 88° (suppl. to ∠EDB)
∠DBC = 72° (suppl. to ∠DBA)
$x° + 72° + 88° = 180°$ (angle sum of a △)
$x = 20$
c ∠DBC = 111° (vert. opp. to ∠ABE)
$x° + 111° + 25° = 180°$ (angle sum of a △)
$x = 44$
3 a ∠BCA = 80° (suppl. adj. angle)
∠BAC = 80° (base ang. of isos. △)
80° + 80° + ∠ABC = 180° (angle sum of △)
∠ABC = 20°
c ∠CBD = ∠CDB (base angles of isos. △)
68° + 2 × ∠CBD = 180° (angle sum of a △)
∠CBD = 56°
∠ABC = 124° (suppl. adj. angles)

4 a ∠EBC = 60° (suppl. adj. angles)
∠ECB = 55° (suppl. adj. angles)
∠BEC = $x°$ (vert. opp. angles)
$x° + 55° + 60° = 180°$ (angle sum of a △)
$x = 65$
c ∠DBC = 70° (corresp. to ∠EAB, EA ∥ DB)
95° = $x° + 70°$ (ext. angle of △DBC)
$x = 25$

e ∠BCE = 40° (suppl. adj. angles)
96° = $x° + 40°$ (ext. angle of △BCE)
$x = 56$

b ∠DCB = 30° (alt. to ∠EDC, ED ∥ BC)
∠ABC + 30° + 100° = 180° (angle sum of a △)
∠ABC = 50°

b ∠ABD = 48° (vert. opp. to ∠ABE)
$x° + 75° + 48° = 180°$ (angle sum of a △)
$x = 57$

b ∠CAB = 81° (alt. to ∠ACD, AB ∥ DC)
∠ABC = 81° (base angles of isos. △)

b $x = 110$ (alt. to ∠EBC, DE ∥ AC)

d 30° + 35° + ∠ABD = 180° (angle sum of a △)
∠ABD = 115°
∠DBC = 65° (suppl. adj. angles)
$x° = 50° + 65°$ (ext. angle of △BCD)
$x = 115$
f acute ∠BAC = 80° (angle of revol'n)
acute ∠ABC = 60° (angle of revol'n)
$x° + 60° + 80° = 180°$ (angle sum of a △)
$x = 40$

5 a $\angle BED = 58°$ (alt. to $\angle CBE$, $AC \parallel DE$)
$x° + 78° + 58° = 180°$ (angle sum of a $\triangle$)
$\qquad x = 44$

b $\angle BDA = x°$ (alt. to $\angle CED$, $BD \parallel CE$)
$x° + 48° + 60° = 180°$ (angle sum of a $\triangle$)
$\qquad x = 72$

c $\angle CED = 55°$ (DEF is a straight line)
$\angle BCE = x°$ (alt. to $\angle ABF$, $BF \parallel CE$)
$x° = 46° + 55°$ (ext. angle of $\triangle CDE$)
$\qquad x = 101$

d $\angle ACD = x° + 42°$ (ext. angle of $\triangle ABC$)
$\angle CAD = x° + 42°$ (base angles of isos. $\triangle DAC$)
$122° = 2x° + 84°$ (ext. angle of $\triangle ACD$)
$\qquad x = 19$

e $\angle BCD = 125°$ (co-int. to $\angle ADC$, $BE \parallel AD$)
$\angle ACD = 55°$ (base angles of isos. $\triangle ACD$)
$\angle BCA = 70°$ ($\angle BCD - \angle ACD$)
$\angle ABC = 70°$ (base angles of isos. $\triangle ABC$)
$x° + 140° = 180°$ (angle sum of $\triangle ABC$)
$\qquad x = 40$

f $\triangle OAB$ and $\triangle OBC$ are isosceles (radii equal)
$\angle ABO = 60°$ (base angles of isos. $\triangle ABO$)
$\angle COB = 120°$ (ext. angle $\triangle ABO$)
$\angle OCB = x°$ (base angles of isos. $\triangle OBC$)
$2x° + 120° = 180°$ (angle sum of $\triangle OBC$)
$\qquad x = 30$

Prep Quiz 11:01C

1 120   **2** 60   **3** 80   **4** 105   **5** 50   **6** 80   **7** 110   **8** 70   **9** 110   **10** 360°

Exercise 11:01C

1 a $\angle CBE = 80°$ (vert. opp. $\angle FBA$)
$\qquad x = 80$ (opp. angles of a par'm)

b $\angle ABE = 78°$ (opp. angles of a par'm)
$\qquad x = 78$ (vert. opp. $\angle ABE$)

c $\angle CBE = 110°$ (vert. opp. $\angle ABF$)
$x° + 60° + 110° + 90° = 360°$ (angle sum of a quad.)
$\qquad x = 100$

d $\angle FBC = 80°$ (suppl. adj. angles)
$\angle CDF = 85°$ (suppl. adj. angles)
$x° + 85° + 80° + 80° = 360°$ (angle sum of a quad.)
$\qquad x = 115$

e $\angle EBC + 60° + 100° + 70° = 360°$ (angle sum of a quad.)
$\angle EBC = 130°$
$\qquad x = 50$ (suppl. adj. angles)

f Reflex $\angle ADC = 360° - 130° = 230°$
(angle sum at point D is $360°$)
$x° + 342° = 360°$ (angle sum of quad. $ABCD$)
$\qquad x = 18$

2 a $\angle CAB + 65° + 145° + 100° = 360°$ (angle sum of a quad.)
$\angle CAB = 50°$
$\angle CAB = \angle ABC$ (base angles of an isos. $\triangle$)
$\angle ABC = 50°$

b $\angle BAC + 70° + 150° + 85° = 360°$
$\qquad$ (angle sum of a quad.)
$\angle BAC = 55°$
$\angle BCA = 55°$ (base angles of an isos. $\triangle$)
$\angle ABC + 55° + 55° = 180°$ (angle sum of a $\triangle$)
$\angle ABC = 70°$

c $\angle CAB + 95° + 80° + 115° = 360°$ (angle sum of a quad.)
$\angle CAB = 70°$
$\angle ABC = 70°$ (base angles of an isos. $\triangle$)

d $\angle EAD = \angle EDA$ (base angles of isos. $\triangle$)
$2 \times \angle EAD + 100° = 180°$ (angle sum of a $\triangle$)
$\angle EAD = 40°$
$\angle BAD + \angle ADC + \angle DCB + \angle ABC = 360°$
$\qquad$ (angle sum of a quad.)
$60° + 110° + 100° + \angle ABC = 360°$
$\angle ABC = 90°$

e $\angle BAC + 80° + 110° + 90° = 360°$ (angle sum of a quad.)
$\angle BAC = 80°$
$\angle ACB = 80°$ (base angles of isos. $\triangle$)
$\angle ABC + 80° + 80° = 180°$ (angle sum of a $\triangle$)
$\angle ABC = 20°$

f $\angle EAD = 80°$ (base angles of isos. $\triangle$)
$\angle BAC + 30° + 80° = 180°$ (angle sum of $\triangle$)
$\angle BAC = 70°$
$\angle ABC = 70°$ (base angle of isos. $\triangle$)

3 a $AE = EB$ (Diag. of a rect. bisect each other
$\qquad$ and are equal)
$\qquad x = 30$ (base angle of isos. $\triangle$)

b $EB = EC$ (Diag. of a rect. bisect each other
$\qquad$ and are equal)
$\angle ECB = x°$ (base angles of isos. $\triangle$)
$x° + x° + 40° = 180°$ (angle sum of a $\triangle$)
$\qquad x = 70$

c $DE = EC$ (Diag. of a rect. bisect each other
$\qquad$ and are equal)
$\qquad x = 32$ (base angles of isos. $\triangle$)

4 a $\angle EAD = x°$ (base angles of isos. $\triangle$)
$\angle ADC = 2x°$ (ext. angle of $\triangle ADE$)
$2x° = 70°$ (opp. angles of par'm are equal)
$\qquad x = 35$

b $\angle GCF = 70°$ (corresp. angles, $AD \parallel BC$)
$\angle GFC = x°$ (corresp. angles, $BE \parallel AF$)
$\angle CGF = 30°$ (vert. opp. angles)
$x° + 30° + 70° = 180°$ (angle sum of a $\triangle$)
$\qquad x = 80$

c $\angle ADB = 40°$ (alt. angles, $AE \parallel BD$)
$\angle ADB = x°$ (alt. angles, $AD \parallel BC$)
$\qquad x = 40$

Investigation 11:02A   The angle sum of a polygon

2

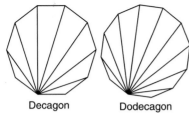

Decagon   Dodecagon

3

No. of sides in polygon	3	4	5	6	7	8	9	10	12
No. of triangles	1	2	3	4	5	6	7	8	10

4 The 'number of triangles' is two less than the 'number of sides'.

5 $n - 2$

6 $(n - 2) \times 180$

7 $\dfrac{(n - 2) \times 180}{n}$

Investigation 11:02B   The exterior angle sum of a convex polygon

1 6   **2** $6 \times 180° = 1080°$ **3** 720°   **4** $1080° - 720° = 360°$

5 (1) 5, 5   (2) $5 \times 180° = 900°$ (3) 540°   (4) $900° - 540° = 360°$ **6** The exterior angles sum to 360°.

Exercise 11:02

1 a i 60° **ii** 120°   **b i** 90° **ii** 90°   **c i** 108° **ii** 52°   **d i** 120° **ii** 60°   **e i** 135° **ii** 45°   **f i** 144° **ii** 36°

2 a 12   **b** 24   **c** 15   **d** 18   **e** 36

4 a square, equilateral, triangle   **b** octagons and squares; equilateral triangles and hexagons

Investigation 11:02A   Regular polygons and tessellations

1 120°   **2** 3   **3** 360°   **4** A regular pentagon will not tessellate because the interior angles (108°) cannot
add at a vertex to give 360°   **5** Square and equilateral triangle.

Investigation 11:02B   Spreadsheet

1 24, 3960, 165   **2** 15840°, 176°   **3 a** 30   **b** 36   **c** $n > 45$

Prep Quiz 11:03

1 and **2**

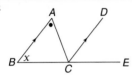

3 ∠DCE   **4** ∠ACD   **5** ∠ACD
6 ∠ACD and ∠DCE   **7** b
8 $180 - a$ **9** c **10** $a = c$

Exercise 11:03

1 a ∠AEF = $x°$ (vert. opp. ∠s)
   ∠AEF = $y°$ (corresp. ∠s, ‖ lines)
   ∴ $x = y$

b ∠DBC = $x°$ (vert. opp. ∠s)
   ∠BDE = $180° - x°$ (co-int. ∠s, $BC ‖ DE$)
   ∠BDE = $180° - y°$ (co-int. ∠s, $DB ‖ EC$)
   ∴ $180 - x = 180 - y$
   ∴ $x = y$

Note: Other proofs may exist for exercises in deductive reasoning.

2

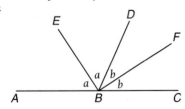

Let ∠ABD be $2a°$ and ∠DBC be $2b°$.
∴ ∠ABC = $2a° + 2b°$ (∠ABD + ∠DBC)
$2(a + b)° = 180°$ (∠ABC is a straight angle)
$(a + b) = 90°$
Now ∠EBD = $a°$ (BE bisects ∠ABD; given)
   ∠DBF = $b°$ (BF bisects ∠DBC; given)
   ∴ ∠EBF = $(a + b)° = 90°$, (∠EBD + ∠DBF)
∴ $EB ⊥ BF$ (Q.E.D.)

3

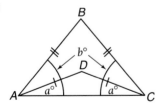

Let ∠DAC and ∠DCA be $a°$ (base angles of isos. △ADC).
Let ∠BAC and ∠BCA be $b°$ (base angles of isos. △ABC).
∴ ∠BAD = $b° - a°$ (∠BAC − ∠DAC)
   ∠BCD = $b° - a°$ (∠BCA − ∠DCA)
∴ ∠BAD = ∠BCD (Q.E.D.)

4

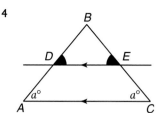

Let ∠BAC and ∠BCA be $a°$ (base angles of isos. △ABC).
∠BDE = $a°$ (corresp. to ∠BAC, DE ∥ AC)
∠BED = $a°$ (corresp. to ∠BCA, DE ∥ AC)
∴ ∠BDE = ∠BED (ie base angles of △DBE are equal)
∴ △DBE is isosceles (Q.E.D.)

5

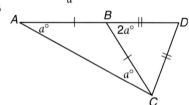

Let ∠BAD and ∠BCD be $a°$ (base angles of isos. △ABC).
∠AED = ∠CFD = 90° (DE ⊥ AB, DF ⊥ BC)
∠EDA = 180° − $a°$ − 90° (angle sum of △AED)
∠FDC = 180° − $a°$ − 90° (angle sum of △DFC)
∴ ∠EDA = ∠FDC (Q.E.D.)

6

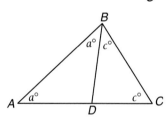

Let ∠BAC and ∠BCA be $a°$ (base angles of isos. △ABC).
∴ ∠DBC = $2a°$ (ext. angle of △ABC)
∠DCB = $2a°$ (base angles of isos. △BDC)
∴ ∠BCD = 2 × ∠BCA (Q.E.D.)

7

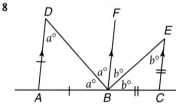

Construction: Draw interval BD.
Let ∠BAD be $a°$ and ∠BCD be $c°$.
∴ ∠ABD = $a°$ (base angles of isos. △ABD)
∠DBC = $c°$ (base angles of isos. △BCD)
$2a° + 2c° = 180°$ (angle sum of △ABC)
$a° + c° = 90°$ (dividing both sides by 2)
∴ ∠ABC = 90°, (∠ABD + ∠DBC) (Q.E.D.)

8

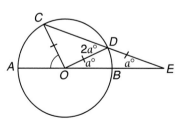

Construction: Draw BF ∥ AD and CE.
Let ∠ABD be $a°$ and ∠CBE be $b°$.
∠ADB = $a°$ (base angles of isos. △ADB)
∠CEB = $b°$ (base angles of isos. △BCE)
∠FBD = $a°$ (alt. to ∠ADB, BF ∥ AD)
∠FBE = $b°$ (alt. to ∠CEB, BF ∥ CE)
$2a° + 2b° = 180°$ (∠ABC is straight)
∴ $a° + b° = 90°$ (dividing both sides by 2)
∠DBE = 90°, (∠FBD + ∠FBE) (Q.E.D.)

9

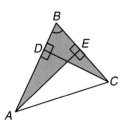

Let ∠DOB and ∠DEO be $a°$ (base angles of isos. △ODE).
∠CDO = $2a°$ (ext. angle of △ODE)
∠OCD = $2a°$ (base angles of isos. △OCD, radii equal)
∴ ∠AOC = ∠DEO + ∠OCD (ext. angle of △OCE)
∴ ∠AOC = $a° + 2a° = 3a°$
∴ ∠AOC = 3 × ∠DOB (Q.E.D.)

10

Let ∠BAE = $x°$, ∠ABE = $y°$ and ∠BCD = $z°$
$x + y = 90$ (comp. ∠s in △ABE)
$z + y = 90$ (comp. ∠s in △BCD)
∴ $x = z$
∴ ∠BAE = ∠BCD

11

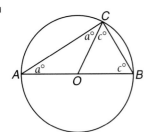

Construction: Draw interval OC
$OA = OC = OB$ (radii of circle)
Let $\angle OAC = a°$ and $\angle OBC = c°$
$\angle ACO = a°$ (base angles of isos. $\triangle ACO$)
$\angle BCO = c°$ (base angles of isos. $\triangle BCO$)
$2a° + 2c° = 180°$ (angle sum of $\triangle ABC$)
$\quad a° + c° = 90°$
$\therefore \angle ACB = 90°$ ($\angle ACO + \angle BCO$) (Q.E.D.)

12

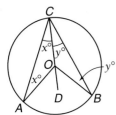

Construction: Join CO and extend it to D.
$OA = OB = OC$ (radii of circle)
Let $\angle ACO = x°$ and $\angle BCO = y°$
$\quad\angle ACB = \angle ACO + \angle BCO$
$\qquad\quad = x° + y°$
$\angle CAO = x°$ (base angles of isos. $\triangle OAC$)
$\angle AOD = 2x°$ (ext. angle of $\triangle OAC$)
Similarly,
$\angle CBO = y°$ and $\angle BOD = 2y°$
$\angle AOB = \angle AOD + \angle BOD$
$\qquad\quad = 2x° + 2y°$
$\qquad\quad = 2(x° + y°)$
$\qquad\quad = 2 \times \angle ACB$ (Q.E.D.)

Prep Quiz 11:04

1 figure C **2** figure D **3** $\angle L$ **4** QP **5** $\angle O$ **6** PO **7** $\angle C$ **8** no **9** no **10** no

Exercise 11:04

1 a

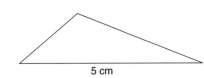

5 cm   5 cm

b

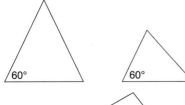

60°   60°

c

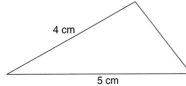

4 cm   4 cm

5 cm   5 cm

d

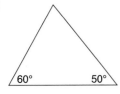

60°   50°   60°   50°

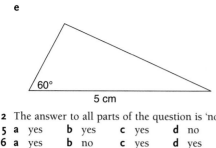 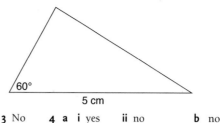

2 The answer to all parts of the question is 'no'. **3** No **4 a i** yes **ii** no **b** no
5 a yes **b** yes **c** yes **d** no **e** yes
6 a yes **b** no **c** yes **d** yes **e** it is between the two sides
  f When the angle is placed between the two sides the positions of the remaining two vertices are fixed.
    Hence there is only one possible answer for the length of the third side and the size of the other angles.
7 a 50° **b** yes **c** yes **d** opposite the smallest angle **e** no **f** yes
  g It has to be placed opposite the same-sized angle.
8 a yes **b** Pythagoras' theorem **c** yes

Prep Quiz 11:05
1 EF **2** ED **3** DF **4** ∠E **5** ∠D **6** ∠F **7** PQ **8** QR **9** 70° **10** no

Exercise 11:05
1 a RHS **b** SSS **c** AAS **d** SAS **e** AAS
2 a yes (SSS) **b** no **c** no **d** no
3 a In △s ABC and CDA
  i AC is common
  ii ∠BAC = ∠DCA (data)
    ∠ABC = ∠CDA (data)
    ∴ △ABC ≡ △CDA (AAS)
  b In △s CED and CAB
    i DC = AC (data)
    ii EC = BC (data)
    iii ∠DCE = ∠ACD (vert. opp. ∠s)
      ∴ △CED ≡ △CAB (SAS)
  c In △s PQN and LMN
    i QN = MN (data)
    ii ∠NPQ = ∠NLM (alt. ∠s PQ // LM)
    iii ∠NQP = ∠NML (alt. ∠s PQ // LM)
      △PQN ≡ △LMN (AAS)
  d In △s POQ and TOS
    i OP = OT (radii of circle)
    ii OQ = OS (radii of circle)
    iii ∠POQ = ∠TOS (data)
      ∴ △POQ ≡ △TOS (SAS)
  e In △s ABC and ADC
    i AC is common
    ii AB = AD (data)
    iii CB = CD (data)
      ∴ △ABC ≡ △ADC (SSS)
  f In △s AOE and COD
    i AO = CO (radii of circle)
    ii EO = DO (radii of circle)
    iii ∠AOE = ∠COD (vert. opp. ∠s)
      ∴ △AOE ≡ △COD (SAS)
4 a In △s ABC and DEC:
  (1) BC = CE (given)
  (2) AC = DC (given)
  (3) ∠ACB = ∠DCE (vert. opp. ∠s)
    ∴ △ABC ≡ △DEC (SAS)
  b In △s ABD and BAC:
    (1) BD = AC (given)
    (2) ∠ABC = ∠BAC (given)
    (3) AB is common
      ∴ △ABD ≡ △BAC (SAS)
  c In △s ABD and ACD:
    (1) AB = AC (given)
    (2) AD is common
    (3) ∠ADB = ∠ADC (given)
      ∴ △ABD ≡ △ACD (RHS)
  d In △s ABC and ADC:
    (1) AB = AD (given)
    (2) BC = DC (given)
    (3) AC is common
      ∴ △ABC ≡ △ADC (SSS)
  e In △s ABD and ACD:
    (1) ∠ABD = ∠ACD (given)
    (2) ∠ADB = ∠ADC (given)
    (3) AD is common
      ∴ △ABD ≡ △ACD (AAS)
  f In △s AOB and COD:
    (1) OA = OC (radii of circle)
    (2) OB = OD (radii of circle)
    (3) ∠AOB = ∠COD (given)
      ∴ △AOB ≡ △COD (SAS)
  g In △s ABF and CDE:
    (1) ∠AFB = ∠CED (given)
    (2) AB = CD (sides of a square are equal)
    (3) ∠ABF = ∠EDC (angles of a square are equal)
      ∴ △ABF ≡ △CDE (AAS)

5 a In △s *ABC* and *DCB*:
   (1) ∠*ACB* = ∠*DBC* (given)
   (2) *AC* = *DB* (given)
   (3) *BC* is common
   ∴ △*ABC* ≡ △*DCB* (SAS)

b In △s *DBC* and *ECB*:
   (1) ∠*BDC* = ∠*CEB* (given)
   (2) ∠*ABC* = ∠*ACB* (given)
   (3) *BC* is common
   ∴ △*DBC* ≡ △*EBC* (AAS)

Exercise 11:06

Note: The word 'matching' can be used in place of 'corresponding' or its abbreviation 'corresp'.

1 a (AAS); *DE* = 10 cm

b (SAS); *DE* = 27 cm

2 a △*ABC* ≡ △*EDF* (SAS)
   ∴ *x* = 38·5 (corresp. sides of cong't △s)

b △*XYZ* ≡ △*LNM* (AAS)
   ∴ *b* = 12·2 (corresp. sides of cong't △s)

c △*ABC* ≡ △*CDE* (SAS)
   ∴ *x* = 50 (corresp. ∠s of cong't △s)

3 a In △s *ABD* and *CBD*
   i *BA* = *BC* (data)
   ii *DA* = *DC* (data)
   iii *BD* is common
   ∴ △*ABD* ≡ △*CBD* (SSS)
   ∴ *a* = 120 (corresp. ∠s of cong't △s)

b In △s *ADB* and *ADC*
   i *AD* is common
   ii *AB* = *AC* (data)
   iii ∠*ADB* = ∠*ADC* = 90° (data)
   ∴ △*ADB* ≡ △*ADC* (RHS)
   ∴ *x* = 4 (corresp. sides of cong't △s)

c In △s *AOB* and *OCD*
   i *OA* = *OC* (radii of circle)
   ii *OB* = *OD* (radii of circle)
   iii ∠*AOB* = ∠*COD* (data)
   ∴ △*OAB* ≡ △*OCD* (SAS)
   ∴ *x* = 8 (corresp. sides of cong't △s)

d In △s *CAB* and *CED*
   i *AC* = *EC* (data)
   ii ∠*ACB* = ∠*ECD* (vert. opp. ∠s)
   iii *BC* = *DC* (data)
   ∴ △*CAB* ≡ △*CED* (SAS)
   ∴ *x* = 98 (corresp. ∠s of cong't △s)

e In △s *BAC* and *DCA*
   i *BA* = *DC* (data)
   ii ∠*BAC* = ∠*DCA* (data)
   iii *CA* is common
   △*BAC* ≡ △*DCA* (SAS)
   ∴ *x* = 29 (corresp. ∠s of cong't △s)

f In △s *AEB* and *BDA*
   i *AB* is common
   ii ∠*EAB* = ∠*DBA* (data)
   iii *AE* = *BD* (data)
   ∴ △*AEB* ≡ △*BDA* (SAS)
   ∴ ∠*ADB* = 85° (corresp. ∠s of cong't △s)
   ∴ *a* + 70 + 85 = 180 (angle sum of △)
   ∴ *a* = 25

4 a In △s *ABC* and *ADC*:
   (1) *AB* = *AD* (given)
   (2) *BC* = *DC* (given)
   (3) *AC* is common
   ∴ △*ABC* ≡ △*ADC* (SSS)
   ∴ ∠*BAC* = ∠*DAC* (corresp. ∠s of cong't △s)

b In △s *ABC* and *DBC*:
   (1) *AC* = *CD* (given)
   (2) *AB* = *DB* (given)
   (3) *BC* is common
   ∴ △*ABC* ≡ △*DBC* (SSS)
   ∴ ∠*ABC* = ∠*CBD* (corresp. ∠s of cong't △s)

c In △s *AXB* and *DXC*:
   (1) *AX* = *XD* (given)
   (2) *BX* = *XC* (given)
   (3) ∠*AXB* = ∠*CXD* (vert. opp. ∠s)
   ∴ △*AXB* ≡ △*DXC* (SAS)
   ∴ ∠*BAX* = ∠*CDX* (corresp. ∠s of cong't △s)
   But ∠*ABX* and ∠*DCX* are alternate angles
   ∴ *AB* // *CD* (equal alt. ∠s)

d In △s *AOD* and *BOD*:
   (1) *AO* = *OB* (radii of a circle)
   (2) *OD* is common
   (3) ∠*ADO* = ∠*BDO* (given)
   ∴ △*AOD* ≡ △*BOD* (RHS)
   ∴ *AD* = *DB* (corresp. sides of cong't △s)

e In △s *OAC* and *OBC*:
   (1) *OA* = *OB* (radii of circle)
   (2) *AC* = *CB* (given)
   (3) *OC* is common
   ∴ △*OAC* ≡ △*OBC* (SSS)
   ∴ ∠*OCA* = ∠*OCB* (corresp. ∠s of cong't △s)
   Now ∠*OCA* + ∠*OCB* = 180° (adj. supp. ∠s)
   ∴ 2 × ∠*OCA* = 180°
   ∴ ∠*OCA* = 90°
   ∴ ∠*OCA* = ∠*OCB* = 90°

f In △s *AOC* and *BOD*:
   i *OA* = *OB* (radii of circle)
   ii *OC* = *OD* (radii of circle)
   iii ∠*AOC* = ∠*BOD* (vert. opp. angles)
   ∴ △*AOC* ≡ △*BOD* (SAS)
   AC = *DB* (corresp. sides of cong. △s)
   ∠*CAO* = ∠*DBO* (corresp. angles of cong. △s)
   ∴ *AC* // *DB* (alt. angles *CAO*, *DBO* are equal)

Exercise 11:07

1
$$\angle BCE = \beta \text{ (alt. } \angle\text{s, } AB \parallel CE)$$
$$\angle ECD = \alpha \text{ (corresp. } \angle\text{s, } AB \parallel CE)$$
$$\therefore \angle BCD = \angle BCE + \angle ECD$$
$$= \alpha + \beta$$

2 $x° + c° = 180°$ (adj. $\angle$s on a st. line)
$y° + b° = 180°$ (adj. $\angle$s on a st. line)
$z° + a° = 180°$ (adj. $\angle$s on a st. line)
$(x° + c°) + (y° + b°) + (z° + a°) = 540°$
$(x° + y° + z°) + (a° + b° + c°) = 540°$
But $x° + y° + z° = 180°$ ($\angle$ sum of a $\triangle$)
$\therefore 180° + (a° + b° + c°) = 540°$
$\therefore a° + b° + c° = 360°$

3

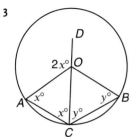

Produce CO to D
$AO = BO = CO$ (radii of circle)
Let $\angle OCA = x°$ and $\angle OCB = y°$
$\therefore \angle ACB = x° + y°$
$\angle OAC = x°$ (base $\angle$s of isos. $\triangle OAC$)
$\angle AOD = 2x°$ (ext. $\angle$ of $\triangle AOC$)
$\angle OBC = y°$ (base $\angle$s of isos. $\triangle OBC$)
$\angle BOD = 2y°$ (ext. $\angle$ of $\triangle BOC$)
Reflex $\angle AOB = \angle AOD + \angle BOD$
$$= 2x° + 2y°$$
$$= 2(x° + y°)$$
$$= 2 \times \angle ACB$$

4

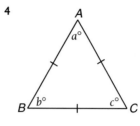

Let the angles be $a°$, $b°$ and $c°$
Since $AB = AC$
$b° = c°$
(base $\angle$s of isos. $\triangle$)
Since $BA = BC$
$a° = c°$
(base $\angle$s of isos. $\triangle$)
$\therefore a° = b° = c°$
$a° + b° + c° = 180°$
($\angle$ sum of $\triangle$)
$\therefore 3a° = 180°$
$\therefore a = 60$
$\therefore a = b = c = 60$

5 a

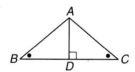

$\angle B = \angle C$ (data)
Draw a perpendicular from A to BC,
meeting BC in D.
In $\triangle$s ABD and ACD
  i $\angle ABD = \angle ACD$ (data)
  ii $\angle ADB = \angle ADC = 90°$ (by construction)
  iii AD is common
$\therefore \triangle ABD \equiv \triangle ACD$ (AAS)
$\therefore AB = AC$ (corresp. sides of cong't $\triangle$s)

b

$\angle A = \angle B = \angle C$ (data)
$\therefore AC = AB$ (using part **a** and $\angle B = \angle C$)
$\therefore AB = CB$ (using part **a** and $\angle A = \angle C$)
$\therefore AB = AC = CB$
$\therefore \triangle ABC$ is equilateral

6 a In $\triangle$s ABD and ACD
  i $AB = AC$ (data)
  ii AD is common
  iii $\angle ADB = \angle ADC = 90°$ (by construction)
    $\therefore \triangle ABD \equiv \triangle ACD$ (RHS)
    $\therefore BD = CD$ (corresp. sides of cong't $\triangle$s)
    $\therefore AD$ bisects BC

b In $\triangle$s ABD and ACD
  i $AB = AC$ (data)
  ii AD is common
  iii $BD = CD$ (data)
    $\therefore \triangle ABD \equiv \triangle ACD$ (SSS)
    $\therefore \angle ADB = \angle ADC$ (corresp. $\angle$s of cong't $\triangle$s)
    $\angle ADB + \angle ADC = 180°$ (adj. supp. $\angle$s)
    $\therefore 2 \times \angle ADB = 180°$
    $\angle ADB = 90°$
    $\therefore AD \perp BC$

7 a $72°$
  b A hexagon. If the radius equals the side length then the triangle is equilateral and $x = 60°$. As $360° \div 60° = 6$, the hexagon is the only polygon for which this will occur.

8 a SAS   **b** corresp. sides of cong't $\triangle$s   **c** SAS   **d** corrresp. sides of cong't $\triangle$s
  e because they are both equal to AS.   **f** isosceles
  g A line drawn from the midpoint of the base of an isosceles triangle to the third vertex is perpendicular to the base.

Exercise 11:08

1 ① quadrilateral   ② trapezium   ③ parallelogram   ④ rectangle   ⑤ square   ⑥ rhombus

2 a alt ∠s and // lines   **b** alt. ∠s and // lines   **c** yes

3 In △s *ABE* and *CDE*:
  (1) *AB* = *DC* (opp. sides of a par'm)
  (2) ∠*BAE* = ∠*DCE* (alt. ∠s, *AB* // *DC*)
  (3) ∠*EBA* = ∠*EDC* (alt. ∠s, *AB* // *DC*)
  ∴ △*ABE* ≡ △*CDE* (AAS)
  ∴ *AE* = *EC* (corresp. sides of cong't △s)
  ∴ *EB* = *ED* (corresp. sides of cong't △s)

  d In △s *ABC* and *CDA*:
  (1) ∠*BAC* = ∠*DCA* (alt. ∠s and // lines)
  (2) ∠*BCA* = ∠*DAC* (alt. ∠s and // lines)
  (3) *AC* is common
  ∴ △*ABC* ≡ △*CDA* (AAS)
  ∴ **i** ∠*ABC* = ∠*CDA* (corresp. ∠s of cong't △s)
  ii *AB* = *DC* (corresp. sides of cont'g △s)
    BC = *AD* (corresp. sides of cong't △s)

4 a Opposite sides of a parallelogram are equal.   **b** Opposite sides of a parallelogram are equal.
  c *AB* = *DC* and *BC* = *AD* proved above. But *AD* = *DC* (given), ∴ *AB* = *DC* = *AD* = *BC*
  d i isosceles   **ii** isosceles   **e** equal ∠s of isos. △   **f** equal ∠s of isos. △
  g alt. ∠s and // lines.   **h** ∠*ADB*, ∠*BDC*, ∠*DBC*
  i

  ∠*BAC* = ∠*ACD* (alt. ∠s, *AB* // *DC*)
  ∠*BCA* = ∠*DAC* (alt. ∠s, *AD* // *BC*)
  But ∠*BAC* = ∠*BCA* (equal ∠s of isos. △)
  ∴ ∠*BAC* = ∠*ACD* = ∠*BCA* = ∠*DAC*
  ∴ *AC* bisects the angles *DAB* and *DCB*.

5 a Diagonals of a parallelogram bisect each other.
  b In △s *ABE* and *CBE*:
  (1) *AE* = *EC* (diag. of par'm bisect each other)
  (2) *BE* is common
  (3) *AB* = *BC* (sides of a rhombus are equal)
  ∴ △*ABE* ≡ △*CBE* (SSS)
  ∴ ∠*AEB* = ∠*BEC* (corresp. ∠s of cong't △s)
  But ∠*AEB* + ∠*BEC* = 180° (adj. supp. ∠s)
  ∴ 2 × ∠*AEB* = 180°
  ∴ ∠*AEB* = 90°
  ∴ ∠*AEB* = ∠*BEC* = 90°

6 a ∠*DAB* = 90° (co-int. ∠s, *AB* // *DC*)
  ∠*ABC* = 90° (co-int. ∠s, *AD* // *BC*)
  ∠*BCD* = 90° (co-int. ∠s, *AB* // *DC*)
  b In △s *ABD* and *DCA*:
  (1) *AB* = *DC* (opp. sides of a par'm are equal)
  (2) *AD* is common
  (3) ∠*ADC* = ∠*DAB* (∠s of a rectangle)
  ∴ △*ABD* ≡ △*DCA* (SAS)
  ∴ *AC* = *DB* (corresp. sides of cong't △s)

7 In △s *ABC* and *CDA*
  (i) *AB* = *CD* (given)
  (ii) *BC* = *DA* (given)
  (iii) *AC* is common
  ∴ △*ABC* ≡ △*CDA* (SSS)
  ∠*BCA* = ∠*CAD* (corresp. angles of cong. △s)
  ∴ *BC* // *DA* (alt. angles equal)
  ∠*BAC* = ∠*DCA* (corresp. angles of cong. △s)
  ∴ *AB* // *CD* (alt. angles equal)
  ∴ Opposite sides are parallel
  ∴ *ABCD* is a parallelogram

8 a Vertically opposite ∠s   **b** SAS   **c** ∠*CBE* (corresp. ∠s of congruent △s)
  d ∠*ADE* and ∠*CBE* are equal alternate ∠s   **e** SAS   **f** Corresp. ∠s of congruent △s
  g Pairs of alternate angles are equal.

9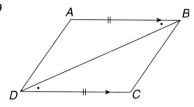

Data: $ABCD$ is a quadrilateral with $AB = DC$ and $AB \parallel DC$.
Aim: To prove $AD \parallel BC$.
Construction: Join BD.
Proof: In $\triangle$s ABD and CBD
(1) $AB = DC$ (data)
(2) BD is common.
(3) $\angle ABD = \angle CDB$ (alt. $\angle$s, $AB \parallel DC$)
$\therefore \triangle ABD \equiv \triangle CBD$ (SAS)
$\therefore \angle ADB = \angle CBD$ (corresp. $\angle$s of cong't $\triangle$s)
But $\angle ADB$ and $\angle CBD$ are also alternate $\angle$s
$\therefore AD \parallel BC$ (pair of alt. $\angle$s are equal)
$\therefore ABCD$ has both pairs of opposite sides parallel.
$\therefore ABCD$ is a parallelogram.

10 Proof: $DC = AB$ (opp. sides of par'm $ABCD$)
$AB = FE$ (opp. sides of par'm $ABFE$)
$\therefore DC = FE$
Also $DC \parallel AB$ and $AB \parallel FE$
$\therefore DC \parallel FE$
$\therefore DC$ and FE are parallel and equal.
$\therefore DCEF$ is a parallelogram.

11 Proof: $AK = KC$ (diag. of par'm bisect each other)
$EA = CG$ (data)
$\therefore AK + EA = KC + CG$
$EK = KG$
Similarly it can be shown that $KH = KF$.
$\therefore$ Diagonals EG and FH bisect each other.
$\therefore EFGH$ is a parallelogram.

12

Proof: $ABCD$ is a parallelogram.
(Both pairs of opposite sides are equal.)
$AB = BC$ (data)
$\therefore ABCD$ is a parallelogram with a pair of adjacent sides equal.
$\therefore ABCD$ is a rhombus. (See definition p. 153.)

13

Proof: $ABCD$ is a parallelogram (opposite $\angle$s equal)
$4x = 360°$ (angle sum of quad.)
$x = 90°$
$\therefore ABCD$ is a parallelogram with one right angle.
$\therefore ABCD$ is a rectangle.

14 a yes   **b** yes   **c** No, because it does not have all its sides equal.
d yes   **e** yes   **f** No, because it does not have all its angles equal.
15 yes

Investigation 11:08   Theorems and their converses
1 If a triangle has all angles equal then it has all its sides equal. (This converse is true.)
2 If a quadrilateral has its diagonals equal then it is a square. (This converse is not true.)
3 If a quadrilateral has its opposite angles equal then it is a parallelogram. (This converse is true.)

Exercise 11:09
1 a 2   **b** $\sqrt{45} = 3\sqrt{5}$ **2 a** yes   **b** no   **c** no
3 a $x = \sqrt{52}$ $y = \sqrt{48}$ **b** $x = \sqrt{27}$ $y = 6$ **c** $x = \sqrt{116}$ $y = \sqrt{20}$
     $= 2\sqrt{13}$ $= 4\sqrt{3}$ $= 3\sqrt{3}$ $= 2\sqrt{29}$ $= 2\sqrt{5}$
4 a 12·8   **b** 4   **c** 9 m   **5 a** $\sqrt{12} = 2\sqrt{3}$ **b** $10\sqrt{3} - 5\sqrt{5} \doteq 6\cdot1$ m   **c** $\sqrt{130}$ cm

Diagnostic Test 11   Deductive geometry
1 a $\angle AFG = x°$ (corresp. $\angle$s, $AB \parallel CD$)
     $x° + 130° = 180°$ (adj. supp. $\angle$s)
           $x = 50$

  b $\angle DBE = \angle EDB$ (base $\angle$s of isos. $\triangle$)
     $2 \times \angle EDB + 40° = 180°$ ($\angle$ sum of $\triangle$)
     $\therefore \angle EDB = 70°$
         $\angle EDB = x°$ (alt. $\angle$s, $AC \parallel DE$)
         $\therefore x = 70$

  c $\angle LON + 90° + 70° + 85° = 360°$ ($\angle$ sum of quad.)
         $\therefore \angle LON = 115°$
            $\angle LOP = x°$ (base $\angle$s of isos. $\triangle$)
           $x° + 115° = 180°$ (adj. supp. $\angle$s)
                $x = 65$
2 a 2340°   **b** 135°   **c** 18

3 a $\angle DBA = x°$ (alt. $\angle$s, $AB \parallel CD$)

$\angle DBA = y°$ (alt. $\angle$s, $AC \parallel BD$)

$\therefore x = y$

c Let $\angle ABC = \angle ACD = x°$

$\therefore \angle CAD = 90° - x°$ (comp. $\angle$s, $\triangle ADC$)

$\therefore \angle ATE = x°$ (comp. $\angle$s, $\triangle ATE$)

$\therefore \angle FTD = x°$ (vert. opp. $\angle$s)

$\therefore \angle ABC = \angle FTD$

4 a SAS **b** SSS **c** AAS

5 a In $\triangle$s ABD and ACD

(1) AD is common.

(2) $AB = AC$ (data)

(3) $BD = CD$ (data)

$\therefore \triangle ABD \equiv \triangle ACD$ (SSS)

$\therefore \angle ABD = \angle ACD$ (corr. $\angle$s of cong. $\triangle$s)

c In $\triangle$s ABX and ACY

(1) $AB = AC$ (data)

(2) $BX = CY$ (data)

(3) $\angle ABX = \angle ACY$ (base $\angle$s of isos. $\triangle$)

$\therefore \triangle ABX \equiv \triangle ACY$ (SAS)

$\therefore AX = AY$ (corr. sides of cong $\triangle$s)

6 a 9 **b** 35° **c** 30°

7 a Let $\angle CAD = a°$

$\angle BCA = a°$ (base $\angle$s) of isos. $\triangle BAC$)

$\angle CBD = 2a°$ (ext. $\angle$ of $\triangle BAC$)

$\angle BCD = 2a°$ (base $\angle$s of isos. $\triangle DBC$)

Now $\angle ACD = \angle BCA + \angle BCD$

$= a° + 2a°$

$= 3a$

$= 3 \times \angle CAD$

c In $\triangle$s CAB and CAD,

i AC is common

ii $AB = AD$ (data)

iii $BC = DC$ (data)

$\therefore \triangle CAB \equiv \triangle CAD$ (SSS)

$\therefore \angle CAB = \angle CAD$ (corresp. $\angle$s of cong't $\triangle$s)

9 a $\sqrt{125}$ cm

b $\sqrt{8}$ cm

c $\sqrt{208}$ cm

b $\angle CBD = \angle CDB$ (base $\angle$s of isos. $\triangle$)

$\therefore \angle ABD = 90° - \angle CBD$

$\angle ADB = 90° - \angle CDB$

$\therefore \angle ABD = \angle ADB$

$\therefore AB = AD$ (equal sides of isos. $\triangle$)

b In $\triangle$s OAB and OCD

(1) $OA = OC$ (radii of circle)

(2) $OB = OD$ (radii of circle)

(3) $AB = CD$ (data)

$\therefore \triangle OAB \equiv \triangle OCD$ (SSS)

$\therefore \angle AOB = \angle COD$ (corr. $\angle$s of cong. $\triangle$s)

b In $\triangle$s ABC and ACD,

i AD is common

ii $\angle ABD = \angle ACD$ (data)

iii $\angle BAD = \angle CAD$ (data)

$\therefore \triangle ABC \equiv \triangle ACD$ (AAS)

$\therefore \angle ADB = \angle ADC$ (corresp. angles of cong't $\triangle$s)

$\angle ADB + \angle ADC = 180°$ (adj. supp. $\angle$s)

$2 \times \angle ADB = 180°$

$\angle ADB = 90°$

$\therefore AD \perp BC$

8 a See Exercise 5:08 question 13

b

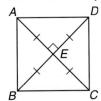

$ABCD$ is a rectangle

(diagonals are equal and bisect each other)

$\triangle ADE \equiv \triangle DCE$ (SAS)

$\therefore AD = DC$ (corresp. sides of cong't $\triangle$s)

$\therefore ABCD$ is a square

(rectangle with a pair of adjacent sides equal)

c One pair of sides is both equal and parallel.

11A Revision Assignment

1 a $\angle BEG = 70°$ (comp. $\angle$s)

$x° + 70° = 180°$ (co-int. $\angle$s, $AB \parallel CD$)

$x = 110$

c $\angle BAC = x°$ (alt. $\angle$s, $DB \parallel AC$)

$\angle BAC = x°$ (base $\angle$s of isos. $\triangle$)

$2x° + 52° = 180°$ ($\angle$ sum of $\triangle$)

$x = 64$

b $\angle EBA = 70°$ (base $\angle$s of isos. $\triangle EAB$)

$\angle DBC = 60°$ ($\angle$ of equil. $\triangle$)

$\therefore \angle EBD = 50°$ (adj. $\angle$s on a st. line)

$\angle BDE = 50°$ (base $\angle$s of isos. $\triangle EBD$)

$x + 50° + 50° = 180°$ ($\angle$ sum of $\triangle$)

$x = 80$

d $\angle BCD + 74° + 138° + 96° = 360°$ ($\angle$ sum of quad.)

$\angle BCD = 52°$

$\angle BDC = x°$ (base $\angle$s of isos. $\triangle$)

$2x° + 52° = 180°$ ($\angle$ sum of $\triangle$)

$x = 64$

2 a 72°, 144° **b** $a = 108, b = 36, c = 36, d = 72$

3 In △s *BED* and *CFD*
  i $BD = CD$ (*D* is midpoint of *BC*)
  ii ∠*BED* = ∠*CFD* (*BE* ⊥ *AD*, *CF* ⊥ *AD*)
  iii ∠*BDE* = ∠*CDF* (vert. opp. angles)
  ∴ △*BED* ≡ △*CFD* (AAS)
    $BE = CF$ (corresp. sides of cong. △s, Q.E.D.)

4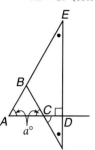

Let ∠*BAC* and ∠*BCA* be $a°$ (base angles of isos. △*ABC*).
∴ ∠*DCF* = $a°$ (vert. opp. ∠*BCA*)
∠*CFD* = 180° − $a°$ − 90° (angle sum of △*CFD*, *FD* ⊥ *CD*)
∠*AED* = 180° − $a°$ − 90° (angle sum of △*AED*)
∴ ∠*CFD* = ∠*AED* (both 90° − $a°$)
∴ △*BEF* is isosceles (base angles equal) (Q.E.D.)

5 18·50 cm (correct to 2 dec. pl.)
6 $CA = CB$ (equal sides in isos. △*CAB*)
  $CB = CD$ (equal sides in isos. △*CBD*)
  ∴ $CA = CD$
  ∴ ∠*CAD* = ∠*CDA* (base ∠s of isos. △*CAD*)

11B Working Mathematically

1 The shape of the lamp shade is based on a square pyramid. The top section of the pyramid and its base have been removed.
2 34   **3** 12 L; 33 L   **4 a** 12   **b** 8
5 a 327 m   **b** 36   **c** $616.65
6 a 15 m   **b** 0·6, 3·4 seconds   **c** 20 m   **d** 2 seconds   **e** 1·4 seconds

Chapter 12: Measurement

Challenge 12:01   Staggered starts
2π metres ≐ 6·3 m

Investigation 12:01A   Skirting board and perimeter

1 No. One wall is 7600 mm long, which is longer than the largest length of skirting board available (6·6 m).
2 Total length required = 27 400 (27·4 m)

3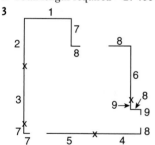

Note: The following is only one possible solution. The numbers show how the 9 skirting boards are used. Joins are indicated by '×'.
Board 1 is 3200 mm long (100 mm waste)
Boards 2, 3, 4, 5, 6 are 3300 mm long.
Board 7 is cut into 3 pieces (1000 mm, 400 mm, 1800 mm)
Board 8 is cut into 4 pieces (600 mm, 1600 mm, 700 mm, 300 mm)
Board 9 is cut into 2 pieces (900 mm, 400 mm)
If joins at corners are not counted the smallest number of joins possible is 4.

4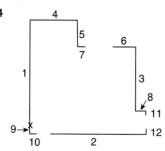

Boards 1 and 2 (6·6 m); Board 3 (4·2 m); Board 4 (3·3 m);
Boards 5 and 6 (1·8 m); Board 7 (600 mm); Board 8 (900 mm);
Board 9 (1·2 m); Boards 10 and 11 (600 mm);
Board 12 (300 mm)
He would have to order: 2 × 6·6 m, 1 × 4·2 m, 1 × 3·3 m, 1 × 1·8 m, 1 × 1·2 m, 1 × 900 mm, 3 × 600 mm, 1 × 300 mm.
This would only require 1 join and give 1·1 m of waste.

Prep Quiz 12:01
1 25·44   **2** 2·04   **3** 32·66   **4** LB   **5** 20   **6** 20   **7** 20   **8** 48   **9** 100   **10** 10

Exercise 12:01

1 **a** 2.5   **b** 4000   **c** 60   **d** 0·06   **e** 0·25
   f 2500   **g** 50 000   **h** 5 000 000   **i** 2   **j** 0·000025
2 **a** 34 m   **b** 24 mm   **c** 22 cm   **d** 15·71 cm   **e** 68 mm
   f 58 cm   **g** 17·9 m   **h** 22·1 mm   **i** 60 m   **j** 23·6 cm
   k 77·1 cm **l** 248·74 mm **m** 2·99 m   **n** 18·38 mm **o** 32·85 cm
3 **a** 34 m   **b** 24 mm   **c** 22 cm   **d** 15·71 cm   **e** 68 mm
   f 58 cm   **g** 17·9 m   **h** 22·1 mm   **i** 60 m   **j** 23·6 cm
   k 77·1 cm **l** 3654·44 mm^2 **m** 0·29 m^2 **n** 25·71 mm^2 **o** 56 cm^2

Investigation 12:01C   Covering floors

Laying tiles **1** 726   **2** 117
Laying carpet **1** 4·25 m, 2·975 m^2 waste, no joins   **2** 5·8 m, 8·555 m^2 waste, yes, there are joins

Prep Quiz 12:02

1 48 cm^2 **2** 25π cm^2 **3** 5 cm   **4** 12π cm   **5** 7
6   **7** 6 cm   **8** 8 cm   **9** 3·5 cm   **10** 9 cm

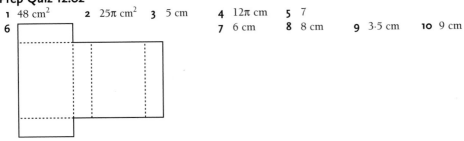

Exercise 12:02

1 **a** 17·0 cm^2 **b** 404·5 cm^2 **c** 48 m^2
2 **a** 84 m^2 **b** 2225 cm^2 **c** 249·6 m^2 **d** 1082·4 cm^2 **e** 640·4 m^2 **f** 293·2 cm^2
3 **a** **i** 1658·76 cm^2 **ii** 760·27 cm^2 **iii** 2419·03 cm^2
   b **i** 424·87 cm^2 **ii** 110·84 cm^2 **iii** 535·71 cm^2
   c **i** 88·22 m^2 **ii** 215·03 m^2 **iii** 303·25 m^2
   d **i** 126·67 cm^2 **ii** 16·08 cm^2 **iii** 142·75 cm^2
   e **i** 38·68 m^2 **ii** 73·49 m^2 **iii** 112·17 m^2
   f **i** 77·41 m^2 **ii** 30·41 m^2 **iii** 107·82 m^2
4 **a** 565·5 cm^2 **b** 199·1 m^2 **c** 161·0 m^2 **d** 515·2 m^2 **e** 1321·0 cm^2 **f** 25·1 m^2 **g** 6·3 m^2 **h** 14·7 m^2
5 **a** 263·1 m^3 **b** 12·0 m^3 **c** 6588·4 cm^3 **6 a** 2·67 m^3 **b** 1·13 m^3 **c** 8·30 m^3
7 **a** 1050 cm^3 **b** 360 cm^3 **c** 308 m^3 **8 a** 960 m^3 **b** 48 m^3 **c** 11·799 m^3
9 **a** 730 cm^2 **b** 209 cm^2 **c** 147 cm^2
10 Surface area = (Perimeter of cross-sectional area × height of prism) + (2 × cross-sectional area) i.e. S = PH + 2A
11 **a** 1249·8 cm^2 (correct to 1 dec. pl.)   **b** 8189 cm^2 (to nearest cm^2)
12 **a** 31·2 m^2 **b** 32·0 m^2 **c** 21·1 m^2
13 **a** 39·2 m^2 **b** 14·7 m^2 **c** 154·7 m^2

Investigation 12:03   Tank sizes

1 **a** 180 L   **b** 450 L   **c** 160 L
2 The three dimensions (measured in metres) have to have a product of 1. To find some, use fractions and then convert to metres (eg $\frac{5}{4} \times \frac{1}{2} \times \frac{8}{5} = 1$). Hence a possible set of dimensions is 1·25 m, 0·5 m, 1·6 m.

Prep Quiz 12:04

1 11   **2** 3   **3** 33 cm^3 **4** Multiply the answer to question 1 by the answer to question 2.
5 11   **6** 3   **7** 33   **8** Yes   **9** Yes   **10** Yes

Exercise 12:04

1 **a** 4320 cm^3 **b** 4160 cm^3 **c** 648 cm^3 **d** 1155 cm^3 **e** 960 cm^3
2 **a** 4934 cm^3 **b** 1352 cm^3 **c** 905 cm^3
3 **a** 292·5 cm^3 **b** 805·266 cm^3 **c** 256·932 cm^3
4 **a** 2293·7 cm^3 **b** 6090·8 cm^3 **c** 1022·2 cm^3
5 **a** 131 m^3 **b** 15 000 cm^3 **c** 1·32 m^3
6 **a** 3435·747 cm^3 **b** 20·79 m^3 **c** 5·625 m^3
7 **a** 13 135·1 cm^3 **b** 179·5 cm^3 **c** 1583·7 cm^3
8 **a** 6232·6 cm^3 **b** 4672·2 cm^3

Investigation 12:04   Perimeter, area and volume

1 a 18 by 12, 20 by 10, 22 by 8, 24 by 6

b

	Length (L)	Breadth (B)	Area (A)	L − B
Rectangle 1	18	12	216	6
Rectangle 2	20	10	200	10
Rectangle 3	22	8	176	14
Rectangle 4	24	6	144	18

c It increases.   **d** 225 cm^2 **e** 625 m^2

2 a 4500 cm^3 **b** 5730 cm^3 (to nearest whole number); yes

Exercise 12:05

1 a 115 m^3; 115 kL   **b** 139 m^3; 139 kL   **c** 92.4 m^3; 92.4 kL   **2** 1.2 m^3, $156

3 a 48.4 kL   **b** 1650 kL   **4 a** 45.0 m^3 **b** 45 kL

5 a 376 m^2; $11 280   **b** 375 000 L   **c** 280   **6 a** 2.3 m^2 **b** 0.339 m^3 **c** 432 kg

7 a 113.1 cm^3 **b** 656.0 g   **8** 4800 g

9 a $45 945   **b** 1537.5 m^3 **c** 51 cm   **10** 76.9 m^2 (correct to 1 dec. pl.)

11 a 3465 L   **b** 77 cm (to the nearest cm)   **c** 235 mm (to the nearest mm)

(Note: (a) the area of 100 mm rainfall is the horizontal area 3.3 m × 10.5 m)

Investigation 12:05   Wallpapering rooms

1.12 rolls. Hence you would need to buy 2 rolls.

1 a 1.8 rolls   **b** 1.4 rolls   **c** 1.2 rolls   **2** 1.6 rolls   **3** 6.5 rolls; you would need to buy 7 rolls.

4 a 22 m   **b** 43 drops   **c** 6.88 rolls

Diagnostic Test 12   Measurement

1 a 23.9 cm   **b** 9.11 m   **2 a** 34 m   **b** 27.8 m

3 a 36 m   **b** 60 cm   **4 a** 15.35 cm   **b** 4.95 m

5 a 11.14 m   **b** 57.12 cm   **c** 30 m   **6 a** 60 cm^2 **b** 76.86 cm^2 **c** 25.83 cm^2

7 a 117.14 m^2 **b** 36 cm^2 **c** 666 m^2 **8 a** 612.6 m^2 **b** 47.5 m^2

9 a 400 cm^2 **b** 704 cm^2 **c** 351.97 cm^2 **10 a** 70.518 m^3 **b** 12 cm^3 **c** 1008 m^3

11 a 972 m^3 **b** 19 m^3 **c** 4 m^3 **12 a** 400 cm^3 **b** 768 cm^3 **c** 324 cm^3

13 a $A = 2\pi rh = 2 \times \pi \times 25 \times 90 = 14\,137.17$ cm^2

$\qquad\qquad\qquad\qquad\qquad$ (or 1.41 m^2)

b $V = \pi r^2 h = \pi \times 25^2 \times 90 = 79\,521.56$ cm^3

$\therefore$ water needed $= \dfrac{3}{4} \times V = 59\,641.17$ cm^3

$\qquad\qquad\qquad = 59.6$ L

$\qquad\qquad\qquad \doteqdot 60$ L

14 a A = left + right + back + front + base

$= (8 \times 2.7) + (8 \times 1.5) + \left(\dfrac{2.7 + 1.5}{2} \times 14\right) \times 2 + (8 \times 14.05)$

$= 175.4$ m^2

so cost is $8 945.40

b V = (Area of side) × width

$= \left(\dfrac{2.7 + 1.5}{2}\right) \times 14 \times 8 = 117.6$ m^3

$\qquad\qquad\qquad\qquad = 117.6$ kL

12A Revision Assignment

1 38.43 m^2; $1537.20   **2** $60 + 25\sqrt{3} \doteqdot 103.3$ cm^2

3 a 12.92 m^2 **b** 4.4 m   **c** 9.7 m (4 × 1.4 + 1.6 + 2.5)

4 $8\pi \doteqdot 25.1$ m^2 **5 a** 56.94 cm **b** 104.36 cm^2

6 (both answers correct to 2 dec. pl.)   **a** 4.47 m^2 **b** 0.50 m^3

7 a 7.6 units   **b** 139.29 unit^2 **c** 582.13 unit^2 **d** 905.385 unit^3

8 a 7163.45 unit^3 **b** 2440 unit^2

1 a complementary angles b supplementary angles c vertically opposite angles d angles at a point
   e corresponding angles f alternate angles g co-interior angles h straight angle
   i reflex angle j revolution
2 Rachel is 13 years old 3 4 times, 3 times 4 34 5 4
6 a 29/3 b 26/4 c Hall and Bagnell d Raine and Harris e 8–15 Feb, 15–29 March, 21–28 June

Chapter 13: Trigonometry

Exercise 13:01

1 a BC b DE c KL d PR e TU f YZ
2 a AB b EF c LM d PQ e ST f XZ
3 a AC b DF c KM d QR e SU f XY
4 a AC b AC c $\angle C$ d $\angle C$
5 a $\frac{5}{12}$ b $\frac{8}{6}$ c $\frac{15}{8}$ 6 a $\frac{12}{13}$ b $\frac{6}{10}$ c $\frac{8}{17}$

Prep Quiz 13:02

1 opp. 2 hyp. 3 adj. 4 $\triangle$I, $\frac{3}{4}$; $\triangle$II, $\frac{6}{8}$ 5 $\triangle$I, $\frac{3}{5}$; $\triangle$II, $\frac{6}{10}$ 6 $\triangle$I, $\frac{4}{5}$; $\triangle$II, $\frac{8}{10}$ 7 Yes 8 Yes 9 Yes 10 Yes

Exercise 13:02

1

	θ	$\frac{o}{h}$	$\frac{a}{h}$	$\frac{o}{a}$
1	30°	0·5	0·9	0·6
2	30°	0·5	0·9	0·6
3	30°	0·5	0·9	0·6

2

	θ	$\frac{o}{h}$	$\frac{a}{h}$	$\frac{o}{a}$
1	50°	0·8	0·6	1·2
2	50°	0·8	0·6	1·2
3	50°	0·8	0·6	1·2

3

	θ	opposite side	adjacent side	hypotenuse	$\frac{o}{h}$	$\frac{a}{h}$	$\frac{o}{a}$
$\triangle BAC$	30°	5·5 cm	9·5 cm	10·8 cm	0·5	0·9	0·6
$\triangle BAD$	45°	7·7 cm	7·6 cm	10·8 cm	0·7	0·7	1·0
$\triangle BAE$	60°	9·4 cm	5·4 cm	10·8 cm	0·9	0·5	1·7

4 a Yes b Yes
5 a i 0·6 ii 0·8 iii 0·7 b i 0·6 ii 0·8 iii 0·7. For an angle of 35° the ratios $\frac{o}{h}$, $\frac{a}{h}$, $\frac{o}{a}$ are constant.

Exercise 13:03

1 a $\sin \theta = \frac{3}{5}$ b $\sin \theta = \frac{5}{13}$ c $\sin \theta = \frac{24}{25}$ 2 a $\sin A = 0.600$ b $\sin A = 0.471$ c $\sin A = 0.923$
   $\cos \theta = \frac{4}{5}$ $\cos \theta = \frac{12}{13}$ $\cos \theta = \frac{7}{25}$ $\cos A = 0.800$ $\cos A = 0.882$ $\cos A = 0.385$
   $\tan \theta = \frac{3}{4}$ $\tan \theta = \frac{5}{12}$ $\tan \theta = \frac{24}{7}$ $\tan A = 0.750$ $\tan A = 0.533$ $\tan A = 2.400$

3 a 15, $\sin \theta = 0.6$, $\cos \theta = 0.8$ b $\sqrt{45}$, $\sin \theta = 0.447$, $\cos \theta = 0.894$ c $\sqrt{8}$, $\sin \theta = 0.707$, $\cos \theta = 0.707$
4 a $YZ = 6$, $\tan X = 0.750$ b $YZ = 6$, $\tan X = 1.2$ c $YZ = 3$, $\tan X = 1.5$

5 a $\sin \theta = \frac{3}{5}$ b $\cos \theta = \dfrac{3}{\sqrt{34}}$ c $\sin 60° = \dfrac{\sqrt{12}}{4}$
   $\cos (90 - \theta) = \frac{3}{5}$ $\sin (90 - \theta) = \dfrac{3}{\sqrt{34}}$ $\cos 30° = \dfrac{\sqrt{12}}{4}$

6 a $\sin \theta = \dfrac{b}{c}$ b $\cos \theta = \dfrac{a}{c}$
   $\cos (90 - \theta) = \dfrac{b}{c}$ $\sin (90 - \theta) = \dfrac{a}{c}$

7 a 65° b 30° c 80°
8 a i $\frac{3}{5}$ ii $\frac{4}{5}$ iii $\frac{3}{4}$ iv $\frac{3}{4}$ b yes

9 a missing side = $\sqrt{3}$, $\sin 30° = \frac{1}{2}$, $\cos 30° = \dfrac{\sqrt{3}}{2}$, $\tan 30° = \dfrac{1}{\sqrt{3}}$ b $\sin 30°$, $\tan 30°$, $\cos 30°$ (ie $\frac{1}{2}$, $\dfrac{\sqrt{3}}{3}$, $\dfrac{\sqrt{3}}{2}$)

10 a $\cos A = \dfrac{\sqrt{15}}{4}$, $\tan A = \dfrac{1}{\sqrt{15}}$ b $\dfrac{\sqrt{7}}{4}$

11 a i $\dfrac{4}{\sqrt{80}} = \dfrac{1}{\sqrt{5}}$ **ii** $\dfrac{4}{\sqrt{52}} = \dfrac{2}{\sqrt{13}}$ **b i** $\dfrac{\sqrt{175}}{20} = \dfrac{\sqrt{7}}{4}$ **ii** $\dfrac{\sqrt{7}}{4}$

12 a $\tan\theta = \dfrac{3}{4}$ and $\tan\theta = \dfrac{m}{5}$. Hence $\dfrac{m}{5} = \dfrac{3}{4}$ and $m = 3.75$.

b $x = 2\sqrt{5}, y = 4\sqrt{5}$

c i $\dfrac{3}{5}$ **ii** $\dfrac{4}{5}$ **iii** 4.8 **iv** 1.4 **v** $\dfrac{4.8}{5} = 0.96$ **vi** $2 \times \sin\theta \times \cos\theta = 2 \times \dfrac{3}{5} \times \dfrac{4}{5}$
$= 0.96$
$\sin 2\theta = 0.96$ (from (v))
$\therefore \sin 2\theta = 2 \times \sin\theta \times \cos\theta$

Exercise 13:04

1 a 16°30′ **b** 38°15′ **c** 73°54′ **d** 305°45′ **e** 40°14′ **f** 100°40′ **g** 12°01′ **h** 238°51′
2 a 17.75° **b** 48.267° **c** 125.717° **d** 88.617° **e** 320.25° **f** 70.9° **g** 241.483° **h** 36.883°
3 a 0.5000 **b** 0.8660 **c** 0.5774 **d** 0.9455 **e** 0.5299 **f** 1.9626 **g** 0.1219 **h** 0.0872
4 a 15° **b** 69° **c** 38° **d** 77° **e** 72° **f** 26° **g** 50° **h** 39° **i** 72°
5 a 0.503 **b** 0.889 **c** 0.609 **d** 0.121 **e** 1.823 **f** 5.323 **g** 0.306 **h** 3.185
6 a 36°52′ **b** 25°28′ **c** 40°10′ **d** 78°28′ **e** 88°13′ **f** 58°34′ **g** 52°26′ **h** 32°00′ **i** 69°28′
7 a 36.87° **b** 25.47° **c** 40.17° **d** 78.46° **e** 88.22° **f** 58.56° **g** 52.43° **h** 32.01° **i** 69.47°
8 a 0.577, 0.5, 0.866 **b** 1.600, 0.848, 0.530 **c** 0.537, 0.473, 0.881
9 a 0.866 **b** 0.883 **c** 1.079
10 a 5 **b** 5.392 **c** No, it does not. **d** 49.5 (correct to 1 dec. pl.)
e No. Substituting $A = 30°$ shows it is not correct.

Practical Activity 13:04 The exact values for the trig. ratios 30°, 60° and 45°

1 $BD = 1, \angle BAD = 30°$ **2** $AD = \sqrt{3}$
3 $\sin 30° = \dfrac{1}{2}$, $\cos 30° = \dfrac{\sqrt{3}}{2}$, $\tan 30° = \dfrac{1}{\sqrt{3}}$, $\sin 60° = \dfrac{\sqrt{3}}{2}$, $\cos 60° = \dfrac{1}{2}$, $\tan 60° = \sqrt{3}$
4 $\angle EDF = \angle EFD$ (base $\angle$s of isosceles $\triangle$)
$\angle EDF + \angle EFD = 90°$ (complementary $\angle$s)
$2 \times \angle EDF = 90°$, $\angle EDF = 45°$ **5** $\sqrt{2}$ **6** $\sin 45° = \dfrac{1}{\sqrt{2}}$, $\cos 45° = \dfrac{1}{\sqrt{2}}$, $\tan 45° = 1$

Prep Quiz 13:05

1 AC **2** BC **3** AB **4** false **5** true **6** true **7** 0.966 **8** 0.477 **9** $4 \times \tan 25°$ (or 1.865 correct to 3 dec. pl.)
10 $4 \div \tan 25°$ (or 8.578 correct to 3 dec. pl.)

Exercise 13:05

1 a 5.9 **b** 5.1 **c** 11.1 **d** 2.5 **e** 15.9 **f** 12.1 **g** 3.8 **h** 6.2 **i** 4.6 **j** 14.4 **k** 3.8 **l** 2.1
2 a 19.4 **b** 9.3 **c** 48.5 **d** 7.2 **e** 7.8 **f** 5.3 **g** 10.2 **h** 22.7 **i** 13.3 **j** 7.1 **k** 13.2 **l** 16.0
3 $\angle ACB = 63°$, $AC = 7\sin 27° \div 3.178$, $AB = 7\cos 27° \div 6.237$
4 5.12 m **5** 5.54 m **6** 13.02 m **7** 1336 m **8** 4.06 m **9** 20.57 m **10** 6.15 cm **11** 2.13 m
12 a 5.37 m **b** 8.45 m **c** 4.4 cm **d** 16.9 cm
13 15.0 cm **14** 8.3 cm **15** 30 cm **16** 20.3 cm **17** 57.2 cm **18** 69.3 cm **19** 300.0 m **20** 35 m
21 5.23 m **22** 54 m² **23 a** 1666 m **b** 200 km/h **24** 15.8 cm²

25 a $\dfrac{a\sqrt{3}}{2}$ **b** $\dfrac{a^2\sqrt{3}}{4}$ **c** $\dfrac{3a^2\sqrt{3}}{2}$ **d i** $6\sqrt{3}$ cm² **ii** $\dfrac{75\sqrt{3}}{2}$ cm² **iii** $150\sqrt{3}$ cm²

Prep Quiz 13:06

1 $\dfrac{12}{13}$ **2** $\dfrac{5}{13}$ **3** $\dfrac{15}{8}$ **4** $\dfrac{15}{17}$ **5** 32° **6** 12° **7** 85° **8** 31°20′ **9** 69°29′ **10** 43°41′

Exercise 13:06

1 a 24° **b** 56° **c** 44° **d** 53° **e** 34° **f** 55° **g** 32° **h** 35° **i** 49°
2 a 36°52′ **b** 45°35′ **c** 54°19′ **d** 36°34′ **e** 36°52′ **f** 54°17′

3 a $\tan x° = \dfrac{3}{4}$, $\sin x° = \dfrac{3}{5}$, $\cos x° = \dfrac{4}{5}$; all give $x = 36°52′$

4 a 27° **b** 36°28′ **5 a** 77° **b** 62°
6 17° **7** 7°8′ **8** 38°0′ **9** 34°15′, 55°45′
10 a 33°41′ **b** 63°26′ **c** 45° **11** 19°45′
12 59°14′ **13** 93°19′ **14 a** 58° (to the nearest degree) **b** 74° (to the nearest degree)

Exercise 13:07

1 68·7 m   **2** 127 m   **3** 317 m   **4** 2·0 m   **5** 58°   **6** 3°20′   **7** 59°36′   **8** 14·458 km
9 76 km, 129 km   **10** 6 km   **11** 58 km   **12** S 31° W   **13** N 16° W, 14·327 km
14 N 27°30′ E   **15** S 31°9′ E   **16** 2·448 km   **17 a** 15·45 m   **b** 16·47 m   **18** 7·7 cm
19 65°   **20** 69° and 111°   **21** 59°29′   **22** 5·11 m   **23** 19°11′, 11·8 cm

24 a $5\sqrt{3}$ **b** $\sqrt{2}$ **c** $4\sqrt{3}$

25 a $\dfrac{100\sqrt{3}}{3}$ cm^2 **b** $\dfrac{20\sqrt{3}}{3}$ m   **c** $9 + 4\sqrt{3}$ cm

Exercise 13:08

1 68 m   **2** 74°   **3** 11 m   **4** 1558 m, 280 km/h
5 a 27·1   **b** 14·4   **c** 0·47   **d** 7·50   **6 a** 23°30′   **b** 33°17′

7 a $\dfrac{XW}{XY} = \cos X \therefore XW = XY \cos X \therefore XW = z \cos X$ **b** $\dfrac{ZW}{YZ} = \cos Z \therefore ZW = YZ \cos Z \therefore ZW = x \cos Z$

     c Since $y = XW + ZW$, then $y = z \cos X + x \cos Z$

8 a In $\triangle ABM$, $\dfrac{AM}{AB} = \sin B \therefore AM = c \sin B$ **b** area of $\triangle ABC = \frac{1}{2} \times BC \times AM = \frac{1}{2} \, ac \sin B$

9 51°   **10** 11·5 km   **11** $\dfrac{16\sqrt{3}}{3}$

12 a $(6\sqrt{3} + 6)$ units   **b** $6\sqrt{6}$ units   **c** $(54 + 18\sqrt{3})$ unit^2

Diagnostic Test 13   Trigonometry

1 a 3·7321   **b** 0·3907   **c** 0·3697   **d** 1·1204   **2 a** 0·431   **b** 1·674   **c** −0·993   **d** −0·306
3 a 50°17′   **b** 47°49′   **c** 4°4′   **d** 73°53′   **4 a** AB   **b** PR   **c** YZ
5 a $\frac{5}{13}$ **b** $\frac{15}{8}$ **c** $\frac{3}{5}$ **6 a** 4·4   **b** 9·0   **c** 14·9   **d** 7·5
7 a 32·0   **b** 6·4   **c** 14·3   **d** 5·7   **8 a** 38°41′   **b** 58°2′   **c** 39°48′   **d** 50°12′

13A   Revision Assignment

1 a 13   **b** 1·8   **c** 32   **2 a** 61°33′   **b** 55°59′   **c** 56°9′
3 a 1500 m   **b i** 975 km   **ii** 1689 km   **4 a** 168 m
5 a i In $\triangle BCT$,   **iii** In $\triangle ACT$,

$\tan 70° = \dfrac{x}{h}$ $\tan 30° = \dfrac{x}{h + 10}$

$\therefore x = h \tan 70°$ $\therefore x = (h + 10) \tan 30°$

   b $x = 7·31$ km (correct to 2 dec. pl.)

   c $BT = \dfrac{x}{\sin 70°}$

       $= 7·78$ km (correct to 2 dec. pl.)

13B   Working Mathematically

1 a *perpendicular* lines   **b** *vertical*, *horizontal*   **c** *concurrent* lines   **d** *reflex* angle
   e *revolution*   **f** *adjacent* angles   **g** *supplementary* angles   **h** *vertically opposite* angles
   i *360°*   **j** *transversal*
2 a *hectare*   **b** *cross-section*   **c** *face*   **d** *vertex*
   e *edge*   **f** axes of *symmetry*   **g** *tally*   **h** *sector (or pie)* graph
   i *bar* graph   **j** *scatter* diagram
3 If the 20° angle is correct, then the angle adjacent to it is 160°. This would make the angle sum of the triangle greater than 180°, which is impossible.
4 a $2\frac{2}{3}$ days   **b** 8 men   **5** $a^2(2\sqrt{3} + 6)$ unit^2
6 Shop B's discount is equivalent to 7·7% (correct to 1 dec. pl.). Hence shop A offers the best discount.

Chapter 14: Vectors

Exercise 14:01

1 a $4\vec{w}$ **b** $\frac{2}{3}\vec{x}$ **c** $-\frac{1}{6}\vec{y}$

2 a $\vec{a} = -\vec{h}$ **b** $\vec{a} = -\frac{1}{3}\vec{f}$ **c** $\vec{b} = 4\vec{l}$ **d** $\vec{b} = -8\vec{k}$

   e $\vec{e} = \frac{1}{3}\vec{c}$ **f** $\vec{d} = -\frac{1}{2}\vec{g}$

3

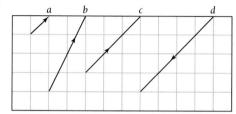

Investigation 14:02   Operating on vectors

	$\overrightarrow{AB}$	$\overrightarrow{BC}$	$\overrightarrow{AC}$
1	$\begin{pmatrix}5\\2\end{pmatrix}$	$\begin{pmatrix}2\\-3\end{pmatrix}$	$\begin{pmatrix}7\\-1\end{pmatrix}$
2	$\begin{pmatrix}-4\\3\end{pmatrix}$	$\begin{pmatrix}-6\\-4\end{pmatrix}$	$\begin{pmatrix}-10\\-1\end{pmatrix}$
3	$\begin{pmatrix}6\\-3\end{pmatrix}$	$\begin{pmatrix}3\\3\end{pmatrix}$	$\begin{pmatrix}9\\0\end{pmatrix}$
4	$\begin{pmatrix}-7\\-3\end{pmatrix}$	$\begin{pmatrix}9\\-1\end{pmatrix}$	$\begin{pmatrix}2\\-4\end{pmatrix}$
5	$\begin{pmatrix}5\\-3\end{pmatrix}$	$\begin{pmatrix}-1\\4\end{pmatrix}$	$\begin{pmatrix}4\\1\end{pmatrix}$
6	$\begin{pmatrix}8\\4\end{pmatrix}$	$\begin{pmatrix}0\\-5\end{pmatrix}$	$\begin{pmatrix}8\\-1\end{pmatrix}$

Exercise 14:02

1

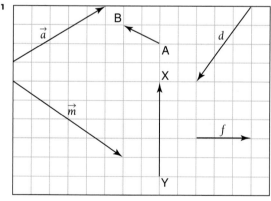

2 a $\begin{pmatrix}11\\-1\end{pmatrix}$ **b** $\begin{pmatrix}2\\-1\end{pmatrix}$ **c** $\begin{pmatrix}-2\\6\end{pmatrix}$ **d** $\begin{pmatrix}-2\\-4\end{pmatrix}$ **e** $\begin{pmatrix}-2\\-4\end{pmatrix}$ **f** $\begin{pmatrix}-3\\5\end{pmatrix}$ **g** $\begin{pmatrix}-8\\5\end{pmatrix}$ **h** $\begin{pmatrix}-4\\3\end{pmatrix}$ **i** $\begin{pmatrix}14\\-1\end{pmatrix}$ **j** $\begin{pmatrix}12\\-9\end{pmatrix}$

3 a $\begin{pmatrix}-6\\4\end{pmatrix}$ **b** $\begin{pmatrix}0\\7\end{pmatrix}$ **c** $\begin{pmatrix}-1\\-1\end{pmatrix}$ **d** $\begin{pmatrix}0\\-1\end{pmatrix}$ **e** $\begin{pmatrix}-2\\8\end{pmatrix}$ **f** $\begin{pmatrix}4\\-4\end{pmatrix}$

4 $\vec{v} = \vec{a} + 2\vec{b} + \vec{x} - \vec{t}$

5 a $2\overrightarrow{CX}$ **b** $\overrightarrow{CX}$ **c** $\frac{1}{2}\overrightarrow{AB}$ **d** $\overrightarrow{CX} + \frac{1}{2}\overrightarrow{AB}$ **e** $2\overrightarrow{CX} + \overrightarrow{AB}$

6 They are parallel and CB is twice the length of XY.

7 a $\overrightarrow{CA} + \overrightarrow{AB}$ **b** $-\left(\overrightarrow{CA} + \overrightarrow{AB}\right) = -\overrightarrow{CA} - \overrightarrow{AB}$ **c** $\overrightarrow{CA} + 2\overrightarrow{AB}$

8 a $\vec{a} + \vec{b}$ **b** $2\left(\vec{a} + \vec{b}\right) = 2\vec{a} + 2\vec{b}$ **c** $-\vec{b} + 2\vec{a} + 2\vec{b} = 2\vec{a} + \vec{b}$ **d** $\vec{b} - \vec{a}$

9 a y **b** $-y + x$ **c** $y - x$ **d** $2y - x$

10

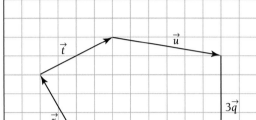

$\vec{r} = \vec{t} + \vec{u} + 3\vec{q} + \vec{s} - 2\vec{p}$

Practical Activity 14:03   Magnitude of a vector

2

Vector	Column vector	Magnitude
$\vec{a}$	$\begin{pmatrix} 2 \\ 3 \end{pmatrix}$	$\sqrt{(2)^2 + (3)^2} = \sqrt{13}$ units
$\vec{b}$	$\begin{pmatrix} -2 \\ 3 \end{pmatrix}$	$\sqrt{(2)^2 + (3)^2} = \sqrt{13}$ units
c	$\begin{pmatrix} 4 \\ 1 \end{pmatrix}$	$\sqrt{(4)^2 + (1)^2} = \sqrt{17}$ units
$\overrightarrow{DE}$	$\begin{pmatrix} -5\frac{1}{2} \\ -8 \end{pmatrix}$	$\sqrt{\left(-5\frac{1}{2}\right)^2 + (-8)^2} = \sqrt{94 \cdot 25}$ units
$\vec{f}$	$\begin{pmatrix} 3 \\ 0 \end{pmatrix}$	$\sqrt{(3)^2 + (0)^2} = \sqrt{9} = 3$ units
g	$\begin{pmatrix} 0 \\ -5 \end{pmatrix}$	$\sqrt{(0)^2 + (-5)^2} = \sqrt{25} = 5$ units

Exercise 14:03

1 $\vec{a} = 2\sqrt{5}$ units $\vec{b} = \sqrt{29}$ units $\vec{c} = 2$ units $\vec{d} = \sqrt{17}$ units $\vec{e} = 5$ units $\vec{f} = 10$ units

2 a 17 units   **b** 10 units   **c** 29 units   **d** 13 units   **e** $2\sqrt{26}$ units

3 a 5 units   **b** 10 units   **c** 17 units   **d** $\sqrt{265}$ units   **e** $\sqrt{117}$ units

Exercise 14:04

1 111 nautical miles bearing 23°   **2** 33·9 km on a bearing of 216°
3 126·8 km on a bearing of 25°   **4** 116·7 km on a bearing of 202°
5 5·83 km/h heading on a bearing of 301°   **6** 140 km/h on a bearing of 60°
7 11·1 km/h on a bearing of 101°
8 a 1 km   **b** 5·83 km/h on a bearing of 301°

Diagnostic Test 14   Vectors

1 a $\vec{v} + \vec{w}$ **b** $\vec{v} - \vec{w}$ **c** $\frac{2}{3}\vec{w}$ **d** $-2\vec{v}$ **e** $\vec{v} + \frac{2}{3}\vec{w}$ **f** $\vec{v} - \frac{1}{3}\vec{w}$

   g $\vec{w} - \vec{v}$ **h** $-2\vec{v} - \vec{w}$ **i** $2\vec{v} + \vec{w}$

2

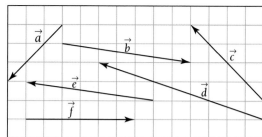

3 a $\begin{pmatrix} 2 \\ 3 \end{pmatrix}$ **b** $\begin{pmatrix} 2 \\ -3 \end{pmatrix}$ **c** $\begin{pmatrix} 0 \\ -4 \end{pmatrix}$ **d** $\begin{pmatrix} 4 \\ 0 \end{pmatrix}$ **e** $\begin{pmatrix} -2 \\ 4 \end{pmatrix}$ **f** $\begin{pmatrix} -1 \\ -3 \end{pmatrix}$

  g $\begin{pmatrix} -1 \\ -1 \end{pmatrix}$ **h** $\begin{pmatrix} 0 \\ 4 \end{pmatrix}$ **i** $\begin{pmatrix} -3 \\ -2 \end{pmatrix}$

4 a $\begin{pmatrix} -1 \\ 0 \end{pmatrix}$ **b** $\begin{pmatrix} 3 \\ -6 \end{pmatrix}$ **c** $\begin{pmatrix} 10 \\ 2 \end{pmatrix}$ **d** $\begin{pmatrix} -4 \\ -14 \end{pmatrix}$ **e** $\begin{pmatrix} -6 \\ 12 \end{pmatrix}$ **f** $\begin{pmatrix} -7 \\ -8 \end{pmatrix}$

5 a 17·0 units **b** 11·7 units **c** 29·0 units **d** 34·0 units **e** 21·1 units **f** 29·4 units

6 a ±4 **b** ±5 **c** ±7·94 **d** ±9·43 **e** ±22·2

7 a 154·70 km on a bearing of 202° **b** 11 knots on a bearing of 344° **c** 209·9 km/h on a bearing of 216°

14A Revision Assignment

1 a

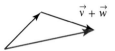
$\vec{v} + \vec{w}$

c

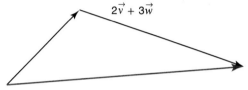
$2\vec{v} + 3\vec{w}$

b

$\vec{v} - \vec{w}$

d

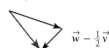
$\vec{w} - \frac{1}{2}\vec{v}$

e $\vec{v} = \begin{pmatrix} 2 \\ 2 \end{pmatrix}$

  $\vec{w} = \begin{pmatrix} 3 \\ -1 \end{pmatrix}$

f $|\vec{v}| = \sqrt{2^2 + 2^2} = \sqrt{8}$ units

  $|\vec{w}| = \sqrt{3^2 + (-1)^2} = \sqrt{10}$ units

g $\left| \begin{pmatrix} 5 \\ 1 \end{pmatrix} \right| = \sqrt{26}$ units

  $\left| \begin{pmatrix} -1 \\ 3 \end{pmatrix} \right| = \sqrt{10}$ units

  $\left| \begin{pmatrix} 13 \\ 1 \end{pmatrix} \right| = \sqrt{170}$ units

  $\left| \begin{pmatrix} 2 \\ -2 \end{pmatrix} \right| = \sqrt{8}$ units

2 a $|\vec{a}| = 5$ km

  $|\vec{b}| = 13$ km

  so total is 18 km

b $\vec{a} + \vec{b} = \begin{pmatrix} 8 \\ -16 \end{pmatrix}$

  so distance is $\sqrt{8^2 + (-16)^2} = 17·9$ km

c

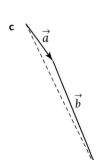

3 a

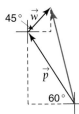

$$\vec{a} = \begin{pmatrix} 800\cos 30 \\ 800\sin 30 \end{pmatrix} = \begin{pmatrix} 692\cdot 8 \\ 400 \end{pmatrix}$$

$$\vec{b} = \begin{pmatrix} 1200\cos 45 \\ -1200\sin 45 \end{pmatrix} = \begin{pmatrix} 848\cdot 5 \\ -848\cdot 5 \end{pmatrix}$$

so resultant vector $\vec{r} = \vec{a} + \vec{b} = \begin{pmatrix} 1541\cdot 3 \\ -448\cdot 5 \end{pmatrix}$

∴ distance is $\quad |\vec{r}| \doteqdot 1605$ km

and directions is $\quad \theta = \tan^{-1}\left(\dfrac{448\cdot 5}{1541\cdot 3}\right) = 16\cdot 2°$

beyond 90° $\quad$ so actual bearing is 116·2°T

b

$$\vec{p} = \begin{pmatrix} -400\cos 60 \\ +400\sin 60 \end{pmatrix} \qquad \vec{w} = \begin{pmatrix} 60\cos 45 \\ 60\sin 45 \end{pmatrix}$$

$$\vec{r} = \vec{p} + \vec{w} = \begin{pmatrix} -157\cdot 6 \\ 388\cdot 8 \end{pmatrix}$$

∴ velocity $\quad = |\vec{r}| = 419$ km/h

and direction is $270 + \theta$ where $\theta = \tan^{-1}\left(\dfrac{388\cdot 8}{157\cdot 6}\right) = 270 + 68 = 338°$T

Chapter 15:   Statistics

Exercise 15:01

1 a i 7 ii 5 iii 5 iv 5·714 $\qquad$ **b** i 4 ii 5 iii 7 iv 6·75 $\qquad$ **c** i 6 ii 24 iii 24 iv 22·6
d i 0·8 ii 1·5 iii 1·5 iv 1·5

2 a 6·05 $\quad$ **b** 64·25 $\quad$ **c** 7 $\qquad$ **d** 2·71 $\quad$ **e** 50·24 $\quad$ **f** 14·78

3 a

Score	Frequency	fx	c.f.	R.F. (d)
5	1	5	1	0·04
6	4	24	5	0·16
7	6	42	11	0·24
8	7	56	18	0·28
9	5	45	23	0·20
10	2	20	25	0·08

$\Sigma f = 25 \quad \Sigma fx = 192$

mode = 8; mean = 7·68; median = 8

b 14; 11 $\quad$ **c** 5 $\quad$ **d** See table in **3a**.

4

Score	Frequency	fx	c.f.
5	2	10	2
6	3	18	5
7	5	35	10
8	4	32	14
9	4	36	18
10	2	20	20

a 7 $\quad$ **b** 7·55 $\quad$ **c** 7·5 $\quad$ **d** 5

5 a range = 4, median = 3·5 $\qquad$ **b** range = 4, median = 2·5

6 a

Children	Frequency	fx	c.f.
0	4	0	4
1	6	6	10
2	9	18	19
3	5	15	24
4	3	12	27
5	0	0	27
6	1	6	28
	28	57	

b 28 $\quad$ **c** 57 $\quad$ **d** 2 $\quad$ **e** above

7

Stem	Leaf	Frequency	c.f.
$6^{(5)}$	88999	5	5
$7^{(0)}$	000012234	9	14
$7^{(5)}$	555566777788	12	26
$8^{(0)}$	00011112344	11	37
$8^{(5)}$	58	2	39
$9^{(0)}$	00012334	8	47
$9^{(5)}$	789	3	50

a Modal class is 75–79 $\qquad$ **b** Median class is 75–79

8 a

Class	Class centre (c.c.)	Freq'cy (f)	f × c.c.	c.f.
64–66	65	25	1625	25
67–69	68	74	5032	99
70–72	71	73	5183	172
73–75	74	24	1776	196
76–78	77	2	154	198

b 14   **c** 67–69
d 69·5 (correct to one dec. pl.)
e 67–69   **f** 172

9 a

Number correct	Tally	Frequency (f)	fx	c.f.
9					3	27	3
10			1	10	4
11				2	22	6
12	ЖТ	5	60	11
13						4	52	15
14	ЖТ ЖТ	10	140	25
15	ЖТ ЖТ	10	150	35
16	ЖТ |||	8	128	43
17	ЖТ ЖТ ||||	14	238	57
18	ЖТ ЖТ		11	198	68
19	ЖТ ЖТ ЖТ ||	17	323	85
20	ЖТ ЖТ ЖТ	15	300	100
		100	1648	

9 b

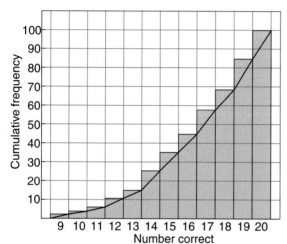

f i

Class	Class centre	f
9–10	9·5	4
11–12	11·5	7
13–14	13·5	14
15–16	15·5	18
17–18	17·5	25
19–20	19·5	32
	Total: 100	

ii

Class	Class centre	f
6–10	8	4
11–15	13	31
16–20	18	65
	Total: 100	

iii

Class	Class centre	f
1–10	5·5	4
11–20	15·5	96
	Total: 100	

Six classes are sufficient to show the characteristics (shape) of the data. As the number of classes is reduced to 3 and then 2, the characteristics (or shape) of the data are lost.

c 17   **d** above   **e** 2 is the best class interval; 5 and 10 give too few classes.

10 a i

Class	Tally	f
0–1			1
2–3		0
4–5	||	2
6–7	||	2
8–9			1
10–11	|||	3
12–13			1
14–15	||	2
16–17	||	2
18–19	|||	3
20–21	||||	4
22–23	||	2
24–25	||	2
26–27	||	2
28–29	|||	3
30–31	|||	3
32–33	||	2
34–35	||	2
36–37			1
38–39	||	2

Σf = 40

ii

Class	Tally	f
0–4	||	2
5–9	||||	4
10–14	ЖТ	5
15–19	ЖТ		6
20–24	ЖТ |||	8
25–29	ЖТ	5
30–34	ЖТ	5
35–39	ЖТ	5

Σf = 40

iii

Class	Tally	f
0–9	ЖТ		6
10–19	ЖТ ЖТ		11
20–29	ЖТ ЖТ |||	13
30–39	ЖТ ЖТ	10

Σf = 40

b i

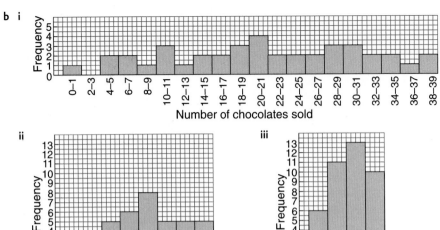

Number of chocolates sold

ii

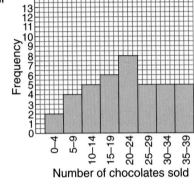

Number of chocolates sold

iii

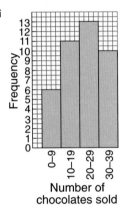

Number of chocolates sold

c Answers may vary, but here, a class interval of 5 gives a good view of trends without losing too much detail.

Prep Quiz 15:02

1 0 **2** 1 **3** 7 **4** Set C **5** yes **6** 8 **7** 8 **8** 8 **9** Set D **10** Set F

Exercise 15:02

1 a 3 **b** 3·5 **c** 13·5 **d** 15·5 **e** 15

2 a 13 **b** 11 **c** 15 **d** 4 **3 a** 4·5 **b** 3 **c** 5·5 **d** 2·5

4

Score	Freq.	Cumulative freq.
2	1	1
3	3	4
4	6	10
5	10	20
6	10	30
7	4	34
8	4	38
9	2	40

$IQR = 2$ using either method.

6 a 20 **b** 4 **c** 8·5

7 a 4 **b** 5

8 a 65 **b** 75 **c** 10

9 a $Q_1 = 21·5, Q_2 = 23, Q_3 = 25·5,$
IQ range = 4

b $Q_1 = 54·5, Q_2 = 63·5, Q_3 = 77,$
IQ range = 22·5

5 a

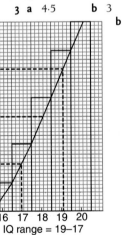

IQ range = 19−17
= 2

b

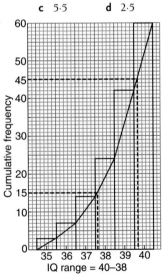

IQ range = 40−38
= 2

Exercise 15:03

1 a i 57 **ii** 32 **iii** 11 **b i** 51 **ii** 20 **iii** 6 **c i** 52 **ii** 25 **iii** 10

2 a (7, 8, 9, 11, 12) **b** (16, 25·5, 28, 33·5, 38) **c** (14, 32·5, 43, 46, 49)

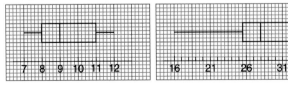

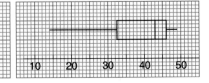

3 a (37, 39·5, 42·5, 44·5, 48)   **b** (59, 71, 76·5, 83, 87)

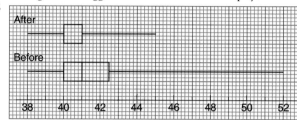

4 a i 25% **ii** 50%   **b i** 50% **ii** 75%   **c i** 3 **ii** 4   **d** Year 10

5 a (17, 20, 20·5, 22, 24)   **6** (26, 38·5, 50·5, 68, 82)

7 a (74, 76, 78, 84, 85)   **b** Ken   **c** Ray

d As the range can be easily affected by an outlier, it is not a good measure of consistency. Ray's lower inter-quartile range would suggest he is the most consistent player.

8

The traffic changes have not reduced the median time for Rick's trip, but they have resulted in more consistent trip times, as indicated by the reduced inter-quartile range. In fact, 75% of the trip times were less than 41 minutes compared to 50% before the changes. This would suggest that the traffic changes had been effective in reducing the variability in the trip times.

Exercise 15:04

1 a i A   **ii** C   **b i** C   **ii** B   **c i** B   **ii** A

2 C, B, A, D

3 a A   **b** C   **c** D   **d** B

4 a 5·4, 2·5   **b** 12·8, 3·3   **c** 5·3, 2·4   **d** 58·9, 19·3

5 a 2·95, 1·12   **b** 10·52, 1·16   **c** 33·4, 13·65   **d** 49·65, 1·48,   **e** 29·2, 10·55

6 a i Set A, 19·1; Set B, 5·4   **ii** The first scores are different. The score of 20 in set A is an outlier.   **iii** Yes

7 a Set A: Mean = 65·9, s.d. = 18·8; Set B: Mean = 68·3, s.d. = 13·7

b The effect of the outlier will be reduced as the number of scores increases.

8 a A   **b** A   **c** B

9 a i George   **ii** George   **iii** Rick

b Rick's lower standard deviation suggests that he is consistently the better player.

10 a B   **b** B   **c** A

11 Maths: $\bar{x} = 69\cdot5$, $\sigma = 14\cdot2$, English: $\bar{x} = 59\cdot4, \sigma = 10\cdot4$. Tom's English marks is the better, relative to the rest of the class.

12 a 70   **b** 62   **c** 63   **d** 18   **e** 40   **f** 48

13 a Mean will be less, s.d. will be greater.   **b** Mean will be greater, s.d. will be less.

c Both mean and s.d. will be greater.

14 a i range = 4, mean = 7, $\sigma \doteq 1\cdot4$ **ii** range = 4, mean = 7, $\sigma \doteq 1\cdot2$ **iii** range = 4, mean = 7, $\sigma \doteq 1\cdot6$

b For all three graphs, the range and mean are the same. The standard deviation is smallest when scores tend to be clustered around the mean (as in case **ii**) and greatest when the scores tend to be further from the mean (as in case **iii**).

c The range does not change, the mean increases by 10 and the standard deviation does not change.

d The range, mean and standard deviation are all multiplied by 10.

Exercise 15:05

1 a B and D. The skew is caused because of the unevenness of the number of students in each age group. School B has a small senior school, while school D has a smaller junior school.

b A   **c i** A   **ii** B   **iii** C or D   **iv** C

2 a class 1   **b i** class 2 **ii** class 2   **c** class 1: mean = 88·7, s.d. = 4·7; class 2: mean = 91·1, s.d. = 5·3

3 a i negatively skewed   **ii** positively skewed   **b** Girls borrow more books than boys.

c Grouped frequency histograms allow a scale to be used to represent large frequencies. If a back-to-back stem-and-leaf plot were used, you would need a large number of leaves in the girls 30–39 column and the boys 1–9 column. This would make the stem-and-leaf plot very wide.

d The distribution would be more uniform. The lowness of the 41–50 column compared to the other columns would make the distribution slightly positively skewed.

4 a topic 1

b topic 1 has the smallest spread of scores. It has a lower standard deviation (15·1) and inter-quartile range (24·5), than that of topic 2.

c topic 1: mean = 61, median = 60; topic 2: mean = 72, median = 78. The results suggest that the class performed much better on topic test 2. This could be because the class was better prepared or perhaps because the test was easier.

5 a weak swimmer   **b** excellent swimmer   **c** $43\frac{1}{3}$ %   **d** 80%   **e** The program was very successful.

6 a

Test 1	
Score	Frequency
1	5
2	5
3	6
4	5
5	2

Test 2	
Score	Frequency
0	4
1	1
2	10
3	4
4	4

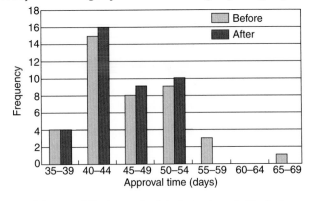

b Test 1 Mean = 2·7   Test 2 Mean = 2·1
        Median = 3   Median = 2

Both the mean and median for Test 2 are lower than that of Test 1.
This suggests that test 2 was more difficult than Test 1.

c The scores in both tests have a standard deviation of 1·26. The inter-quartile range for Test 1 is 2 while for Test 2 is 1. This would suggest that the scores for Test 1 have a greater spread than those of Test 2.

7 a This shows that the median is 160 cm, the middle half of the scores lie in the range 153 to 168 cm and the 30 heights lie in the range 135 cm to 178 cm.

b Yes. The median class is 160–164 and this contains the median score of the box-and-whiskers graph and it is possible for the middle half of the scores to be in the range 153 cm to 168 cm and the range to be 135 cm to 178 cm.

8 Both brands have the same median, but brand X has a larger inter-quartile range, a lower minimum and a lower maximum. This would suggest that brand Y will be the best performer.

9 a The data for group 1 is positively skewed, while that for group 2 is close to normally distributed. The mean for group 1 would be in the 120s while that for group 2 is in the 140s. The shape suggests that group 1 is fitter than group 2.

b Group 1: Median = 129   Group 2: Median = 146
        IQ range = 135–127   IQ range = 154–137
              = 8   = 17

Group 1 has a lower median and its scores are not as spread. Hence group 1 is overall a fitter group than group 2.

10 a The data could be organised into a grouped frequency distribution table using classes of 35–39, 40–44, 45–49, etc. This would give 7 classes. Using class intervals of 30–39, 40–49 etc, would result in only 4 classes and would not show the differences between the two sets of data.
Stem-and-leaf plots would probably not be appropriate because of the number of leaves needed on the 4 stem (40–49) or the 4° stem (40–44). Either stem-and-leaf plot would probably be too wide.
The best way to display the data is a double-column graph with one column for 'before' and another column for 'after'.

b Either the mean or median could be used as measures of cluster, while the standard deviation is probably the best measure of spread to use even though the spread of both sets of data is similar.

c Council's new procedures have reduced the average time taken to approve applications. The median time has been reduced from 45 days to 44 days. The 'after' application times also have a smaller spread than the 'before' times, indicating that the scores are closer to the mean. This would indicate that the new procedures have resulted in more consistent approval times.

Diagnostic Test 15   Statistics

1 a 14   **b** 13   **c** 15   **d** 13·06 (to 2 dec. pl.)   **e** 12   **f** $\frac{18}{117}$ (or 0·15)   **g** 2·83

2

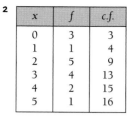

x	f	c.f.
0	3	3
1	1	4
2	5	9
3	4	13
4	2	15
5	1	16

a

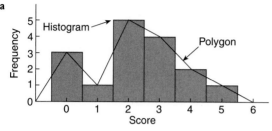

b

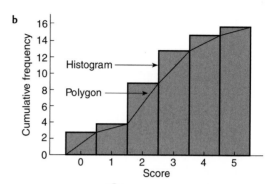

3

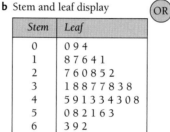

Class	Class centre	Tally	Freq.	c.f.
0–9	4.5	|||	3	3
10–19	14.5	|||||	5	8
20–29	24.5	|||||		6	14
30–39	34.5	||||| |||	8	22
40–49	44.5	||||| ||||	9	31
50–59	54.5	|||||		6	37
60–69	64.5	|||	3	40

b Stem and leaf display

Stem	Leaf
0	0 9 4
1	8 7 6 4 1
2	7 6 0 8 5 2
3	1 8 8 7 7 8 3 8
4	5 9 1 3 3 4 3 0 8
5	0 8 2 1 6 3
6	3 9 2

(OR) Ordered stem and leaf display

Stem	Leaf
0	0 4 9
1	1 4 6 7 8
2	0 2 5 6 7 8
3	1 3 7 7 8 8 8 8
4	0 1 3 3 3 4 5 8 9
5	0 1 2 3 6 8
6	2 3 9

c 2.5   **d** 12

4 a (7.5)   **b**

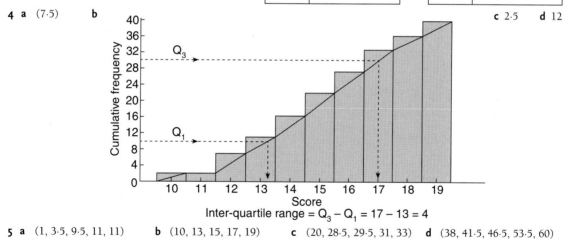

Inter-quartile range = $Q_3 - Q_1$ = 17 − 13 = 4

5 a (1, 3.5, 9.5, 11, 11)   **b** (10, 13, 15, 17, 19)   **c** (20, 28.5, 29.5, 31, 33)   **d** (38, 41.5, 46.5, 53.5, 60)

6 a

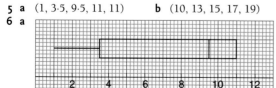

b

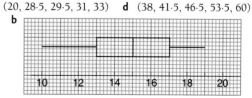

c

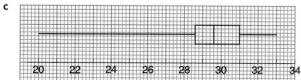

7 a 25   **b** range = 60, inter-quartile range = 22

8 Test A: s.d. = 2·00   Test B: s.d. = 4·15   Test C: s.d. = 4·52.

A mark of 15 is more impressive for Test C as it is 1·11 standard deviations above the mean (while it is only 1·00 for test A and 0·72 for Test B).

9 a

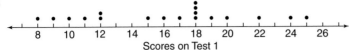

Scores on Test 1

b   Scores   **c**

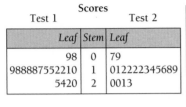

Test 1		Test 2
Leaf	Stem	Leaf
98	0	79
988887552210	1	012222345689
5420	2	0013

15A Revision Assignment

1 a Yes, 64 is an outlier.   **b i** (64, 71·5, 73, 76, 81)   **ii** (70, 72, 73, 76 81)   **c i** 4·5   **ii** 4

    d It is positively skewed.

2 Without Jenny's score, the mean will be greater and the s.d. will be less.

3 Nick: mean = 78, s.d. = 4·07   Dylan: mean = 78, s.d. = 5·06

    Nick is the more consistent golfer (because of his smaller s.d.)

4 a The scores cluster around 6 with a regular spread on each side. The distribution is reasonably symmetrical.

    b The scores are skewed to the right (negatively skewed), while the score 1 is an outlier.

5 Year 4 have clearly performed better. The mean and median are both 66·5 compared to the mean and median for year 3, which are 49·8 and 48 respectively. Both sets of results have a similar spread, especially if the score of 35 in the year 4 results is ignored, as it is an outlier. The year 3 results are positively skewed, while the year 4 results are reasonably uniform. All of the year 4 results, with the exception of the outlier, are above the year 3 mean and median.

15B Working Mathematically

1 14   **2** 6

3 a ÷ 3·8 cm ÷ 210 = 0·018 cm   **b** 0·25 cm ÷ 0·018 cm ÷ 13·8 times longer

4 26·3 cm   **5** 18·75 m

6 a i early morning on Saturday   **ii** Mon, Tue, Wed afternoon

    b Many young people go out on Friday evening and are coming home on Saturday early in the morning. They could be tired or driving under the influence of alcohol and hence more likely to be involved in an accident.

Chapter 16:   Probability

Exercise 16:01

1 Answers will vary.

2 a even chance   **b** improbable   **c** probable   **d** impossible   **e** certain   **f** even chance

3 a $\frac{13}{20}$ **b** $\frac{7}{20}$ **c** 1   **d** 0   **e** 1   **f** $\frac{7}{20}$

4 a $\frac{20}{100}$ [or $\frac{1}{5}$]   **b** $\frac{80}{100}$ [or $\frac{4}{5}$]   **c** $\frac{16}{100}$ [or $\frac{4}{25}$]   **d** $\frac{84}{100}$ [or $\frac{21}{25}$]

5 a $\frac{1}{2}$ **b** $\frac{1}{2}$ **c** 0   **d** $\frac{1}{13}$ **e** $\frac{12}{13}$ **f** $\frac{3}{13}$ **g** $\frac{1}{4}$ **h** $\frac{3}{4}$ **i** $\frac{2}{13}$

6 a 1   **b** 1   **c** No, unless the number of boys is the same as the number of girls.

7 a $\frac{1}{4}$ **b** $\frac{1}{2}$ **c** $\frac{3}{200}$ **d** $\frac{1}{200}$ **e** $\frac{3}{4}$ **f** $\frac{159}{200}$ **g** $\frac{197}{200}$ **h** $\frac{41}{200}$ **i** $\frac{1}{50}$

8 a This is untrue, as most phone numbers in a suburb (and perhaps a state) start with the same number.

    b The trees would not be present in equal numbers. If koalas live on Koala Mountain, there is probably a large percentage of gum trees. The statement is illogical.

9 a 'Out'   **b i** 5 times   **ii** 20 times   **c** $\frac{1}{3}$ **d** $\frac{1}{5}$

10 ABC, ACB, BAC, BCA, CAB, CBA   **a** $\frac{1}{2}$ **b** $\frac{1}{3}$ **c** $\frac{1}{3}$ **d** $\frac{2}{3}$ **e** $\frac{1}{3}$

11 a $\frac{7}{10}$ **b** $\frac{1}{5}$ **c** $\frac{1}{10}$ **d** $\frac{4}{5}$ **e** $\frac{3}{10}$ **f** 0 **g** 1 **h** $\frac{7}{10}$

12 a $\frac{1}{4}$ **b** $\frac{1}{8}$ **c** $\frac{1}{12}$ **d** $\frac{5}{36}$ **e** $\frac{1}{9}$ **f** $\frac{13}{36}$ **g** $\frac{5}{12}$ **h** $\frac{31}{72}$ **i** $\frac{25}{72}$ **j** $\frac{3}{4}$ **k** $\frac{17}{24}$

13 a 50% **b** 38% **c** 1% **d** 20% **e** 80% **f** 77% **g** 23%

14 a $\frac{3}{20}$ **b** $\frac{17}{20}$ **c** $\frac{67}{100}$ **d** $\frac{33}{100}$ **e** $\frac{47}{50}$ **f** $\frac{3}{50}$ **g** $\frac{1}{100}$

15 a $\frac{3}{20}$ **b** $\frac{17}{20}$ **c** $\frac{3}{25}$ **d** $\frac{9}{50}$ **e** $\frac{11}{20}$ **f** $\frac{9}{20}$ **g** $\frac{3}{10}$ **h** $\frac{3}{20}$ **i** $\frac{17}{20}$

16 a $\frac{16}{17}$ **b** 0·75 **c** 63% **d** 0·875

e 99·5%. No, as \$135 is 1·35% of \$10 000 and this is clearly more than 0·5%. (There is 1 chance in 200 that I will die this year. 200 × \$135 = \$27 000. As I am insured for only \$10 000, it does not represent good value.)

17 a $\frac{1}{125}$ **b** $\frac{124}{125}$

18 a $\frac{4}{25}$ **b** $\frac{7}{50}$ **c** $\frac{43}{100}$ **d** $\frac{43}{50}$ **e** $\frac{3}{10}$ **f** $\frac{1}{2}$

19

Result	Tally	Freq.	Experimental probability
2	||	2	2/80 or 0·025 or 2·5%
3	ЖЖ	5	5/80 or 0·0625 or 6·25%
4	ЖЖ |	6	6/80 or 0·075 or 7·5%
5	ЖЖ |||	8	8/80 or 0·1 or 10%
6	ЖЖ ЖЖ |	11	11/80 or 0·1375 or 13·75%
7	ЖЖ ЖЖ ||||	14	14/80 or 0·175 or 17·5%
8	ЖЖ ЖЖ ||	12	12/80 or 0·15 or 15%
9	ЖЖ ||||	9	9/80 or 0·1125 or 11·25%
10	ЖЖ |	6	6/80 or 0·075 or 7·5%
11	||||	4	4/80 or 0·05 or 5%
12	|||	3	3/80 or 0·0375 or 3·75%
	Totals:	80	80/80 1·0000 100%

20

Number of heads	Tally	Freq.	Experimental probability
0	ЖЖ |	6	$\frac{3}{25}$, 12%
1	ЖЖ ЖЖ ЖЖ |||	18	$\frac{9}{25}$, 36%
2	ЖЖ ЖЖ ЖЖ ||||	19	$\frac{19}{50}$, 38%
3	ЖЖ ||	7	$\frac{7}{50}$, 14%

a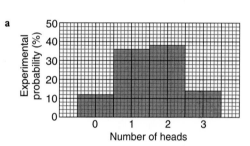

b '2 heads' is the most likely outcome.

21 a i 0·12 **ii** 0·07 **iii** 0·04 **b i** 0·62 **ii** 0·38 **c i** 0·42 **ii** 0·58

d Jan tends to throw her darts towards the bottom right side of the board.

Prep Quiz 16:02

1 1, 2, 3, 4, 5, 6 **2** head, tail **3** J, Q, K of hearts, of diamonds, of clubs and of spades
4 Wagga Wagga wins, Armidale wins, there is a draw. **5** 1, 2, 3, 4, 5, 6, 7, 8, 9
6 (1, 6), (2, 5), (3, 4), (4, 3), (5, 2), (6, 1) **7** (1, 1) **8** (1, 2), (2, 1) **9** (1, 3), (2, 2), (3, 1)
10 (1, 4), (2, 3), (3, 2), (4, 1)

Exercise 16:02

1 a (moon, blue), (moon, green), (moon, red), (spoon, blue), (spoon, green), (spoon, red), (star, blue), (star, green), (star, red), (crown, blue), (crown, green), (crown, red)

b

	blue	*green*	*red*
moon	✓	✓	✓
spoon	✓	✓	✓
star	✓	✓	✓
crown	✓	✓	✓

c

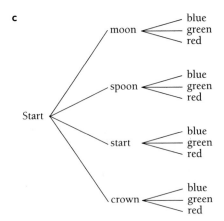

2 a (head, blue), (head, green), (head, red), (tail, blue), (tail, green), (tail, red)

b

	blue	*green*	*red*
head	✓	✓	✓
tail	✓	✓	✓

c

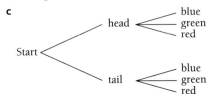

3 a (head, 5♦), (head, 5♠), (head, 10♥), (head, 9♣), (head, 3♦), (tail, 5♦), (tail, 5♠), (tail, 10♥), (tail, 9♣), (tail, 3♦)

b

	5♦	*5♠*	*10♥*	*9♣*	*3♦*
head	✓	✓	✓	✓	✓
tail	✓	✓	✓	✓	✓

c

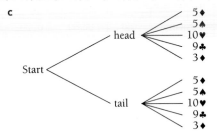

4 a (1, blue), (1, green), (1, red), (2, blue), (2, green), (2, red), (3, blue), (3, green), (3, red), (4, blue), (4, green), (4, red), (5, blue), (5, green), (5 red), (6, blue), (6, green), (6, red)

b

	blue	*green*	*red*
1	✓	✓	✓
2	✓	✓	✓
3	✓	✓	✓
4	✓	✓	✓
5	✓	✓	✓
6	✓	✓	✓

c

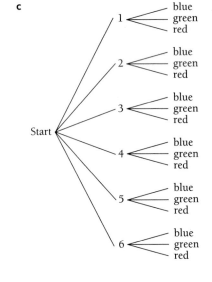

5 a 8　　**b** 24　　**c** 20　　**d** 30　　**e** 12　　**f** 15

6 24　　**7 a** 9　　**b** 3　　**c** 5　　**d** 4

8

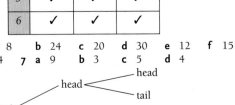

a 4　　**b** 3　　**c** 1

9

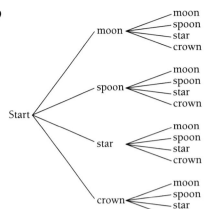

a 16   **b** 7   **c** 9

10 a no   **b** 20   **c** 14   **d** 6   **e** 4   **f** 10   **g** 10   **h** yes

11 a $\frac{1}{169}$ (ie $\frac{1}{13} \times \frac{1}{13}$)   **b** $\frac{1}{221}$ (ie $\frac{1}{13} \times \frac{3}{51}$)

Exercise 16:03

1 independent   **2** dependent   **3** dependent   **4** dependent   **5** dependent   **6** independent
7 dependent   **8** dependent   **9** independent   **10** dependent   **11** independent

12 a $\frac{1}{3}$ **b** $\frac{1}{3}$ **c** $\frac{1}{2}$ **d** No. At this stage, the ring is just as likely to be in box A as box B.
    e In this case there would be 1 chance in 3 of the ring being in box A and 2 chances in 3 of it being in the remaining box. (This problem is called the Monty Hull paradox.)

13 a $\frac{3}{10}$ **b** yes, $\frac{1}{3}$ **c** 1   **d** dependent

14 a

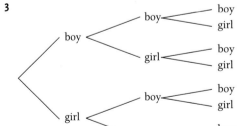

b 6   **c** $\frac{1}{6}$ **15 a** 12 ways   **b** $\frac{1}{12}$ **c** 0

16 a 6   **b** 1   **c** $\frac{1}{6}$

17 a 6   **b** B, C, D, E or F   **c** 5
    d 30   **e** $\frac{1}{30}$

Exercise 16:04

1 a 4   **b** i $\frac{1}{4}$ ii $\frac{1}{2}$ iii $\frac{3}{4}$

2 a $\frac{1}{36}$ **b** $\frac{1}{6}$ **c** $\frac{1}{36}$ **d** $\frac{1}{18}$ **e** $\frac{1}{12}$ **f** $\frac{1}{9}$ **g** $\frac{5}{36}$ **h** $\frac{1}{6}$ **i** $\frac{5}{36}$ **j** $\frac{1}{9}$ **k** $\frac{1}{12}$ **l** $\frac{1}{18}$
    m $\frac{1}{36}$ **n** 0   **o** $\frac{3}{4}$ (or $\frac{27}{36}$)   **p** $\frac{1}{4}$ **q** $\frac{1}{4}$ **r** $\frac{1}{2}$ **s** 1, parts p, q and r represent all possible outcomes. Therefore their sum is 1.   **t** 'a sum of 5', 'a sum of 9' (Other answers are also possible.)

3

```
                        ┌── boy
              ┌── boy ──┤
              │         └── girl
       ┌ boy ─┤
       │      │         ┌── boy
       │      └── girl ─┤
       │                └── girl
  ─────┤
       │                ┌── boy
       │      ┌── boy ──┤
       │      │         └── girl
       └ girl ┤
              │         ┌── boy
              └── girl ─┤
                        └── girl
```

a 8   **b** 3   **c** i $\frac{1}{8}$ ii $\frac{3}{8}$ iii $\frac{1}{4}$ iv $\frac{1}{2}$
4 a $\frac{1}{12}$ **b** $\frac{1}{12}$ **c** $\frac{1}{2}$ **d** $\frac{1}{2}$ **e** $\frac{1}{4}$ **f** $\frac{1}{4}$
5 a $\frac{1}{3}$ **b** $\frac{5}{9}$ **c** $\frac{1}{3}$ **d** $\frac{2}{3}$
6 a $\frac{3}{8}$ **b** $\frac{3}{8}$ **c** $\frac{1}{2}$ **d** $\frac{1}{8}$ **e** $\frac{7}{8}$ **f** $\frac{3}{4}$ **g** $\frac{1}{2}$

7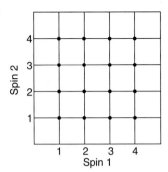

a 16   **b i** $\frac{1}{4}$ **ii** $\frac{7}{16}$ **iii** $\frac{1}{4}$ **iv** $\frac{1}{2}$ **v** $\frac{1}{4}$

8 a 6   **b i** $\frac{1}{6}$ **ii** $\frac{2}{3}$ **iii** $\frac{2}{3}$ **iv** 1

9 a

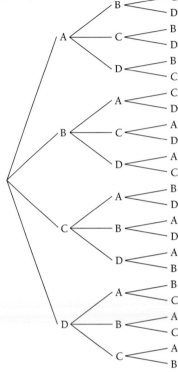

b i $\frac{1}{24}$ **ii** 0

c i $\frac{1}{4}$ **ii** $\frac{1}{6}$

10 a

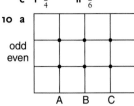

b 6

c i $\frac{1}{6}$ **ii** $\frac{5}{6}$ **iii** $\frac{2}{3}$

11 a

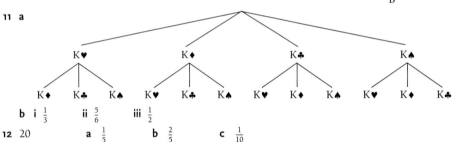

b i $\frac{1}{3}$ **ii** $\frac{5}{6}$ **iii** $\frac{1}{2}$

12 20   **a** $\frac{1}{5}$ **b** $\frac{2}{5}$ **c** $\frac{1}{10}$

Exercise 16:05

1 a 342   **b** 301   **c i** $\frac{301}{600}$ **ii** $\frac{299}{600}$ **iii** $\frac{342}{600}$ (or $\frac{57}{100}$)   **iv** $\frac{258}{600}$ (or $\frac{43}{100}$)   **v** $\frac{103}{600}$ **vi** $\frac{62}{600}$ (or $\frac{31}{300}$)
d $\frac{239}{301}$ **e** $\frac{239}{342}$

2 a $\frac{315}{1000}$ (or $\frac{63}{200}$)   **b** $\frac{393}{1000}$ **c** $\frac{169}{1000}$ **d** $\frac{461}{1000}$ **e** $\frac{63}{339}$ (or $\frac{21}{113}$)   **f** $\frac{83}{268}$

3 a 0·47   **b** 0·40   **c** 0·77   **d** 0·16   **e** 0·31

4 a $\frac{236}{2461}$ **b** $\frac{122}{2461}$ **c** $\frac{1734}{2461}$ **d** $\frac{358}{2461}$ **e** 0   **f** 1   **g** $\frac{628}{2461}$

5 a $\frac{86}{181}$ **b** $\frac{42}{181}$ **c** $\frac{95}{181}$

6

	male	female	totals
Library	10	20	30
Psychology	30	30	60
Mathematics	50	10	60
totals	90	60	150

a $\frac{60}{150}$ (or $\frac{2}{5}$)   **b** $\frac{30}{150}$ (or $\frac{1}{5}$)
c $\frac{10}{150}$ (or $\frac{1}{15}$)   **d** $\frac{30}{150}$ (or $\frac{1}{5}$)

7 a $\frac{1}{39}$ **b** 0   **c** $\frac{19}{39}$ **d** $\frac{28}{39}$ **e** $\frac{2}{39}$

8 a $\frac{31}{87}$ **b** $\frac{17}{87}$ **c** $\frac{14}{87}$ **d** $\frac{50}{87}$

9 a i $\frac{210}{300}$ (or $\frac{7}{10}$)   **ii** $\frac{160}{300}$ (or $\frac{8}{15}$)   **iii** $\frac{230}{300}$ (or $\frac{23}{30}$)   **iv** $\frac{70}{300}$ (or $\frac{7}{30}$)   **b i** $\frac{70}{300}$ (or $\frac{7}{30}$)

    ii $\frac{20}{300}$ (or $\frac{1}{15}$).   **c** No. The group of people who are not athletes are likely to have a far greater percentage in the 'heavy' category.

10 a i 32·7%   **ii** 0·6%   **iii** 18·8%   **iv** 97·8%   **v** 66·7%

    b i 30·2%   **ii** 0·9%   **iii** 18·7%   **iv** 96·5%   **v** 68·9%

The decrease of 37·5% in fatalities in the ACT was a decrease of only 6 fatalities, which is only about 0·3% of the national toll of 1737.

Exercise 16:06

1 a Results will vary.   **b** theoretical probability $= \frac{1}{8}$

2 Allot a number from the dice to each shirt. Throw the dice 52 times, recording the results. Count the number of times a result was repeated. Provided Lachlan continues to randomly choose from the six shirts, you would expect that a similar number of repetitions would occur in the second year. Each week the chance of choosing the same shirt as the previous week is $\frac{1}{6}$. So you would expect repetition to occur $\frac{1}{6}$ of the time.

3 Results will vary.

4 a It is impossible to throw a 1 (January) with two dice. It is far more likely that a 7 will be thrown (probability $= \frac{1}{6}$) than a 12 (probability $= \frac{1}{36}$). The likelihood of weddings is not the same for each month anyway.

    b How many weddings do we expect to be invited to each year? Which months are popular for weddings? Discuss other problems.

    c Each of 52 playing cards could represent a week of the year, but still, some weeks will be more popular than others because of climate and holidays.

5 Results will differ. It would not be reasonable to multiply the results of the first stimulation by ten as the result would be that Heather plays in either all games or no games. This is clearly unreasonable.

6 Results will differ. Each simulation may be different. Campers could be asked to pay in advance or at least pay a deposit. Advertising vacant sites could attract passing travellers. Discuss any other ideas.

7 a Results will differ.   **b** Minimum time for two sets is 20 weeks.

8 Results will vary, but on average five 6's should occur.

9 Results will vary.

Diagnostic Test 16   Chance and simulation experiments

1 a $\frac{1}{10}$ **b i** $\frac{1}{50}$ **ii** $\frac{1}{5}$ **iii** $\frac{49}{50}$ **iv** $\frac{3}{10}$

2 a $\frac{3}{44}$ **b** $\frac{41}{44}$ **c** 0. It is obviously possible that I could play very badly and score higher than 109, so the real probability (theoretical) would be greater than zero.

3 a (1, head), (1, tail),
(2, head), (2, tail),
(3, head), (3, tail),
(4, head), (4, tail),
(5, head), (5, tail),
(6, head), (6 tail)

b

	head	tail
1	✓	✓
2	✓	✓
3	✓	✓
4	✓	✓
5	✓	✓
6	✓	✓

c

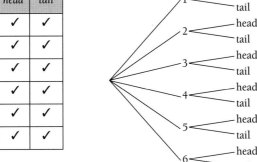

4 a

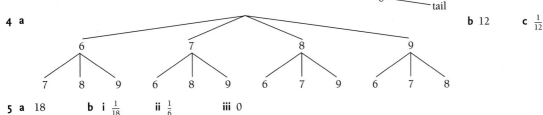

b 12   **c** $\frac{1}{12}$

5 a 18   **b i** $\frac{1}{18}$ **ii** $\frac{1}{6}$ **iii** 0

6 a

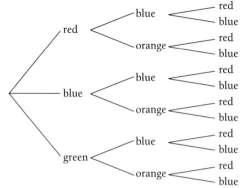

6 b $\frac{5}{12}$

7 a $\frac{3}{4}$ **b** $\frac{1}{4}$

8 a $\frac{22}{110}$ (or $\frac{1}{5}$)   **b** $\frac{32}{110}$ (or $\frac{16}{55}$)

    c $\frac{55}{110}$ (or $\frac{1}{2}$)   **d** $\frac{12}{110}$ (or $\frac{6}{55}$)

9 a $\frac{1}{15}$ **b** $\frac{7}{10}$ **c** $\frac{3}{10}$ **d** 1

10 a $\frac{35}{85}$ (or $\frac{7}{17}$)   **b** $\frac{7}{85}$ **c** $\frac{28}{85}$ **d** $\frac{42}{85}$

16A Revision Assignment

1 a $\frac{7}{20}$ **b** $\frac{1}{10}$ **c** $\frac{13}{20}$

2 a $\frac{5}{36}$ **b** $\frac{1}{12}$ **c** $\frac{5}{12}$ **d** $\frac{5}{18}$

3 a $\frac{2}{5}$ **b** $\frac{1}{10}$ **c** $\frac{1}{2}$ **d** 0

4 a $\frac{4}{13}$ **b** $\frac{5}{13}$ **c** $\frac{4}{13}$ **d** $\frac{9}{13}$

16B Working Mathematically

1 a 3   **b** 18   **c** 3

2 a twice yearly   **b** monthly   **c** $500
   d 30 days   **e** $100

3 a 8   **b** 24   **c** 24   **d** 8   **e** 4·14

5 a

a	0	1	2	3	4	5	6
n	1	3	5	7	9	11	13

   b i even   **ii** even   **iii** odd   **iv** even   **v** odd

   c $(2a + 1)(2b + 1) = 4ab + 2a + 2b + 1$

                   = even + even + even + odd

                   = odd

6 a 27·5%   **b** 75·4%   **c** 13·1%   **d** 93·3%   **e** No, there are probably fewer female motocyclists.
   f passenger, 0–4 years   **g** 26–39 years

5 a $\frac{1}{16}$ **b** $\frac{3}{8}$

   c $\frac{1}{4}$ **d** $\frac{11}{16}$

6 a $\frac{2}{5}$ **b** $\frac{3}{5}$

Chapter 17: Logic — an introduction

Exercise 17:01

1 a T   **b** Not a proposition   **c** F   **d** T   **e** Not a proposition
   f F   **g** T   **h** T   **i** T   **j** T

Exercise 17:02

1 a T   **b** T   **c** T   **d** T   **e** F   **f** T   **g** T   **h** T   **i** F   **j** F

Exercise 17:03

1 a i All even numbers are divisible by 2 and all odd numbers are divisible by 3.
    ii All even numbers are divisible by 2 or all odd numbers are divisible by 3.

b

p	q	$p \wedge q$	$p \vee q$
T	F	F	T

2 a i A hexagon has 5 sides and a quadrilateral with only two parallel sides is a trapezium.
    ii Either a hexagon has 5 sides or a quadrilateral with only two parallel sides is a trapezium.

b

m	n	$m \wedge n$	$m \vee n$
F	T	F	T

3 a i Today I have homework and this book has 20 chapters.

ii Either today I have homework or this book has 20 chapters.

b

a	b	$a \wedge b$	$a \vee b$
F	F	F	F

4 a i A revolution has 360° and the angle sum of a quadrilateral is the same as a revolution.

ii Either a revolution has 360° or the angle sum of a quadrilateral is the same as a revolution.

b

s	t	$s \wedge t$	$s \vee t$
T	T	T	T

5 a i $\sqrt{(-64)} = -8$ and $\sqrt[3]{(-64)} = -4$

ii $\sqrt{(-64)} = -8$ or $\sqrt[3]{(-64)} = -4$

b

p	q	$p \wedge q$	$p \vee q$
F	T	F	T

6 Since both propositions cannot be true and x is true, then y must be false. Therefore Rajiv will not play golf this weekend.

Exercise 17:04

1 a i All trapeziums are not parallelograms.

ii Either all squares are rhombuses or all trapeziums are parallelograms.

iii All squares are rhombuses and all trapeziums are parallelograms.

iv All squares are rhombuses and all trapeziums are not parallelograms.

v All squares are not rhombuses and all trapeziums are parallelograms.

b

s	t	$\neg s$	$\neg t$	$s \vee t$	$s \wedge t$	$s \vee \neg t$	$\neg s \wedge t$
T	F	F	T	T	F	T	F

So (i), (ii) and (iv) are true propositions.

2 a i $\neg c$ **ii** $\neg c \wedge d$ **iii** $c \vee \neg d$ **iv** $\neg c \wedge \neg d$ **v** $c \vee d$

b

c	d	$\neg c$	$\neg d$	$\neg c \wedge d$	$c \vee \neg d$	$\neg c \wedge \neg d$	$c \vee d$
F	T	T	F	T	F	F	T

So (i), (ii) and (v) are true.

3 p: Michael is not a good swimmer.

q: The diagonals of a rectangle are equal.

4 a

m	n	$\neg m$	$\neg n$	$m \wedge n$	$\neg m \wedge n$	$\neg m \wedge \neg n$	$\neg(m \wedge n)$
T	T	F	F	T	F	F	F

b $\neg m$: All mammals do not breathe air.

$\neg n$: All pentagons do not have 5 sides.

$m \wedge n$: All mammals breathe air and all pentagons have 5 sides.

$\neg m \wedge n$: All mammals do not breathe air and all pentagons have 5 sides.

$\neg m \wedge \neg n$: All mammals do not breathe air and all pentagons do not have 5 sides.

$\neg(m \wedge n)$: It is not right that all mammals breathe air and all pentagons have 5 sides.

5 Today rain is not predicted and I will not play tennis.

6 p is false and q is true.

7

p	q	$\neg p$	$\neg q$	$p \wedge q$	$p \vee q$	$\neg p \wedge \neg q$	$\neg p \vee \neg q$
T	T	F	F	T	T	F	F
T	F	F	T	F	T	F	T
F	T	T	F	F	T	F	T
F	F	T	T	F	F	T	T

Investigation 17:04   The whole truth and nothing but the truth!

Table 1

p	q	r	$q \vee r$	$p \vee q$	$p \vee r$	$(p \vee q) \vee r$	$p \vee (p \vee r)$
T	T	T	T	T	T	T	T
T	T	F	T	T	T	T	T
T	F	T	T	T	T	T	T
F	T	T	T	T	T	T	T
T	F	F	F	T	T	T	T
F	T	F	T	T	F	T	T
F	F	T	T	F	T	T	T
F	F	F	F	F	F	F	F

Table 2

p	q	r	$q \vee r$	$p \wedge q$	$p \wedge r$	$p \wedge (q \vee r)$	$(p \wedge q) \vee (p \wedge r)$
T	T	T	T	T	T	T	T
T	T	F	T	T	F	T	T
T	F	T	T	F	T	T	T
F	T	T	T	F	F	F	F
T	F	F	F	F	F	F	F
F	T	F	T	F	F	F	F
F	F	T	T	F	F	F	F
F	F	F	F	F	F	F	F

Table 3

p	q	r	$q \wedge r$	$p \vee q$	$p \vee r$	$p \vee (q \wedge r)$	$(p \vee q) \wedge (p \vee r)$
T	T	T	T	T	T	T	T
T	T	F	F	T	T	T	T
T	F	T	F	T	T	T	T
F	T	T	T	T	T	T	T
T	F	F	F	T	T	T	T
F	T	F	F	T	F	F	F
F	F	T	F	F	T	F	F
F	F	F	F	F	F	F	F

Exercise 17:05

1 a

p	q	$\neg p$	$\neg q$	$p \vee q$	$\neg(p \vee q)$	$\neg p \wedge \neg q$
T	T	F	F	T	F	F
T	F	F	T	T	F	F
F	T	T	F	T	F	F
F	F	T	T	F	T	T

b $\neg(p \vee q)$: It is not true that I have a pet cat or that I live in a brick house.
$\neg p \wedge \neg q$: I do not have a pet cat and I do not live in a brick house.
These statements are logically equivalent.

2 a

m	n	$\neg m$	$\neg n$	$m \wedge n$	$\neg(m \wedge n)$	$\neg m \vee \neg n$
T	T	F	F	T	F	F
T	F	F	T	F	T	T
F	T	T	F	F	T	T
F	F	T	T	F	T	T

b $\neg(m \wedge n)$: It is not true that **both** Minh plays tennis well **and** that George is a good algebra student.

$\neg m \vee \neg n$: **Either** Minh does **not** play tennis well **or** George is not a good algebra student.

These are logically equivalent statements.

3 a i I play a team sport **and** its **either** rugby **or** soccer.

ii I play a team sport **and** its rugby **or** I play a team sport **and** its soccer.

b

r	s	t	$r \vee s$	$t \wedge r$	$t \wedge s$	$t \wedge (r \vee s)$	$(t \wedge r) \vee (t \wedge s)$
T	T	T	T	T	T	T	T
T	T	F	T	F	F	F	F
T	F	T	T	T	F	T	T
F	T	T	T	F	T	T	T
T	F	F	T	F	F	F	F
F	T	F	T	F	F	F	F
F	F	T	F	F	F	F	F
F	F	F	F	F	F	F	F

4 a i $s \vee (p \wedge u)$: **Either** Jon is from South America **or** he speaks Spanish **and** is studying at university.

ii $(s \vee p) \wedge (s \vee u)$: Jon is **either** from South America **or** speaks Spanish **and** is **either** from South America **or** is studying at university.

b

s	p	u	$p \wedge u$	$s \vee p$	$s \vee u$	$s \vee (p \wedge u)$	$(s \vee p) \wedge (s \vee u)$
T	T	T	T	T	T	T	T
T	T	F	F	T	T	T	T
T	F	T	F	T	T	T	T
F	T	T	T	T	T	T	T
T	F	F	F	T	T	T	T
F	T	F	F	T	F	F	F
F	F	T	F	F	T	F	F
F	F	F	F	F	F	F	F

5 a i $(a \wedge b) \vee c$ **ii** $(a \vee c) \wedge (b \vee c)$

a	b	c	$a \wedge b$	$a \vee c$	$b \vee c$	$(a \wedge b) \vee c$	$(a \vee c) \wedge (b \vee c)$
T	T	T	T	T	T	T	T
T	T	F	T	T	T	T	T
T	F	T	F	T	T	T	T
F	T	T	F	T	T	T	T
T	F	F	F	T	F	F	F
F	T	F	F	F	T	F	F
F	F	T	F	T	T	T	T
F	F	F	F	F	F	F	F

Exercise 17:06

1 a If it is raining then I will take my umbrella.
  c If it is raining then I will not take my umbrella.
  d If I take my umbrella it does not necessarily mean that it is raining.

b

p	q	$p \rightarrow q$
T	T	T
T	F	F
F	T	T
F	F	T

2 a If Tony is in Germany then he is in Europe.
  b Tony is either not in Germany or he is in Europe.

c

g	e	$\neg g$	$g \rightarrow e$	$\neg g \vee e$
T	T	F	T	T
T	F	F	F	F
F	T	T	T	T
F	F	T	T	T

  d They are equivalent statements.
  e Even if Tony is not in Germany, he could still be in Europe so $\neg g \rightarrow e$ is still true. However, if Tony is in Germany then he must be in Europe so $g \rightarrow \neg e$ is false.

3 a My grandmother is coming for dinner. We still have ice cream for dessert. **b** $a \rightarrow b$

c

a	b	$a \rightarrow b$
T	T	T
T	F	F
F	T	T
F	F	T

d

$b \rightarrow a$
T
T
F
T

4 a Hyun Ju will either go to the beach or play tennis.
  b If the weather is fine Hyun Ju will either go to the beach or play tennis.
  c If the weather is fine Hyun Ju will go to the beach or if the weather is fine Hyun Ju will play tennis.

d

f	t	b	$b \vee t$	$f \rightarrow b$	$f \rightarrow t$	$f \rightarrow (b \vee t)$	$(f \rightarrow b) \vee (f \rightarrow t)$
T	T	T	T	T	T	T	T
T	T	F	T	F	T	T	T
T	F	T	T	T	F	T	T
F	T	T	T	T	T	T	T
T	F	F	F	F	F	F	F
F	T	F	T	T	T	T	T
F	F	T	T	T	T	T	T
F	F	F	F	T	T	T	T

  e Since $f \rightarrow (b \vee t)$ is true, if it is fine then Hyun Ju will play tennis or go to the beach, but the fact that she has gone to the beach or is playing tennis does not necessarily mean that the weather is fine.

5 a

b	t	s	$b \wedge s$	$b \rightarrow t$	$b \rightarrow s$	$b \rightarrow (t \wedge s)$	$(b \rightarrow t) \wedge (b \rightarrow s)$
T	T	T	T	T	T	T	T
T	T	F	F	T	F	F	F
T	F	T	F	F	T	F	F
F	T	T	T	T	T	T	T
T	F	F	F	F	F	F	F
F	T	F	F	T	T	T	T
F	F	T	F	T	T	T	T
F	F	F	F	T	T	T	T

  b i If Dan is in Bangkok then he is in both Thailand and South East Asia.
  ii If Dan is in Bangkok then he is in Thailand and if Dan is in Bangkok then he is in South East Asia.

Diagnostic Test 17   Logic — an introduction

1 **a** Not a proposition   **b** F   **c** T   **d** T   **e** F   **f** F
   g Not a proposition   **h** F   **i** T   **j** F

2 **a** **i** The Athens Olympic Games were held in 2004 and Athens is in Greece.   T
      ii The Athens Olympic Games were held in 2004 or Athens is in Greece.   T
   b **i** Parallelograms have all sides equal and the opposite sides of a parallelogram are equal.   F
      ii Parallelograms have all sides equal or the opposite sides of a parallelogram are equal.   T
   c **i** A square root of 16 is 4 and the cubed root of 64 is 4.   T
      ii A square root of 16 is 4 or the cubed root of 64 is 4.   T

3

p	q	$\neg p$	$\neg q$	$p \wedge q$	$\neg(p \wedge q)$	$\neg p \vee \neg q$
T	T	F	F	T	F	F
T	F	F	T	F	T	T
F	T	T	F	F	T	T
F	F	T	T	F	T	T

4

p	q	$\neg p$	$\neg q$	$p \vee q$	$\neg(p \vee q)$	$\neg p \wedge \neg q$
T	T	F	F	T	F	F
T	F	F	T	T	F	F
F	T	T	F	T	F	F
F	F	T	T	F	T	T

5 **a** If Tony is in the Antarctic for his holiday then he is cold.
   b If Tony is cold then he is in the Antarctic for his holiday.
   c If he is cold he need not be in the Antarctic, he could be anywhere that is cold.

   d

a	c	$a \rightarrow c$	$c \rightarrow a$
T	T	T	T
T	F	F	T
F	T	T	F
F	F	T	T

17A Revision Assignment

1 **a** T   **b** Not a proposition   **c** T   **d** F   **e** T   **f** T
2 **a** F   **b** T   **c** T   **d** T   **e** F   **f** F

3 **a** **i** The square root of negative 1 is negative 1 AND the cube root of negative 1 is negative 1.
      ii The square root of −1 is −1 OR the cube root of −1 is −1.

   b

p	q	$p \wedge q$	$p \vee q$	$\neg p$	$\neg q$
F	T	F	T	T	F

   c **i** $\sqrt{-1}$ is −1 AND $\sqrt[3]{-1}$ is NOT −1.
      ii $\sqrt{-1}$ is NOT −1 AND $\sqrt[3]{-1}$ is −1.
      iii The statements $\sqrt{-1}$ is −1 and $\sqrt[3]{-1}$ is −1 are not both true.
      iv $\sqrt{-1}$ is NOT −1 OR $\sqrt[3]{-1}$ is NOT −1.

   d

p	q	$\neg p$	$\neg q$	$p \wedge q$	$\neg(p \wedge q)$	$\neg p \vee \neg q$
T	T	F	F	T	F	F
T	F	F	T	F	T	T
F	T	T	F	F	T	T
F	F	T	T	F	T	T
					identical columns	
					∴ logically equivalent	

Answers to ID Cards

ID Card 1 (Metric Units) page xiv

1 metres
2 decimetres
3 centimetres
4 millimetres
5 kilometres
6 square metres
7 square centimetres
8 square kilometres
9 hectares
10 cubic metres
11 cubic centimetres
12 seconds
13 minutes
14 hours
15 metres per second
16 kilometres per hour
17 grams
18 milligrams
19 kilograms
20 tonnes
21 litres
22 millilitres
23 kilolitres
24 degrees Celsius

ID Card 2 (Symbols) page xiv

1 is equal to
2 is approximately equal to
3 is not equal to
4 is less than
5 is less than or equal to
6 is not less than
7 is greater than
8 is greater than or equal to
9 4 squared
10 4 cubed
11 the square root of 2
12 the cube root of 2
13 is perpendicular to
14 is parallel to
15 is congruent to
16 is similar to
17 per cent
18 therefore
19 for example
20 that is
21 pi
22 the sum of
23 the mean
24 probability of event E

ID Card 3 (Language) page xv

1 $6 - 2 = 4$
2 $6 + 2 = 8$
3 $6 \div 2 = 3$
4 $6 - 2 = 4$
5 $6 \div 2 = 3$
6 2
7 6
8 $6 \times 2 = 12$
9 $6 - 2 = 4$
10 $6 \times 2 = 12$
11 $2 + 6 = 8$
12 $6 - 2 = 4$
13 $6^2 = 36$
14 $\sqrt{36} = 6$
15 $6 - 2 = 4$
16 $6 \times 2 = 12$
17 $(6 + 2) \div 2 = 4$
18 $6 + 2 = 8$
19 $6^2 = 36$
20 $6 - 2 = 4$
21 $6 - 2 = 4$
22 $6 + 2 = 8$
23 $6 \div 2 = 3$
24 $6 + 2 = 8$

ID Card 4 (Language) page xvi

1 square
2 rectangle
3 parallelogram
4 rhombus
5 trapezium
6 regular pentagon
7 regular hexagon
8 regular octagon
9 kite
10 scalene triangle
11 isosceles triangle
12 equilateral triangle
13 circle
14 oval (or ellipse)
15 cube
16 rectangular prism
17 triangular prism
18 square pyramid
19 rectangular pyramid
20 triangular pyramid
21 cylinder
22 cone
23 sphere
24 hemisphere

ID Card 5 (Language) page xvii

1 point A
2 interval AB
3 line AB
4 ray AB
5 collinear points
6 midpoint
7 number line
8 diagonals
9 acute-angled triangle
10 right-angled triangle
11 obtuse-angled triangle
12 vertices
13 $\triangle ABC$
14 hypotenuse
15 $180°$
16 $a° + b°$
17 $360°$
18 [b] $a° = b°$
19 $a° = 60°$
20 $3 \times 180° = 540°$
21 AB is a diameter: OC is a radius.
22 circumference
23 semicircle
24 AB is a tangent. CD is an arc. EF is a chord.

ID Card 6 (Language) page xviii

1 parallel lines
2 perpendicular lines
3 vertical, horizontal
4 concurrent lines
5 angle ABC or CBA
6 acute angle
7 right angle
8 obtuse angle
9 straight angle
10 reflex angle
11 revolution
12 adjacent angles
13 complementary angles
14 supplementary angles
15 vertically opposite angles
16 $360°$
17 transversal
18 corresponding angles
19 alternate angles
20 co-interior angles
21 bisecting an interval
22 bisecting an angle
23 $\angle CAB = 60°$
24 CD is perpendicular to AB

ID Card 7 (Language) page xix

1 anno Domini
2 before Christ
3 ante meridiem
4 post meridiem
5 hectare
6 regular shapes
7 net of a cube
8 cross-section
9 face
10 vertex
11 edge
12 axes of symmetry
13 reflection (or flip)
14 translation (or slide)
15 rotation (or turn)
16 tessellation
17 coordinates
18 tally
19 picture graph
20 column graph
21 line graph
22 sector (or pie) graph
23 bar graph
24 scatter diagram